D0561040

The Chemistry

of

PETROLEUM HYDROCARBONS

EDITED BY

BENJAMIN T. BROOKS

STEWART S. KURTZ JR.

CECIL E. BOORD

LOUIS SCHMERLING

VOLUME II

BOOK DIVISION

REINHOLD PUBLISHING CORPORATION

*Publishers of Chemical Engineering Catalog; Chemical Materials
Catalog; Materials & Methods; Automatic Control;
Advertising Management of American Chemical Society*

430 Park Ave., New York 22, N. Y.

1955

Copyright 1955 by

REINHOLD PUBLISHING CORPORATION

All rights reserved
Library of Congress Catalog Card Number: 54-12805

PRINTED IN U.S.A. BY THE MAPLE PRESS COMPANY

Library
State College
Indiana, Penna.

547.2 B791
v.2, c.1

Dedicated to the late
VLADIMIR N. IPATIEFF
and
FRANK C. WHITMORE

PREFACE

When the Editors considered the plan and scope of these volumes, it was realized that so much excellent research had been published and the technology involving hydrocarbon chemistry had progressed to such a degree, that the work could easily be of encyclopedic dimensions. It was decided that, in order to keep the work within reasonable bounds of space and publication costs, it would be necessary to limit its scope largely to scientific fundamentals. This has necessitated leaving out much of the process engineering, apparatus design, and analytical and testing methods relating to petroleum refining, and many uses of petroleum products.

The subjects of some of the chapters have been covered in individual treatises, in some cases by the same authors who have contributed these special chapters to the present work. However, it seemed advisable and opportune to bring together for review in one treatise the chemistry of the hydrocarbons as we now know it.

As will be apparent from an inspection of the subjects discussed, the fundamental chemistry of many industrial processes involving hydrocarbon chemistry is included. Also, since the study of hydrocarbon reactions has been greatly enriched and stimulated by theoretical considerations, the probable mechanisms of the reactions are discussed.

In general, the objective has been to discuss the chemistry of the hydrocarbons themselves rather than to extend it to the chemistry of the derivatives made from them, for this would have entailed a very large part of the whole field of organic chemistry, if the extension were carried very far.

The study of the composition of petroleums in recent years has profited by the application of many physical methods, which in numerous cases have been of the greatest importance in throwing light on the structure of the more complex hydrocarbons present in petroleum oils. We have therefore thought it desirable to include competent discussions of such physical methods.

The Editors are happy to acknowledge their great indebtedness to the many authors who have contributed chapters on special subjects and without whose assistance the present work would have been impossible. In the early planning of the undertaking, we were highly gratified by the enthusiastic interest and approval of these authors of the purpose and scope of "The Chemistry of Petroleum Hydrocarbons."

Benjamin T. Brooks
Cecil E. Boord
Stewart S. Kurtz
Louis Schmerling

CONTENTS

CHAPTER 22

MECHANISMS FOR THE THERMAL DECOMPOSITION OF HYDROCARBONS

E. W. R. Steacie and S. Bywater

National Research Council, Ottawa, Canada

Studies of the thermal decomposition of hydrocarbons have been carried out over a considerable period of years, during which time many mechanisms have been proposed. The earliest appears to be that of Berthelot,[3] who suggested the formation of acetylene as an intermediate in every hydrocarbon decomposition together with polymerization to more complex hydrocarbons and their subsequent decomposition. More accurate analyses by later workers showed acetylene to be a minor product and this theory quickly fell into disrepute.

Other investigators brought forward the conception of what might be described as the direct molecular rearrangement, i.e., a primary break in the hydrocarbon chain accompanied by the *simultaneous* shift of hydrogen atoms to produce an olefin and a shorter-chain saturated hydrocarbon or hydrogen molecule. Thorpe and Young[53] were early exponents of this theory. Haber[15] contended that the primary break occurred at the terminal C—C bond, always producing methane. Later workers showed that in general the hydrocarbon chain may rupture in any position, and that the over-all reaction is the sum of these individual steps.

The next development was the concept of free-radical intermediates. Thus Bone and Coward[6] assumed the formation of $-CH_3$, $=CH_2$ and $\equiv CH$ radicals in the thermal decomposition of ethane. These radicals were then assumed to be hydrogenated to methane, decomposed to carbon, or recombined. Hague and Wheeler[16] considered that methane split on thermal decomposition to give methylene and a hydrogen molecule. The free-radical mechanism received its strongest impetus in the hands of Rice,[35] who considered that methyl, ethyl, propyl, and similar higher radicals were the only reaction intermediates and worked out detailed mechanisms using plausible values for the activation energies of the various radical reactions. He was able to show that this type of mechanism was quite compatible with the over-all experimental kinetics.

The early theories were based on experimental data which involved very high extents of conversion. Thus the products which were isolated were in many cases due to subsequent reaction of the initial products. A closer understanding of the true mechanism has come hand in hand with more accurate analysis, and today the only two mechanisms which have any support are the direct molecular rearrangement, together with free radical schemes of the type suggested by Rice.

Direct molecular rearrangement is the simplest mechanism and requires little clarification. The specific rate of reaction of simple molecules can be expressed by the well-known Arrhenius equation:

$$k = A \cdot e^{-E/RT}$$

where A is the frequency factor which may be considered to be proportional to the number of molecular collisions per cubic centimeter per second, and E is the activation energy for the reaction. The reacting molecules are those in the wide distribution of molecular velocities which have a kinetic energy greater than E. Activation by means of molecular collisions is possible even for unimolecular reactions, according to the theory of Lindemann,[27] if a finite time interval occurs between the collision and the decomposition of the energy-rich molecule formed in it. This theory accounts for the dependence of reaction order on pressure found in many reactions. In many hydrocarbon decompositions the specific rate is greater than calculated by the above formula. This could of course be taken to indicate a chain reaction and is so interpreted by many authors. Even in reactions inhibited with nitric oxide, where it is commonly supposed that the radical chains are completely suppressed, the discrepancy still occurs. It is therefore necessary to assume that for complex molecules decomposing by a molecular mechanism, the energy associated with the numerous internal degrees of freedom is convertible into activation energy as well as the translational kinetic energy. The maximum rate then becomes:

$$k = A \cdot e^{-E/RT} \cdot \frac{(E/RT)^{\left(\frac{n}{2}-1\right)}}{\left(\frac{n}{2}-1\right)!}$$

where n is the number of "square terms" associated with the internal and external degrees of freedom.

If this theory is correct, and the nitric-oxide-inhibited decompositions of hydrocarbons are indeed molecular reactions, not all the vibrational degrees of freedom participate, for the experimental results are compatible with the participation of some five to twenty square terms only. The maximum rate is never attained. Nor does there seem to be any correlation with molecular complexity, for in the decomposition of normal hydrocarbons, from methane to heptane, the n value required experimentally varies quite randomly with molecular size.

A radical chain mechanism of the type suggested by Rice involves a primary C—C bond split to form free radicals. These undergo a series of reactions, specifically, abstraction of a hydrogen atom from the hydrocarbon substrate forming a different radical, thermal decomposition of the longer chain radicals, and recombination of radicals to terminate the chains. Each primary C—C bond split thus results in the decomposition of several hydrocarbon molecules, the extent of the chain process depending on the relative rates of the propagation and termination reactions. The kinetic chain length (N) is defined as the number of times the propagation steps occur for each chain initiation step. Thermal decompositions are not an ideal method of studying the subsequent radical reactions since these are faster than the primary reaction involving the C—C bond split. The rate and activation energy of the over-all reaction are thus determined to the largest extent by the primary reaction. Most of the knowledge of radical reactions in the thermal decomposition of hydrocarbons comes from studies of the photochemical and photosensitized reactions of hydrocarbons, ketones, mercury alkyls, and aldehydes. In these cases the activation energy for the primary split never appears in the kinetic analysis, and the over-all activation energy is usually some simple function of the relative activation energies of the various radical reactions. It is also possible to work at lower temperatures, where side reactions cause less trouble. Thus activation energies and steric factors of radical reactions can be estimated independently and their importance judged in purely thermal decompositions.

Another important source of information lies in the determination of bond dissociation energies. A knowledge of these factors permits the identification of the weakest bond in the molecule. Also, since the theoretical over-all activation energy is a function of the initial bond dissociation energy and the activation energies of the various radical reactions, a comparison between theory and experiment is possible.

It has been proven beyond doubt that radical chains occur in hydrocarbon decompositions. The only question so far unsettled is to what extent they are responsible for the total reaction. Paneth and co-workers[31,32] first demonstrated the presence of methyl radicals in the decomposition of lead tetramethyl vapor. The vapor was streamed at high velocity in the presence of hydrogen as carrier gas through a long tube of hard glass. A furnace around part of the tube was used to decompose some lead tetramethyl, thus producing a lead mirror on the tube at this point. The furnace was then moved upstream so that the reaction products flowed over the original mirror. This was found to be removed even at distances up to 30 cm from the point of decomposition, presumably due to the reaction:

$$Pb + 4CH_3 \rightarrow Pb(CH_3)_4$$

The method was modified by Rice and co-workers,[37,38] who showed that many other metallic mirrors would remove radicals and that mirrors can be removed by radicals formed in the thermal decomposition of hydrocarbons, ketones, and ethers. The method has been widely used to determine various properties of radicals and to prove that the results are produced by radicals and not by other factors, for example, the presence of a carrier gas. The radicals responsible for mirror removal have been identified by condensing out the reaction products and reacting them with alcoholic mercuric bromide. Various alkyl mercury bromides could then be isolated by sublimation. In this way the presence of methyl, ethyl, and propyl radicals has been detected.

In a similar manner Gorin[14] and later Blacet and co-workers[4,5] have added iodine vapor in the photolysis of aldehydes. The presence of alkyl iodides in the reaction products indicates the presence of radicals, since clearly iodides would not be formed if the original decomposition was proceeding by a direct molecular rearrangement. It is supposed that the reaction of iodine with radicals is extremely fast and thus any products other than iodides are formed by a simultaneously occurring molecular reaction. In this way the ratio of iodides to hydrocarbons in the products gives an estimate of the relative importance of the two types of mechanism. The method is, however, susceptible to difficulties of interpretation, and the results are not unequivocal.

Recently, the mass spectrometer has been used as a powerful tool to detect free radicals. The method relies on the fact that the ionization potential (I_R) of a radical (R) is always less than the appearance potential (A_R) of the R^+ ion directly from the parent hydrocarbon. Thus by having a fine leak of the products of a reaction into the mass spectrometer tube and using an ionizing potential intermediate between the two values mentioned, the concentration of R^+ ions at the collector plate gives a direct measure of the initial concentration of R radicals, since none can be formed directly from the hydrocarbon molecules. The experimental difficulties are severe but can be overcome, and the final result is unequivocal. The method was first used by Eltenton,[11] who investigated the concentration of methyl, ethyl, and other radicals in hydrocarbons decomposing thermally and when sensitized by lead tetramethyl. Robertson[39] has detected methyl radicals in the pyrolysis of methane on a platinum filament and ethyl radicals in butane decomposed in the same way. Lossing[28] has been able to identify methyl radicals in various homogeneous thermal decompositions.

In photochemical reactions many radicals have been detected by observation of their absorption spectra. This method has lately received much attention with the development of high-intensity discharges that produce high radical concentrations in the gas phase. Work in this field has been described by Porter[34] and by Herzberg and Ramsay.[17] Unfortunately, up to the present time no one has been able to detect the presence of the very important methyl radical by absorption spectroscopy.

For the special case where the radical is a hydrogen atom, other methods are known which give directly hydrogen-atom concentrations. Thus hydrogen atoms can be detected by their reducing action on solid oxides and dyes, by their heat of recombination on a platinum surface, by the ortho-para conversion, by exchange reactions with deuterium, and by other similar methods.

All the above-mentioned methods demonstrate directly the presence of radicals in thermal and photochemical decompositions. Many other indirect methods exist, depending on kinetic interpretation of reaction rates and products.

Rice Mechanisms for the Thermal Decomposition of Hydrocarbons

Since it is generally agreed that a free-radical process is at least partly responsible for the decomposition of hydrocarbons, it is worthwhile to discuss the Rice-type mechanisms. The first assumption of Rice[35] was that reaction is initiated by a C—C bond split. This is a very reasonable assumption, since it is known that the C—C bond in hydrocarbons is considerably weaker than the C—H bond. Two free radicals are thus produced whose subsequent reactions decide the reaction products. Three basic types of radical reaction occur[36,38] which have been widely studied by photochemical methods.

(1) Hydrogen Abstraction Reactions

$$R_1- + RH \rightarrow R_1H + R-$$

Activation energies for this type of reaction where R_1- is H, CH_3, C_2H_5 are known reasonably well at the present time, and in many cases frequency factors are also known.

(2) Thermal Decomposition Reactions

$$R.CH_2.CH_2- \rightarrow R- + CH_2=CH_2$$
$$R.CH_2CH_2- \rightarrow R \cdot CH=CH_2 + H$$

The larger radicals (C_2H_5, C_3H_7........) are thermally unstable at temperatures *below* those at which the parent compound (RH) decomposes. The activation energy for the reaction is much lower than that for the decomposition of the parent hydrocarbon owing to the fact that only one bond (C—C or C—H) has to be broken in order that the residue may rearrange *simultaneously* to form an olefin, an exothermic process which reduces the energy required to produce the over-all reaction.

(3) Radical Interactions

$$R_1— + R_2— \rightarrow \text{stable products}$$

The products may be the saturated molecule R_1R_2 or alternatively one radical may abstract a hydrogen atom from the other, producing an alkane and an alkene (disproportionation). Evidence exists that the activation energy is slightly higher in the latter case. Both reactions are limited in rate by the low radical concentration in the system.

A typical free-radical mechanism could be expressed in terms of the following reactions:

$$
\begin{aligned}
\text{Initiation:} \quad & R_1H \rightarrow R_2— + R_3— && \ldots k_1 \\
\text{Propagation:} \left\{ \begin{array}{l} R_2— + R_1H \rightarrow R_2H + R_1— \\ R_3— + R_1H \rightarrow R_3H + R_1— \\ R_1— \rightarrow C_2H_4 + R_3— \end{array} \right. && \begin{array}{l} \ldots k_2 \\ \ldots k_3 \\ \ldots k_4 \end{array} \\
\text{Termination:} \quad & R_1— + R_3— \rightarrow \text{products} && \ldots k_5
\end{aligned}
$$

where the hydrocarbon splits at a C—C bond forming two radicals, R_2 and R_3, which abstract hydrogen atoms from the parent hydrocarbon, forming radical R_1. R_1 is thermally unstable, forming an olefin and regenerating R_3 which can again produce R_1 from the hydrocarbon. This process repeats until terminated by interaction of the radicals R_1 and R_3. The principal products are decided by the way in which R_1 breaks to form intermediates. The stationary state treatment may be applied to this scheme since the concentration of radicals is small. This gives the following relation for the rate of decomposition of the hydrocarbon,

$$-\frac{d[R_1H]}{dt} = \sqrt{\frac{k_1 k_2 k_4}{k_5}}\,[R_1H]$$

where $[R_1H]$ denotes the concentration of the hydrocarbon. In this way a radical chain mechanism *can* produce a reaction which is first order and whose over-all activation energy

$$\left(\frac{E_1}{2} + \frac{E_2}{2} + \frac{E_4}{2} - \frac{E_5}{2} \text{ in this case}\right)$$

is lower than the bond dissociation energy of the primary step (E_1). In the example above

$$\frac{E_2}{2} + \frac{E_4}{2} \text{ will be less than } \frac{E_1}{2}$$

since, in general,

$$\frac{E_2}{2} \approx 4 \text{ kcal and } \frac{E_4}{2} \approx 10\text{–}15 \text{ kcal, whereas}$$

$$\frac{E_1}{2} \approx 40 \text{ kcal}$$

It must be emphasized that this scheme is quite arbitrary and the results would be considerably modified by choosing a different scheme. Thus if the radical recombination step had been postulated as:

$$R_1\text{—} + R_1\text{—} \rightarrow \text{products}$$
or
$$R_3\text{—} + R_3\text{—} \rightarrow \text{products}$$

the predicted over-all reaction order would be one-half or three halves, respectively. Similarly, postulating a bimolecular chain initiation step would produce over-all second order kinetics. The over-all kinetics produced by assuming various types of mechanism have been evaluated by Goldfinger, Letort, and Niclause,[12] who present a table from which the over-all order can be found, given any order of initiation and termination.

Rice could, therefore, by a suitable choice of reaction steps, and by assuming plausible values for the activation energies of the various steps, successfully predict reaction order and over-all activation energy. The distribution of products could be predicted in a similar way by postulating that normal radicals break at a C—C bond and isoradicals break at a C—H bond on thermal decomposition. Further it was assumed that all secondary C—H bonds and all tertiary C—H bonds are 1200 cal and 4,000 cal weaker, respectively, than primary C—H bonds. In this way the results in Table 1 were obtained.[35]

TABLE 1. COMPARISON OF THE PRODUCTS PREDICTED BY THE RICE MECHANISMS WITH THOSE OBTAINED EXPERIMENTALLY

	H_2	CH_4	C_2H_6	C_2H_4	C_3H_6	$C_4H_8{}^{iso}$	$C_4H_8{}^N$	C_5H_{10}	Hydrocarbon decomposed
Calc.	20	30	—	30	20	—	—	—	} Propane
Exp.	20	30	—	←50→		—	—	—	
Calc.	26	24	0	0	26	24	—	—	} Isobutane
Exp.	25	23	2	←—50——→			—	—	
Calc.	6	30	13	6.5	20	22	8.5	0	} Isopentane
Exp.	6	30	24	—	15	←20→		4	

Product (%)

Qualitatively there is no doubt that radical chain mechanisms of this type give a reasonably good explanation of the observed facts in hydrocarbon decompositions. The difficulty arises when attempts are made to make the schemes quantitative. Firstly experimental constants of many elementary steps are now reasonably well-known. Often they are markedly different from the values Rice had to assume. Thus, to bring back agreement with the observed over-all activation energy the scheme must be modified. This tends to change the predicted reaction order. In many cases frequency factors also are known, so that it becomes possible to compare the absolute rates of various elementary steps, to assess their relative importance, and thus to calculate radical concentrations and probable termination reactions. Once again it is difficult to reconcile evidence of this type with the observed reaction order. To summarize: radical steps must be chosen to be in agreement with (1) observed reaction order, (2) experimental activation energy, (3) known rates of elementary reactions, (4) known products. It is difficult to find a scheme which is consistent with all these requirements. Also, from inhibition experiments an experimental evaluation of the kinetic chain length can be made. This usually is too low compared with the value calculated from the known characteristics of radical reactions.

Bond Energies

It is important to know the amount of energy required to break any particular bond in a hydrocarbon, since this factor decides which bond will preferentially break at high temperatures; also it is the most important factor deciding the over-all activation energy of the reaction, assuming either a free radical or a molecular mechanism. Bond energies can be defined in different ways, resulting in different numerical values. Thus the "bond dissociation energy" is defined as the amount of energy required to split a defined bond and separate the resultant radicals at $0°K$, and is the important quantity from the point of view of reaction kinetics. "Average bond energies," often more simply termed "bond energies," represent the average energy necessary to break a bond when all bonds in the molecule are simultaneously split. The two are obviously identical for diatomic molecules but differ widely for polyatomic molecules.

As an example to illustrate the terminology, consider the molecule CH_4. The bond dissociation energy of C—H in methane is the heat of reaction at $0°K$ of the process:

$$CH_{4(gas)} \rightarrow CH_{3(gas)} + H_{(gas)}$$

whereas the average bond energy is one quarter of the heat of reaction at $0°K$ of the process:

$$CH_{4(gas)} \rightarrow C_{(gas)} + 4H_{(gas)}$$

The heat of the first reaction is 102 kilocalories and of the second is 347.5 kilocalories, thus the C—H bond dissociation energy in methane is 102 kilocalories, whereas the average bond energy is 86.9 kilocalories. The latter value is calculated from thermochemical data and is dependent on the value assigned to the latent heat of sublimation of graphite, and the former is an experimental quantity derived from kinetic measurements. The relationship between the two is simply that in this case the sum of the individual bond dissociation energies in CH_4, CH_3, CH_2, and CH, which differ widely, must be equal to four times the average bond energy. Tables of bond energies as given, for instance, by Pauling[33] are average bond energies and bear no *direct* relation to the problems of hydrocarbon decomposition; therefore bond dissociation energy determinations alone will be considered here.

The earliest work on bond dissociation energies in complex molecules was initiated by Polanyi[7] and co-workers, who investigated the pyrolysis of a series of iodides in a fast flow system using a carrier gas and low iodide pressures. Under these conditions they assumed that secondary reactions were unimportant and the measured activation energies corresponded to those of the reactions:

$$R \cdot I \rightarrow R— + I$$

There is strong evidence that the activation energies of the reverse reactions are zero, and so the measured activation energy becomes equal to the heat of reaction and hence to the $R—I$ bond dissociation energy

$$(\Delta H = E_{forward} - E_{reverse})$$

By combination of the experimental RI bond dissociation energies with standard thermochemical data, the $R—H$ bond dissociation energies can be found.

Most of the values so obtained are open to doubt, since no temperature coefficient was measured and E was calculated arbitrarily by use of the following relation:

$$k = 10^{13}e^{-E/RT}$$

In practice unimolecular reactions can have frequency factors differing widely from 10^{13}, so that the use of this relation can produce serious errors. There is also doubt in other cases as to whether subsequent radical reactions had really been eliminated, since even when a fast flow system is used the radical lifetimes are short compared with contact times. The data are therefore quantitatively unreliable but do show characteristic trends in the hydrocarbon series.

A few bond dissociation energies have been measured by Kistiakowsky,

Van Artsdalen[1,20,23] and co-workers by a detailed kinetic study of the photobromination of hydrocarbons. Evidence was given that the experimental activation energy refers to the reaction:

$$Br + RH \rightarrow R— + HBr$$

The activation energy of the reverse reaction was estimated. Since the heat of reaction is the difference between the activation energies of the forward and reverse reactions, identification of the observed activation energy with that of the forward reaction enables the heat of reaction to be calculated. The R—H bond dissociation energy can then be calculated using standard thermochemical data. The mechanism seems to be best established in the case of methane and reasonably well in the case of ethane. The calculated bond dissociation energies should be correct to within three kilocalories in these cases.

Many bond dissociation energies have been measured by Szwarc[50] and co-workers by pyrolysis of hydrocarbons in a fast flow system in the presence of a large excess of toluene. The high rate of flow should ensure that product molecules do not react further and thus complicate the kinetics. The free radicals formed will react preferentially with the toluene which is in large excess, and in this way radical chains are inhibited. In the exchange, benzyl radicals are formed which are highly stabilized by resonance and consequently unreactive. These, therefore, should merely dimerize. The simplicity of the reaction can be checked by isolating the dibenzyl and comparing it to the quantities of other products. As in the above cases, the observed activation energy is equated to the bond dissociation energy in question. The technique is limited to compounds having a bond weaker than the C—H bond in toluene, otherwise the reaction is complicated by the thermal decomposition of the latter. Analyses of the products show that in spite of the precautions taken side reactions do occur, but it is assumed that their effect on the measured activation energy is negligible. The method has the further disadvantages that owing to the high flow rate, the exact gas temperature is a little uncertain, and pressures of reactants can be varied over only a limited range. It is therefore difficult to check if the reaction does correspond to a simple unimolecular reaction. However, the technique is very powerful and bond dissociation energies can be measured in the best cases to within 2 to 3 kilocalories. In other cases the supposed mechanisms have by no means been well-established and the results are open to doubt.

Electron impact data provide a valuable check on the kinetically determined bond dissociation energies. The method[18,46,47] depends on the observation of appearance potentials ($A_{(R)}$) for the following types of reaction in a mass spectrometer.

$$R\text{—}H \;\rightarrow\; R^+ + H + e^- \qquad A_\text{I}(R^+)$$
$$R\text{—} \;\rightarrow\; R^+ + e^- \qquad A_\text{II}(R^+)$$
$$R\text{—}R_1 \;\rightarrow\; R_1^+ + R\text{—} + e^- \qquad A_\text{III}(R_1^+)$$
$$R_1\text{—}H \;\rightarrow\; R_1^+ + H + e^- \qquad A_\text{IV}(R_1^+)$$

Conditions are arranged in the instrument so that the observed ion current corresponds to each of the reactions in turn. The electron bombarding energy is gradually increased and the corresponding ion current measured. The appearance potential is the minimum potential required to produce the given ion. Curves of the type of Figure 1 are produced where

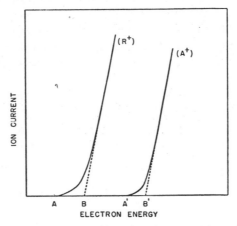

Fig. 1. Typical ionization waves as given in a mass spectrometer (diagrammatic).

point A or B can be imagined to be the required potential. The potential scale is established by observing the ionization curve of argon whose ionization potential is accurately known from spectroscopic measurements. Thus the error in interpretation is reduced, since AB will be roughly equal to $A'B'$, and either method of extrapolation gives results which are roughly equivalent. The difference is, however, still too large for the required accuracy. Stevenson[47] has put forward evidence that the initial break points (A, A') correspond to separation of products with only thermal energies. In this case the appearance potentials correspond to heats of reaction. Thus the bond dissociation energy $D_{(R\text{–}H)}$ can be found in the following two ways, assuming that the reverse reactions require zero activation energy.

Direct method $\quad D_{(R\text{–}H)} = A_\text{I}(R^+) - A_\text{II}(R^+)$

Indirect method $\quad D_{(R\text{–}H)} = A_\text{III}(R_\text{I}^+) - A_\text{IV}(R_\text{I}^+)$
$$+ \; Hf(RH) + Hf(R_1H) - Hf(RR_1)$$

The terms $Hf(\;\;)$ represent the heats of formation of the compounds indicated in parentheses. The indirect method can be checked using several different compounds (R_I = CH_3, C_2H_5, etc.). All cases should give the same value for $D_{(R-H)}$. The agreement obtained by these independent measurements is taken by Stevenson[47] to indicate that the initial break method is correct and the products do separate with no extra kinetic energy since otherwise differences would be observed due to the separation of the various particles with different amounts of kinetic energy. Similarly, it also suggests that the reverse reactions have zero activation energy.

All the methods of measurement of R—H bond dissociation energies yield values of the corresponding R—R bond dissociation energy by combination of the data with the heats of formation of R—R and R—H. The reliability of bond dissociation energy measurements can be indicated by the comparison of values obtained by the different methods in Table 2.

TABLE 2. BOND DISSOCIATION ENERGIES

Bond	Investigator			
	Polanyi	Stevenson	Kistiakowsky	Szwarc
CH_3—H	102.5	101.4	102	—
C_2H_5—H	97.5	96.8	98	96
n-C_3H_7—H	95.0	99	—	~100
n-C_4H_9—H	94	101	—	—
iso-C_3H_7—H	89	93.5	—	94
tert-C_4H_9—H	86	—	—	89
CH_3—CH_3	87	83.4	85.6	—
CH_3—C_2H_5	85	81.1	83.8	—
C_2H_5—C_2H_5	—	79.1	82.4	—

Inhibition of Thermal Decompositions

The addition of a few per cent of nitric oxide has a pronounced retarding effect on the rate of decomposition of a hydrocarbon. The rate is progressively decreased until over an extensive range of NO pressures no change in rate is observed. A similar effect is observed with propylene addition, although in this case larger quantities are required. The limiting rate is, however, the same[48] in many cases (Figure 2). The nitric oxide is slowly consumed, but there is usually a residual amount at the end of the reaction.

The maximally inhibited reaction has been studied extensively by Hinshelwood and co-workers over a large range of hydrocarbons. The over-all activation energy is usually slightly larger than for the normal reaction at high pressures. The activation energy of the inhibited reaction decreases[21] (except for ethane and propane) from a high value at low pressures and becomes independent of pressure at high pressures. This behavior is, in fact, the same as that of the normal reaction. With ethane, in both cases the activation energy is independent of pressure. The reac-

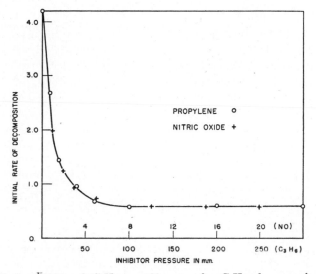

FIG. 2. Effect of NO and C_3H_6 on 100 mm. of n C_5H_{12} decomposing at 530°C, plotted from the data of Stubbs and Hinshelwood:[48]

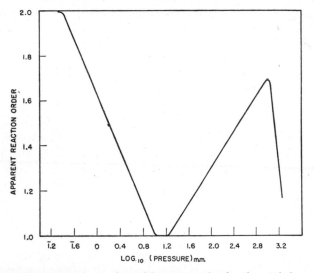

FIG. 3. Variation of reaction order with pressure in the thermal decomposition of n-pentane (diagrammatic) after Hinshelwood 49 et al.

tion order of the inhibited reaction with respect to hydrocarbon pressure is complicated[49] except for ethane, and possibly propane, where the order approaches two at very low pressures and is approximately unity over a very wide range at high pressures. Typical behavior is shown in Figure 3. The change in order in going from low to medium pressures could be accounted for by assuming a normal unimolecular reaction with collisional activation. The subsequent changes, if this is truly a molecular mechanism, would involve a complex activation scheme. The products of the maximally inhibited reaction are within the limits of accuracy achieved experimentally identical with the normal reaction products (Steacie and Folkins,[43] Ingold, Stubbs, and Hinshelwood[22]).

Nitric oxide and propylene react rapidly with free radicals. The products formed have not been identified, but it is generally supposed that the reaction proceeds in the nitric oxide case by the following reactions:

$$CH_3 + NO \rightarrow CH_3NO$$
$$CH_3NO \rightarrow CH_2{=}NOH$$
$$CH_2{=}NOH \rightarrow products$$

The final products may be HCN, CO, NH_3, H_2O, etc.[51,52] The fact that nitric oxide drastically reduces the rate of thermal decompositions is generally agreed to be strong evidence for the presence of radical chains in these reactions. There is, however, still controversy regarding the nature of the residual reaction in the presence of nitric oxide. Three possibilities exist, namely; (1) The residual reaction is still a radical chain reaction in which the average chain length is shorter since the nitric oxide has interrupted many chains by removal of the chain carrier.[43] (2) The residual reaction is a molecular (one-stage) process.[48] (3) The residual reaction corresponds to a stationary state, where as many chains are initiated by the nitric oxide as it terminates.[10]

The third possibility is unlikely and is not usually considered. Steacie and Folkins argued that the identity of products in the normal and inhibited reactions is strong evidence for the inhibited reaction being a shorter-chain radical process, since it is unlikely that two widely different mechanisms would yield the same products. Stubbs and Hinshelwood[48] considered that this evidence is still compatible with the idea of a molecular reaction in the presence of NO, since for a given C—C split a radical reaction can be written down yielding the same products as the direct molecular rearrangement. This is undoubtedly true, but in order to do so it is necessary to choose certain specific radical reactions and ignore others which are known to be more probable from the large mass of evidence now accumulated on radical reactions.

Both Steacie and Folkins[43] and Klute and Walters[24] have investigated the effect of nitric oxide on thermal decompositions sensitized by compounds which easily split into free radicals. In both cases it was shown that some residual chain reaction must be occurring in the presence of nitric oxide.

Hinshelwood and co-workers, however, argue with considerable justification that the fact that both C_3H_6 and NO produce the same limiting rate is strong evidence for a direct molecular reaction. In photochemical reactions the presence or absence of chains can be checked by measuring quantum yields. Thus Mitchell and Hinshelwood[30] found that 3 per cent of nitric oxide reduced the quantum yield from 186 to 1.14 in the photolysis of acetaldehyde, so that the residual chain length with NO present must be at most one or two units. The quantum yield of NO disappearance was about unity, suggesting that NO reacts with every radical produced. Similarly LeRoy and Steacie[26] found that nitric oxide completely inhibits chains in the photosensitized decomposition of ethylene. It is important, however, to note that conditions (particularly temperature) are quite different in photochemical reactions as compared with thermal decompositions.

Hinshelwood and co-workers call the ratio of uninhibited to maximally inhibited rates the "mean chain length" of the radical reaction. This is only equivalent approximately to the true free radical chain length if the hydrocarbon *initially* reacts to equal amounts by splitting into two free radicals and by rearranging directly. The mean chain length is in fact equivalent to:

$$1 + N \cdot \frac{\text{(rate of radical initiation)}}{\text{(rate of molecular initiation)}}$$

If the rate of radical initiation is small, then the true radical chain length (N) can be many times the mean chain length. This does not mean that the products are not produced predominantly by the free-radical mechanism, since the effect of one initial free radical split in the hydrocarbon produces $2N$ product molecules, whereas one molecular rearrangement produces just two product molecules. The mean chain length, in fact, gives the ratio of products produced by the free-radical and molecular reactions. In practice mean chain lengths between 2 and 20 are found under various conditions with hydrocarbons. The relative rates of the steps in free-radical reactions known to date make it necessary that a chain mechanism should have fairly long chains, so that if the maximally inhibited rate is truly molecular, it is necessary to assume that the *initial* radical split occurs less frequently than the molecular rearrangement.

While the nitric oxide technique has established without doubt the fact that radical mechanisms are responsible for a large proportion of the products of the decomposition of hydrocarbons, the presence or absence of a direct molecular reaction accompanying the chain process has not been definitely proved. All these reactions are, in practice, carried out at large conversions, where products are undergoing secondary reactions. Propylene is itself produced in many hydrocarbon decompositions and the reaction is self-inhibiting to some extent. The ultimate solution of the problem of the mechanism of the inhibited reactions appears to lie in experiments carried out at very low conversions (1 to 2 per cent), where it will be reasonably certain that the curious effects of the inhibited reaction are not in fact due to subsequent reactions of the primary products.

The Thermal Decomposition of Ethane

It is worthwhile to consider one hydrocarbon in more detail in order to find out how the mechanisms proposed for thermal decompositions agree quantitatively with experiment. Ethane is the most suitable hydrocarbon to investigate since the reactions of methyl and ethyl radicals have been studied in greatest detail. Only one type of radical (CH_3) is produced in the initial reaction step, a factor which simplifies the kinetic mechanisms. By comparison, a discussion of the thermal decomposition of butane would involve three radicals (CH_3, C_2H_5, C_3H_7) and two different chain initiation reactions. The kinetics become, therefore, more complex, and in addition there exist few quantitative data on the reactions of propyl radicals.

Marek and McCluer[29] investigated the thermal decomposition of ethane by flowing the gas through a heated tube and analyzing for ethylene and hydrogen in the outgoing gas stream. Sachsse,[41] Kuchler and Thiele,[25] and Steacie and Shane,[44] measured the rate of decomposition by measuring the pressure rise in a closed vessel at high temperatures. The over-all reaction corresponds to the process,

$$C_2H_6 \rightarrow C_2H_4 + H_2$$

and therefore to a doubling of the pressure at 100 per cent reaction in the absence of side reactions. Some product analyses were usually also made to verify the validity of the method.

There exists some divergence in the results obtained, especially between Marek and McCluer's rates, which are much higher than the rest, and those of the other authors. Neglecting Marek and McCluer's results, the best straight line through the experimental points of the other workers yields the rate equation

$$\log_{10} k_1 = 15.09 - \frac{74,000}{2.3RT} \ \text{sec}^{-1}$$

where k_1 is the apparent first-order reaction constant for the decomposition. This is shown in Figure 4. The reaction is approximately first order with respect to ethane concentration, but the apparent first-order rate constants fall off badly at high conversions and at low initial ethane pressures. The back reaction becomes important at low conversions and rates must therefore be corrected for this, or alternatively measurements of initial rates must be made. This lowers the accuracy of the experimental data. The reaction products are almost exclusively ethylene and hydrogen in almost equal proportions, together with a small quantity (2 to 5 per cent of the ethylene) of methane and a trace of high-boiling liquid.

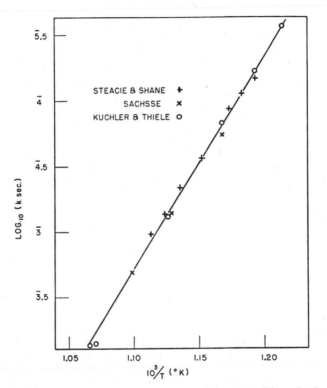

Fig. 4. Activation energy for the thermal decomposition of ethane.

The reaction is strongly inhibited by nitric oxide.[45,19,42] A few millimeters of nitric oxide reduce the rate of decomposition to a limiting value of about one-tenth of the original rate. The activation energy of the fully inhibited reaction is constant over a wide pressure range at 74.7 kilocalories according to Ingold, Stubbs, and Hinshelwood[21] and 77.3 kilocalories according to Steacie and Shane.[45] The inhibited reaction is first order with respect to ethane concentration at high pressures. The order begins to increase below about 250 mm initial pressure, becoming approximately second order at 2 mm initial pressure, in accordance with the collision theory of unimolecular reactions.

A free-radical scheme for the thermal decomposition must be based on the following reactions:

$$C_2H_6 \rightarrow 2CH_3 \tag{1}$$
$$CH_3 + C_2H_6 \rightarrow CH_4 + C_2H_5 \tag{2}$$
$$C_2H_5 \rightarrow C_2H_4 + H \tag{3}$$
$$H + C_2H_6 \rightarrow C_2H_5 + H_2 \tag{4}$$
$$C_2H_5 + C_2H_5 \rightarrow C_4H_{10} \tag{5a}$$
$$H + C_2H_5 \rightarrow C_2H_6 \tag{5b}$$
$$CH_3 + C_2H_5 \rightarrow C_3H_8 \tag{5c}$$
$$H + CH_3 \rightarrow CH_4 \tag{5d}$$
$$CH_3 + CH_3 \rightarrow C_2H_6 \tag{5e}$$
$$H + H \rightarrow H_2 \tag{5f}$$

The occurrence of reactions (1) to (4) has been substantiated by investigations of the reactions of the radicals concerned, largely by photochemical studies. The following six chain termination steps pose a more difficult problem. No solution of the rate equations can be obtained unless the mechanism is simplified to include one or at most two termination steps only. In the original scheme of Rice and Herzfeld it was assumed arbitrarily that reaction (5b) was predominant, largely in order to make the theory agree with experiment. It is now possible, however, to estimate the relative importance of the individual termination steps. The following data (Table 3) are available in the literature for the rate

TABLE 3. RATE CONSTANTS OF THE RADICAL REACTIONS IN THE THERMAL DECOMPOSITION OF ETHANE

Reaction	A	E (kcal)	Reference
(1)	1×10^{13} (sec)$^{-1}$	86.0	assuming a unimolecular reaction
(2)	2×10^{11}	10.4	[54]
(3)	3×10^{14}	39.5	[8]
(4)	1.2×10^{14}	9.0	[40]
(4)	3.4×10^{12}	6.8	[2]
(5e)	7×10^{13}	0.0	[13]

constants of reactions (1) to (5) where A, the frequency factor, is expressed in cc mole^{-1} sec^{-1}, unless otherwise stated. The difference in rates reported for reaction (4) indicates that these values may be subject to considerable error; but the permissible error is very large in the following argument.

Let us consider the thermal decomposition at 824°K and one atmosphere pressure. Now if the termination steps involving methyl radicals (5c, 5d, and 5e) are so slow as to be negligible, then using the stationary-state method of calculation:

$$\frac{d[CH_3]}{dt} = 2k_1[C_2H_6] - k_2[CH_3][C_2H_6] = 0$$

$$\therefore [CH_3] = \frac{2k_1}{k_2}$$

Under the above conditions, and using the appropriate rate constants, the concentration of methyl radicals in the system will be 8×10^{-19} mole per cubic centimeter. The occurrence of steps (5c), (5d), or (5e) would lower the concentration, since this involves extra reactions removing methyl radicals. The change in concentration must however be small, as shown by the following argument. At a methyl radical concentration of 8×10^{-19} mole per cc, and with the above rate constants, reaction (2) will remove methyl radicals at the rate of 4×10^{-15} mole per cc per second, and reaction (5e) at the rate of 4.5×10^{-23} mole per cc per second. At CH_3 concentrations below 8×10^{-19} mole per cc, the termination reaction is even less important. Thus since 8×10^{-19} mole per cc is a maximum concentration, reaction (5e) can only exert a minute effect on the radical concentration. A similar argument applies to reactions (5c) and (5d), so that the value obtained above for the methyl radical concentration must be correct to within the limits of accuracy to which the constants k_1 and k_2 are known. In a similar manner the concentration of hydrogen atoms is decided almost entirely by their rate of formation by reaction (3) and their rate of removal by reaction (4), and in the steady state the hydrogen-atom concentration is given by the following relations:

$$\frac{d[H]}{dt} = k_3[C_2H_5] - k_4[H][C_2H_6] = 0$$

$$\therefore [H] = 5 \times 10^{-3}[C_2H_5]$$

This argument is, however, not applicable to determination of the ethyl radical concentration, since this radical is regenerated repeatedly by the series of reactions (2), (3), and (4). Reactions (3) and (4) proceed at equal rates according to the preceding formula. Thus the ethyl radicals produced by (3) are destroyed by (4), and the propagation steps have no effect on the ethyl radical concentration, which is simply decided by the rates of reactions (2) and (5) according to the following equation:

$$\frac{d[C_2H_5]}{dt} = k_2[CH_3][C_2H_6] - k_{5a}[C_2H_5]^2 - k_{5b}[H][C_2H_5] - k_{5c}[C_2H_5][CH_3] = 0$$

Substitution of the values of k_2, $[H]$, $[CH_3]$ given above in this equation and assuming that all the reactions (5) have a rate constant of 7×10^{13} cc $mole^{-1}sec^{-1}$, gives a value of 8×10^{-15} mole per cc for the ethyl radical concentration. This value is considerably higher than for the other radicals since only slow chain termination steps remove ethyl radicals.

At 950°K, the highest temperature which has been studied experimentally, repetition of the argument gives the following values:

$[CH_3] = 4 \times 10^{-16}$ $[C_2H_5] = 2.5 \times 10^{-13}$ $[H] = 2 \times 10^{-14}$ (all in mole/cc)

Using the assumptions mentioned and neglecting reaction (5f) since the recombination of hydrogen atoms certainly proceeds by means of triple collisions which occur very infrequently, the rates of the various termination reactions in mole $cc^{-1}sec^{-1}$ given in Table 4 are obtained.

TABLE 4. RATES OF THE TERMINATION REACTIONS AT ONE ATMOSPHERE PRESSURE

Reaction	Rate (824°K)	Rate (950°K)
(5a) $C_2H_5 + C_2H_5$	5×10^{-15}	5×10^{-12}
(5b) $H + C_2H_5$	2×10^{-17}	4×10^{-13}
(5c) $CH_3 + C_2H_5$	4×10^{-19}	7×10^{-15}
(5d) $H + CH_3$	2×10^{-21}	6×10^{-16}
(5e) $CH_3 + CH_3$	4×10^{-23}	1×10^{-17}

Table 4 shows that reaction (5a) is predominant at all temperatures and high pressures. Allowing, however, for errors in the above calculation, reaction (5b) should also be considered since it will be increasingly important at low pressures. The inclusion of reaction (5c) would be desirable, but in this case the rate equations become too complex. Even the solution of the series of equations (1), (2), (3), (4), (5a), (5b) is impossible exactly, but a reasonable approximation is obtained by assuming that the termination steps do not appreciably change the hydrogen-atom and methyl radical concentrations. This yields the following expression for the rate of decomposition of ethane:

$$- \frac{d[C_2H_6]}{dt} = \frac{2^{1/2}k_1^{1/2}k_3[C_2H_6]^{1/2}}{k_5^{1/2} \left\{ 1 + \dfrac{k_3}{k_4[C_2H_6]} \right\}^{1/2}}$$

At high pressures and low temperatures, this equation predicts a half-order reaction of rate

$$\frac{2^{1/2}k_1^{1/2}k_3[C_2H_6]^{1/2}}{k_5^{1/2}}$$

and activation energy 83 kilocalories

$$\left(\frac{E_1}{2} + E_3 - \frac{E_5}{2} \right)$$

and a rate

$$\frac{2^{1/2}k_1^{1/2}k_3^{1/2}k_4^{1/2}[C_2H_6]}{k_5^{1/2}}$$

at higher temperatures and lower pressures with an activation energy of 67 kilocalories

$$\left(\frac{E_1}{2} + \frac{E_3}{2} + \frac{E_4}{2} - \frac{E_5}{2} \right)$$

The latter case corresponds to the original mechanism proposed by Rice. It must be emphasized that these predictions only apply to initial rates of decomposition since the equations are not in an integrated form. The contributions of reactions (5a) and (5b) are measured relatively by the factors 1 and

$$\frac{k_3}{k_4[C_2H_6]}$$

respectively. Now the term

$$\frac{k_3}{k_4[C_2H_6]}$$

assumes the values shown in Table 5 under various conditions. In this

TABLE 5. VARIATION OF THE FACTOR $\dfrac{k_3}{k_4[C_2H_6]}$ WITH REACTION CONDITIONS

T, °K		Initial Pressure of Ethane		
	760 mm	400 mm	100 mm	10 mm
824°	1×10^{-3}	3×10^{-3}	1×10^{-2}	1×10^{-1}
	(1×10^{-2})	(2×10^{-2})	(9×10^{-2})	(9×10^{-1})
950°	2×10^{-2}	4×10^{-2}	2×10^{-1}	2.0
	(2×10^{-1})	(4×10^{-1})	(1.5)	(15)

table, the two sets of figures at each characteristic temperature and pressure correspond to the two available estimates for the constants of reaction (4). On changing from low temperatures and high pressures to high temperatures and low pressures the dominant termination mechanism must change over, and with it the reaction order and activation energy.

The experimental results of most workers were extrapolated to very high pressures, usually by plotting the reciprocal of the first-order rate constant against reciprocal pressure. These are the results plotted in Figure 4. This type of extrapolation is, of course, only valid if the reaction is really first order changing to second order at low pressures. Since this has not been proved, probably it is better to state the experimental results in the following way. Sachsse's results indicate an activation energy between 70 and 73 kilocalories, the values varying randomly over the pressure range 20 to 200 mm, results below 20 mm being completely inaccurate. Steacie and Shane's results indicate an activation energy of average value 74 kilocalories over the pressure range 130 to 500 mm, if the measurement at the highest temperature is neglected due to the large variation of rate with pressure at this temperature. Steacie and Shane considered that their results indicated an activation energy of 70 kilocalories. It seems likely therefore that the best experimental value is 72 ± 2 kilocalories in the pressure range 20 to 500 mm. The results of Kuchler and Thiele cannot be considered in detail since their paper contains only values of rate constants extrapolated to infinite pressure. The experimental results fall intermediate between the two extremes predicted theoretically and suggest that the mechanism is complex with probably termination reactions (5a) and (5b), and perhaps others, playing an important role.

Recently it has been suggested that reaction (1) has a frequency factor of 10^{17} rather than 10^{13}. If so the importance of reaction (5c) is increased. At one atmosphere pressure reaction (5a) is then probably still dominant but at a few millimeters pressure reactions (5a), (5b) and (5c) must occur. Approximate solution of the series of equations becomes impossible, but the general conclusion that more than one termination reaction must be considered, is still valid.

The free-radical mechanism predicts a reaction order varying from one-half at high pressures to three halves at low pressures, taking into account a change from unimolecular to bimolecular chain initiation at low pressures in accord with the collisional theory of activation. This predicted change is in qualitative agreement with the observed drop of first-order constants with decreasing pressure. Experimentally, the reaction is approximately first order at high pressures, but it must be borne in mind that it is difficult to distinguish between a first-order and a half-order reaction by merely changing the initial pressure over a limited range and observing drifts in "first-order" constants. Kuchler and Thiele[25] have suggested that even at high pressures chain initiation is a bimolecular process, in which case the theory predicts a first-order reaction at these pressures. This suggestion, of course, cannot be reconciled with their process of extrapolating rate constants to infinite pressure, a process which infers that the reaction is unimolecular, at least at high pressures.

Agreement is therefore reasonably good between theory and experiment, bearing in mind the experimental difficulties and the impossibility of taking into account all possible termination mechanisms which could be important over a wide range of conditions and also the possibility of quite large numerical errors in the values in Table 5.

The nitric-oxide-inhibited thermal decomposition has been shown by Hobbs and Hinshelwood[19] to obey the following relation between rate of decomposition and nitric oxide concentration:

$$\frac{\rho - \rho_\infty}{\rho_0 - \rho_\infty} = -\gamma[NO] + [1 + \gamma^2[NO]^2]^{1/2}$$

where ρ is the rate at any nitric oxide concentration, ρ_∞ is the limiting rate attained at high nitric oxide concentrations and ρ_0 is the normal rate in absence of nitric oxide. Nitric oxide must inhibit the reaction by removing rapidly either CH_3, C_2H_5, or H radicals from the reaction to form inactive products. Since it was shown in an earlier section that the ethyl radical concentration must be much higher than the hydrogen-atom or methyl radical concentration, it seems likely that nitric oxide reacts preferentially with this radical. Making the likely assumption that the reaction between ethyl radicals and nitric oxide proceeds at the same rate as that between methyl radicals and nitric oxide as measured by Durham and Steacie,[9] then at 824°K, using 10 per cent nitric oxide, the reaction

$$C_2H_5 + NO \rightarrow \text{inactive products} \qquad (6)$$

is about thirty times as fast as reaction (3) and thus should be able to reduce drastically the ethyl radical concentration. An analysis of the set of rate equations (1), (2), (3), (4), (5a), (5b), and (6), using the steady-state method of calculation, produces an equation of the type found experimentally by Hobbs and Hinshelwood, where γ has the value:

$$\frac{k_6}{2^{3/2} k_1^{1/2} k_5^{1/2} [C_2H_6]^{1/2}} \times \frac{1}{\left[1 + \dfrac{k_3}{k_4 [C_2H_6]} \right]^{1/2}}$$

This is a satisfactory check with experiment except that it predicts that γ should be proportional to $[C_2H_6]^{-0.5}$ whereas experimentally γ was found to be proportional to $[C_2H_6]^{-0.8}$. The theoretical expression was, however, derived assuming unimolecular chain initiation. If it is assumed that chain initiation is bimolecular at lower pressures, then qualitatively the theory predicts that γ should be inversely proportional to some power of the ethane concentration between 0.5 and unity. Hobbs and Hinshelwood assumed that nitric oxide stops chains by reacting with methyl radicals instead of ethyl radicals and concluded that their data were best explained by assuming unimolecular chain initiation over the whole pressure range and termination by a mixture of binary and ternary collisions. This is unlikely since it seems from modern evidence that third body restrictions do not apply to the recombination of methyl, and probably ethyl, radicals. It also seems likely that ethyl radicals will be preferentially removed. Hinshelwood and co-workers[49] have also produced evidence in a later paper that bimolecular initiation occurs to increasing extents below pressures of 250 mm in the nitric-oxide-inhibited decomposition of ethane.

Stavely[42] has measured "mean chain lengths" of the radical reaction by the nitric oxide method. Values found vary from 20.6 at 50 mm to 6.4 at 500 mm, all at 620°C. These cannot be the true radical chain lengths since the values are totally incompatible with the rate constant values given above. The real chain length as measured by the relative rates of propagation and termination reactions must be several thousand units. If the inhibited reaction is molecular, therefore, these results can only be interpreted by assuming that the molecular rearrangement directly to ethylene and hydrogen must occur much more frequently than a split of an ethane molecule into two methyl radicals.

A similar analysis could be carried out in detail of the thermal decomposition of higher hydrocarbons. The problem becomes increasingly difficult as in these cases more than one type of radical is produced in the initial step and the rate constants for the reactions of higher alkyl radicals are not as yet known. The general inference that radical reactions play an important role in hydrocarbon decompositions is, however, clear. No simple free-radical mechanism can be expected to give quantitative agreement with experiment over a wide range of pressures due to mechanism changes which occur with changing experimental conditions.

The presence or absence of a concomitant molecular reaction accounting for some 10 to 50 per cent of the products depending on the hydrocarbon cannot as yet be proved or disproved. It is virtually impossible to explain the fact that both propylene and nitric oxide produce the same limiting low rate of decomposition when added to various hydrocarbons without assuming that the residual reaction is of a different type and, hence, probably molecular. There exists, however, a discrepancy between these experiments and photochemical experiments, since the former indicate that nitric oxide is only about ten times more efficient than propylene in removing radicals, whilst the latter indicate that the ratio should be many powers of ten higher. The ratio can be measured by determination of the rate constants of the reactions of methyl radicals produced photochemically with propylene and nitric oxide separately. The answer to this and to the other quantitative discrepancies lies in further experimental work at low conversions, where the experimental data are less ambiguous.

References

1. Anderson, H. G., and Van Artsdalen, E. R., *J. Chem. Phys.*, **12**, 479 (1944).
2. Berlie, M. R., and LeRoy, D. J., *J. Chem. Phys.*, **20**, 200 (1952).
3. Berthelot, M., *Ann. Chim.*, **IV 9**, 445 (1866).
4. Blacet, F. E., and Heldman, J. D., *J. Am. Chem. Soc.*, **64**, 889 (1942).
5. Blacet, F. E., and Loeffler, D. E., *J. Am. Chem. Soc.*, **64**, 893 (1942).
6. Bone, W. A., and Coward, H. F., *J. Chem. Soc.*, **93**, 1197 (1908).
7. Butler, E. T., and Polanyi, M., *Trans. Faraday Soc.*, **39**, 19 (1943).
8. Bywater, S., and Steacie, E. W. R., *J. Chem. Phys.*, **19**, 326 (1951).
9. Durham, R. W., and Steacie, E. W. R., *J. Chem. Phys.*, **20**, 582 (1952).
10. Echols, L. S., and Pease, R. N., *J. Am. Chem. Soc.*, **61**, 1024 (1939).
11. Eltenton, G. C., *J. Chem. Phys.*, **15**, 445 (1947).
12. Goldfinger, P., Letort, M., and Niclause, M., "Contribution to the Study of Molecular Structure," Liege, Besoer, 1948.
13. Gomer, R., and Kistiakowsky, G. B., *J. Chem. Phys.*, **19**, 85 (1951).

Library
State College
Indiana, Penna.

547.2   B791

v. 2, c.1

14. Gorin, E., *Acta Physicochim. URSS*, **9**, 681 (1938).
15. Haber, F., *Ber.*, **29**, 2691 (1896).
16. Hague, E. N., and Wheeler, R. V., *J. Chem. Soc.*, 378 (1929).
17. Herzberg, G., and Ramsay, D. A., *Discussions Faraday Soc.*, **9**, 80 (1950).
18. Hipple, J. A., and Stevenson, D. P., *Phys. Rev.*, **63**, 121 (1943).
19. Hobbs, J. E., and Hinshelwood, C. N., *Proc. Roy. Soc. (London)*, **A162**, 557 (1937).
20. Hormats, E. I., and Van Artsdalen, E. R., *J. Chem. Phys.*, **19**, 778 (1951).
21. Ingold, K. U., Stubbs, F. J., and Hinshelwood, C. N., *Proc. Roy. Soc. (London)*, **A203**, 486 (1950).
22. Ingold, K. U., Stubbs, F. J., and Hinshelwood, C. N., *Proc. Roy. Soc. (London)*, **A208**, 285 (1951).
23. Kistiakowsky, G. B., and Van Artsdalen, E. R., *J. Chem. Phys.*, **12**, 469 (1944).
24. Klute, C. H., and Walters, W. D., *J. Am. Chem. Soc.*, **67**, 550 (1945).
25. Kuchler, L., and Thiele, H., *Z. physik. Chem.*, **B42**, 359 (1939).
26. LeRoy, D. J., and Steacie, E. W. R., *J. Chem. Phys.*, **10**, 676 (1942).
27. Lindemann, F. A., *Trans. Faraday Soc.*, **17**, 598 (1922).
28. Lossing, F. P., Ingold, K. U., and Tickner, A. W., *Discussions Faraday Soc.* **14**, 34 (1953).
29. Marek, L. F., and McCluer, W. B., *Ind. Eng. Chem.*, **23**, 878 (1931).
30. Mitchell, J. W., and Hinshelwood, C. N., *Proc. Roy. Soc. (London)*, **A159**, 32 (1937).
31. Paneth, F., and Hofeditz, W., *Ber.*, **62B**, 1335 (1929).
32. Paneth, F., and Lautsch, W., *Ber.*, **64B**, 2708 (1931).
33. Pauling, L., "Nature of the Chemical Bond," Ithaca, New York, Cornell University Press, 1948.
34. Porter, G., *Discussions Faraday Soc.*, **9**, 60 (1950).
35. Rice, F. O., *J. Am. Chem. Soc.*, **53**, 1959 (1931).
36. Rice, F. O., and Herzfeld, K. F., *J. Am. Chem. Soc.*, **56**, 284 (1934).
37. Rice, F. O., Johnston, W. R., and Evering, B. L., *J. Am. Chem. Soc.*, **54**, 3529 (1932).
38. Rice, F. O., and Rice, K. K., "The Aliphatic Free Radicals," Baltimore, Johns Hopkins Press, 1935.
39. Robertson, A. J. B., *Proc. Roy. Soc. (London)*, **A199**, 394 (1949).
40. Roberts, R., and Darwent, B. deB., *Discussions Faraday Soc.* **14**, 55 (1953).
41. Sachsse, H., *Z. physik. Chem.* **B31**, 79 (1935).
42. Stavely, L. A. K., *Proc. Roy. Soc. (London)*, **A162**, 557 (1937).
43. Steacie, E. W. R., and Folkins, H. O., *Can. J. Research*, **B18**, 1 (1940).
44. Steacie, E. W. R., and Shane, G., *Can. J. Research*, **B18**, 203 (1940).
45. Steacie, E. W. R., and Shane, G., *Can. J. Research*, **B18**, 351 (1940).
46. Stevenson, D. P., *J. Chem. Phys.*, **10**, 291 (1942).
47. Stevenson, D. P., *Discussions Faraday Soc.*, **10**, 35, (1951).
48. Stubbs, F. J., and Hinshelwood, C. N., *Proc. Roy. Soc. (London)*, **A200**, 458 (1950).
49. Stubbs, F. J., Ingold, K. U., Spall, B. C., Danby, C. J., and Hinshelwood, C. N., *Proc. Roy. Soc. (London)*, **A214**, 20 (1952).
50. Szwarc, M., *Chem. Rev.*, **47**, 75 (1950).
51. Taylor, H. A., and Bender, H., *J. Chem. Phys.*, **9**, 761 (1941).
52. Thompson, H. W., and Meissner, M., *Nature*, **139**, 1018 (1937).
53. Thorpe, T. E., and Young, J., *Proc. Roy. Soc. (London)*, **21**, 184 (1873).
54. Trotman-Dickenson, A. F., Birchard, J. R., and Steacie, E. W. R., *J. Chem. Phys.*, **19**, 163 (1951).

CHAPTER 23

CONDITIONS AND RESULTS OF THERMAL CRACKING FOR GASOLINE

Joel H. Hirsch and E. K. Fisher

Gulf Research & Development Company

In any list of the most significant commercial developments of the last century, thermal cracking would have an important place. From its inception with the development of the Burton Still in 1912[5] to the general acceptance of catalytic cracking in 1944, over four billion barrels of thermally cracked gasoline were produced. Without thermal cracking the widespread development of the automobile would have been impossible, since straight-run gasoline alone would not have been adequate in quantity or quality. Although new refinery construction is now largely devoted to catalytic cracking, 2,200,000 barrels per day of thermal capacity are still in operation[3] and several auxiliary uses give promise of some resurgence, especially in the viscosity breaking of vacuum-reduced crudes and the cracking of certain refractory catalytic cycle stocks.

Thermal cracking as it is practiced to produce gasoline may be defined as a series of decomposition and condensation reactions which take place at elevated temperatures. The decomposition reactions are usually endothermic and the condensation reactions are exothermic. Decomposition usually predominates to the extent that the over-all effect is moderately endothermic.

Over the period from 1912 to 1944 a very large number of thermal cracking processes were in use; a still larger number appeared in the technical and patent literature. Notwithstanding a wide variety of names and a considerable period of development, thermal cracking as it finally evolved was substantially a single process, the similarities being more marked than the differences.

Broadly, the processes were classified into two major categories—liquid phase and vapor phase. These designations have more historical than scientific significance; but the literature, and particularly the patent literature, tended to turn on this method of classification. The phase conditions were the focal point of a number of patent lawsuits and, it is important to understand the basis for these distinctions.

Liquid Phase vs Vapor Phase

The use of liquid and vapor phase to characterize cracking processes grew out of the method by which the processes were practiced in the early days. The Burton process, which is generally recognized to be the first commercially successful cracking process for the production of gasoline, was conducted in an externally heated, horizontal, cylindrical tank. The temperature was maintained just below the boiling point of the charge at the highest pressure which could be held safely. Originally this pressure was 75 psig, but later improvements in vessel construction permitted a maximum of 95 psig. The temperature in the still was normally about 750°F. A liquid level was maintained, and most of the cracking took place in the liquid phase, the product gasoline distilling over. Hence, the inception of liquid-phase cracking.

As the art progressed the liquid-phase cracking units went through a stage where they resembled steam boilers. Notable among these were the Burton-Clark and Jenkins stills. The Burton-Clark process[2,6] circulated oil through a multiplicity of tubes much like a water tube boiler. The cracking took place in the liquid phase in what would be the steam drum of a boiler. A thermo-siphon effect caused the oil to circulate through the tubes and up into the drum with cracked vapors passing out the top of the drum. The Jenkins process[16] provided a considerable improvement by using a propeller to circulate the oil through the tubes. This circulation was so rapid that the necessary heat of cracking could be supplied to the contents of the drum with a very small increase in temperature of the oil passing through the tubes. Thus coking of the tubes was minimized.

Other early workers, among them Hall,[13] Rittman,[24] Greenstreet,[12] and Ramage,[23] endeavored to operate wholly in the vapor phase. They did this by maintaining the pressure as low as possible at appropriately high temperatures. Vapor-phase operations were usually conducted in heated pipes; sometimes a number of pipes were used in parallel, and sometimes they were connected in series to form a long serpentine coil.

As the art developed, liquid-phase processes were practiced in tubular systems similar to vapor-phase processes, except that these were conducted under the highest pressures that materials limitations would permit, with the avowed purpose of maintaining the oil in the liquid phase. This work paralleled the development of the tubular pipe still for crude oil distillation, the heating element of a tubular liquid-phase cracking process being really a high-pressure pipe still. Notable examples of the more successful liquid-phase cracking processes were the Tube and Tank,[15] Cross,[7] Dubbs,[10] and Holmes-Manley[1] processes. These processes generally employed a high-pressure pipe still, followed by a reaction drum. The oil was supposed to have been heated in the coil and allowed to crack in the reaction drum, although an appreciable portion of the cracking actually took place in the coil.

In the early art there were several schools of thought as to the preferred method of carrying out a given cracking reaction. Some people preferred conducting the cracking in a tubular coil only. Some preferred a coil and a horizontal reaction vessel. Some preferred a coil and a vertical vessel with the reactants flowing upward and some with the reactants flowing downward. Considerable difference of opinion existed as to the merits of these systems, and many reports and articles were written, particularly about the relative merits of coil-only cracking versus coil-and-drum cracking. It can now be said that for all practical purposes there was substantially no difference, and the same yield and quality of products could be obtained with any given oil in any of the several types of cracking apparatus that were commonly used. If one were to draw any distinctions, and these would be fine ones, it might be said that a coil alone would be preferred for mild viscosity breaking of heavy residual stocks. For topped crudes and gas-oils, on the other hand, any of the systems work about equally well. It was preferable to operate upflow in the reaction drum when more extensive treatment was desired on the heavier portions of the oil. In this way the light materials vaporized out and the heavy oils remained in the reaction zone until the desired treatment was obtained. This was carried to its final degree in the various coking processes. On the other hand, when more severe treatment of the vapor components was desired, such as with gas-oils and some topped crudes, the downflow-type reaction chamber had considerable popularity. In this case the unvaporized fractions fell through the reaction chamber and were drawn off quickly, while the vapors were held a longer period and the desired treatment obtained. This method was especially effective in producing low-viscosity residual fuel oil from a number of topped crudes.

The pressures used in the so-called "liquid phase" processes varied from about 200 psig in the Dubbs process to 600 psig in the Cross process. It was the opinion of the inventors that the reactions took place in the liquid phase, just as in the Burton and Jenkins processes, and there was some evidence that this was the case. For example, the effect of each thrust of the oil charging pump at the inlet of the cracking coil could be observed by a corresponding pulsation of the pressure gauge connected to the reaction chamber outlet. Subsequent investigation revealed that the processes operated in what might be described as the mixed phase—both vapor and liquid being present; but the establishment of this fact required many years of work and many thousands of dollars' expense. The record of it is spread over volumes of court records. What was perhaps the distinguishing feature was the operating pressure, since high-pressure processes tend to make products of one type and low-pressure processes those of another. Although the terms "liquid phase" and "vapor phase" were applied, these terms were more honored in the breach than in the observance.

The confusion over the terms "liquid phase" and "vapor phase" as applied to cracking arose from the fact that fluids under pressure exhibit properties closely resembling both liquids and vapors. This is illustrated by the diagram, Figure 1. If a mixture such as a hydrocarbon oil is heated at constant pressure, as defined by the line $ABCD$, the first bubble of vapor will appear at the bubble point, B, and the amount of liquid will gradually decrease until the last drop evaporates at C. As the temperature is further raised to D, the homogeneous vapor becomes superheated. If, on the other hand, the pressure is first raised at constant temperature to point E and the fluid is heated to point F and then expanded to point D, no perceptible transition can be observed.

This is well illustrated with a sample of gasoline containing a blue dye. As the gasoline is heated through the route $ABCD$, the liquid begins to boil at point B, and the dye concentrates in the liquid phase as the oil is vaporized until at point C the entire solid settles out on the walls of the sample tube. If, on the other hand, the dye solution is first raised in pressure to point E, which is well above the top of the border curve, and then heated to point F, no evidence of segregation is observed. The pressure may even be lowered to point D without any evidence of the dye's separating out. Thus the system has passed from liquid to vapor with no perceptible line of demarcation between the two phases. It has also been found that highly compressed water vapor when above its critical pressure and critical temperature will dissolve solids such as sodium chloride. Thus, under the conditions which exist in a cracking coil, it is possible to go from a liquid to a vapor without ever having any evidence of a transition. This phenomenon is described very effectively in Taylor's "A Treatise on Physical Chemistry":[26]

" . . . the only definite difference between a gas and a liquid is the property of liquids of forming an independent surface, that is, one not determined by the wall of the container.

"Other differences between gases and liquids are of degree and not fundamental. Unless this distinguishing property of independent surface is exhibited it is not possible to give a strict definition which will classify a dense fluid as either liquid or gas."

The preceding discussion deals with a border curve for a simple mixture; that is, where no chemical change takes place. In a cracking apparatus the

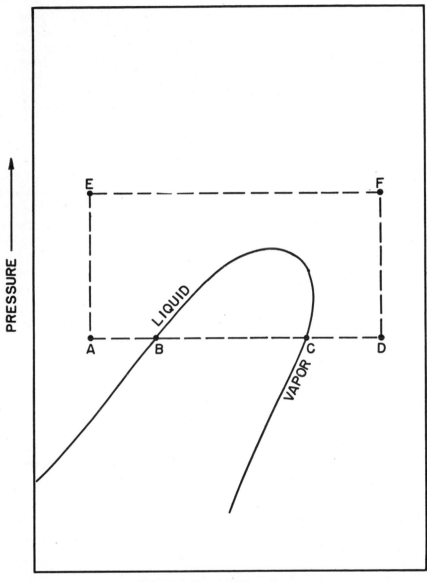

FIG. 1. Liquid-vapor phase relationship for petroleum fractions.

problem is further complicated by another dimension, the extent of cracking. In other words, three dimensions are present—temperature, pressure, and composition—and the border curve thus becomes a border surface.

A cracking unit can be operated in such a way that it is impossible to tell whether it is in the liquid phase or the vapor phase, since the stream could travel from inlet to outlet without ever passing through the two-phase region defined by the border surface. Only if the pressure-temperature curve for the stream passes through the border surface can it be definitely said that the process is not in a single phase, and then it will be neither liquid phase nor vapor phase, but mixed phase. The same reactions can occur either inside or outside the border surface, and the phase conditions under which the reactions are taking place are unimportant to the results.

Basically, the yields and product characteristics from thermal cracking are controlled by three major variables: character of feed to the reaction zone, extent of cracking or conversion per pass, and pressure. Many other variables have a secondary or related effect, but none has the same importance as these three.

Relation of Temperature

Just as phase conditions were once thought to have an important influence on cracking, but were really a result rather than a cause, other variables which were thought to be independent have been shown by further investigation to be intensive rather than extensive properties of the system. A good example is reaction temperature. Temperature is the major factor controlling the rate of cracking reactions and it, together with reaction time, governs the extent of conversion that will take place in any given apparatus. The fundamental axiom of cracking is that it is a time-temperature function, and to a considerable extent these variables are interchangeable. That is, at increased temperature, a given amount of cracking will be accomplished in a shorter time. However, it was long believed that temperature had a very important effect on the quality of products made in a cracking unit. For example, it was thought that high temperature produced improved antiknock properties. Careful analysis of the data indicates that the effect of temperature, per se, on the octane number of cracked gasolines is minor. The observed cracking temperature was really a measure of something else. High octane number comes from increased conversion per pass and is normally associated with greater refractoriness of the oil fed to the cracking zone. Thus, stocks of low aniline point and low paraffinicity, as expressed by Watson's characterization factor,[27,28] tend to produce high-octane gasoline on cracking. In any given cracking unit a higher temperature is required in order to attain a given conversion per pass with a more refractory stock or an increased conversion per pass with a given stock. Under conditions where high temperatures were attained, the systems usually were thought to be in the vapor phase. Thus high temperature and vapor phase became associated with high-octane-number gasoline when they were not the underlying causes, but only the apparent results, of other operating variables. If sufficient time were built into an apparatus or the charge rate sufficiently reduced, gasoline octane numbers could be obtained in liquid-phase cracking at relatively moderate temperatures which would be comparable with those normally associated with high-temperature vapor-phase cracking. This is illustrated by Keith, Ward, and Rubin.[17] Their data indicate that at a given crack per pass and operating pressure, anti-knock values attained at temperatures varying from 800 to 1000°F can all be represented by a single line. Their findings are summarized as follows: "Thus, it is seen that there is very little evidence of temperature effect—the factors determining the anti-knock by this method being crack per pass and pressure of formation."

The preceding discussion has been devoted to consideration of the factors normally thought to affect thermal cracking operations, in an effort to see which ones have substance. Thus it is seen that stock character, conversion per pass, and pressure are controlling, and that phase conditions and temperature are much less important than was formerly believed.

Yields from Thermal Cracking

The yields from thermal cracking were originally measured in three quantities, namely, gas, cracked gasoline, and cracked tar or fuel oil. In some instances coking or non-residuum operations were conducted, in which case the major products were gas, cracked gasoline, and coke. Fairly good yield correlations were developed for the major products, but detailed product analyses of the type now available from catalytic cracking were largely unknown because of the lack of rapid and accurate analytical facilities in the period when thermal cracking was most widely employed.

The most important single factor in determining the yield of cracked gasoline from a given oil is the change in hydrogen content. In fact, it can be shown that thermal cracking is in a large measure a matter of hydrogen balance and that the results of a wide range of operations can be defined by the change in hydrogen content. The following equation presents a good generalized expression of the cracked gasoline yield for a wide range of cracking operations and a variety of processes.

$$N = \frac{115(H_C - H_T)}{3.09 + (H_C + H_T)} \tag{1}$$

where N = volume per cent 400°F E.P. cracked gasoline, total butane retention
$\quad H_C$ = weight per cent hydrogen in fresh charge
$\quad H_T$ = weight per cent hydrogen in cracked fuel oil

This equation is presented graphically in Figure 2. The cracked gasoline yield from a great variety of stocks, distillate and residual, cracked and virgin, and under a variety of operating conditions is predicted with an average deviation of about 3 per cent. The equation is also applicable,

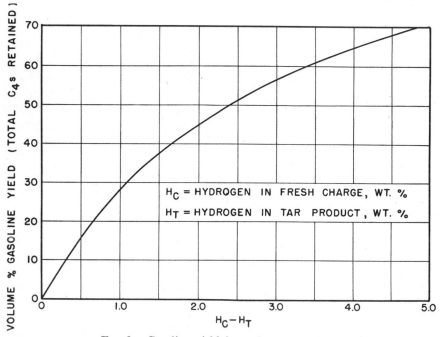

FIG. 2.   Gasoline yield from thermal cracking.

with slight modification, to coking or non-residuum operations. The fact that cracking yields can be expressed so simply as the difference in hydrogen content between the charge stock and cracked fuel oil explains why it has been possible to correlate gasoline yield as a function of the API gravities of the charge stock and cracked fuel oil. Hydrogen content, of course, is fairly accurately indicated by the API gravity of the oil. Therefore, when running to the same fuel oil gravity with a given charge stock, the ultimate yield of cracked gasoline is only moderately affected by other operating conditions and is substantially the same for all processes. Next to hydrogen content, pressure is the most important secondary variable—decreasing pressure producing more gas and less fuel oil for a given gasoline yield—but even pressure has a relatively minor effect on yields.

Having estimated the yield of cracked gasoline from Equation (1), it is possible to calculate the yield of cracked fuel oil from the following equation:

$$T = \frac{92.2 - N}{0.95} \tag{2}$$

where T = volume per cent cracked fuel oil
   N = volume per cent 400°F E.P. cracked gasoline, total butane retention

and the yield of dry gas (C_3's and lighter) from the following equation:

$$G = 1.4 + 0.168N \tag{3}$$

where G = weight per cent butane-free gas
   N = volume per cent 400°F E.P. cracked gasoline, total butane retention

These three equations give reasonably satisfactory results for most stocks and processes at operating pressures of 200 to 1000 psig and 800 to 1000°F reaction temperature. Below 100 psig and above 1050°F there may be some increase in gas formation, possibly as a result of over-cracking; that is, further cracking of the gasoline produced early in the reaction.

Characteristics of Products from Thermal Cracking

In general, the high-pressure processes, that is, 200 to 1000 psig, make a gasoline product that is characterized as fairly saturated, low in diolefins, and capable of being readily treated to make finished gasoline. The composition of cracked gasolines is the subject of another chapter and will not be discussed here, but it is believed that some generalizations may be apropos. At cracking pressures of 200 to 1000 psig and any given conversion per pass, the octane number of cracked gasoline is largely dependent on the characteristics of the fresh charge to the cracking unit. When producing 12° API cracked fuel oil and operating at a conversion per pass of about 20 per cent; the octane numbers of the 10 RVP, 400°F E.P. cracked gasoline are represented approximately by the curves on Figure 3. The C_4-free gas from high pressure cracking operations has approximately the following composition:

TABLE 1. COMPOSITION OF BUTANE-FREE GAS

Hydrogen	4
Methane	42
Ethylene	4
Ethane	24
Propylene	8
Propane	18
	——
Total	100

At cracking pressures below 100 psig, the gasoline and gas are much higher in unsaturated components. The gasoline has somewhat higher octane number, but an increased amount of undesirable diolefins. This becomes increasingly worse as the pressure approaches atmospheric. These low-pressure operations usually took place at correspondingly high temperatures of 1050 to 1150°F, because in any given apparatus the reaction time is very short at low pressure. Such processes as the Hall,

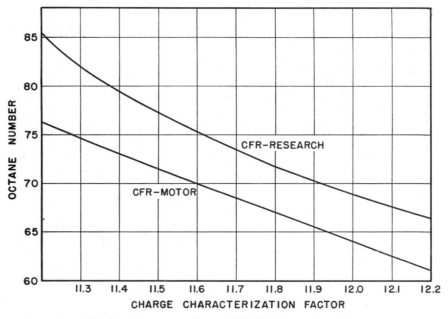

Fig. 3.   Octane number of 10 RVP cracked gasoline.

Greenstreet, Rittman, etc. were characterized by the high antiknock properties of the gasoline and the highly olefinic nature of the gasoline and cracked gas.

One seeming anomaly was the de Florez process,[9] which was classified as a vapor-phase process but produced gasoline and gas quite similar to that from the high pressure or "liquid phase" processes. This caused speculation in the early years, but was resolved when improved testing and calculative techniques became available. Like the low-pressure "vapor phase" processes, the de Florez process did not have a back pressure valve at the outlet of the reaction coil. The reaction coil transfer line discharged into a separating tower in which the cracked fuel was withdrawn from the bottom, and the gasoline and vaporized components passed overhead. The pressure in this tower was of the order of 50 psig, but although the outlet pressure of the de Florez cracking coil was quite low, the inlet pressure was high, being of the order of 500 to 600 psig. In passing through the long coil the pressure decreased, but most of the pressure drop occurred near the outlet. Studies in later years showed that the bulk of the cracking was taking place at high pressures; that is, pressures above 200 psig, the mean pressure for most of the cracking being about 300 psig. The pressure did not fall until near the coil outlet, when substantially all of the cracking had been completed. Unlike the de Florez process, those processes that were distinguished by "vapor phase" type products had the reaction tubes connected in parallel, permitting the whole reaction system to operate at low pressure.

Previously it was brought out that the yields of cracked gasoline, gas, and fuel oil were largely determined by the hydrogen content of the fresh charge and cracked fuel oil, and that this, in turn, was closely related to the API gravities of these two streams. Thus, all cracking units produce about the same yields when operating to the same fuel oil gravity on a given charge stock. However, the most important quality of cracked fuel oil is not its gravity but its viscosity, and not all processes produce the same viscosity fuel oil for a given gravity. The fuel-oil viscosity appears to be more nearly a function of operating conditions and process sequence than most of the other yields and properties from thermal cracking. Most oils undergo considerable change in viscosity as they pass through a cracking unit. The lighter oils such as gas-oils produce cracked fuel oils higher in viscosity than the initial charge stock, the fuel oil being composed mainly of second-order condensation products of the reaction. Heavy residual stocks produce cracked fuel oils lower in viscosity than the initial charge stock. This is called viscosity breaking or vis-breaking. Topped crudes on the other hand produce fuel oils of intermediate viscosity. The fuel oil is a mixture of the vis-broken virgin bottoms and the condensed materials from gas-oil cracking.

Just how the operation takes place has a significant effect on the final viscosity of the fuel oil. For example, it has been found that if the heavy virgin gas-oil is removed from the vis-broken residuum, it can be replaced by refractory light cycle stock from cracking of the lighter components. This lighter material, although poorer in hydrogen and potential gasoline-making properties, is a superior medium for cutting the viscosity of the heavy bottoms. On the other hand, the virgin gas-oil extracted from the heavy bottoms, being richer in hydrogen, will make more gasoline than the light refractory cycle stock would if it had been recycled to extinction. The net effect is that removal of a poor viscosity cutting medium and replacing it with a good viscosity cutter, but a poor cracking stock, produces higher over-all yields of gasoline and lower yields of fuel oil of a given viscosity specification. This operation is known as "running heavy and blending back." One way in which it can be accomplished is by charging a reduced crude to a viscosity-breaking coil, removing the gas-oil overhead, cracking the light gas-oil in one coil and the heavy gas-oil in another. The bottoms are subjected to vacuum reduction and the gas-oil removed is charged to the heavy gas-oil cracking coil. The cracked tars from the light and heavy gas-oil coils are blended with the vacuum bottoms, together with sufficient light cycle stock to make the required specification fuel oil.

Viscosity Blending

Viscosity-blending calculations are of considerable importance in any effort to predict over-all yields from a cracking operation. Frequently,

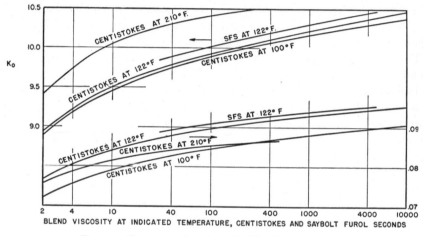

Fig. 4.   Constants for viscosity blending equation.

blending experiments are conducted to gain information on this subject; or, lacking them, various graphical procedures are used. One procedure that has been found convenient is based on the use of Watson's characterization factor in the following manner.

Study of the correlations of characterization factor with gravity and viscosity by Watson, *et al.*,[27,28] shows that, for a given viscosity and temperature, the characterization factor, K, is a linear function of API gravity, G:

$$K = K_0 + mG \tag{4}$$

where the constants, K_0 and m, are functions of viscosity and temperature (see Figure 4). It has also been demonstrated that API gravity and characterization factor can be averaged on a weight basis:[25]

$$G_B = G_L X + G_H(1 - X) \tag{5}$$
$$K_B = K_L X + K_H(1 - X) \tag{6}$$

where X is the weight fraction of light oil in the blend and the subscripts B, L, and H refer to blend, light oil and heavy oil properties, respectively. Substituting G_B and K_B in Equation (4), and solving for X, gives:

$$X = \frac{K_H - K_0 - mG_H}{K_H - K_L + m(G_L - G_H)} \tag{7}$$

The weight ratio of light oil to heavy oil is:

$$\frac{X}{1 - X} \tag{8}$$

The volume ratio of light oil to heavy oil is:

$$\frac{X}{1 - X}\left[\frac{S_H}{S_L}\right] \tag{9}$$

where S is the specific gravity.

The average deviation for values of X, using Equation (7), on known blends is ± 0.024.

The effectiveness of any given cracking coil for reducing the viscosity of a charge stock is a function of several factors of the operation and charge stock, not all of which are fully understood. Change in viscosity for any given operation in going from fresh charge to cracked fuel oil can be fairly well expressed by plotting the difference in characterization factor between the charge and fuel oil against the difference in gravity or hydrogen content. Although these relationships will vary with charge stocks and with cracking units, they do provide a fairly good procedure for interpolation.

Conditions Conducive to Coking

One of the early operators of thermal cracking once commented that the twin specters of cracking plant operation were corrosion and coke. Both of these problems were largely solved as the art progressed. No better proof of this could be found than the fact that while the early Burton stills operated for about 24 hours and then had to shut down for cleaning and repairs, a modern combination thermal cracking unit operates many months between shutdowns. Although all of the factors affecting coke formation have not been determined, enough is known to permit fairly trouble-free operation. In general, it seems that at least two conditions must be present for coke to form in a cracking unit; one of these is a result of chemical factors and the other physical. Cracked tars— the ones that are most likely to produce coke—are formed in secondary reactions by condensation of the initial products. Unless these compounds are present, coking is not likely to occur; in fact, they can be present up to a certain concentration without difficulty. Even if they are present in considerable quantity, coking will not necessarily occur unless certain physical conditions are present. Previous discussion dealt with border curves and border surfaces, which defined the phase conditions in cracking systems. There, it was pointed out that the same cracking reactions could take place either inside or outside the border surface. It appears that only when the operating conditions are too close to the border surface is there danger of coke formation. If the entire operation is conducted outside the surface coke will not deposit; or, if the operation is well inside the border surface, no difficulty will be encountered. It is only under conditions where the operation is close to the dew-point surface that difficulty may occur, and then only if coke-forming bodies are present. This is analogous to the settling out of the blue dye in the experiments with the gasoline described earlier.

These conditions may occur either on heating or cooling of a cracked stream. In fact, one of the places where coking was most frequently experienced in the early days of thermal cracking was in the transfer line connecting the cracking zone with the first tower. Here, in cooling, the stream crossed the border surface and coking resulted. This was overcome by the simple expedient known as "quenching." By injecting a quantity of oil recycled from one of the towers, the transfer line contents were cooled quickly to a point inside the border surface. If the dew-point surface is crossed rapidly, coking is avoided. It is only when this crossing occurs slowly that trouble occurs.

Heat Effects in Thermal Cracking

In general, thermal cracking operations are preponderantly endothermic, as previously stated. The reactions taking place in the cracking zone are a combination of decomposition and condensation. The decomposition reactions predominate, and since they are endothermic they more than offset the condensation reactions that are exothermic. The heat of cracking at standard conditions amounts to about 350 Btu's per pound of gas plus gasoline formed. The heat of cracking reactions may be estimated fairly accurately from the following equation:

$$H = \frac{50,000(M_c - M_p)}{M_c M_p} \tag{10}$$

where H = heat of cracking, Btu/lb at 77°F and 1 atm
M_c = molecular weight of charge to reaction zone
M_p = molecular weight of products from reaction zone

There seems to be some confusion in the literature in regard to the appropriate heat of cracking for use in equipment design. This arises from the fact that some heats of cracking are given at reaction conditions rather than at standard conditions. If the heat of cracking is determined from a heat balance where the datum level is taken at some reference temperature such as 32°, 60°, or 77°F, the heat of reaction is determined by difference after correcting for all losses and is the heat of reaction at the datum temperature. This is the value customarily determined by use of standard heats of combustion.

On the other hand, some data reported in the literature have been determined by heating hydrocarbon oils in bench-scale, continuous-flow equipment. The reaction zone is maintained under isothermal conditions by external electric windings. The heat input required to maintain constant temperature is measured on an electric watt meter. The heat of cracking determined in this case is the heat of reaction at operating conditions. This is usually higher than the heat of reaction at standard conditions.

Reaction Rates

Reaction velocity data for thermal cracking are usually correlated by means of the first-order reaction equation:

$$\frac{dx}{dt} = K(a - x) \tag{11}$$

which integrates to:

$$\ln \frac{a}{a - x} = Kt \tag{12}$$

where x = fraction of the feed converted, in this instance the weight fraction of gas plus 400°F E.P. gasoline formed

a = weight fraction of unconverted feed entering the reaction zone ($a = 1.0$ if no gas or gasoline is present in the feed)

t = reaction time, sec

K = reaction velocity constant, sec^{-1}

When a pure compound is cracked it is quite simple to determine $(a - x)$ or the amount of that compound remaining at time (t), and x as the difference between the amount present at the inlet of the reaction zone and that present at time (t). With mixtures, especially those present in a cracking coil, where decomposition and condensation proceed simultaneously, the extent of conversion must be defined somewhat arbitrarily. Use of the weight fraction of gas plus gasoline formed as an index of conversion has been found satisfactory for this purpose.

Plots of reaction velocity constants against the reciprocal of the absolute temperature give straight lines that are approximately parallel for a wide variety of hydrocarbons, both pure compounds and mixtures, when conversion is defined as described above. Figure 5 presents a correlation of cracking reaction velocity constants at 800°F for petroleum oils as a function of the API gravity and average boiling point. The effect of temperature on reaction velocity constants is given in Figure 6.

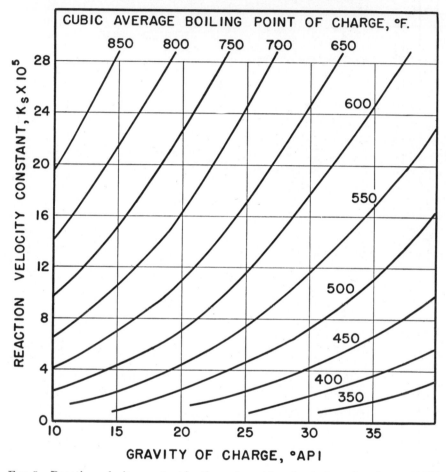

Fig. 5.   Reaction velocity constant for thermal cracking of petroleum fractions at 800°F.

It should be noted that the reaction velocity constants at 800°F, obtained from Figure 5, are for heater feed (i.e., oil charged to the reaction zone), not for fresh feed to the cracking unit. Only for once-through-type cracking operations is Figure 5 directly applicable. For single recycle stream units the characterization factor and the API gravity of the heater feed can be approximated in the following manner. Figure 7 gives the difference in characterization factor between the

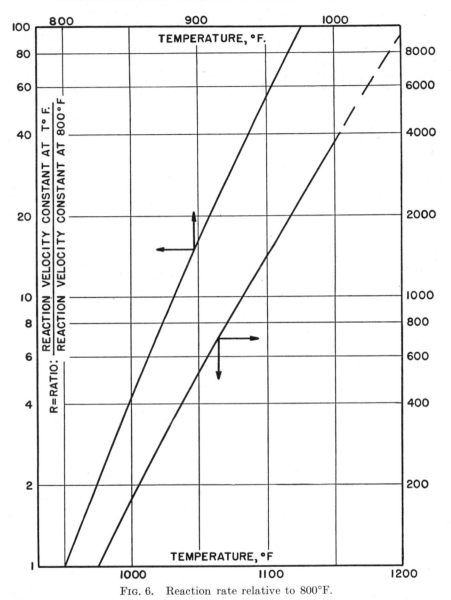

Fig. 6. Reaction rate relative to 800°F.

fresh feed and recycle as a function of the ultimate yield of gas plus gasoline from the unit. The characterization factor of the heater feed is then calculated from the following equations:

$$K_H = K_F - (K_F - K_R)(1 - f) = K_F - \Delta K(1 - f) = K_F - \Delta K \left(1 - \frac{x}{y}\right)$$

where K_H = Watson's characterization factor of the heater feed
K_F =   "   "   "   "   " fresh feed
K_R =   "   "   "   "   " recycle
f = weight fraction of fresh feed in heater feed = x/y
x = conversion per pass, weight fraction gas plus gasoline formed, based on heater feed
y = ultimate yield, weight fraction gas plus gasoline formed, based on fresh feed.

In a similar manner the API gravity of the heater feed can be calculated from Figure 8 and the following equation:

$$G_H = G_F - (G_F - G_R)(1 - f) = G_F - \Delta G(1 - f) = G_F - \Delta G \left(1 - \frac{x}{y} \right)$$

K_F = WATSON CHARACTERIZATION FACTOR OF FRESH CHARGE
K_R = CHARACTERIZATION FACTOR OF RECYCLE

FIG. 7. Recycle characterization factor.

where G_H, G_F, and G_R are the API gravities of the heater feed, fresh feed, and recycle, respectively, and all other terms are as defined above. The cubic average boiling point can be calculated from the equation:

$$\text{Cubic average boiling point (°F)} = (K_H S_H)^3 - 460$$

where S_H is specific gravity of heater feed. The reaction velocity constant of the heater feed at 800°F can then be obtained from Figure 5.

For combination units the situation is more complicated. Several fresh and recycle streams pass through a single fractionating system and are segregated on the basis of boiling range for charging to the various cracking heaters. It is almost impossible to determine the characteristics of the various heater feed streams without actual operating data, and it is for problems of this type that small-scale laboratory pilot units have great utility. The proposed commercial operation can thus be simulated, with all of the cracking zones operating in unison, and the characteristics of the various streams determined.

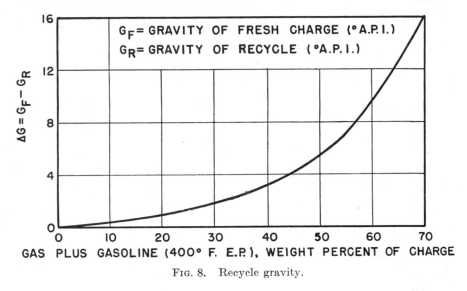

FIG. 8.   Recycle gravity.

Thermal Reforming

Thermal reforming is a special type of cracking process for converting low-octane naphthas into high-octane gasolines. In addition to octane improvement, it also provides an effective method for increasing gasoline volatility. Reforming is particularly useful when seasonal variations require a large range in vapor-pressure specifications.

Reforming is carried out under relatively severe conditions—950°F to 1075°F and 250 to 1000 psig. Because of the high temperature and short contact time, reaction chambers are not usually employed. Recycling is not used because substantially all of the octane improvement obtainable can be attained in a single pass without coke formation.

Reforming changes the chemical composition of the naphtha. The formation of low-molecular-weight hydrocarbons results in a product richer in low-boiling fractions than the charge stock. Paraffins in the virgin naphtha are to a considerable extent converted to olefins, and naphthenes are dehydrogenated to aromatics. This change in chemical composition is highly significant and is largely responsible for the improvement in octane number. In addition, thermal reforming produces large yields of propane-propylene and butane-butylenes. These can be polymerized to produce a high-octane polymer gasoline which is an excellent blending material for improving the quality of other gasolines.

Reforming converts a portion of the charge to gas and cracked fuel oil with a corresponding loss in gasoline yield. The greater the reforming severity the higher the octane number of the gasoline, but the lower the yield because of degradation to less valuable by-products. Tetraethyl lead may also be used to increase the octane number, the optimum reforming level being determined by an economic balance between the cost of TEL required and the loss in yield due to thermal reforming.[11]

Two well-known variations of the thermal reforming process are the Polyform process[4,21] and the Gas Reversion process,[4] in both of which the joint conversion of naphtha and hydrocarbon gases takes place. In the Polyform process the charge naphtha absorbs the C_3- and C_4-hydrocarbons formed on reforming, and the mixture is then charged to the furnace coil. In the Gas Reversion process, the charge naphtha and the recycle gas stream are heated in two separate coils and combined in a third coil for the final conversion.

Yields and properties of gasoline from the two processes are similar, provided the operating conditions and charge stocks are comparable. Additional C_3 or C_4 from other sources may be added to either process, in which case the quantity and quality of these streams become additional variables. Both processes derive their advantages from additional gasoline yield from the circulated gas and from more severe operating conditions made possible by the dilution effect of the added gas. Gasolines of 76–80 CFR M octane numbers may be produced in high yields, whereas the practical ceiling for conventional reforming is 70–72 CFR M octane number.

Physical Apparatus for Commercial Thermal Cracking

Just as there was a wide divergence in the process conceptions in the early days of the cracking art, there were many proposed types of apparatus for carrying out the processes. Gradually these ideas as to processes and apparatus converged, until the present day combination thermal cracking units built by any of several construction companies would be quite similar. The flow diagram for a typical combination thermal cracking unit is shown in Figure 9.

The term "combination process" results from combining several separate operations into one self-contained system. Thus, crude distillation, light oil cracking, heavy oil cracking, viscosity breaking, and naphtha reforming can be integrated to make considerable savings in total investment and operating costs. This is the result of reduced handling of intermediate products, conservation of waste heat from the cracking

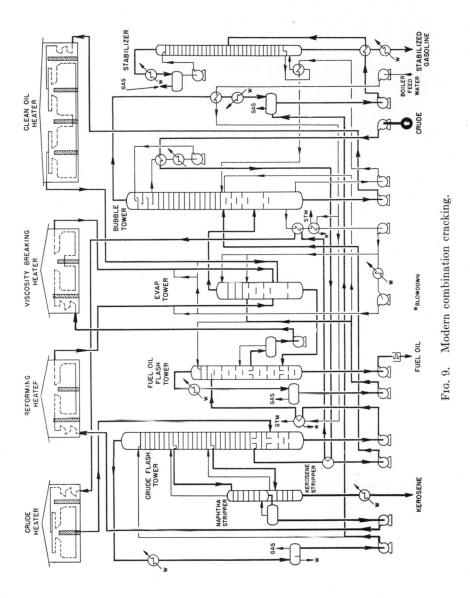

FIG. 9. Modern combination cracking.

operations, and reduced labor and investment requirements per unit of capacity.

Referring to Figure 9, it will be seen that crude petroleum enters the unit through a heat exchange system, being pumped first through the trap tray reflux cooler on the bubble tower, then through the light gas-oil cooler on the crude flash tower, then through the bottoms reflux cooler on the bubble tower, and finally to the crude heater. The oil flows through the convection section of the heater and then through two radiant sections in parallel, and leaves the heater at 700°F and 25 psig. It is then flashed into the crude flash tower. In the crude flash tower a number of fractions pass upward. The straight-run gasoline comes off the top of the tower at a temperature of 270°F and goes to a receiver. The straight-run gasoline is pumped to the cracked gasoline receiver of the cracking section, the mixture then flowing to the stabilizer.

The second stream from the crude flash tower is naphtha, which comes off at 370°F and passes to a naphtha sidestream stripper. The stripped virgin naphtha is collected in an accumulator and then pumped to the reforming heater, where it passes first through the convection section and then through two radiant sections in series. The reformed naphtha leaves the heater at 940°F and 750 psig, passing to the evaporator tower. The third stream from the crude flash tower is kerosene, which comes off at 445°F and passes through a sidestream stripper and cooler to storage. The fourth stream is light gas-oil, which comes off the crude tower at 550°F, is heat-exchanged with the incoming crude, and then pumped into the bubble tower, where it comprises a portion of the feed to the clean oil heater. The bottoms from the crude flash tower are pumped through a steam generator and then used as intermediate reflux in the fuel-oil flash tower. In the fuel-oil flash tower this oil flows downward over baffles along with condensed fractions from the cracked fuel oil. The combined stream passes into an accumulator at 615°F and is pumped to the viscosity-breaking heater.

In the viscosity-breaking heater the stream flows first through a convection section, then through two radiant sections in series. The cracked effluent leaves the viscosity-breaking heater at 885°F and 240 psig, passing into the evaporator tower.

The streams from all three cracking heaters merge in the evaporator tower and are separated according to boiling range. The reformed naphtha and light gas-oil from vis-breaking, plus the clean oil heater recycle, pass overhead to the bubble tower. In the bubble tower the cracked and reformed gasoline passes overhead through condensers and coolers to the cracked gasoline receiver, where it mixes with the straight-run gasoline and is pumped to the stabilizer. The combined gasoline streams leave the bottom of the stabilizer and pass to storage.

In the bottom of the bubble tower, light gas-oil from vis-breaking topped crude and recycle gas-oil from the clean oil heater are combined and pumped to the clean oil heater. In the clean oil heater this stream passes first through the convection section, and then through two radiant sections in parallel, and finally through two more radiant sections in parallel. The clean oil heater effluent leaves the heater at 940°F and 500 psig, and passes into the evaporator tower. In the evaporator tower the light fractions pass overhead, as previously described. The bottoms from the evaporator tower comprising a blend of cracked fuel oil from clean oil cracking, vis-breaking, and reforming flow to the fuel-oil flash tower. This stream leaves the evaporator at 805°F and 220 psig. It flashes into the fuel-oil flash tower, which is operated at 6 psig. The flashed fuel oil from the bottom of this tower is pumped through a submerged cooler to storage. The flashed vapors pass upward in the fuel-oil flash tower, a portion being condensed into the viscosity breaker feed and a portion passing overhead through a condenser into a flash distillate receiver. The flash distillate is pumped into the evaporator tower, where it serves as an intermediate reflux, vaporizing a portion which is suitable for clean oil feed and carrying it into the bubble tower.

All of the cracking furnaces are designed with several bridge walls to permit independent firing of the various radiant sections. This provides maximum flexibility, since each section can be operated substantially as an independent heater.

Cracking Coil Design

The heart of the thermal cracking process is the cracking furnace or heater, and as a result of considerable research and correlation studies, it is possible to design them with a high degree of reliability. Here again there is a considerable difference of opinion as to just how a cracking furnace should be designed, and there are several adaptations which are about equally successful. One school of thought prefers rapid heating of the oil, followed by a soaking section in which the cracking reactions are permitted to take place under mildly heated conditions. The heat supplied in the soaking section just about compensates for the heat of cracking. This soaking section is usually in a portion of the furnace where it is out of sight of the flames, and a large share of the heat is by convection from the hot gases. The soaking section in furnaces of this type functions much like the reaction chamber in the coil-and-drum-type cracking unit. Other cracking experts see no particular reason to use a soaking zone and

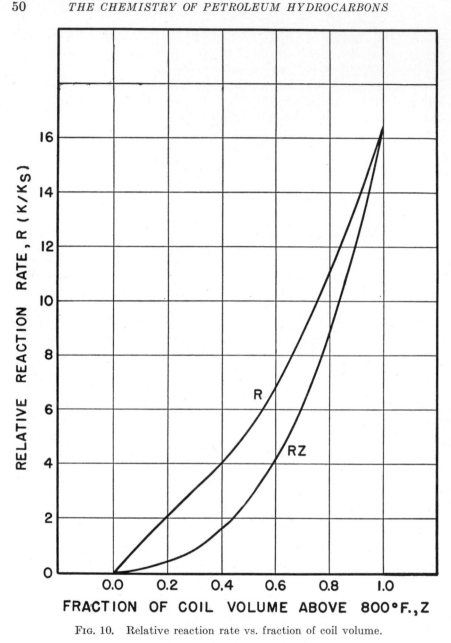

Fig. 10.   Relative reaction rate vs. fraction of coil volume.

do all of the cracking in tubes operating at the same heat density. It is the opinion of the authors that either system will operate successfully when the cracking furnace has been properly designed.

The following procedure is applicable to any of the accepted cracking systems. This presentation is an abridgement of a projected publication of a detailed method for cracking furnace design.

In the design of commercial cracking coils, it is often necessary to project laboratory pilot-plant data into commercial reaction coils. With a knowledge of radiant heat transfer calculation methods, such as those presented by Lobo and Evans,[19] it is possible to calculate the amount of heat transferred to a commercial heating coil. A procedure presented by Hirsch, Crawford, and Holloway[14] may then be used to calculate the extent of cracking and the pressure drop developed in the commercial coil.

The first step in this procedure is to develop reaction velocity constant data from laboratory pilot-plant runs. This is accomplished through use of an equation which takes into consideration the substantially constant pressure operation of the laboratory coil. Having the reaction velocity constant, it can be used for commercial design in the point-to-point equation, which takes into consideration the variation in fluid density resulting from the change in pressure through the reaction zone.

Where a preliminary estimate of the amount of cracking is required, a short-cut method using a simplified equation is available. The steps necessary for these calculations are listed below and then explained individually.

(1) Calculate reaction velocity constants (Equation 13).
(2) Calculate 800°F point.
(3) Calculate pressure drop and cracking progressively to the furnace outlet (Equation 14).

Reaction Velocity Constant. Because the usual laboratory coil operates at substantially constant pressure, the precise cracking equation (14) may be simplified as follows:[14]

$$\left(v_0 + \frac{a\Delta v}{x}\right)\ln\frac{a}{a-x} - \Delta v = \frac{K_sC}{W}\int_0^1 RdZ = \frac{K_s}{W}\int_0^C RdC \qquad (13)$$

Knowing the laboratory coil volume and temperature gradient and the results from a pilot-plant run, all terms in the above equation except the reaction velocity constant K_s are fixed, and K_s can be evaluated.

Nomenclature

a = weight fraction of 400°F plus material in reaction coil feed
C = coil volume above reference temperature (800°F), cu ft
K_s = reaction velocity constant at reference temperature (800°F)
R = relative reaction rate, K/K_s (Figure 6)
v_0 = fluid specific volume at reference temperature, cu ft/lb
v_1 = fluid specific volume at coil outlet, cu ft/lb
$\Delta v = v_1 - v_0$
W = flow rate through reaction coil, lb/sec
x = gas plus gasoline formed in coil, wt fraction of coil feed
Z = fraction of total coil volume above 800°F

Calculation of 800°F Point. Using the radiant heat density calculated by the method of Lobo and Evans[19] the 800°F point in the furnace is calculated, and the pressure drop to this point is determined. Thus, the furnace volume above 800°F is calculated.

Pressure Drop and Cracking to Furnace Outlet. Using the point-to-point conversion equation (14) previously referred to, it is possible to calculate the pressure drop and cracking in several sections progressively through the furnace. This can be done at intermediate values of $Z = 0.3$, $Z = 0.6$, $Z = 0.8$, and $Z = 1.0$. In cases where a definite temperature gradient is known and used, it is usually sufficiently accurate to use only three sections, $Z = 0.3$, $Z = 0.7$, and $Z = 1.0$.

In calculating fluid density through the coil, it is assumed that the stream consists of three components: gas (C_3's and lighter), gasoline (C_4 to 400°F), and heavier material assumed to be the same as the furnace feed. In case the relative proportions of gas and gasoline and their physical properties are not available from pilot-plant runs, they must be determined from correlations or estimated. Average gas properties which may be used are mol wt = 26, $T_c = 510$°R, and $P_c = 750$ psia. Similarly, average gasoline properties are mol wt = 110, $T_c = 1035$°R, and $P_c = 562$ psia. To calculate the density of the stream at any point, the specific volume of each component is calculated and multiplied by the respective weight fraction. The density is the reciprocal of the sum of the partial specific volumes.

The pressure drop through a section is calculated from the Fanning equation. Calculate the Reynolds modulus at the 800°F point and determine the friction factor from conventional published sources.[22] If the friction factor is greater than 0.005 use the value determined, otherwise use 0.005 throughout the remainder of the calculations. The density used in the pressure-drop equation is the log mean of the densities at the inlet and outlet of the section.[14]

Production of gas plus gasoline is determined by a trial and error solution of equation (14). Preliminary assumption of the pressure and amount of cracking are necessary to calculate the temperature, pressure drop, and amount of cracking.

If the calculated pressure agrees within 10 per cent of the value assumed, the conversion may be calculated. After solution of the conversion equation, if the calculated value agrees within 10 per cent of the assumed figure, proceed to the next point in the coil.

$$\ln\left(\frac{a}{a-x}\right) = \frac{K_s C}{W}\left[\rho_1 \int_{Z_1}^{Z_2} RdZ - \left(\frac{\rho_1 - \rho_2}{Z_2 - Z_1}\right)\left(\int_{Z_1}^{Z_2} RZdZ - Z_1 \int_{Z_1}^{Z_2} RdZ\right)\right] \quad (14)$$

Nomenclature

a = weight fraction of 400°F plus material in reaction coil at reference temperature (800°F)

C = total coil volume above reference temperature (800°F), cu ft

K_s = reaction velocity constant at reference temperature (800°F)

R = relative reaction rate, K/K_s

W = flow rate through reaction coil, lb/sec

x = gas plus gasoline formed, weight fraction of coil feed

Z = fraction of total coil volume about 800°F

ρ = density, lb/cu ft

To avoid some unnecessary repetition of the calculations and for preliminary estimates, it has been found desirable to employ certain approximate methods to estimate in advance the required coil volume and inlet pressure, or amount of cracking and outlet temperature, etc. For this purpose, a modified equation (15) may be used. This is applied in one step over the entire coil from 800°F to the heater outlet. Use of this equation requires knowledge of the temperature gradient in order that $\int RdZ$ and $\int RZdZ$ may be calculated. The limitations of the equation are given in the original publication.[14]

$$\ln\left(\frac{a}{a-x}\right) = \frac{K_s C}{W}\left[\rho_1 \int_0^1 RdZ - (\rho_1 - \rho_2) \int_0^1 RZdZ\right] \quad (15)$$

The nomenclature for this equation is the same as for Equation (14).

Sample Calculation

This calculating procedure can be applied in either of two ways: (1) in the design of a new cracking heater, or (2) the adaptation of an existing heater to a new service. The following example deals with a problem of the latter type.

Adaptation of an Existing Furnace to a Vis-breaking Operation.

An existing gas-oil cracking coil is to be used for vis-breaking 8.5° API vacuum-reduced West Texas Crude. The quantity of this material available is 5,000 BPSD. From pilot-plant runs it has been determined that the reaction velocity constant for this stock at 800°F is 11.8×10^{-5}; other properties are shown in Table 2.

TABLE 2. CHARGE STOCK PROPERTIES

Virgin West-Texas Vacuum Bottoms

Vol % on crude	9.9
°API	8.5
Specific gravity, 60/60	1.0107
Carbon residue, wt %	19.8
Sulfur, wt %	2.90
Viscosity, SUS, 100°	787,000
Viscosity, SUS, 210°	6,930
Melting point (R and B), °F	117
Penetration (D5)	168
Characterization factor, K	11.48
Mol wt	620
P_c, psia.	115
T_c °R	1,780
K_S, reaction velocity constant at 800°F.	11.8×10^{-5}
μ_c, centipoises	0.0218
π_1 (density term)	0.1500

An example of the heat transfer calculations is not given here, but similar calculations have been given in the literature.[18,19,30] The results of the heat transfer calculations are summarized below along with pertinent data on the commercial coil.

COMMERCIAL COIL CHARACTERISTICS

Section	Convection	Radiant
Exposed surface, sq ft	534	3,568
Volume per tube, cu ft	0.5617	2.3010
Volume per return bend, cu. ft.	0.0852	0.1260
Total volume, cu ft	38.81	237.89
Total equivalent length, ft	1,805	5,213
Number of tubes	60	98

RESULTS OF HEAT TRANSFER CALCULATION

Total heat required	15,653,000 Btu/hr
Preliminary pressure drop in convection section	35 psi
Preliminary pressure drop in radiant section	106 psi
Total net heat input	22,126,000 Btu/hr
Temp. oil entering convection section	675 °F
Temp. oil leaving convection section	722 °F
Pressure at convection section inlet	355.0 psia
Pressure at convection section outlet	319.9 psia
Radiant section required heat density	3,689 Btu/hr/sq ft

Cracking and Pressure Drop in Radiant Section

Calculate 800°F Point

$H_{800} - H_{722} = 437.0 - 379.7 = 57.3$

$\dfrac{57.3 \times 73{,}625}{3{,}689} = 1{,}143$ sq ft tube surface required

$\dfrac{1{,}143 \times 5{,}213}{3{,}568} = 1{,}670$ equivalent ft to 800°F

$5{,}213 - 1{,}670 = 3{,}543$ equivalent ft above 800°F

$3{,}568 - 1{,}143 = 2{,}425$ sq ft surface above 800°F

$\rho_{800}{}^{\circ} = 49.4$ lb/cu ft

$\rho_{722}{}^{\circ} = 50.9$ lb/cu ft

$\rho_{av} = 50.15$ lb/cu ft

$\Delta P = \dfrac{2 \times 0.005 \times (266.6)^2 \times 1{,}670}{32.2 \times 0.312 \times 50.15 \times 144} = 16.4$ psi

$319.9 - 16.4 = 303.5$ psia at 800°F

$\dfrac{1{,}143}{36.408} = 31.4$ tubes required to 800°F

$31.4 \times 2.4270 = 76.21$ cu ft to 800°F

$237.89 - 76.21 = 161.68$ cu ft above 800°F

Cracking and ΔP From 800°F to $Z = 0.2$

$\dfrac{2{,}425 \times 0.2 \times 3{,}689}{73{,}625} = 24.30$ Btu/lb oil heat input

Assume cracking = 0.008 wt fraction gas plus gasoline

Enthalpy at 800°	437.00 Btu/lb
	24.30
	461.30
Heat of cracking 350 (0.008)	−2.80
Enthalpy at $Z - 0.2$	458.50 Btu/lb

	x	820°	830°
Gas	0.0016	716	724
Gasoline	0.0064	582	590
Oil	0.9920	453	460
	1.000	(454.8)	(462.0)

$3.7/7.2 = 5 + 820 = 825°F$, $1{,}285°R$

$R = 2.1$, $RZ = 0.42$, $\int R dZ = 0.21$, $\int RZ dZ = 0.042$ (Figure 10)

Assume $P = 295$ psia

	x	$T°R$	P	T_R	P_R		v	xv	ρ_2
		1,285	295					0.02517	39.73
Gas	0.0016	(461)	(643)	2.78	0.46	1.00	1.811		
Gasoline	0.0064	(1085)	(390)	1.18	0.76	0.83	0.310		
Oil	0.9920	(1780)	(115)	0.72	2.56	(0.1163)	0.02045		

Parenthetical numbers in columns under $T°R$ and P are critical temperatures and pressures used in calculating T_R and P_R. In column under μ (0.1163) is a density term used to calculate the specific volume, v, of the liquid oil phase.[29]

$$\text{Oil} = \frac{0.1500}{0.1163 \times 1.0107 \times 62.426} = 0.02045$$

$$\text{Gasoline} = \frac{10.73 \times 1,285 \times 0.83}{295 \times 125} = 0.310$$

$$\text{Gas} = \frac{10.73 \times 1,285 \times 1.00}{295 \times 25.8} = 1.811$$

$$\rho_{av} = \frac{49.4 - 39.73}{\ln 49.4/39.73} = 44.4$$

$$\Delta P = \frac{0.491 \times 3,543 \times 0.2}{44.4} = 7.9$$

$$303.5 - 7.9 = \underline{\underline{295.6}} \text{ vs 295 assumed}$$

$$\ln \frac{a}{a-x} = \frac{11.8 \times 10^{-5} \times 161.68}{20.45} \left[49.4(0.21) - \frac{10.3}{0.2}(0.042) \right] \quad \text{(Equation 14)}$$

$$= 93.29(10.38 - 2.16)$$
$$= 0.00767$$

$$\log \frac{a}{a-x} = 0.00333$$

$$\frac{a}{a-x} = 1.0077$$

$$x = \underline{\underline{0.0077}} \text{ vs 0.008 assumed}$$

At $Z = 0.2$, $x = 0.0077$, $H = 458.61$,

$$T = 825°F, P = 295.6, \rho = 39.73, \ln \frac{a}{a-x} - x = 0.00767$$

Section Z = 0.2 to Z = 0.4

Assume $x = 0.024$

Heat content, 825°F	458.61 Btu/lb
	24.30
	————
	482.91
Heat of cracking 350 (0.0240 − 0.0077)	−5.70
	————
	477.21 Btu/lb

	x	840°	850°
Gas	0.005	733	742
Gasoline	0.019	598	608
Oil	0.976	468	474
	1.00	(471.80)	(477.89)

$$5.41/6.09 = 8.9 + 840 = 849°F$$
$$R = 4.0, RZ = 1.6, \smallint RdZ = 0.61, \smallint RZDZ = 0.20$$

Assume $P = 285$

	x	T	P	T_R	P_R	μ	v	xv	ρ_2
		1,309	285					0.03619	27.63
Gas	0.005			2.84	0.44	1·00	1.910		
Gasoline	0.019			1.21	0.73	0·850	0.335		
Oil	0.976			0.74	2.48	(0.1145)	0.02077		

$$\text{Oil} = \frac{0.002378}{0.1145} = 0.02077$$

$$\text{Gasoline} = \frac{10.73 \times 1309 \times 0.850}{285 \times 125} = 0.335$$

$$\text{Gas} = \frac{10.73 \times 1309 \times 1.00}{285 \times 25.8} = 1.910$$

$$\rho_{\text{av}} = \frac{39.73 - 27.63}{\ln 39.73/27.63} = \frac{12.10}{0.362} = 33.4$$

$$\Delta P = \frac{0.491 \times 708.6}{33.4} = 10.4 \text{ psi}$$

$$295.6 - 10.4 = \underline{285.2} \text{ psia vs 285 assumed}$$

$$\ln \frac{a}{a-x} = 0.00767 + 93.29 \times 10^{-5} \left[39.73(0.61) - \frac{12.10}{0.2}(0.20 - 0.2(0.61)) \right]$$

$$= 0.00767 + 93.29 \times 10^{-5}(24.2 - 4.84)$$

$$= 0.00767 + 0.01806 = 0.02573$$

$$\log \frac{a}{a-x} = 0.01118$$

$$\frac{a}{a-x} = 1.0261$$

$$x = \underline{0.0254} \text{ vs 0.024 assumed}$$

At $Z = 0.4$, $x = 0.0254$, $T = 849°F$, $P = 285.2$ psia

$$\rho = 27.63, \ H = 476.71, \ \ln \frac{a}{a-x} = 0.02573$$

Section $Z = 0.4$ to $Z = 0.7$

Assume $x = 0.0600$

Heat content 849°F   476.71 Btu/lb

                                                   36.45

                                                  513.16

Heat of cracking $350(0.0600 - 0.0254)$ -12.12

                                                  501.04 Btu/lb

	x	870°	880°
Gas	0.012	760	769
Gasoline	0.048	626	634
Oil	0.940	485	493
		(495.07)	(503.08)

$$5.97/8.01 = 7.4 + 870 = 877°F$$

$$R = 8.8, \ RZ = 6.15, \ \int R dZ = 1.92, \ \int RZ dZ = 1.16$$

Assume $P = 260$ psia

	x	T	P	T_R	P_R	μ	v	xv	ρ_2
		1,337	260					0.06383	15.67
Gas	0.012			2.90	0.40	1.00	2.137		
Gasoline	0.048			1.23	0.67	0.87	0.384		
Oil	0.940			0.75	2.26	(0.1132)	0.02101		

$$\text{Oil} = \frac{0.002378}{0.1132} = 0.02101$$

$$\text{Gasoline} = \frac{10.73 \times 1,337 \times 0.87}{260 \times 125} = 0.384$$

$$\text{Gas} = \frac{10.73 \times 1,337 \times 1.00}{260 \times 25.8} = 2.137$$

$$\rho_{av} = \frac{27.63 - 15.67}{\ln 27.63/15.67} = \frac{11.96}{0.568} = 21.05$$

$$\Delta P = \frac{0.491 \times 1,062.9}{21.05} = 24.8$$

$$285.2 - 24.8 = \underline{\underline{260.4}} \text{ vs } 260 \text{ assumed}$$

$$\ln \frac{a}{a-x} = 0.02573 + 93.29 \times 10^{-5} \left[27.63(1.92) - \frac{11.96}{0.3}(1.16 - 0.4(1.92)) \right]$$

$$= 0.02573 + 93.29 \times 10^{-5}(53.1 - 15.5)$$

$$= 0.02573 + 0.03508 = 0.06081$$

$$\log \frac{a}{a-x} = 0.02645$$

$$\frac{a}{a-x} = 1.0628$$

$$x = \underline{\underline{0.0591}} \text{ vs } 0.0600 \text{ assumed}$$

At $Z = 0.7$, $x = 0.0591$, $T = 877°F$, $P = 260.4$,

$$\rho = 15.67, \ln \frac{a}{a-x} = 0.06081, H = 501.36$$

Section $Z = 0.7$ to $Z = 1.0$

Assume $x = 0.100$

Heat content, 877°F	501.36 Btu/lb
	36.45
	————
	537.81
Heat of cracking $350(0.100 - 0.0591)$	-14.32
	————
	523.49 Btu/lb

	x	890°	910°
Gas	0.020	779	797
Gasoline	0.080	640	656
Oil	0.900	497	513
		(513.8)	(530.4)

$$\frac{9.69 \times 20}{16.6} = 11.7 + 890 = 902°F$$

$$R = 16.5, RZ = 16.5, \int R dZ = 3.79, \int RZ dZ = 3.39$$

Assume $P = 215$ psia

	x	T	P	T_R	P_R		v	xv	ρ_2
		1,362	215					0.11163	8.96
Gas	0.020			2.96	0.34	1.00	2.64		
Gasoline	0.080			1.26	0.55	0.90	0.491		
Oil	0.900			0.765	1.87	(0.1095)	0.02172		

$$\text{Oil} = \frac{0.002378}{0.1095} = 0.02172$$

$$\text{Gasoline} = \frac{10.73 \times 1,362 \times 0.90}{215 \times 125} = 0.491$$

$$\text{Gas} = \frac{10.73 \times 1,362 \times 1.00}{215 \times 25.8} = 2.64$$

$$\rho_{av} = \frac{15.67 - 8.96}{\ln 15.67/8.96} = \frac{6.71}{0.557} = 12.0$$

$$\Delta P = \frac{0.491 \times 1,062.9}{12.0} = 43.5$$

$$260.4 - 43.5 = 216.9 \text{ psia vs 215 assumed}$$

$$\ln \frac{a}{a-x} = 0.06081 + 93.29 \left[15.67(3.79) - \frac{6.71}{0.3} (3.39 - 0.7(3.79)) \right]$$

$$= 0.06081 + 93.29 \,(42.85)$$
$$= 0.06081 + 0.03997 = 0.10078$$

$$\log \frac{a}{a-x} = 0.04382$$

$$\frac{a}{a-x} = 1.1062$$

$$x = 9.60 \text{ vs 10.0 assumed}$$

SUMMARY OF RESULTS

	x	P	T	ρ	Cu ft
Convection inlet		355.0	675		0
Radiant inlet		319.9	722	50.9	38.81
800°F point	0	303.5	800	49.4	115.02
$Z = 0.2$	0.77	295.6	825	39.7	147.36
$= 0.4$	2.54	285.2	849	27.6	179.70
$= 0.7$	5.91	260.4	877	15.7	228.81
Outlet	9.60	216.9	902	9.0	276.72

The above procedure has been subjected to the most careful check against a wide variety of commercial thermal cracking operations. Some thirty sets of test data on commercial units have been studied. In many cases these units were so equipped that samples could be obtained at intermediate points in the cracking coils, and the data compared with the results by calculation. These runs covered a wide range of conversions per pass, temperature gradient shapes, and heater feed characteristics. Both cylindrical and box-type furnaces were tested, and the heater feed stocks covered the whole range of refractoriness from virgin East Texas fractions to cracked cycle stock derived from Mirando Crude. The calculated conversions checked the observed data within an average deviation of about 15 per cent.

References

1. Anon., *The Texaco Star*, **9**, 12 (1922).
2. Anon., *Oil Gas J.*, **23**, No. 41, 109 (1925).
3. Anon., *Ibid.*, **51**, No. 46, 312 (1953).

4. Bogk, J., Ostergaard, P., and Smoley, E. R., *Proc. Am. Petroleum Inst.* [III], 17 (1940).
5. Burton, W. M., U. S. Patent 1,049,667 (1912).
6. Clark, E. M., U. S. Patent 1,388,514 (1921).
7. Cross, R., U. S. Patent 1,255,138 (1918).
8. Clarke, L., "Manual for Process Engineering Calculations," 1st. ed., New York, McGraw-Hill Book Co., Inc., 1947.
9. de Florez, L., *Proc. Am. Petroleum Inst.* (Dec. 1930).
10. Dubbs, J. A., U. S. Patent 1,123,502 (1915).
11. Feuchter, C. E., *Oil Gas J.*, **48**, No. 11, 62 (1949).
12. Greenstreet, C. J., U. S. Patent 1, 110,923 (1914).
13. Hall, W. A., *J. Inst. Petroleum Tech.*, **1**, 147 (1915).
14. Hirsch, J. H., Crawford, C. L., and Holloway, C., *Ind. Eng. Chem.*, **38**, 885 (1946).
15. Howard, F. A., Natl. Petroleum News, **14**, No. 47, 17 (1922).
16. Jenkins, U. S., U. S. Patent 1,226,526 (1917).
17. Keith, P. C., Ward, J. T., and Rubin, L. C., *Proc. Am. Petroleum Inst.* (May 1933).
18. Kern, D. A., "Process Heat Transfer," 1st ed., New York, McGraw-Hill Book Co., Inc., 1950.
19. Lobo, W. A. and Evans, J. E., *Trans. Am. Inst. Chem. Engrs.*, **35**, 743 (1939).
20. Nelson, W. L., *Oil Gas J.*, **50**, No. 39, 75 (1952).
21. Offut, W. C., Fogle, M. C., and Beuther, H., *Petroleum Refiner*, **25**, 554 (1946).
22. Perry, J. H., "Chemical Engineering Handbook," 3rd ed., New York, McGraw-Hill Book Co., Inc., 1950.
23. Ramage, A. S., U. S. Patent 1,403,194 and 1,409,404.
24. Rittman, W. F., Dutton, C. B., and Dean, E. W., *U. S. Bur. Mines Bull.*, **114** (1915).
25. Smith, R. L. and Watson, K. M., *Ind. Eng. Chem.*, **29**, 1408 (1937).
26. Taylor, H. S., "Treatise on Physical Chemistry," 2nd ed., New York, D. Van Nostrand Co., Inc., 1931, Vol. 1, page 231.
27. Watson, K. M., and Nelson, E. F., *Ind. Eng. Chem.*, **25**, 880 (1933).
28. Watson, K. M., Nelson, E. F., and Murphy, G. B., *Ind. Eng. Chem.*, **27**, 1460 (1935).
29. Watson, K. M., *Ind. Eng. Chem.*, **35**, 398 (1943).
30. Wilson, D. W., Lobo, W. E., and Hottel, H. C., *Ind. Eng. Chem.*, **24**, 486 (1932).

CHAPTER 24

COMPOSITION OF SYNTHETIC AND CRACKED GASOLINES

A. N. Sachanen

Socony-Vacuum Oil Co., Paulsboro, N. J.

In addition to straight-run petroleum products, various synthetic fuels are manufactured from petroleum by thermal and catalytic processes. As a result, the chemical composition of synthetic fuels differs from that of the original straight-run charging stocks to an extent depending upon the process and the process conditions. The most important synthetic fuels to be discussed in this chapter are alkylates, polymer gasolines, cracked and reformed fuels, and hydrogenation products. Like straight-run products, the synthetic fuels consist predominantly of hydrocarbons. In general, the amount of nonhydrocarbon components in synthetic fuels is less than in straight-run products, particularly of high-boiling type. Such fuels as alkylates, polymer gasolines, and some hydrogenation fuels are almost exclusively hydrocarbons. In some cases the synthetic fuels are predominantly paraffinic or olefinic, but in most cases they contain all types; paraffins, cycloparaffins, aromatic and unsaturated hydrocarbons. Unsaturation is a characteristic property of polymer and cracked gasolines.

Alkylates

Commercial alkylates, produced mostly by low-temperature catalytic alkylation of butenes with isobutane, are entirely paraffinic. In contrast to straight-run and cracked gasolines, the paraffins of alkylates are highly branched, mostly trimethylpentanes. The composition depends on the catalyst used for the alkylation, as the data of Table 1 show (Glasgow et al.[3]).

Polymer Gasolines

Commercial polymer gasolines are manufactured by catalytic polymerization of propene and butenes. Polymerized isobutylene is mostly diisobutene consisting of two isomers: predominantly 2,2,4-trimethylpentene-1 and partially 2,2,4-trimethylpentene-2. Copolymers or codimers of isobutylene and normal butenes consist mainly of various isomeric trimethylpentenes, the proportion of which depends on the catalyst used

TABLE 1. HYDROCARBONS OF DEPENTANIZED BUTENE-ISOBUTANE ALKYLATE
[Per cent by Volume]

	Sulfuric Acid Process	Hydrofluoric Acid Process
2,2-Dimethylbutane	0.6 ± 0.4	
2,3-Dimethylbutane	5.5 ± 1.0	2.1 ± 0.5
2- and 3-Methylpentane	2.7 ± 0.8	
2,2,3-Trimethylbutane	3.6 ± 0.5	2.6 ± 0.5
2- and 3-Methylhexane	3.1 ± 0.5	1.9 ± 0.5
2,2,4-Trimethylpentane	30.1 ± 0.6	41.7 ± 0.5
2,5- and 2,4-Dimethylhexane	8.1 ± 1.2	13.4 ± 1.2
2,2,3-Trimethylpentane	1.8 ± 0.8	2.9 ± 1.2
2,3,4-Trimethylpentane	9.3 ± 1.2	9.4 ± 2.0
2,3,3-Trimethylpentane	14.5 ± 1.2	10.0 ± 2.0
2,3-Dimethylhexane	3.7 ± 1.2	6.2 ± 2.0
2,2,5-Trimethylhexane	12.7 ± 0.8	3.4 ± 1.0
Other isoparaffins	4.3 ± 0.5	6.4 ± 0.5

for polymerization. The composition of hydrogenated copolymers or hydrocodimers is given in Table 2 (Glasgow et al.[3]). The position of the double bonds in the original (nonhydrogenated) copolymers remains unknown.

TABLE 2. HYDROCARBONS OF DEPENTANIZED HYDROCODIMER
(Per cent by volume)

	Hot Sulfuric Acid Process	Phosphoric Acid Process
C_6- and C_7-Hydrocarbons	1.2 ± 0.5	3.6 ± 0.5
2,2,4-Trimethylpentane	35.4 ± 1.0	9.9 ± 0.8
2,2,3-Trimethylpentane	26.0 ± 2.0	9.2 ± 3.0
2,3,4-Trimethylpentane	19.0 ± 2.0	43.9 ± 2.0
2,3,3-Trimethylpentane	7.5 ± 1.5	8.6 ± 2.0
Other hydrocarbons	11.4	24.8

Polymer gasolines, produced on a large scale by catalytic polymerization of refinery gases, are polymers and copolymers of propene, butenes, and isobutylene, which are present in the refinery gases. Consequently, such gasolines consist of hexenes, heptenes, and octenes. If the polymerization conditions are mild, the polymer gasolines are entirely olefinic. Otherwise, the gasolines may contain a small amount of paraffins, cycloparaffins and aromatics, as a result of secondary reactions. The olefins of polymer gasolines are highly branched. A large portion of the olefins consists of tetraalkylethylenes.

Cracked Gasolines

Whereas the composition of straight-run products depends entirely on the nature of crude oils, the composition of cracked gasolines is governed

TABLE 3. HYDROCARBONS IN FRACTIONS OF CRACKED MID-CONTINENT NAPHTHA (THERMAL AND CATALYTIC)

Hydrocarbon Number	Hydrocarbon	% by Volume	
		Thermal	Catalytic
C$_4$-Fraction	Isobutane	0.7	2.7
	n-Butane	66.6	27.0
	Isobutylene	1.1	1.7
	1-Butene	1.5	4.9
	2-Butenes	30.1	63.7
C$_5$-Fraction	2,2-Dimethylpropane	0.1	—
	2-Methylbutane	20.4	51.8
	n-Pentane	35.2	6.7
	Cyclopentane	2.4	0.9
	3-Methyl-1-butene	2.4	0.6
	1-Pentene	12.6	2.1
	2-Methyl-1-butene	8.2	7.6
	trans-2-Pentene	9.5	9.2
	2-Methyl-2-butene	6.8	17.3
	Cyclopentene	2.4	1.8
C$_6$-Fraction	2,2-Dimethylbutane	0.3	0.2
	2,3-Dimethylbutane	1.1	9.0
	2-Methylpentane	10.7	29.1
	3-Methylpentane	7.7	18.5
	n-Hexane	23.0	5.2
	Methylcyclopentane	7.3	3.7
	Cyclohexane	3.4	0.7
	Benzene	1.3	0.9
	3- and 4-Methyl-1-pentene	5.4	1.5
	cis-4-Methyl-2-pentene	3.8	2.6
	2-Methyl-1-pentene	3.8	5.0
	1-Hexene	8.8	0.4
	2-Ethyl-1-butene	0.4	2.8
	2-Methyl-2-pentene	3.8	5.6
	trans-3-Methyl-2-pentene	2.3	2.7
	cis- and trans-2- and 3-Hexene	6.9	4.9
	cis-3-Methyl-2-pentene	0.8	1.4
	2,3-Dimethyl-2-butene	0.3	0.4
	3-Methyl-1-cyclopentene	1.9	1.9
	1- and 4-Methyl-1-cyclopentene	5.8	1.5
	Cyclohexene	1.1	0.3
	Conjugated and nonconjugated diolefins	0.1	0.2
C$_7$-Fraction	2,2- and 2,4-Dimethylpentane		1.9
	3,3-Dimethylpentane		0.7
	2,3-Dimethylpentane		16.9

TABLE 3. HYDROCARBONS IN FRACTIONS OF CRACKED MID-CONTINENT NAPHTHA (THERMAL AND CATALYTIC). (*Continued*)

Hydrocarbon	% by Volume	
	Thermal	Catalytic
2-Methylhexane		6.5
3-Methylhexane		11.5
n-Heptane		4.4
1,1-Dimethylcyclopentane		0.2
trans-1, 3-Dimethylcyclopentane		0.7
trans-1, 2-Dimethylcyclopentane		7.9
cis-1, 2-Dimethylcyclopentane		1.8
Methylcyclohexane		7.1
Ethylcyclopentane		1.4
Toluene		6.9
Olefins		28.4
Conjugated and nonconjugated diolefins		0.6
3- and 4-Methyl-1-cyclohexene		2.4
1-Methyl-1-cyclohexene		0.7

not only by the nature of charging stocks but mostly by the variables of cracking. Hence the composition of catalytically cracked gasolines is different from that of noncatalytically (thermally) cracked gasolines produced from the same charging stock. Moreover, with the same charging stock and the same process, the temperature- and pressure conditions of the process will very much affect the composition of cracked gasolines and other products.

The presence of unsaturated hydrocarbons in cracked products enormously complicates the identification and determination of the hydrocarbons present. Only during the last five years, with the aid of mass-, infrared- and ultraviolet spectroscopy, has it been possible to identify and determine the hydrocarbons of cracked gasolines, at least in the C_5- to C_9-fractions.

Cady, Marschner, and Cropper[1] reported the data on hydrocarbons identified in the thermal and catalytic gasolines produced from the same Mid-Continent oil. The data are summarized in Table 3, in which the content of hydrocarbons is given as the per cent of a fraction indicated.

As far as the thermally (noncatalytically) cracked gasolines are concerned, a striking similarity in the composition of saturated hydrocarbons of straight-run and thermal gasolines from the same crude must be pointed out. The data on Table 3 are to be compared with the data of Table 1 of Chapter 2, pertaining to the hydrocarbons in straight-run products also from a Mid-Continent crude oil. Normal paraffins followed by slightly branched ones (one methyl group in a branch) are the predominating paraffins in the C_4-C_6 fractions of the thermal gasoline. The content of methylcyclopentane is comparable to that of cyclohexane. Similar results were obtained by Young[7] for the C_7-fraction of a thermally cracked gasoline, i.e., straight-chain or slightly branched paraffinic hydrocarbons predominating and an approximately even distribution of cyclopentane and cyclohexane homologs.

Of the unsaturated hydrocarbons present in thermal gasoline (Table 3), open-chain olefins are more abundant than cycloolefins. Diolefins are present in insignificant amounts. Similarly to paraffins, the most abundant open-chain olefins are straight-chain or slightly branched structures.

It should be borne in mind that the above data on the hydrocarbons present in thermally cracked gasolines relate to commercial gasolines produced under relatively moderate temperatures (about 450 to 500°C) and pressures (about 500 lbs/sq in). Higher temperatures and lower pressures of cracking shift the composition of cracked gasolines to a higher percentage of aromatic and unsaturated hydrocarbons, including open-chain and cyclic diolefins.

In addition to the information on the composition of a catalytic gasoline by Cady *et al.* (Table 3), the data reported by Melpolder, Brown, Young, and Headington[5] are summarized in Table 4. These authors extended the identification of hydrocarbons to C_8-hydrocarbons. In general, the agreement between the data of Tables 3 and 4 on identification and relative abundance of hydrocarbons is quite satisfactory.

The composition of catalytically cracked gasolines and other fractions is governed by the isomerization and hydrogen transfer effects of cracking catalysts (silica-alumina). As a result, catalytic gasolines are rich in branched paraffins, branched open-chain olefins, alkyl cyclopentanes, cyclopentenes, and aromatics. Tables 3 and 4 show clearly that normal paraffins from pentane to octane, abundant in straight-run and thermal gasolines from Mid-Continent crudes, are present in catalytically cracked gasolines in relatively small amounts. Of the paraffins, branched paraffins with one methyl group in the branch, such as methylbutanes and methylpentanes, are the most abundant. In general, alkyl cyclopentanes are more abundant than alkyl cyclohexanes. Like thermal gasolines catalytically cracked gasolines are richer in open-chain olefins than in cyclic olefins. Normal olefins are quite abundant, as well as branched olefins, particularly those with one or two branched methyl groups. Of the cyclic olefins, alkyl cyclopentenes, particularly methyl- and dimethylcyclopentenes seem to be predominant. Catalytic gasolines are richer in aromatic hydrocarbons than straight-run or thermal gasolines from the same crude oil.

Just as in the case of thermal gasolines, the composition of catalytic gasolines changes when more severe conditions of catalytic cracking are

TABLE 4. COMPOSITION OF CRACKED GASOLINE (BOILING RANGE 35 TO 218°C, FLUID CATALYTIC CRACKING)

Hydrocarbon	% by Volume
Propane	0.13
Isobutane	0.81
n-Butane	1.32
Isopentane	5.55
n-Pentane	1.14
2,3-Dimethylbutane	0.70
2-Methylpentane	1.71
3-Methylpentane	1.31
n-Hexane	0.43
2,4-Dimethylpentane	0.22
2,3-Dimethylpentane	0.088
2-Methylhexane	0.77
3-Methylhexane	0.77
n-Heptane	0.46
2,5-Dimethylhexane	0.20
2,4-Dimethylhexane	0.11
2,3-Dimethylhexane	0.10
2-Methylheptane	0.41
4-Methylheptane	0.13
3,4-Dimethylhexane	0.10
3-Ethylhexane	0.048
3-Methylheptane	0.43
n-Octane	0.22
C$_9$-Paraffins and higher	7.53
Cyclopentane	0.14
Methylcyclopentane	0.96
Cyclohexane	0.12
1,1-Dimethylcyclopentane	0.053
1-*trans*-3- and 1-*cis*-3-Dimethylcyclopentane	0.36
1-*trans*-2-Dimethylcyclopentane	0.18
1-*cis*-2-Dimethylcyclopentane	0.11
Methylcyclohexane	0.35
Ethylcyclopentane	0.20
1,1,3-Trimethylcyclopentane	0.061
1-*trans*-2-*cis*-4-Trimethylcyclopentane	0.072
1-*trans*-2-*cis*-3-Trimethylcyclopentane	0.057
1,1,2-Trimethylcyclopentane	0.010
1-*cis*-2-*trans*-4-Trimethylcyclopentane	0.096
1-*cis*-2-*trans*-3-Trimethylcyclopentane	0.019
1-*cis*-2-*cis*-4-Trimethylcyclopentane	0.035
1-*trans*-4-Dimethylcyclohexane	0.074
1,1-Dimethylcyclohexane	0.024
1-*cis*-3-Dimethylcyclohexane	0.13
1-Methyl-*cis*-3- and 1-Methyl-*trans*-3-ethylcyclopentane	0.28
1-Methyl-*trans*-2-ethylcyclopentane	0.021
1-*trans*-2-Dimethylcyclohexane	0.050

benzene
—toxicity
—replaced
tetramethyl (lead
vapor phase

TABLE 4. COMPOSITION OF CRACKED GASOLINE (BOILING RANGE 35 TO 218°C, FLUID CATALYTIC CRACKING). (*Continued*)

$C_6 - C_8$

Hydrocarbon	% by Volume
1-*cis*-4-Dimethylcyclohexane	0.060
1-*trans*-3-Dimethylcyclohexane	0.066
Isopropylcyclopentane	0.022
1-Methyl-*cis*-2-ethylcyclopentane	0.031
1-*cis*-2-Dimethylcyclohexane	0.004
C_9- and higher Cycloparaffins	5.55
Dicycloparaffins	0.75
Isobutylene	0.91
1-Butene	0.64
trans-2-Butene	1.35
cis-2-Butene	1.05
1-Pentene	1.20
2-Methyl-1-butene	0.71
trans-2-Pentene	0.43
cis-2-Pentene	3.97
2-Methyl-2-butene	4.61
3,3-Dimethyl-1-butene	0.21
3-Methyl-1-pentene	0.27
2,3-Dimethyl-1-butene	0.98
2-Methyl-1-pentene	0.61
1-Hexene	0.57
2-Ethyl-1-butene	0.25
2-Methyl-2-pentene	0.85
cis- and *trans*-3- and *cis*- and *trans*-2-Hexenes	1.79
cis- and *trans*-3-Methyl-2-pentene	2.55
2,3-Dimethyl-2-butene	0.40
2,2-Dimethylpentenes	0.006
2,3-Dimethylpentenes	0.48
2,4-Dimethylpentenes	0.11
2-Methylhexenes	1.24
3-Methylhexenes and 2-Ethylpentenes	1.42
3-Ethylpentenes	0.13
n-Heptenes	1.20
Trimethylpentenes and Dimethylhexenes	0.41
2-Methylheptenes	0.45
3-Methylheptenes	0.73
4-Methylheptenes	0.40
3-Ethylhexenes	0.088
n-Octenes	0.23
C_9-Olefins	4.75
Cyclopentene	0.40
Methylcyclopentenes	0.75
Cyclohexene	0.015
1,1-Dimethylcyclopentenes	0.012
1,2- and 1,3-Dimethylcyclopentenes	1.58
Methylcyclohexenes	0.42

employed. Glasgow, Willingham, and Rossini[4] published the data on the composition of a catalytically cracked gasoline produced by so-called two-pass or repeated catalytic cracking. As the result of more severe cracking conditions, the content of unsaturated hydrocarbons drastically

TABLE 4. COMPOSITION OF CRACKED GASOLINE (BOILING RANGE 35 TO 218°C, FLUID CATALYTIC CRACKING). (*Continued*)

Hydrocarbon	% by Volume
Ethylcyclopentenes	0.26
Trimethylcyclopentenes	0.48
1,1-Dimethylcyclohexenes	0.051
1-Methyl-1-ethylcyclopentenes	0.047
1-Methyl-2-ethylcyclopentenes	0.14
1,2-, 1,3- and 1,4-Dimethylcyclohexenes	0.15
C_9-Cycloolefins	1.94
C_9-Dicycloolefins	0.09
Benzene	0.21
Toluene	2.32
Ethylbenzene	1.07
o-Xylene	1.20
m-Xylene	2.30
p-Xylene	0.84
Isopropylbenzene	0.18
n-Propylbenzene	0.16
Methylethylbenzenes	0.96
Trimethylbenzenes	4.98
Butylbenzenes	3.90
Amylbenzenes	1.78
Hexylbenzenes	0.56
Heptylbenzenes	0.052
Alkenylbenzenes from $C_6H_5.C_3H_5$ to $C_6H_5.C_7H_{13}$	2.177
Dicyclic aromatics	1.3
Total	100.0

decreases (to about 4 per cent of total gasoline studied by Glasgow *et al.*, as compared with about 40 per cent of the gasolines represented in Tables 3 and 4) and the content of isoparaffins and aromatics greatly increases.

Catalytically and thermally cracked gas-oils and heavier products are highly aromatic. The catalytic gas-oils are more aromatic and less olefinic than the thermal ones. The aromatic hydrocarbons of the cracked gas-oils are predominantly condensed. Charlet, Lanneau, and Johnson[2] give the following composition for a heavy catalytic gas (cycle)-oil of specific gravity 0.921, boiling range 213 to 482°C under atmospheric pressure:

	% by weight
Benzenes	5
Naphthalenes	15
Phenanthrenes	40
4 Fused rings	30
5 Fused rings	10

Carcinogenic properties of some polycyclic aromatic hydrocarbons present in catalytic gas-oils and other high-boiling aromatic petroleum products should be mentioned.

Within certain groups of isomeric hydrocarbons, the distribution of the isomers actually determined in catalytically cracked gasolines is fairly close to the relative proportions calculated for the thermodynamic equilibrium at cracking temperatures, i.e., 450 to 500°C. First of all, it is applicable to various isomers of olefins that are very reactive in the presence of catalysts at high temperatures. Cady *et al.*[1] found, for instance, that the relative proportions of isomeric methylbutenes or methylpentenes in the catalytic gasoline studied corresponded very closely to the thermodynamic equilibrium at 470°C. In the same way, the relative amounts of isomeric C_8 or C_9 aromatic hydrocarbons in catalytic gasolines are almost equal to the amounts calculated for the thermodynamic equilibria (Streiff and Rossini[3]). The ratio of cyclohexane to methylcyclopentane found for two catalytic gasolines represented in Tables 3 and 4, 1:6 and 1:8, respectively, is not too far from the equilibrium ratio 1:10. The groups of less reactive isomeric paraffins usually do not follow this relationship.

The composition of reformed gasolines depends upon the process of reforming. The gasolines produced by thermal reforming and polyforming are similar to thermally cracked gasolines but are more aromatic. In contrast, the gasolines produced by catalytic reforming of cycloparaffinic naphthas are predominantly aromatic, owing to the specific dehydrogenation effect of the catalyst on cycloparaffinic hydrocarbons. Read[6] gives the following composition of a catalytically reformed naphtha produced from a Gulf Coast straight-run gasoline:

	% by Volume
Benzene	3.5
Toluene	12.0
Xylenes	11.9
Ethylbenzene	2.0
C_9-plus-aromatics	26.2

Hydrogenation gasolines and other products produced by destructive hydrogenation of gas-oils and residues differ from cracked products by total absence of unsaturated hydrocarbons. In this respect and in many others, the hydrogenation and straight-run products are quite similar.

The composition of hydrogenation gasolines depends upon the charging stock and the conditions of the process as well, as it does for cracked gasolines. Hydrogenation gasolines high in paraffins are produced by destructive hydrogenation of paraffinic gas-oils and residues. Cycloparaffinic and aromatic stocks, particularly under high-temperature conditions of hydrogenation, yield hydrogenation gasolines rich in cycloparaffins and aromatics. The data on individual hydrocarbons identified in hydrogenation products are not available at the present time.

Table 5 summarizes the most reliable data on the percentage of main

TABLE 5. COMPOSITION OF SYNTHETIC GASOLINES (END POINT 200°C)

Process	Charging Stock	% by Volume			
		Paraffins	Cyclo-paraffins	Unsatu-rates	Aro-matics
Thermal, mixed-phase	Paraffinic gas-oil	37	16	39	8
Thermal, mixed-phase	Naphthenic gas-oil	30	25	30	15
Thermal, vapor-phase	Gas-oil	20	15	45	20
Reforming, thermal	Naphtha	35	30	20	15
Polyforming	Naphtha, gas	24	18	36	22
Catalytic	Paraffinic gas-oil	40	15	30	15
Catalytic	Naphthenic gas-oil	25	15	35	20
Catalytic, high conversion	Gas-oil	40	15	5	40
Reforming, catalytic	Naphthenic naphtha	40	10	0	50
Hydrogenation	Paraffinic stock	65	30	0	5
Hydrogenation	Naphthenic stock	45	47	0	8

hydrocarbon classes in synthetic gasolines. It is understood that the composition of gasolines may deviate from the figures given in the table because of variations in charging stocks or conditions of the process. The composition of catalytically cracked gasolines is particularly sensitive to the changes in temperature, contact time, and activity of the catalyst.

References

1. Cady, W. E., Marschner, R. F., and Cropper, W. P., *Ind. Eng. Chem.*, **44**, 1859 (1952).
2. Charlet, E. M., Lanneau, K. P., and Johnson, F. B., Cleveland, Meeting Am. Chem. Soc., April 1951, Symposium on the Chemical Composition of Petroleum, p. 105.
3. Glasgow, A. R., Streiff, A. J., Willingham, C. B., and Rossini, F. D., *J. Research Natl. Bur. Standards*, **38**, 537 (1947).
4. Glasgow, A. R., Willingham, C. B., and Rossini, F. D., *Ind. Eng. Chem.*, **41**, 2292 (1949).
5. Melpolder, F. W., Brown, R. A., Young, W. S., and Headington, C. E., *Ind. Eng. Chem.*, **44**, 1142 (1952).
6. Read, D., *Petroleum Processing*, 839 (June 1952).
7. Young, W. S., *Natl. Petr. News* (March 6, 1946).
8. Streiff, A. J., and Rossini, F. D., *J. Research Natl. Bur. Standards*, **39**, 303 (1947).

CHAPTER 25

ACETYLENE BY THE PYROLYSIS OF LIGHT HYDROCARBONS

LEONARD KRAMER AND JOHN HAPPEL

Chemical Engineering Department, New York University,
University Heights, New York 53, N. Y.

Recent interest in the use of acetylene has been stimulated by the development of processes for its production from low-molecular-weight hydrocarbons. These processes all involve the noncatalytic pyrolysis of the hydrocarbons at high temperatures as the initial process step. The acetylene is produced in a relatively dilute gaseous mixture and is concentrated and purified in subsequent recovery operations.

To secure reasonably high yields in the primary pyrolysis, temperatures in excess of 1200°C are necessary; the optimum condition has not been defined. Other important operating conditions are short contact times, rapid quenching of reaction products, and low partial pressures of feed and product. The latter condition is obtained by operating under vacuum or through the addition of diluents. The present survey has as its object a critical study of available data on the primary pyrolysis step. The system adopted here is to consider the problem from three viewpoints: equilibrium, kinetics, and mechanism of the reactions involved.

Equilibrium Considerations

The pyrolysis of hydrocarbons to acetylene at high temperatures is considered to go through a series of consecutive reactions, each of which is reversible.[44,45,51,83,86,92] The primary products are not directly related to the final equilibrium products, which are carbon and hydrogen together with small amounts of acetylene, ethylene, and methane. Therefore, in producing acetylene from hydrocarbons, the reactions are quenched before equilibrium is reached.

The products are a function only of temperature, pressure, and contact time, if the feed is a single reactant. If these variables result in product concentrations such that the degree of conversion is small compared to that at equilibrium, then only the kinetics of the forward reactions need be considered. The equilibrium constant limits the concentrations attainable. Storch[87] has employed the ratio K/R as a measure of the approach to equilibrium attained at various reaction conditions. K is the ratio of partial pressure terms, in atmospheres, at equilibrium; R is the ratio of these same terms at the conditions of the experiment. Table 1 defines K and R for several reactions that will be considered. Values of log K at various temperatures have been plotted for the reactions of Table 1. These are shown in Figure 1. The data are based on one mole of reacting substance, except for methane. Free energy and heat of reaction data for calculating K have been obtained from Bureau of Standards Circular C-461.[72] These reactions are not intended to give all the steps in acetylene production; rather, they are given to show only those stable products which immediately precede acetylene formation.

TABLE 1. REACTIONS INVOLVED IN ACETYLENE FORMATION AND EQUILIBRIUM CONSTANTS

Reaction		Equilibrium Constant*,†
(1)	$2CH_4 \rightleftharpoons C_2H_4 + 2H_2$	$K_1 = \dfrac{P_{C_2H_4}P_{H_2}^2}{P^2_{CH_4}}$
(2)	$C_2H_6 \rightleftharpoons C_2H_4 + H_2$	$K_2 = \dfrac{P_{C_2H_4}P_{H_2}}{P_{C_2H_6}}$
(3)	$C_3H_8 \rightleftharpoons C_2H_4 + CH_4$	$K_3 = \dfrac{P_{C_2H_4}P_{CH_4}}{P_{C_3H_8}}$
(4)	$C_3H_8 \rightleftharpoons C_3H_6 + H_2$	$K_4 = \dfrac{P_{C_3H_6}P_{H_2}}{P_{C_3H_8}}$
(5)	$C_4H_{10} \rightleftharpoons C_2H_4 + C_2H_6$	$K_5 = \dfrac{P_{C_2H_6}P_{C_2H_4}}{P_{C_4H_{10}}}$
(6)	$C_4H_{10} \rightleftharpoons C_3H_6 + CH_4$	$K_6 = \dfrac{P_{CH_4}P_{C_3H_6}}{P_{C_4H_{10}}}$
(7)	$C_4H_{10} \rightleftharpoons C_4H_8 + H_2$	$K_7 = \dfrac{P_{C_4H_8}P_{H_2}}{P_{C_4H_{10}}}$
(I)‡	$C_2H_4 \rightleftharpoons C_2H_2 + H_2$	$K_I = \dfrac{P_{C_2H_2}P_{H_2}}{P_{C_2H_4}}$
(II)‡	$C_3H_6 \rightleftharpoons C_2H_2 + CH_4$	$K_{II} = \dfrac{P_{CH_4}P_{C_2H_2}}{P_{C_3H_6}}$
(III)‡	$2CH_4 \rightleftharpoons C_2H_2 + 3H_2$	$K_{III} = \dfrac{P_{C_2H_2}P_{H_2}^3}{P^2_{CH_4}}$

* Partial pressures are expressed in atmospheres.

† The same terms occur as shown in R but are taken at the conditions of the experiment and therefore are not necessarily at equilibrium.

‡ Roman numerals refer to reactions yielding acetylene as a product.

Tables 2, 3, and 4 present the data of several investigators. R has been calculated and compared with K for both the production of intermediate and its decomposition to acetylene. Where the ratio K/R is equal to or greater than 10, the kinetics of the reverse reactions are considered small. K/R can theoretically never be less than 1.0.

Table 2 contains the data for methane pyrolysis. Not all the runs of a

given investigator are tabulated, but only those where the greatest
extent of decomposition has taken place and the acetylene concentration
is high. These are the conditions which would be closest to equilibrium.
Rudder and Biederman[73] present data with K_1/R_1 greater than K_I/R_I by

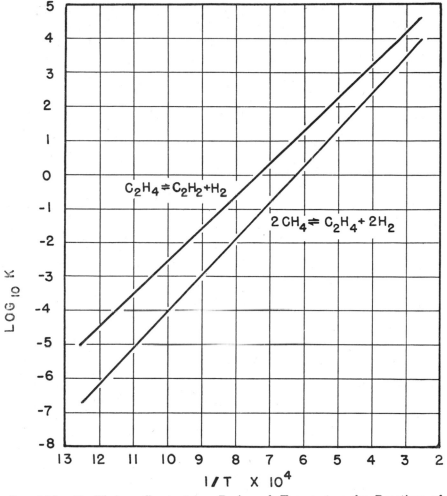

FIG. 1(a). Equilibrium Constant vs. Reciprocal Temperature for Reactions of
Table 1.

a factor of at least 3x. Though not tabulated for all runs, K_I/R_I is generally less than 10. This would indicate that the intermediate, ethylene,
is being produced from methane but rapidly decomposes to acetylene,
maintaining approximately equilibrium concentrations. The data of

Stanley and Nash,[80] Smith, *et al.*,[79] Tropsch and Egloff,[92] Fischer and Pichler,[19] and Storch and Golden[88] are consistent with this concept.

TABLE 2. APPROACH TO EQUILIBRIUM: METHANE PYROLYSIS

Line	Temp, °C	Time (sec)	R_1*	K_1	K_1/R_1	R_I	K_I	K_I/R_I	Reference
1	1000	1.81	8.16×10^{-3}	1.86×10^{-2}	2.28	1.08×10^{-1}	2.52×10^{-1}	2.34	(73)
2	1100	1.35	2.66×10^{-3}	1.00×10^{-1}	37.6	2.79×10^{-1}	8.91×10^{-1}	3.19	(80)
3	1150	0.22	5.0×10^{-3}	1.78×10^{-1}	35.6	6.2×10^{-1}	1.58	2.50	(80)
4	1200	0.41	1.4×10^{-4}	3.16×10^{-1}	2250	3.7×10^{-3}	2.24	6.1×10^2	(73)
5	1200	0.23	1.9×10^{-2}	3.16×10^{-1}	17	5.63×10^{-1}	2.24	3.98	(79)
6	1400	0.014	6.7×10^{-3}	2.24	330	1.86×10^{-1}	14.1	76	(92)
						R_{III}	K_{III}	K_{III}/R_{III}	
7	1260	0.20				2.3×10^{-1}	2.24	9.73	(58)
8	1300	0.098				5.1×10^{-3}	3.98	7.8×10^2	(73)
9	1450	0.01				1.56	70.8	45.4	(58)
10	1500	0.005				2.27	158.5	69.8	(58)
11	1500	0.034				0.13	158.5	1220	(73)
12	1500	0.0042				7.5×10^{-3}	158.5	21×10^3	(88)
13	1500	0.0042				1.0×10^{-3}	158.5	158.5×10^3	(88)

* Nomenclature is consistent with that of Table 1.

If it is accepted, therefore, that the formation of acetylene from methane passes through ethylene as an intermediate, then the decomposition of methane may be considered without considering reverse reactions.

TABLE 3. APPROACH TO EQUILIBRIUM: ETHANE AND ETHYLENE

Line Ethane	Temp, °C	Time, sec	R_2	K_2	K_2/R_2	R_I	K_I	K_I/R_I	Reference
1	900	0.048	2.06	3.98	1.93	0.03	0.071	23.6	(60)
2	975	0.013	0.82	10.0	12.2	0.011	0.224	20.0	(31)
3	1032	0.008	4.12	17.8	4.33	0.058	0.447	7.7	(31)
4*	1400	0.00088	0.574	251	437	0.020	15.9	795	(92)
5*	1400	0.00164	—	251	—	0.047	15.9	340	(92)
Ethylene									
1	1150	0.044				0.10	2.51	25.1	(93)
2	1400	0.0084				0.17	14.1	83.0	(93)

* Estimated.

Table 3 contains data on the pyrolysis of ethane and ethylene. In the decomposition of ethane, the formation of ethylene proceeds more rapidly than the disappearance of ethylene to acetylene. Thus, the ethylene accumulates and approaches an equilibrium with ethane and hydrogen. Ethane decomposition must therefore be considered as complicated by the reverse reaction, ethylene hydrogenation. The rapid disappearance of ethane to ethylene is significant in the decomposition of methane and will be further discussed under "Mechanism." The data for propane indicate that the decomposition of propane via reaction (3), Table 1, that is, with ethylene as an intermediate, is far from equilibrium. Simultaneously, the decomposition through propylene as an intermediate, reaction (4), Table 1, is essentially at equilibrium at even the shortest contact times. However, all propane disappears in less than 5.5×10^{-4} seconds at temperatures above 1100°C; this makes it difficult to decide in which direction the decomposition of propane proceeds, since the ethylene present is also a product of propylene pyrolysis.[93] K/R for acetylene production is very close to 1.0 for the propylene intermediate but is usually greater than 10.0 for the ethylene intermediate. This would

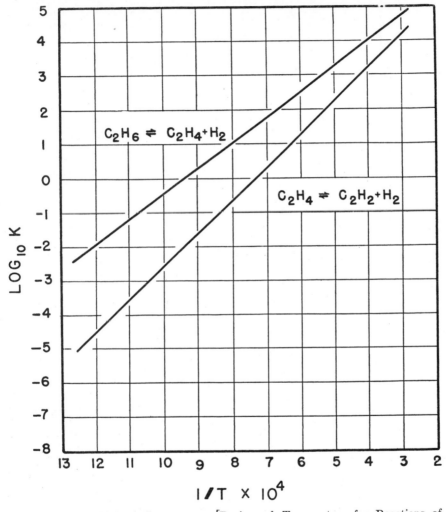

Fig. 1(b). Equilibrium Constant vs. [Reciprocal Temperature for Reactions of Table 1.

indicate that the demethanation of propylene to acetylene proceeds more rapidly than the dehydrogenation of ethylene.

n-Butane and isobutane behave similarly to propane in that they decompose to secondary and tertiary products too fast for the direction

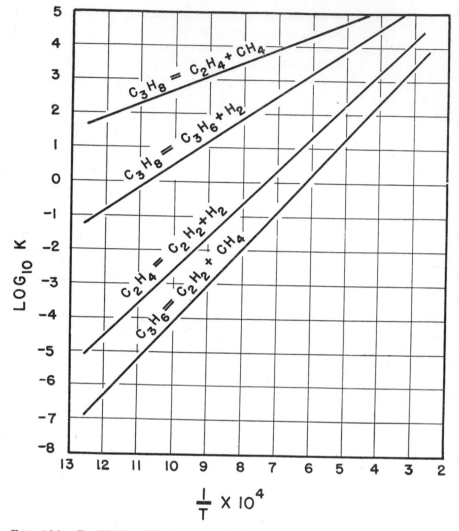

FIG. 1(c). Equilibrium Constant vs. Reciprocal Temp. for the Reactions of Table 1.

of the initial decomposition to be studied. This is true at all temperatures over 1000°C; that is, where acetylene is an important product. K/R has roughly the same values for acetylene from propylene or ethylene as are found in propane pyrolysis; this would indicate that the nature of the initial reactant does not have too great an effect on the rate of acetylene formation if the initial reactant is a three-carbon or higher hydrocarbon. Owing to the aforementioned factors, the production of acetylene from

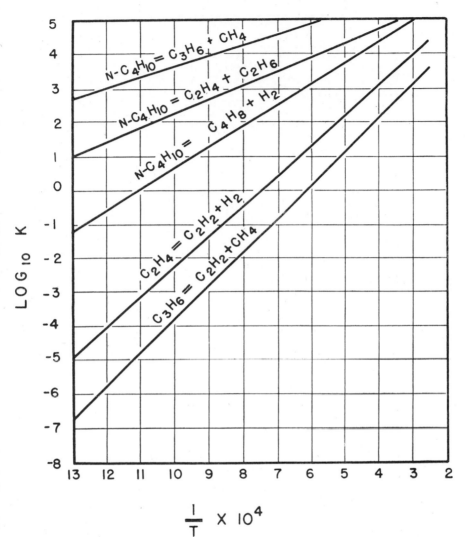

FIG. 1(d). Equilibrium Constant vs. Reciprocal Temp. for the Reactions of Table 1.

propane and the butanes will be considered from the aspect of acetylene formation rather than feed-disappearance.

Effect of Temperature and Pressure on Equilibrium. The effect of temperature is clearly shown in Figure 1. Both the decomposition of reactant to intermediate and intermediate to acetylene are favored by increasing the temperature.

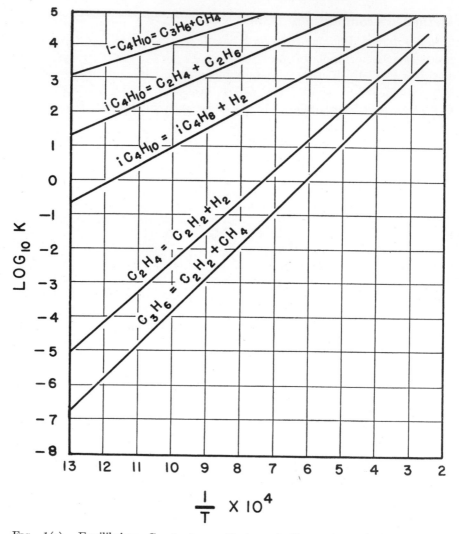

FIG. 1(e). Equilibrium Constant vs. Reciprocal Temp. for the Reactions of Table 1.

In addition, a pressure decrease should favor all the reactions, because all yield an increase in the total number of moles. The introduction of inert gases should have the same effect as a pressure reduction. Dilution with hydrogen, however, should suppress the formation of acetylene; hydrogen is always the product of at least one stage of the reactant decomposition to acetylene.

Methane Decomposition—Kinetics

Below 700°C, Bone and Coward[6] found that methane decomposition proceeds at a negligible rate; at temperatures above 700°C, they found an initial rate of nth order, n being much greater than 1.0, but the order became first as the extent of decomposition increased. Acetylene appears as a product of reaction only at first, but rapidly decomposes to carbon and hydrogen.

Holliday *et al.*[35,36] observed that hydrogen had a marked retardation effect on the rate of methane decomposition, reducing it practically to zero at some fixed ratio:

$$K_p' = (p_{CH_4})^2/(p_{CH_4})^3 \tag{1}$$

where p represents the partial pressure of a component in any consistent pressure units. This ratio, K_p', is itself a function of temperature and in many ways behaves as a true equilibrium constant. Holliday and Exell postulate that methane decomposes to carbon and hydrogen through acetylene. It is the acetylene decomposition that is retarded by hydrogen; the small amount of acetylene that does not decompose is capable of maintaining large concentrations of methane via the equilibrium:

$$K_p = \frac{(p_{C_2H_2})(p_{C_2H_2})^3}{(p_{CH_4})^2} \tag{2}$$

At small but constant partial pressures of acetylene,

$$K_p' = \frac{(p_{C_2H_2})}{K_p} = \frac{(p_{CH_4})^2}{(p_{H_2})^3} \tag{1}$$

This effect is not important at temperatures above 1000°C, owing to the rapid increase of K_p with temperature (Figure 1). Holliday, *et al.* conclude that the retardation effect of hydrogen is due to its effect on acetylene decomposition and not on the decomposition of methane.

Peters and Meyer[57] cracked methane to acetylene, benzene, carbon and hydrogen over hot tungsten coils and in porcelain tubes. The reaction was stopped far short of equilibrium where acetylene concentrations were quite high. Though the temperature data of these authors are very approximate, several trends are apparent. The maximum conversion to acetylene occurred at the highest temperature, 3000°C, and the shortest contact time, 0.0001 sec. A decrease in the partial pressure of methane resulted in higher conversions to acetylene and lower conversions to coke and liquid products.

Frolich[24,25] studied the effect of pressure reduction and hydrogen dilution on the yield of acetylene. With pressure ranging from 20 to

760 mm, the ethylene percentage remained constant; the acetylene concentration increased from 1.9 to 2.4 per cent, and the hydrogen yield increased from 10 to 30 per cent. Thus, while the increase of pressure raised the conversion of methane, the yield of ethylene and acetylene decreased. Hydrogen dilution of the feed resulted in a sixfold increase in the ratio of acetylene to carbon in the product. Similar results are reported by Frost,[26] who observed a 95 per cent conversion to acetylene at 1800°K and one atmosphere; at one-tenth atmosphere the same conversion resulted at 1500°K.

The data of several investigators have been used to calculate first-order rate constants for methane decomposition. These are presented in Table 4. The first-order rate constant, k_1, is calculated from the integrated form of the equation:

$$-\frac{dC}{dt} = k_1 C \tag{3}$$

That is,
$$ln\, C_1/C_2 = k_1(t_2 - t_1) \tag{4}$$

where C_1 = methane concentration in   (mole fraction)
C_2 = methane concentration out (mole fraction)
$t_2 - t_1$ = contact time   (see Equation 6)

The application of a first-order rate equation to the decomposition of methane is due largely to the work of Kassel.[44] This author measured the isothermal rate of decomposition of methane in silica bulbs by following pressure rise. An induction period was observed which decreased with packing or with increasing pressure. These effects of pressure and packing are also indicative of a heat transfer problem rather than a kinetic effect, but because of a lack of experimental detail, this is only conjecture. Kassel suggests the use of Equation (3) to temperatures of 1500°C, where it begins to deviate badly. The value of k_1 he suggests is given by:

$$k_1 = 1.0 \times 10^{-12} e^{-79,385/RT} \text{ sec}^{-1} \tag{5}$$

where R is the gas constant and T is in degrees Kelvin. This equation is plotted as a dashed line in Figure 2.

None of the data presented in Table 4 are sufficiently different from the rest to warrant condemning or discarding them. However, sufficient differences exist to make the experimental techniques employed of interest. Rudder and Biederman[73] employed a carbon grain resistance furnace to obtain the temperatures required. They used a platinum vs platinum rhodium thermocouple to measure gas temperatures. Wheeler and Wood[96] ran reactions in silica and chrome-iron tubes of approximately the same surface-to-volume ratio, S/V. However, the runs of line 5, Table 4, were made with surface-to-volume ratio about 15 times

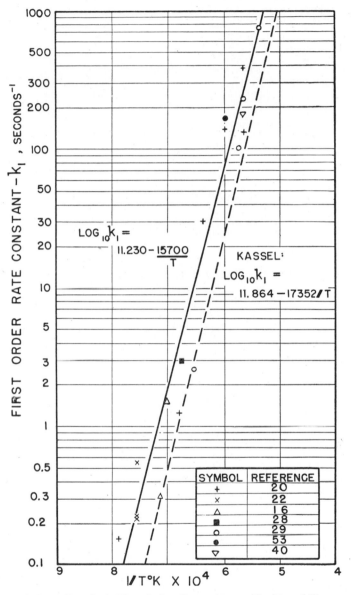

TABLE 4. FIRST-ORDER RATE CONSTANTS METHANE PYROLYSIS

Line—Runs	Temp, °C	Pressure Range, mm Hg	Conc. Range CH_4 Vol % in	Conc. Range CH_4 Vol % out	Cont. Time Range, sec	k_1 sec^{-1} Range	k avg.	Reference
1—2	900	760	100	84.8–67.5	27.1–63.4	0.0062–0.0061	0.0062	(73)
2—10	1000	760	100	86.9–34.5	1.03–13.7	0.2650–0.0777	0.1582	(73)
3—6	1050	760	96 + 4N_2	42.7–26.9	2.6–11.2	0.3110–0.1135	0.2182	(96)
4—5	1050	760	94.4 + 5.6 N_2	55.5–29.9	2.0–9.0	0.2650–0.1282	0.2220	(96)
5—5	1050	760	92.5 + 7.5 N_2	73.3–40.7	0.3–3.7	0.7760–0.2210	0.5430	(96)
6—3	1100	760	92.5 + N_2	78.2–60	0.52–1.35	0.345–0.319	0.328	(80)
7—5	1150	760	92.5	78.6–48.1	0.15–0.5	2.390–1.075	1.555	(80)
8—2	1200	105	100	63.0–58.5	0.41–0.39	1.375–1.121	1.248	(73)
9—2	1200	760	100	76.4–46.1	0.11–0.23	2.49–3.37	2.93	(79)
10—1	1260	760	25CH_4 50H_2 bal. inert	15*	0.20	2.55	2.55	(19)
11—4	1300	85–142	100	83.2–13.8	0.0095–0.0975	46.20–12.35	29.89	(73)
12—5	1400	34–206	100	29.4–9.5	0.0077–0.0234	225–65	134	(73)
13—5	1400	50	100	63.1–18.8	0.0023–0.0140	200–119	164	(92)
14—1	1450	760	25CH_4 50H_2 inert	9.0*	0.010	102	102	(19)
15—7	1500	35–99	100	52.7–2.2	0.0012–0.0339	700–112	370	(73)
16—2	1500	35–55	43–66 + H_2	4.5–3.3	0.0135–0.0321	168–93.3	130	(73)
17—4	1500	760	10–25 + CO_2	14.2–4.3	0.0032–0.0042	201–127	176	(88)
18—1	1500	760	25CH_4 + 50H_2 + inert	8*	0.005	228	228	(19)
19—1	1600	760	" "	1.8*	0.004	659	659	(19)

* Estimated.

that of lines 3 and 4. The k_1's obtained are generally higher, but not enough to warrant a differentiation between them. The effect is probably due to the sensitivity of temperature gradient in an annulus to different flow rates, as pointed out by Storch.[87] Stanley and Nash[80] used a quartz tube as a reactor; Smith, Grandone and Rall[79] used sillimanite tubes. Storch and Golden[88] were primarily interested in obtaining data on methane pyrolysis with steam or carbon dioxide as diluents. Only the center 10 cm of a 20-cm tube is taken as effective reactor volume, as suggested by Storch. Tropsch *et al.*[92] used 3-mm I D porcelain tubes in a furnace heated by silicon carbide glo bars. A single thermocouple at the half-way point along the outside of the reactor was used to measure temperature.

The contact time in all cases has been calculated, assuming an isothermal reactor with negligible pressure drop:

$$t = \frac{V_R}{\left(\frac{(V_0 + V_1)}{2}\right)\left(\frac{T_R}{T_A}\right)\left(\frac{\pi_A}{\pi_R}\right)} \tag{6}$$

where t = contact time in seconds

V_R = reactor volume, effective

V_0 and V_1 = flow volume/sec in and out, respectively, at ambient pressure, π_A, and temperature, T_A, at which volumes are measured

T_R and π_R = reactor pressure and temperature

Most contact times in Table 4 were taken directly from Storch.[86]

The data summarized in Table 4 show a definite increase in k_1 with temperature. In addition to this, at a given temperature there is a definite decrease in k_1 with increasing extent of reaction; that is, the products of reaction inhibit the decomposition of methane. The values of k_1 avg are plotted in Figure 2 as $\log_{10} k_1$ *vs* $1/T$. This plot of k_1 avg in Figure 2 and the data of Kassel from static experiments are seen to be in good agreement. The equation obtained from Figure 2 is:

$$\log_{10} k = 11.230 - \frac{15,700}{T} \tag{7}$$

Kassel's data yield:

$$\log_{10} k = 11.864 - \frac{17,352}{T} \tag{8}$$

Equation (7) represents the decomposition of methane at a wide variety of temperatures, pressures, and feed compositions; k_1, as calculated from Equation (7), also represents the average rate of decomposition over a wide range of conversions. Thus, Equation (7) in conjunction with Equation (3) permits the estimation of the extent of decomposition of methane. It is also necessary to estimate the product distribution; that is, the conversion to acetylene and ethylene, especially the former.

Conversion of Methane to Acetylene and Ethylene: Pressure and Dilution Effects. The net conversion to acetylene and ethylene depends upon their rate of formation from methane and upon their decomposition to carbon and hydrogen. If the decomposition of methane is assumed to be first order, then any effect of pressure must be due to its effect on the decomposition of ethylene and acetylene.

Pease[55] found the disappearance of acetylene to be homogeneous and bimolecular at temperatures of 400 to 600°C and pressures around one atmosphere. Rimarski[69] found that dilution with inert gases tends to decrease the rate of acetylene decomposition. Both of these effects were confirmed by Schäpfer and Brunner.[75]

Thus, in the cracking of methane to acetylene, either a decrease in pressure or the addition of inert gases to the feed should result in higher yields.

The effect of temperature on the yield of acetylene and ethylene has been discussed under "Equilibrium." Storch[87] has attempted to correlate the conversion to acetylene and ethylene with the average partial pressure of methane; the product of the average partial pressure of methane and the conversion to acetylene and ethylene is represented as a constant which has the dimensions of pressure and is a function of temperature. This constant has been calculated for the data summarized in Table 4. The average partial pressure of methane, $\bar{p}_{CH_4}$, has been calculated, assuming that the decomposition of methane follows Equation (3); that is,

$$-\ln \left(\frac{p_1}{p_0}\right) = kt \tag{9A}$$

p_0, p_1 = initial and final partial pressure of methane, respectively, at time 0 and t
$\quad t$ = contact time, seconds
$\quad k$ = first-order rate constant, sec^{-1}
Then:

$$\bar{p}_{CH_4} = \frac{\int_0^t p_0 e^{-kt} dt}{t} \tag{10}$$

$$= \frac{p_0}{kt}[1 - e^{-kt}] \tag{10A}$$

It was found that this product, $(\bar{p}_{CH_4})$ (conversion to $C_2H_2 + C_2H_4$), did not yield a satisfactory constant. For instance, at 1000°C, the values ranged from 9.4 to 45.5 mm Hg; also, no relation of this constant to temperature is evident. Over all temperatures and pressures, the variation is about 2000 per cent. However, this "constant" disregards the effect of total pressure or of added inert gases on the decomposition of acetylene.

On inspecting the data summarized in Table 4, it appeared that the "constant" suggested by Storch, when divided by the square root of the total pressure, would yield a somewhat more reliable constant; that is,

$$\frac{(\bar{p}_{CH_4})(\text{conversion to acetylene and ethylene})}{(\pi)^{1/2}} = k_3 \text{ (mm Hg)}^{1/2} \tag{11}$$

where π is the total pressure of the system in mm Hg, $\bar{p}_{CH_4}$ is the average partial pressure of methane (Equation 10A), and $k_3 = 1.05 \pm$

0.445 for all the data summarized in Table 4 regardless of temperature, total pressure, or nature or quantity of diluent present in the feed. It is obvious that any combination of terms leading to a conversion to ethylene and acetylene greater than 1.0 is not realizable; Equation (11) is generally not useful at total conversions of methane greater than 90 per cent. Table 5 lists some values of the predicted conversion (Equation 11) and the actual conversion obtained experimentally. It is obvious that Equation (11) generally is conservative. That is, it predicts yields lower than those obtained, especially at high temperatures (1300 to 1400°C). However, considering the numerous sources of the data and wide variety of experimental conditions, the agreement of 50 per cent is very good.

TABLE 5. CALCULATED AND EXPERIMENTAL CONVERSIONS OF METHANE
TO ACETYLENE AND ETHYLENE

	Temp, °C	Time, sec	k (Fig. 2) sec^{-1}	π Total Pressure mm Hg	$\bar{p}_{CH_4}$ Calc Eq. (9) mm Hg	Conversion Calc.	Conversion Exper.	Diluent	Reference
(1)	1000	11.5	0.07	760	520	5.58	3.5	none	(73)
(2)	1050	2.6	0.20	760	566	5.13	6.0	5% N$_2$	(96)
(3)	1050	0.45	0.20	760	663	4.37	5.2	5% N$_2$	(96)
(4)	1100	0.87	0.6	760	547	5.29	4.3	?	(80)
(5)	1150	0.22	0.88	760	639	4.53	8.8	?	(80)
(6)	1200	0.39	3.6	105	56	19.1	16.0	none	(73)
(7)	1200	0.23	3.6	760	517	5.62	8.50	none	(79)
(8)	1300	0.0149	14.0	85	75.6	12.8	4.0	none	(73)
(9)	1300	0.0095	14.0	151	143	8.8	11.0	none	(73)
(10)	1400	0.0104	70.0	206	146	10.35	27.0	none	(73)
(11)	1400	0.0077	70.0	134	104	11.75	20.0	none	(73)
(12)	1400	0.0140	70.0	50	32	23.4	29.1	none	(53)
(13)	1500	0.0012	170	60	54	15.1	20.0	none	(73)
(14)	1500	0.0135	170	35	5.9	10.5	23.0	50% H$_2$	(73)
(15)	1500	0.0032	170	760	147	20.0	29.5	75% CO$_2$	(88)
(16)	1500	0.0032	170	760	58.4	49.8	23.3	90% CO$_2$	(88)
(17)	1500	0.0050	170	760	128	22.6	55.0	50% H$_2$ 25% N$_2$	(19)

Finally, it would be useful to predict the fraction of the conversion to ethylene and acetylene that is acetylene.

The data summarized in Table 4 and equilibrium data at one atmosphere total pressure are compared in Table 6. Thus, it is possible through Equations (9), (11), and Table 6 to predict the yield of acetylene when methane is cracked under a wide variety of conditions.

Surface Effects. The effect of surface was investigated by Holliday, et al.[55,56] and found to be negligible. Kassel considered the above author's work inconclusive because only clean surfaces, that is, free of coke, were tested. Kassel[44] therefore ran tests of homogeneity with a twentyfold variation in surface-to-volume ratio, and with both clean and unclean

TABLE 6. PERCENTAGE OF ACETYLENE IN ACETYLENE-ETHYLENE CUT

Temp, °C	Equilibrium % Acetylene	Table 4 Data Average Values % Acetylene
1000	15	15
1100	60	25
1200	90	40
1300	>90	60
1400	>90	80
1500	>90	>90

The differences at higher temperatures are due to two things:

(A) The data of Table 4 are obtained at pressures well below one atmosphere.

(B) Hydrogen is formed by the net reaction:

$$CH_4 \rightarrow C + 2H_2$$

as well as by the dehydrogenation of ethylene to acetylene. This extra hydrogen tends to lower the ratio of acetylene to ethylene.

packing. This author also concludes that the effect of surface is negligible for methane decomposition.

Also, as has been pointed out previously, the decomposition of the products is largely homogeneous; therefore, surface should have little effect on either conversion of methane or yield of products.

Catalysis. Many efforts have been made to find homogeneous or heterogeneous catalysts for acetylene production from methane. Hessels, et al.[32] have tried sulfur, oxygen, and chlorine, and also their compounds with hydrogen. They observed little effect on the cracking of methane or yield of unsaturates. Huntington and Lu[37] obtained similar results with methyl chloride. Steam, carbon dioxide,[88] titanium tetrachloride,[73] and hydrogen chloride[73] have been added with no effect on the reaction.

Although the above gases may not exert catalytic effects, they do behave as inerts which are easily removed; this is of practical importance because of the low concentrations of acetylene obtained in the product stream of commercial cracking units.

Although no positive catalysts are known for the production of acetylene from methane, many materials have marked negative effects on acetylene yields. These materials tend to promote the total decomposition of methane to carbon and hydrogen. Among those metals most commonly mentioned are iron, nickel, cobalt, copper, platinum, and palladium.[80,95] It is obvious that equipment for the thermal cracking of methane should not include these metals or their oxides.

Mechanism of Methane Pyrolysis to Acetylene

The pyrolysis of methane to acetylene has been considered to go through steps involving ethane and ethylene. As will be seen, the first stable product is generally agreed to be ethane. Because the decomposition of ethane and ethylene will be considered separately, only the initial steps in the decomposition of methane will be considered; that is, those steps leading to ethane.

Among the first mechanisms presented to account for the formation of acetylene from methane was that of Holliday, et al.[35,36] These authors postulated a direct molecular mechanism:

$$(8) \qquad\qquad 2CH_4 \rightleftharpoons C_2H_2 + 3H_2$$

Kassel[44] has shown that the rate of formation of acetylene is much too high for the mechanism as given by Equation (8); if the energy of activation obtained by Kassel is even approximately correct, 79 k cal/mol, the observed rate is much too high.

Hague and Wheeler[30] have postulated a route through butadiene and ethylene which eliminates acetylene as an intermediate, preferring ethylene. Their major arguments are concerned with temperatures under 1000°C and with reactions leading to aromatic products. Because acetylene formation is not important where either of the two conditions given above prevail, it is pointless to study this mechanism.

There is little argument at the present time about the initial stable product of methane decomposition. Storch[86,87] cracked methane on a carbon filament suspended in a bulb cooled to low temperature. The product obtained depended upon the degree of cooling, the extent of dehydrogenation increasing with increasing temperature of the coolant. The data are summarized in Table 7.

TABLE 7. METHANE CRACKING IN CARBON FILAMENT BULB

Coolant	Temperature of Coolant	Produced
N_2	−195°C	95% conv. to ethane
O_2	−182°C	ethylene and acetylene
CO_2 + alcohol	−70°C	carbon and hydrogen
Ice and water	0°C	carbon and hydrogen

The drastic cooling with liquid nitrogen removes the initial product from the reaction zone. Less drastic cooling permits the return of this initial product to the wire for further cracking. The relatively mild cooling obtained with solid carbon dioxide or ice permits total cracking. The conclusion is that ethane is the primary stable product of methane cracking. The energy of activation observed by Storch was 77 ± 10 k cal/mol, in good agreement with other investigators.

It is largely because of this work done by Storch that a path through stable products is generally accepted as:

$$(9) \qquad 2CH_4 \rightarrow C_2H_6 \rightarrow C_2H_4 \rightarrow C_2H_2 \rightarrow 2C + H_2$$
$$(+H_2) \quad (+H_2) \quad (+H_2)$$

Free-Radical Role in Methane Decomposition. A method frequently employed to detect free radicals involves the use of nitric oxide. It was found[33] that the addition of small amounts of NO reduced a rate of reaction to some limiting value. Addition of more NO after this limiting reaction rate was reached did not reduce it further. The conclusion is that the NO is combining with the free radicals and removing them as reactants. When the limiting rate is reached, all the radicals are reacted; the residual rate is due to that portion of the reaction which proceeds by purely molecular mechanisms.

Hobbs and Hinshelwood[34] have investigated the effect of nitric oxide on methane decomposition. They found an effective chain-length of 4.7 at 850°C and 100 mm of methane. Maximum inhibition occurred at a pressure of 3.2 mm Hg of NO. The quantitative effect is not definite, owing to some reaction of the methane with nitric oxide. This method of determining a free-radical mechanism does not yield information concerning the nature of the radical involved.

Methylene Radicals. A mechanism for the decomposition of methane through methylene radicals was first postulated by Kassel.[44] He presented the following five steps for the total decomposition of methane to carbon and hydrogen:

$$(1) \qquad CH_4 \rightleftharpoons CH_2 + H_2$$
$$(2) \quad CH_2 + CH_4 \rightarrow C_2H_6$$
$$(3) \qquad C_2H_6 \rightarrow C_2H_4 + H_2$$
$$(4) \qquad C_2H_4 \rightarrow C_2H_2 + H_2$$
$$(5) \qquad C_2H_2 \rightarrow 2C + H_2$$

Ethane is the first stable product formed in agreement with presently accepted fact. This reaction mechanism results in the following rate equation:

$$\frac{-d(CH_4)}{dt} = \frac{a(CH_4)^2 - b(H_2)^4}{c(H_2)^3 + d(H_2)^2 + e(H_2) + f(CH_4)} \qquad (12)$$

where a, b, c, d, e, f are constants and the brackets enclose concentration terms. This equation reduces to:

$$\frac{-d(CH_4)}{dt} = k(CH_4) \qquad (3)$$

at low hydrogen concentrations, in agreement with the first-order rate observed by Kassel.

Much of the criticism leveled at this mechanism has been directed against the first step; that is, a split of methane into a methylene radical and a hydrogen molecule.

Bawn and Milsted[2] prepared methylene radicals by reacting methylene bromide with sodium vapor:

$$(10) \qquad CH_2Br_2 + 2Na \ (v) \rightarrow CH_2 + 2NaBr$$

If hydrogen is present as a diluent, methane is the principal product; ethylene is present in traces.

Rice and Glasbrook[67a] were able to isolate the products of reaction of methylene radicals with tellurium, selenium, arsenic, and antimony mirrors. The product with tellurium is an analog of formaldehyde, $(CH_2Te)_n$.

Fischer[18] has given the heats of reaction data for the hydrogenation of carbon monoxide to methylene. His data indicate a heat of formation of 30 to 40 k cal/gm mole for methylene from graphite and hydrogen.

Burton, *et al.*[10] find that methylene behaves more like a molecule than a radical; that is, it is similar to carbon monoxide, its half-life being a function of its environment.

Bawn and Tipper[3] investigated the reactions of methylene in hydrogen and nitrogen atmospheres. They found the ratio,

$$\left(\frac{\text{Conversion to methane}}{\text{Conversion to ethylene}}\right)$$

in nitrogen much less than the same ratio in a hydrogen atmosphere. They conclude that both of the following reactions can occur:

(11) $$CH_2 + H_2 \rightarrow CH_4$$
(12) $$2CH_2 \rightarrow C_2H_4$$

A more complete summary of the evidence for and the properties of methylene radicals is presented by Barrow, *et al.*[1]

The first evidence for the existence of methylene radicals in the decomposition of methane was presented by Mecke.[48] He claims to have observed the radicals spectroscopically when methane was cracked at 800 to 900°C in quartz.

Belchetz, *et al.*[4,5] cracked methane at very low pressures and allowed the product to impinge on cooled mirrors of iodine and tellurium. They emphasize the fact that the mirrors were placed within one mean free path of the wire. These authors claim to have isolated the reaction products of methylene with iodine, methylene iodide, and with tellurium, telluro formaldehyde. When the mirror is placed at distances greater than one mean free path from the wire, only methyl radicals were observed. They conclude, "methyl radicals are produced but are essentially secondary products."

Steacie[83] regards Belchetz' early work as doubtful because it is not reproducible. Steacie also regards the later work done as dubious because of the small amounts of material with which Belchetz *et al.* worked.

Rice and Glasebrook[67] cracked methane, ethane, and propane in a tubular furnace at 800 to 1000°C and passed the products of reaction over iodine and tellurium mirrors. They could not detect any of the reaction products of methylene but did find those of methyl radicals.

Pearson, et al.[54] obtained methylene radicals by decomposing ketene and diazomethane:

$$(13) \qquad CH_2=C=O \rightarrow CH_2 + CO$$
$$(14)\ CH_2=N-N=CH_2 \rightarrow 2CH_2 + N_2$$

In diazomethane or in ketene, the half-life of the methylene radical was too long to be measured in their apparatus. In methane, however, the half-life was approximately equal to the time necessary to traverse one mean free path, 0.001 second. They found a reaction between methylene and methane could occur at temperatures over 800°C.

In the work of Belchetz and Rideal, the tellurium and iodine mirrors were placed at one mean free path from the hot wire. In Rice's experiments, the distances were much greater. This might account for the failure of Rice to detect methylene radicals.

Rosenbloom[71] studied the reactions of methylene in a hydrogen atmosphere. The methylene was produced by irradiating ketene with ultraviolet light that had been filtered through hydrogen to remove the bands causing the reaction:

$$(15)\ H_2 \rightleftharpoons 2H$$

The principal products obtained are ethane and ethylene. The conversion to methane increases with increasing temperatures. Rosenbloom postulates the following reactions yielding ethane and methyl radicals:

$$(16) \qquad CH_2 + H_2 \rightleftharpoons CH_3 + H$$
$$(17)\ CH_2 + CH_4 \rightleftharpoons 2CH_3$$
$$(18) \qquad 2CH_3 \rightleftharpoons C_2H_6$$

Both ethane and methyl radicals are known products of the methane decomposition.

Belchetz and Rideal cite the similarity of energies of activation obtained by them for methane and ethane cracking as proof of the fact that the initial split is the same in both cases:

$$CH_4 \rightleftharpoons CH_2 + H_2 \qquad E_{act} = 95\ k\ cal$$
$$C_2H_6 \rightleftharpoons CH_3-CH- + H_2 \qquad E_{act} \approx 95\ k\ cal$$

This very argument of Belchetz et al. is, however, an indication of the fact that very probably the filament used to crack the hydrocarbon was a complicating factor. The value of about 95 k cal as the energy of activation for cracking all hydrocarbons up to butane would indicate some sort of surface catalysis.

It is interesting to note that the work of Storch in determining the primary product of methane pyrolysis was also done on a carbon filament. However, the postulation of ethane as an initial stable product has caused no "furor" such as that by the postulation of methylene as the initial radical.

Role of Methyl Radicals. Rice and Dooley[64] prefer a mechanism involving methyl radicals as the primary reaction product in the methane decomposition:

(19) $\qquad CH_4 \rightleftharpoons CH_3 + H$ (chain initiating)
(20) $CH_3 + CH_4 \rightleftharpoons C_2H_6 + H$ (chain propagating)
(21) $\qquad H + CH_4 \rightleftharpoons CH_3 + H_2$ (chain propagating)
(22) $\qquad 2H \rightleftharpoons H_2$ (chain ending)
(23) $\qquad 2CH_3 \rightleftharpoons C_2H_6$ (chain ending)
(24) $\qquad H + CH_3 \rightleftharpoons CH_4$ (chain ending)

This mechanism also predicts ethane as the initial stable product. If (19) is considered unimolecular, then reaction (22) must be the predominant terminating step in order that the kinetics be first order. This has not been confirmed.

The evidence for the presence of methyl radicals, however, is very conclusive.

Rice, *et al.*[61,62,64,65,67] have made many attempts to detect methylene radicals in the decomposition of methane, using metal mirrors. They have not found methylene but only methyl radicals. In addition, Robertson[70] and Eltonton[16,17] have followed the course of methane decomposition, using a mass spectrometer to pick up radicals, and have observed only methyl radicals.

Additional Radical Mechanisms. Bawn and Tipper[3] studied the reactions of methyl radicals and proposed the following mechanism.

(25) $CH_3 + CH_3 \rightleftharpoons C_2H_6$ (3 body since inert gas increased the yield of ethane)
(26) $\qquad 2CH_3 \rightleftharpoons CH_4 + CH_2$ (rate determining for carbon production)
(27) $CH_3 + CH_2 \rightleftharpoons CH_4 + CH$ (very fast, $E_{act} = 20$ k cal)
(28) $CH_3 + CH \rightleftharpoons CH_4 + C$ (exothermic)

If ethane is assumed to be a necessary intermediate in the formation of acetylene from methane, reaction (25) would show why an inert gas would increase the yields of acetylene. Also, thermodynamically, a decrease in pressure should have no effect on any of the reactions except (28). This would account for the reduction in coking with a reduction in pressure. There is no direct evidence for this mechanism.

At very high temperatures, such as those attained in the arc, many radicals other than methyl and methylene have been detected. Thus, Peters and Wagner[59] cracked mixtures of methane and hydrogen in low energy arcs. They determined methyl, methylene and methyne ($CH_\equiv$) radicals. With high energy arcs, only methyne and C_2 radicals were observed. They suggest acetylene from:

(29) $2CH \rightleftharpoons C_2H_2$
(30) $2H + C_2 \rightleftharpoons C_2H_2$

Similarly, Letort and Duval[46] observed methylene radicals in the arc cracking of methane by reacting the product stream with tellurium mirrors.

Frish and Kagan[23] observed only methyne radicals in both flow and static experiments indicating it as an intermediate in acetylene formation.

Finally Briner, *et al.*[7] observed methyne, carbon plus (C^+) and C_2 radicals in a high-frequency discharge at normal ambient temperatures, with methane nitrogen and hydrogen in the feed.

Conclusions. Further data on the decomposition of methane is needed, especially that data at high temperatures and low conversions.

Much of the basis for assuming a first-order reaction is due to Kassel.[44] He followed the change of pressure at constant volume with respect to time and found

$$\frac{dp}{dt} = kp^0 \tag{13}$$

where p = pressure and p^0 is the initial methane pressure. As Laidler[45] points out, this assumes that the increase of pressure is a measure of the decomposition of methane. If it assumed that methane decomposes only to ethane, ethylene and hydrogen, then the pressure rise actually measures ethylene formation rather than methane disappearance. With a complete range of products produced, that is, ethane, ethylene, acetylene, carbon and hydrogen, a relation between pressure rise and decomposition of methane could not be made without a complete product analysis.

As Laidler[45] points out, the true order of reaction can be determined by plotting:

$$-\ln \left(\frac{dc}{dt}\right) \text{ vs } \ln C$$

and determining the slope. If the plot obtained exhibits curvature, the reaction is complicated and does not have a simple order. Figure 3 presents the data of Tropsch and Egloff.[92] As closely as possible, the initial order of reaction is seen to be 0.517. Similarly plotted, the data of Rudder and Biederman at temperatures of 900 and 1000°C yield orders of 0.525 and 0.71, respectively. Wheeler and Wood's data yield an order of 1.95, the only order greater than 1.0.

The data used to calculate these orders generally involved too great an extent of decomposition for an initial rate to be determined accurately. Therefore it is not claimed that the values given represent the true order. The results do indicate that the postulation of first-order kinetics is not completely substantiated. On the other hand, first-order kinetics do best represent the data available. Thus, the correlations under "kinetics" used a first-order equation. It will be remembered, however, that these correlations were only accurate to about 50 per cent when used to predict conversions to acetylene and ethylene. At best, the present data indicate

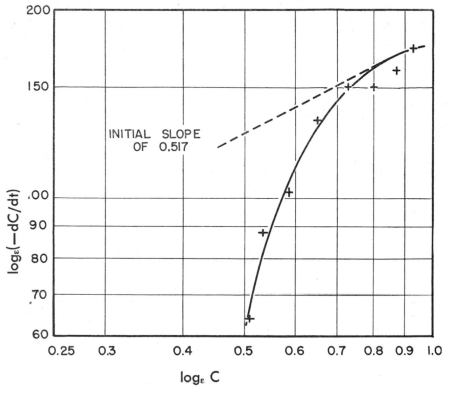

INITIAL SLOPE
OF 0.517

Fig. 3.   Methane Pyrolysis, "True Order," 1400°C.—50^{mm} Hg.[53]

but do not substantiate first-order kinetics. Therefore, before any mechanism is considered proven, it would be best if an order, first or otherwise, would be confirmed at low conversions.

Kinetics of the Pyrolysis of Ethane to Acetylene

It has already been pointed out under equilibrium considerations that the pyrolysis of ethane is complicated by the reverse reaction, ethylene hydrogenation. Kassel *et al.*[60] have investigated the rate of hydrogen formation. These authors found the initial dehydrogenation of ethane to ethylene is first order between 200 and 1500 mm Hg pressure and propose the following equation:

$$\frac{d(H_2)}{dt} = k(C_2H_6) - k'(H_2)(C_2H_4) \tag{14}$$

At temperatures between 650 and 700°C and at contact times greater than 0.25 second, acetylene is not an important product of ethane pyrolysis. At these longer contact times, acetylene seems to remain at some equilibrium concentration of about 2 per cent by volume of the off gas. Liquid products, methane and hydrogen, constitute the main products, with coke appearing at 850°C.[28] At temperatures greater than 1000°C, acetylene becomes important, but ethane does not appear in the product except at the shortest contact times. At 1400°C, for instance, the ethane concentration is negligible at 0.56 millisecond.[92]

The various equations which will be presented refer to the initial stages of ethane decomposition. As the extent of decomposition increases, the first-order rate constant, k_4, decreases sharply; k_4 is defined by:

$$\frac{-d(C_2H_6)}{dt} = k_4(C_2H_6) \tag{15}$$

where (C_2H_6) = concentration of ethane, mole fraction. These constants are given in Table 8 for varying extents of decomposition at 750°C and 1400°C. The data of several investigators have been recalculated to yield k_4, and these values are plotted in Figure 4. The rate equations suggested by Marek and McClure[47] and Steacie and Shane[85] have also been plotted on Figure 4. Relative to the data plotted, Steacie is generally conservative up to 1000°C; that is, the rate predicted is lower than that observed. Marek's equation fits the data somewhat better. Above 1000°C, the data are too sparse in the region of low conversions to test the equations.

TABLE 8. ETHANE CRACKING

Time, seconds	Total Conversion, %	k_4 sec^{-1}	Reference
First-Order Constants 750°C—760 mm Hg Pressure			
0.38	38.0	1.74	(60)
2.90	64.2	0.50	(60)
9.10	66.9	0.17	(60)
13.10	71.3	0.13	(60)
1400°C—50 mm Hg Pressure			
0.28×10^{-3}	81.5	7,800	(92)
0.33×10^{-3}	95.3	13,350	(92)
0.41×10^{-3}	95.9	9,550	(92)
0.56×10^{-3}	97.2	7,780	(92)
0.88×10^{-3}	98.6	5,850	(92)

If the conservative equation of Steacie is used to calculate the average rate of approach to 99.9 per cent of equilibrium, the times plotted in

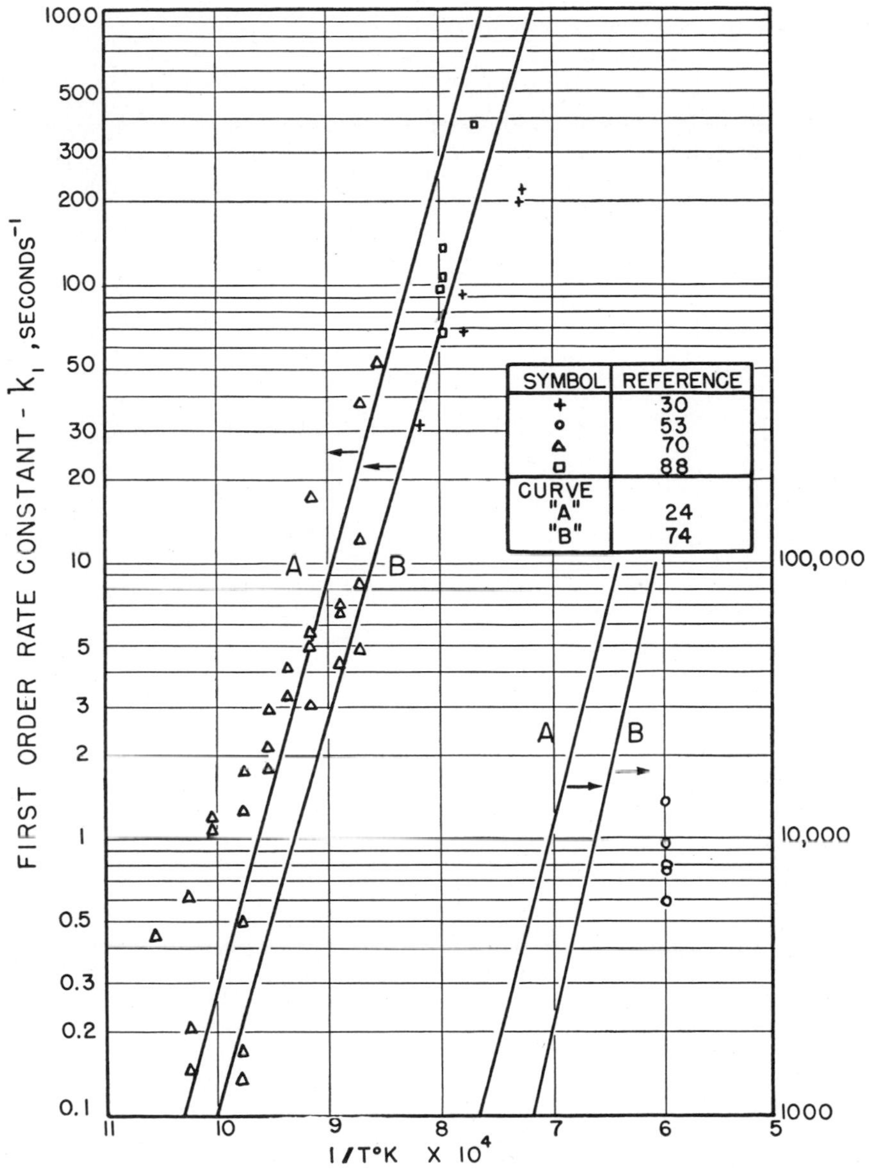

FIG. 4. Ethane Pyrolysis-First Order Rate Constants, Sec. -1 Reciprocal Temp., $(1/T \times 10^4)$.

Figure 5 are obtained. At temperatures greater than 1100°C, the equilibrium concentration of ethane is, for all practical purposes, negligible. Figure 5 indicates that at temperatures near 1000°C, the time for ethane to reach 99.9 per cent of equilibrium is 10^{-2} second; at 1400°C this falls to 10^{-4} second.

During the time in which ethane is falling to negligible concentrations, the ethylene concentration reaches a maximum.

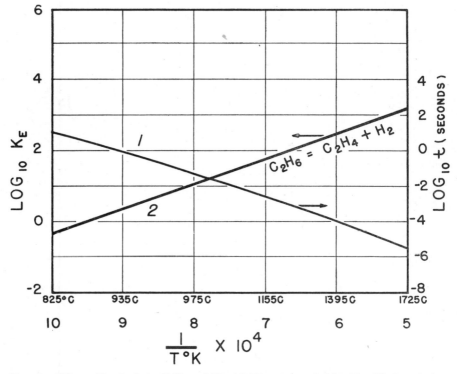

FIG. 5.   Ethane Pyrolysis to C_2H_4 and H_2. (1) Time to reach 99% Equilibrium (using equation of Reference 74). (2) Equilibrium Constants—(Fig. 2).

Figure 6 presents the data of Tropsch and Egloff[92] on acetylene and ethylene concentrations during the pyrolysis of pure ethane at 1400°C and 50 mm pressure. The ethane percentage has been estimated from the value of n in an analysis for C_nH_{2n+2} by assuming only ethane and methane are present. Other investigators[20,31] present data at varying conditions of temperature and pressure that bear a strong resemblance to the data of Tropsch, but they indicate that longer times are necessary for the ethylene maximum to appear. The fact that the feeds were diluted with up to 90 per cent hydrogen may account for this discrepancy.

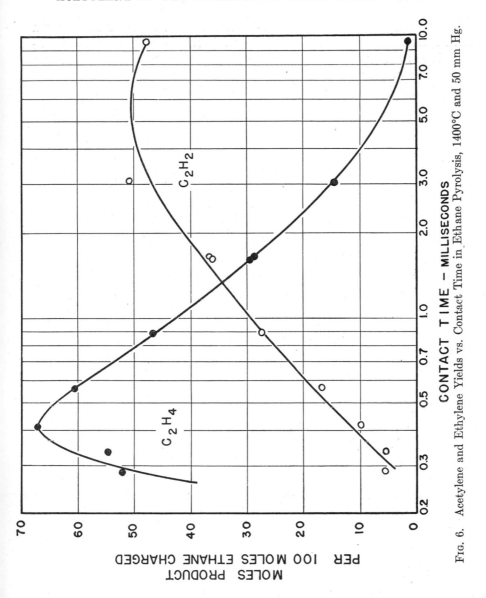

FIG. 6. Acetylene and Ethylene Yields vs. Contact Time in Ethane Pyrolysis, 1400°C and 50 mm Hg.

The discrepancies between these authors' data and the data shown in Figure 6 are not as striking as the similarities. In each case, the conversion to acetylene rises sharply as the conversion to ethylene falls from a maximum. It is well to remember that the ethane has, for all practical purposes, disappeared when the ethylene reaches a maximum.

The foregoing discussion applies to those conditions where acetylene is an important product. It indicates that acetylene formation in ethane pyrolysis is linked directly to the decomposition of ethylene. It is of interest, therefore, to investigate the pyrolysis of ethylene to acetylene. Before considering ethylene, however, the significance of the preceding discussion as applied to the pyrolysis of methane may be indicated.

Ethane in Methane Pyrolysis. The primary stable product in the pyrolysis of methane is generally considered to be ethane. Yet, the concentration of ethane never rises to more than a few per cent, and generally is negligible. The reason for this is apparent upon an examination of the rate constants for the disappearance of methane and ethane. Whereas the value for methane rises to a value less than 200 at 1400°C, ethane has a value of approximately 10^5 at this same temperature. It is obvious, therefore, that even at the short periods involved in the cracking of methane, sufficient time is available for ethane to crack further to ethylene and acetylene.

Pyrolysis of Ethylene to Acetylene. Molera and Stubbs[49] find the thermal decomposition of ethylene in the range 593 to 743°C to be first order to 250 mm Hg and second order at higher pressures. Acetylene is not an important product at temperatures below 800°C and does not seem to form at all at temperatures under 600°C.[8,15,38] There is no doubt that at lower temperatures and higher pressures, the polymerization of ethylene prevails over its decomposition. At higher temperatures, polymerization shows up only at the shortest times as a contraction in the volume of gas. The decomposition soon takes over, masking the polymerization completely. Decomposition prevails at temperatures greater than 800°C. At 1400°C, no contraction is observed even at the shortest times.[93]

The pyrolysis of ethylene has been studied under a wide variety of conditions by many investigators.[20,93,77] Some important results will be considered.

Temperature. Regardless of what other conditions are present, an increase in temperature favors both the rate of disappearance of ethylene and the conversion to acetylene. At high temperatures, greater than 1000°C, the product distribution is effected less than the rate. With respect to temperature, it must be made clear that the contact times are adjusted so that excessive coking does not occur. At 1000°C and higher, the times are measured in milliseconds.

Pressure. A pressure decrease favors the rate of ethylene decomposition and the production of acetylene. As noted,[49] the reaction becomes first order as the pressure is lowered.

Diluents. At 625°C and conversions under 3 per cent, Burk *et al.*[8] have found that inerts tend to increase the yield of acetylene and decrease polymerization. At one atmosphere total pressure and 100 per cent ethylene, negligible acetylene but a 30 per cent yield of propylene was obtained. With 75 per cent of nitrogen in the feed, the yield of propylene fell to 17 per cent, whereas that of acetylene rose to 15 per cent. The methane yield was the same for both runs, but that of hydrogen increased tenfold in the second run.

At all temperatures, the effect of dilution with nitrogen is the same as that of reducing the total pressure, although nitrogen dilution seems to give slightly higher yields of acetylene.

Hydrogen dilution does not cause the rate of ethylene decomposition to change greatly from that of pure ethylene at one atmosphere. However, the yields of acetylene are almost doubled.

The effect of dilution with methane is uncertain since the methane reacts under the conditions studied to yield both ethylene and acetylene. The effects of these variables at 1000°C and 1400°C are presented in Table 9.

TABLE 9. ETHYLENE PYROLYSIS

Total Pressure, mm Hg	Diluent and Volume, %	Conversion of Ethylene, %	Yield of Acetylene, % (Based on Ethylene Converted)
1000°C			
760	none	8.5	16.5
76	none	13.0	32.1
76	CH_4 50	4.9	69.3
760	CH_4 44	2.5	40.0
760	N_2 49.5	9.9	30.3
760	H_2 44.5	6.4	12.5
1400°C			
50	none	90.2	60.2
76	CH_4 50	91.6	89.3
76	H_2 86	91.1	92.3
76	H_2 75	97.0	87.1
12.7	H_2 50	98.7	73.5

Qualitatively, the data of Table 9 may be summarized as follows: The conversion of ethylene to acetylene is favored by an increase in temperature, a decrease in pressure, and the addition of inert gases as diluents. In addition, it is necessary to maintain very short contact times in order to avoid the complete decomposition to coke and hydrogen. It is interesting that these are identical to the conditions favoring acetylene formation from methane and ethane.

Mechanism of Ethane Decomposition

Because of its importance in the Rice free-radical mechanisms, the pyrolysis of ethane to ethylene and hydrogen has been thoroughly investigated. Pease[56] found the reaction to be homogeneous and of first order. These conclusions are supported by many other investigations.[13,22,47,53,85] The presently accepted[31] value of the over-all energy of activation for the reaction:

$$(31) \qquad\qquad C_2H_6 \rightleftharpoons C_2H_4 + H_2$$

is 69,800, as found by Sachsse.[74] This value results from a study in which polymers and methane were among the products of reaction. Rice and Dooley have calculated the energy of activation from data on ethylene hydrogenation:

$$(32) \qquad\qquad C_2H_4 + H_2 \rightleftharpoons C_2H_6$$

For (32), $E_{act} = 43.15$ k cal/mol and $\Delta E_{react} = 31.24$ k cal/mol. The sum of these is E_{act} for (31) $= 74.39$ k cal/mol, somewhat higher than the value obtained by Sachsse. Two mechanisms have been proposed to account for the preceding conclusions; one is molecular and the other, free radical.

Free-Radical Mechanisms. Rice and Herzfeld[67] have postulated the course of reaction as follows:

(1)	$C_2H_6 \rightarrow 2CH_3$	$E_1 = 84$ k cal
(2)	$CH_3 + C_2H_6 \rightarrow CH_4 + C_2H_5$	$E_2 = 8$ k cal
(3)	$C_2H_5 \rightarrow C_2H_4 + H$	$E_3 = 40$ k cal
(4)	$H + C_2H_6 \rightarrow C_2H_5 + H_2$	$E_4 = 7$ k cal
(5)	$H + C_2H_5 \rightarrow C_2H_6$	$E_5 = 0$ k cal

The values of E are those presently accepted, as quoted in Laidler,[45] and are not those of Rice and Herzfeld. This mechanism leads to first-order kinetics:[83]

$$\frac{-d(C_2H_6)}{dt} = k(C_2H_6) \qquad\qquad (16)$$

$$\log k = \frac{1}{2} \log \frac{k_1 k_3 k_4}{2k_5} \qquad\qquad (17)$$

where k_1, k_2, k_3, k_4, k_5 refer to reaction one through five, above. Thus, the over-all energy of activation is:

$$E_{overall} - \tfrac{1}{2}(E_1 + E_3 + E_4 - E_5) = 65.5 \text{ k cal}$$

which is reasonably close to the accepted value, 69.8. Other reactions might conceivably end the reaction chain. Some of those possible are:

$$(6) \quad 2C_2H_5 \rightarrow C_4H_{10}$$
$$(7) \quad H + CH_3 \rightarrow CH_4$$
$$(8) \quad H + H \rightarrow H_2$$

but only reaction (5) yields first-order kinetics. Reactions (7) and (8) may occur to only a slight extent; because of the simple nature of the particles involved, these reactions probably must be stabilized in a three-body collision. Steric effects may be important in reaction (6). Therefore, although (5) is not the only possible chain-terminating reaction, it may be the only reaction occurring to any great extent. The fact that the free-radical mechanism can account for the correct order and over-all energy of activation is indirect evidence in its own support. In addition, attempts have been made to obtain more direct evidence.

The effect of nitric oxide on the ethane decomposition has been the subject of many investigations. Stavely[81] found that the rate of decomposition fell to a minimum value of 8 per cent of the uninhibited rate as the concentration of nitric oxide was increased. Stavely and Hinshelwood,[82] also studying the nitric-oxide-inhibited reaction, found that the average chain lengths were much shorter than those expected from the postulated free-radical mechanism. These authors conclude that both free-radical and molecular mechanisms are operating. This conclusion is borne out by Steacie and Shane,[85] who found the energy of activation for the fully inhibited reaction to be 77.3 k cal as compared to that of Stavely, 74 k cal. Either of these is higher than 69.8 k cal, the accepted value for the uninhibited reaction. Ingold *et al.*[43] have tested the effect of nitric oxide and propylene in ethane decomposition. Propylene acts in a manner similar to nitric oxide, but does not act as an oxidizing agent. Ingold reaches the same conclusions, that both mechanisms operate.

Attempts to detect radicals, using metal mirrors, have been made by Rice and Dooley.[63] By using standard mirrors, these authors have obtained a value of E_{act} for a split into methyl radicals equal to 79.5 $\pm$ 3 k cal. However, as Steacie[83] points out, owing to the poor definition of the reactor space, the uncertainty is more likely to be ± 10 k cal and would therefore include the values of 74 and 77, arrived at using the inhibition methods.

Eltenton[16,17] has detected methyl radicals in the ethane decomposition by following the reaction with a mass spectrometer.

Rice and Wall[92] have studied ethane decomposition at 600°C, using a feed of 50 per cent each C_2H_6 and C_2D_6. The extent of mixing, that is, the presence of both hydrogen and deuterium in a single molecule, was measured. The hydrogen was highly exchanged but the methane generally showed much less exchange. This would be expected because the methane decomposition into methyl radicals would not be very fast at 600°C.

The effect of NO, which suppresses the radical mechanism, is to increase the exchange in hydrogen and to decrease it in methane. Packing had no effect on the rate of exchange. While the simple molecular mechanism does not offer an explanation of these results, the Rice mechanisms do explain these high exchange rates.

The evidence for the free-radical mechanism is very strong. However, the residual reaction rate in the presence of nitric oxide indicates that much reaction occurs by a straight molecular mechanism. It would seem, therefore, that both mechanisms do operate. The fact that the average chain length is much shorter than expected would point to the fact that the chains are few in number but quite long.

Methane in Thermal Decomposition of Ethane. Methane always appears as a product of the thermal decomposition of ethane. Many studies have been made to determine whether it is a primary or secondary product of the decomposition and also what conditions favor its formation.

Bone and Coward[6] cracked ethane at 800°C in the presence of hydrogen and obtained a 41 per cent yield of methane. The same conditions with nitrogen as a diluent yielded only 18 per cent methane. Bone and Coward conclude that methane arises as a result of the hydrogenation of methyl radicals. Ethylene behaved similarly to ethane. Gardner[27] found the decomposition of ethane similar to that of other hydrocarbons, the cracking process yielding an olefin and the paraffin:

$$(33) \qquad (2C_2H_6) \rightleftharpoons C_2H_4 + 2CH_4$$

This mechanism leads to second-order kinetics for the formation of methane as observed, but the energy of activation observed is consistently greater than 65 k cal, whereas the value based on other hydrocarbons should be 63 ± 0.5 k cal.[9] Travers[91] found that a large excess of hydrogen suppressed the formation of ethylene, but did not stop the formation of methane. Travers finds the rate of formation of methane to be:

$$\frac{d(CH_4)}{dt} \propto (C_2H_4)[(C_2H_6) + (CH_4) + (H_2)] \qquad (18)$$

That is, methane is formed when ethylene collides with any of the other three molecules. Schutt[78] has found the primary products to be only ethylene and hydrogen. These facts indicate that methane is a secondary reaction product.

Danby,[12] using mass spectrometric and kinetic data, finds methane as a product at the very beginning of the ethane decomposition. The initial rate of methane formation is of the same order as the decomposition of ethane to ethylene and hydrogen. However, as the ethylene accumulates, the order of methane formation becomes second with respect to ethylene. Nitric oxide reduces the decomposition rate of ethane to ethylene and hydrogen to a limiting rate, but hardly affects the rate of methane formation. The consumption of nitric oxide is roughly two moles for every mole of methane produced. Danby postulates the following reaction to account for methane formation:

$$(34) \qquad C_2H_6 \rightleftharpoons CH_2 + CH_4$$

This accounts satisfactorily for the observed effects. It may be noted that this mechanism lends support to Kassel's mechanism for the decomposition of methane.

Ethylene Decomposition. The mechanism of the ethylene decomposition to acetylene has not been thoroughly investigated with regard to determining the mechanism.

Line and Leroy[47] have studied the decomposition in the presence of excited mercury atoms. They find that acetylene formation is not inhibited by nitric oxide and conclude a molecular mechanism for this reaction:

$$(35) \qquad C_2H_4 \rightarrow C_2H_4{}^* \rightarrow C_2H_2 + H_2$$

The rate of acetylene formation is independent of temperature if the effect of bimolecular collisions is taken into account. These collisions tend to stabilize excited ethylene molecules.

Rice has been unable to isolate radicals in the decomposition of ethylene. However, if the primary split is:

$$(36) \qquad C_2H_4 \rightarrow 2CH_2$$

This may be due to his inability to detect methylene radicals under the conditions of the experiment. Kassel assigns a value of 77 k cal as the E_{act} of reaction (35). At temperatures over 600°C, therefore, an appreciable rate would be possible. The value of 77 k cal is open to question. If the initial split of the double bond yields the radicals, a value of 125 to 150 k cal is not unreasonable.[83] However, if the radicals reorganize to bivalent carbon, such as is present in carbon monoxide, the E_{act} would be much lower and the value given by Kassel is reasonable.

Pyrolysis of Higher Hydrocarbons

Pyrolysis of Propane. It is well known that the energy of activation of the cracking process decreases slightly as the molecular weight of the paraffin being cracked increases.[60] This means that the temperature level necessary for cracking at useful rates decreases. For this reason, the first commercial thermal cracking process in this country for the production of acetylene used propane as a feed.

The initial pyrolysis of propane proceeds in two main directions.[21,40]

(37) $C_3H_8 \rightarrow C_2H_4 + CH_4$
(37A) $C_3H_8 \rightarrow C_3H_6 + H_2$

Some ethane is also formed; it may arise as a primary product[78] or by the hydrogenation of ethylene.

(37B) $(2C_3H_8) \rightarrow 2C_2H_6 + C_2H_4$

Temperature has a marked effect on the distribution of products. At temperatures between 600 to 700°C the ratio is $C_2H_4:C_3H_6 \simeq 1:1.$[47]

At higher temperatures, ethylene is the main product[29,76]; below 650°C, propylene predominates. The yield of acetylene is negligible below 800°C. The decomposition of propane is first order.

$$-\frac{d(C_3H_8)}{dt} = k(C_3H_8) \tag{19}$$

where (C_3H_8) = mole fraction
k = first-order rate constant given by:

$$\log k = 13.46 - \frac{63,300}{2.3RT} \tag{20}$$

Equation (19) is the equation of Steacie and Puddington[84] and is reasonably consistent with other equations obtained over the temperature range 550 to 700°C.

A pressure increase from one to seven atmospheres had little effect on the distribution of products,[14] but below one atmosphere the products are a function of the initial partial pressure of propane.[84]

The effect of pressure may be due to its effect on propylene decomposition. Szwarc[89] found the decomposition to be first order from 6 to 9 mm Hg:

$$-\frac{d(C_3H_6)}{dt} = k(C_3H_6) \tag{21}$$

where $\log k = 13.04 - \frac{77,000}{2.3RT} \tag{22}$

At 570 to 650 mm, Ingold[42] finds E_{act} equal to 57.1 k cal. This difference of almost 20 k cal is indicative of a difference in mechanism in the two pressure ranges.

When propane is cracked at temperatures above 1000°C, where acetylene is definitely an important product, the high yields are obtained as a result of the decomposition of ethylene and propylene. Tropsch and Egloff[92] have cracked propane at 50 mm Hg and 1100° and 1400°C.

The data of these authors at 1100°C are presented in Figure 7. The top curve gives the value of n in an analysis for C_nH_{2n+2} at different contact times. The conversion to ethane is generally less than 5 per cent,

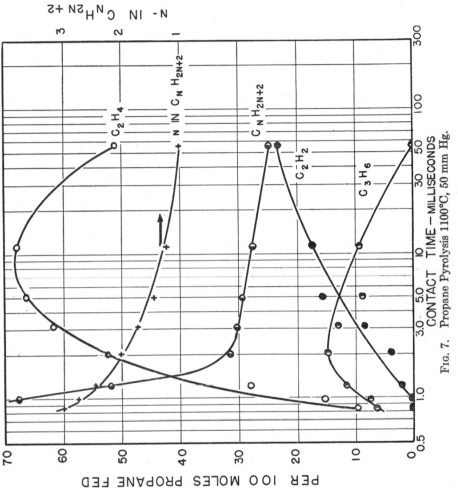

Fig. 7.   Propane Pyrolysis 1100°C, 50 mm Hg.

based on the propane cracked. Therefore, n is a rough measure of the relative amounts of propane and methane. When $n = 1.5$, at 5.13×10^{-3} second, the percentage of propane is already far less than 5 per cent, whereas the ethylene and methane are close to their maximum values. The percentage of methane increases slightly at higher times, but acetylene increases almost sevenfold to 21 per cent. Ethylene and propylene concentrations fall from the maximum during this increase in the yield of acetylene.

The data at 1400°C are even more striking. The percentage of propane falls to less than 5 per cent in 0.39 millisecond. The percentage of ethylene

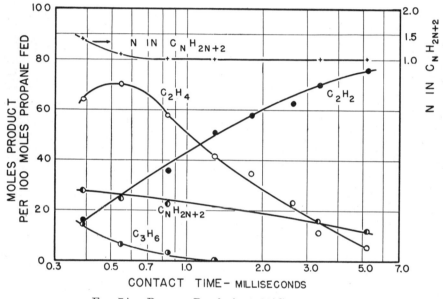

FIG. 7A.   Propane Pyrolysis, 1400°C, 50 mm Hg.

reaches a maximum in 0.50 millisecond and falls rapidly to under 5 per cent in 5 milliseconds. In the time between 0.5 and 5.0 milliseconds, the percentage of acetylene continues to climb almost to a maximum. The yields of ethylene and acetylene are shown at various times in Figure 7A.

It has been shown that, in the pyrolysis of propane, acetylene is derived from the cracking of the primary reaction product ethylene, and possibly propylene. It is more likely that propylene decomposes to ethylene and methane before yielding acetylene.

In the pyrolysis of methane, ethane, and propane, acetylene is the direct result of the pyrolysis of ethylene. It is not unreasonable, therefore, to find the same conditions favoring high acetylene yields for all three hydrocarbons; that is, low partial pressure of hydrocarbon, high temperature, and low contact times.

Pyrolysis of Butanes. The pyrolysis of butanes to acetylene differs from that of propane in minor respects only. The greater variety of possible primary products is one difference, and the cracking of branched chains is another.

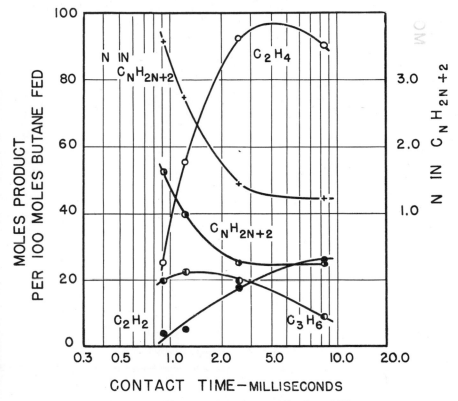

Fig. 8.   *n*-Butane Pyrolysis 1100°C, 50 mm Hg.

The possible reaction products in the decomposition of *n*-butane are: 1-butene and 2-butene and hydrogen; methane and propylene; ethane and ethylene. The data of several authors[28,29,41,50] indicate that the decomposition to butenes occurs to less than 20 per cent of the *n*-butane reacted. In addition, temperatures greater than 700°C favor ethylene, whereas temperatures below this favor propylene.

The data of Tropsch and Egloff[92] for the pyrolysis of *n*-butane are presented in Figure 8. It is very evident that again ethylene is the most important product preceding acetylene formation.

The pyrolysis of isobutane does not yield ethane and ethylene as primary product to any large extent; the main products are isobutylene and hydrogen, and methane and propylene. Ethylene is a product in the decomposition of propylene and isobutylene. Isobutylene also decomposes at temperatures up to 925°C to yield methyl acetylene as a primary

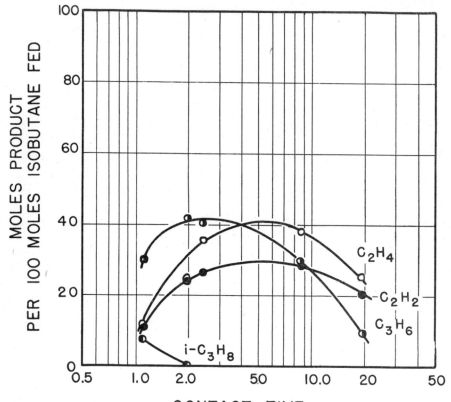

Fig. 9.   *i*-Butane Pyrolysis, 1100°C, 50 mm Hg.

product.[66,68] In addition, unpublished experimental work by Kramer and Happel at temperatures to 1000°C, indicates that no acetylene is produced in the decomposition of isobutylene if the contact time is sufficiently short.

However, the data of Tropsch and Egloff for isobutane at 1100°C (Figure 9) show that propylene and ethylene are the main products preceding acetylene. The conclusion must be that very little isobutylene is found when isobutane is cracked at 1100°C. Figure 9 indicates, in fact, that propylene is initially produced in much larger amounts than any other olefin including ethylene.

Industrial Aspects. It has been shown that the production of acetylene by pyrolysis of the hydrocarbons methane through butanes is possible. It may be stressed that the conditions necessary for conversions to acetylene are high temperature, low partial pressure of feed and product, and very short times of contact. Only the latter condition is desirable from an industrial viewpoint.

The employment of temperatures above 1100°C means that only a limited number of refractories are feasible. The need for stability in reducing atmospheres during cracking and oxidizing atmospheres during heating has practically limited the choice to aluminum oxide refractories.

The need for low partial pressures of hydrocarbon in the feed and acetylene in the product means either vacuum operation or dilution of the feed. Both cause inefficient use of reactor space. Vacuum operation introduces a need for gas tightness and mechanical strength. Dilution of the feed causes a low thermal efficiency.

In addition, those hydrocarbons which are easiest to crack, the butanes and propane, introduce the highest raw-material costs. It is doubtful, in fact, whether butane can be economically cracked to acetylene.

The large supply and low cost of methane from natural gas, or as a by-product of the Fischer-Tropsch-type synthesis, make it a likely feed for acetylene production by straight thermal cracking.

References

1. Barrow, R. F., Pearson, T. G., and Purcell, R. H., *Trans. Faraday Soc.*, **35**, 880 (1939).
2. Bawn, C. E. H., and Milsted, J., *Ibid.*, **35**, 889 (1939).
3. Bawn, C. E. H., and Tipper, C. F. H., *Discussions of Faraday Soc.*, No. 2, 104 (1947).
4. Beeck, O., *Rev. Modern Physics*, **20**, 127 (1948).
5. Belchetz, L., *Trans. Faraday Soc.*, **30**, 170 (1934).
6. Belchetz, L., and Rideal, E. K., *J. Am. Chem. Soc.*, **51**, 116 (1935).
7. Bone, W. A., and Coward, H. F., *J. Chem. Soc.*, **93**, 1197 (1908).
8. Briner, E., Desbaillets, J., and Paillard, H., *Helv. Chim. Acta*, **21**, 115 (1938).
9. Burk, R. E., Baldwin, B. G., and Whitacre, C. H., *Ind. Eng. Chem.*, **29**, 326 (1937).
10. Burk, R. E., Laskowski, L., and Lankelma, H. P., *J. Am. Chem. Soc.*, **63**, 3248 (1941).
11. Burton, M., Davis, T. W., Gordon, A., and Taylor, H. A., *Ibid.*, **63**, 1956 (1941).
12. Danby, C. J., *et al.*, *Proc. Roy. Soc.* (*London*), **A218**, 450 (1953).
13. Eastwood, S. C., and Potas, A. E., *Petroleum Engr.*, **19**, 43 (1948).
14. Egloff, G., Thomas, C. C., and Linn, C. B., *Ind. Eng. Chem.*, **28**, 1283 (1936).
15. Egloff, G., and Wilson, E., *Ibid.*, **27**, 917 (1935).
16. Eltenton, G. C., *J. Chem. Phys.*, **10**, 403 (1942).

17. Eltenton, G. C., *Ibid.*, **15,** 455, 465, 474 (1947).
18. Fischer, F., *Ber.*, **A 71,** 56 (1938).
19. Fischer, F., and Pichler, *Brennstoff-Chem.*, **13,** 381 (1932).
20. Fischer, F., and Pichler, *Ibid.*, **13,** 406 (1932).
21. Frey, F. E., and Hepp, H. J., *Ind. Eng. Chem.*, **25,** 441 (1933).
22. Frey, F. E., and Smith, D. F., *Ibid.*, **20,** 948 (1928).
23. Frish, S. E., and Kagan, Y. M., *Bull. Acad. Sci.* (U.R.S.S.) Ser. Phys., **9,** 238 (1945).
24. Frolich, P. K., White, A., and Dayton, H. P., *Ind. Eng. Chem.*, **22,** 20 (1930).
25. Frolich, P. K., White, A., Uhrmacher, R. R., and Tufts, L. T., *Ibid.*, **22,** 23 (1930).
26. Frost, A. V., *Khim. Teoret.*, No. 2, 98; *Chem. Abs.*, **29,** 5626 (1935).
27. Gardner, A. W., *Fuel*, **4,** 430 (1925).
28. Groll, H. P. A., *Ind. Eng. Chem.*, **25,** 784 (1933).
29. Hague, E. N., and Wheeler, R. V., *J. Am. Chem. Soc.*, **51,** 378 (1929).
30. Hague, E. N., and Wheeler, R. V., *J. Chem. Soc.*, **(1929),** 378.
31. Hepp, H. J., Spessard, F. P., and Randall, J. H., *Ind. Eng. Chem.*, **41,** 2531 (1949).
32. Hessels, W. J., Van Krevelin, D. W., and Waterman, H. I., *J. Soc. Chem. Ind.*, **58 T,** 323 (1939).
33. Hinshelwood, C. N., and Hobbs, J. E., *Proc. Roy. Soc.* (London), **A 154,** 335 (1936).
34. Hinschelwood, C. N., and Hobbs, J. E., *Ibid.*, **A 167,** 439, 447 (1938).
35. Holliday, G. C., and Exell, H. C., *J. Chem. Soc.*, **(1929),** 1066.
36. Holliday, G. C., and Gooderham, W. J., *Ibid.*, **(1931),** 1594.
37. Huntington, R. L., and Lu, H. C., *Refiner Natural Gasoline Mfr.*, **20,** 390 (1941).
38. Hurd, C. D., *Ind. Eng. Chem.*, **26,** 50 (1934).
39. Hurd, C. D. and Eilers, L. K., *Ibid.*, **26,** 776 (1934).
40. Hurd, C. D., and Pilgrim, F. D., *J. Am. Chem. Soc.*, **55,** 4902 (1933).
41. Hurd, C. D. and Spence, L. W., *Ibid.*, **51,** 3353 (1929).
42. Ingold, K. W., and Stubbs, J. F., *J. Chem. Soc.*, **(1951)** 1749.
43. Ingold, K. W., Stubbs, J. F., and Hinshelwood, C. N., *Proc. Roy. Soc.* (London), **A 203,** 486 (1950).
44. Kassel, L. S., and Storch, H. H., *J. Am. Chem. Soc.*, **59,** 1240 (1937).
45. Laidler, K. J., "Chemical Kinetics," New York, McGraw-Hill Book Co., Inc., 1950.
46. Letort, M., and Duval, X., *Compt. rend.*, **219,** 452 (1944).
47. Line, D., and LeRoy, D. J., *J. Chem. Phys.*, **13,** 307 (1945).
48. Marek, L. F., and McClure, W. B., *Ind. Eng. Chem.*, **23,** 878 (1931).
49. Mecke, R., *Zt. Physik. Chem.*, **7 B,** 108, 120 (1930).
50. Molera, M. J., and Stubbs, F. J., *J. Chem. Soc.*, **(1952),** 381.
51. Neuhaus, M., and Marek, L. F., *Ind. Eng. Chem.*, **24,** 400 (1932).
52. Nieuwland, J. A., and Vogt, R. L., "The Chemistry of Acetylene," New York, Reinhold Publishing Corp., 1945.
53. Paul, R. E., and Marek, L. F., *Ind. Eng. Chem.*, **26,** 454 (1934).
54. Pearson, T. G., Purcell, R. H., and Saigh, G. S., *J. Chem. Soc.*, **(1938),** 409.
55. Pease, R. N., *J. Am. Chem. Soc.*, **51,** 3470 (1929).
56. Pease, R. N., *Ibid.*, **54,** 1878 (1932).
57. Peters, K., and Meyer, K., *Brennst. Chem.*, **10,** 324 (1929).
58. Peters, K., and Wagner, O. H., *Ibid.*, **12,** 67 (1931).
59. Peters, K., and Wagner, O. H., *Z. physik. Chem.*, **153,** A 161 (1931).

60. Potolovski, L., and Atal'You A, *Petroleum Engr.*, **10**, No. 11, 40 (1939).
61. Rice, F. O., *J. Am. Chem. Soc.*, **55**, 4329 (1933).
62. Rice, F. O., *Ibid.*, **61**, 213 (1939).
63. Rice, F. O., and Dooley, M. D., *Ibid.*, **55**, 4245 (1933).
64. Rice, F. O., and Dooley, M. D., *Ibid.*, **56**, 2747 (1934).
65. Rice, F. O. and Evering, B. L., *Ibid.*, **56**, 2105 (1934).
66. Rice, F. O. and Haynes, W. S., *Ibid.*, **70**, 964 (1948).
67. Rice, F. O. and Herzfeld, K. F., *Ibid.*, **56**, 284 (1934).
67a. Rice, F. O., and Glasebrook, A. L., *Ibid.*, **56**, 2381 (1934).
68. Rice, F. O. and Wall, L., *Ibid.*, **72**, 3967 (1950).
69. Rimarsky, W., *Z. angew. Chem.*, **42**, 933 (1929).
70. Robertson, A. J. B., *Proc. Roy. Soc.* (London), **A 199**, 394 (1949).
71. Rosenbloom, C., *J. Am. Chem. Soc.*, **60**, 2819 (1938).
72. Rossini, F. D., *et al.*, "Selected Values of Properties of Hydrocarbons," U. S. Gov't. Printing Office, Washington D.C., 1947.
73. Rudder, D., and Biedermann, H., *Bull. soc. chim.*, **47**, 710 (1930).
74. Sachsse, H., *Z. physik. Chem.*, **B 31**, 79 (1935).
75. Schäpfer, P., and Brunner, M., *Helv. Chim. Acta,* **13**, 1125 (1930).
76. Schneider, H., and Frolich, P. K., *Ind. Eng. Chem.*, **23**, 1405 (1931).
77. Schultze, G. R., and Muller, K. L., *Oel, Kohle, Erdoel u. Teer*, **15**, 215 (1939).
78. Schutt, H. C., *Chem. Engr. Prog.*, **43**, 103 (1947).
79. Smith, H. H., *et al.*, *Bur. of Mines, Repts. Inv.* 3143.
80. Stanley, H. M., and Nash, A. W., *J. Soc. Chem. Ind.*, **48**, 1 T (1929).
81. Stavely, L. A. K., *Proc. Roy. Soc.* (London), **162 A**, 557 (1937).
82. Stavely, L. A. K. and Hinshelwood, C. N., *J. Chem. Soc.*, **(1937)**, 15.
83. Steacie, E. W. R., "Atomic and Free Radical Reactions," New York, Reinhold Publishing Corp., 1946.
84. Steacie, E. W. R. and Puddington, I. E., *Can. J. Research*, **16B**, 411 (1938).
85. Steacie, E. W. R. and Shanc, G. P., *Ibid.*, **18B**, 351 (1940).
86. Storch, H. H., *J. Am. Chem. Soc.*, **54**, 4185 (1932).
87. Storch, H. H., *Ind. Eng. Chem.*, **26**, 56 (1934).
88. Storch, H. H., and Golden, P. L., *Ibid.*, **25**, 768 (1933).
89. Szwarc, M., *J. Chem. Phys.*, **17**, 284, 292 (1949).
90. Taylor, H., *et al.*, *Ibid.*, **5**, 203 (1937).
91. Travers, M. W., *Trans. Faraday Soc.*, **32**, 236 (1936).
92. Tropsch, H., and Egloff, G., *Ind. Eng. Chem.*, **27**, 1063 (1935).
93. Tropsch, H., Parrish, C. G., and Egloff, G., *Ibid.*, **28**, 581 (1936).
94. Wall, L. A., and Moore, W. J., *J. Am. Chem. Soc.*, **73**, 2840 (1951).
95. Wheeler, R. V., and Wood, W. L., *Fuel*, **7**, 535 (1928).
96. Wheeler, R. V., and Wood, W. L., *Ibid.*, **9**, 567 (1930).

CHAPTER 26

PYROLYTIC REACTIONS OF AROMATIC HYDROCARBONS

C. R. KINNEY

Pennsylvania State University

The appearance of aromatic hydrocarbons in high-temperature processes such as the cracking of petroleum in the range of 400 to 600°C, the coking of coal at 800 to 1100°C, and the pyrolysis of methane at temperatures as high as 1200°C demonstrates the remarkable thermal stability of aromatic hydrocarbons. This stability is due to unusually strong carbon-to-carbon bonds, and was recognized by Haber in a rule (1896) which states that "the C—C linkage in the aromatic series is more stable than the C—H linkage, the reverse of which is true in the aliphatic series."[21] The basis for the greater stability of C—C bonds in aromatic structures may be found in the fact that this structural arrangement is related to the very stable structure of crystalline graphite; whereas the C—C bonds of aliphatic hydrocarbons are similar to those in the less thermally stable diamond crystal.

Thermodynamic evidence for greater C—C bond strength in aromatic compounds is available in the observation that the heat of formation of aromatic structures is always greater than that calculated from normal bond energies of aliphatic double and single bonds. This greater evolution of energy, during the formation of aromatic compounds, results in shorter C—C bond distances, greater bond strengths, and greater thermal stability. In recent years this difference in energy has been called resonance energy[34] and is explained on the basis of "contributions" made by various Kekulé, Dewar, and other olefinic structures that may be drawn for an aromatic nucleus. The quantities of energy involved in resonance are relatively large,[32] amounting to nearly 40 Calories* for benzene,[13] 75 for naphthalene, 105 for anthracene, and so on. The amount of this energy may be roughly correlated with the number of ring bonds in the

---

* Kilogram-calories will be designated by "Calories."

aromatic structure and the double bond character of the bonds,[33] which decrease from one-half in benzene to one-third in graphite.

In the following discussion of individual aromatics, marked differences are observed in the thermal behavior of the mixed aliphatic-aromatic hydrocarbons compared with that of the unsubstituted aromatics. For this reason the two groups are described separately, the unsubstituted aromatics first and their derivatives subsequently.

Unsubstituted Aromatic Hydrocarbons

Benzene. The free energy of formation of benzene from elemental carbon and hydrogen is positive at all temperatures,[39]

$$\Delta F° = 17,200 + 43T$$

Benzene, therefore, despite 39.4 Calories[32] of resonance energy released during its formation, is thermally unstable in respect to its elements. No doubt graphite is similarly stabilized by resonance, and presumably this effect is largely cancelled out.

Furthermore, the activation energy of the thermal decomposition of benzene appears to be surprisingly low. Mead and Burk[26] obtained a value of only 50 Calories per mole from studies in the range of 750 to 852°C, which is considerably less than some 65 Calories reported for paraffinic hydrocarbons. On this basis, benzene would be expected to be decomposed with even greater ease than open-chain paraffins. Experimentally, benzene is fairly easily decomposed, but with the important difference that the decomposition involves only the dissociation of hydrogen and not the rupture of C—C bonds in the nucleus.

The dissociation of hydrogen is accompanied by the condensation of the radicals formed, a reaction which is found to be reversible.

$$2C_6H_6 \rightleftharpoons C_6H_5 - C_6H_5 + H_2$$

The lowest temperature at which decomposition to biphenyl has been reported is 300°C in a glass bomb tube. At 485°C under 250 atmospheres, 1 to 2 per cent conversion occurs, and at 525°, under a high but undetermined pressure, 73 per cent is converted to biphenyl in 48 hours. The reaction is reversed to the extent of 92.3 per cent when biphenyl is heated with hydrogen under 200 atmospheres at 500°C. Presumably, the effect of pressure is to speed up the rate of these reactions and not to change the position of equilibrium.

In flowing systems at atmospheric pressure, the conversion of benzene to biphenyl amounts to 2.5 per cent per pass at 550°C, 4.5 per cent at 650°C and 10 to 30 per cent at 750°C, depending on conditions, with an ultimate recycle yield of about 82 per cent and 18 per cent of higher condensation products, including coke and losses. At temperatures above 750°C, higher single-pass yields of biphenyl are obtained, but losses due to further condensation become excessive and the ultimate yields of biphenyl decrease. The manufacture of biphenyl is important because of its use as a heat-transfer medium (Dowtherm), retaining nearly 80 per cent as much latent heat as steam under similar conditions. Diphenyl ether is usually admixed to give a lower-melting product.

Since the characteristic reaction of benzene on pyrolysis is the dissociation of hydrogen with condensation of the resulting radicals, it is not surprising that, in addition to biphenyl, 1,4-, 1,3- and 1,2-diphenylbenzene, 1,3,5-triphenylbenzene, and triphenylene have been identified among the products. The mechanism by which triphenylene is formed has not been proven, but condensation of 1,2-diphenylbenzene appears much more likely than a trimolecular reaction involving three molecules of benzene. However, it has been reported that no triphenylene is pro-

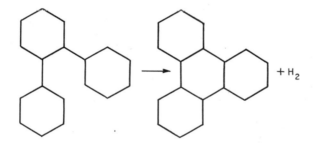

duced when 1,2-diphenylbenzene is pyrolyzed. In addition to the polyphenyls mentioned above, small amounts of resinous material and coke or carbon are produced. No doubt the latter are formed by the multiple condensation of benzene nuclei; as Brooks[5] has said of the pyrolysis of aromatic hydrocarbons, " . . . the result is chemical condensation, carbon-to-carbon combination to larger and larger molecules and eventually to coke . . . ." This mechanism is developed in greater detail by Sachanen.[39]

At temperatures maintained in metallurgical coke ovens in the range of 800 to 1100°C, the rate of decomposition of benzene to coke increases rapidly, as shown in Table 1.[23] At temperatures of 1000 to 1100°C the carbonization of benzene is very extensive. However, decomposition of benzene to carbon is depressed by the presence of hydrogen, which is a normal component of coke-oven gas. For example, at 1000°C and at a contact time of 23 seconds, the per cent of carbon of the benzene feed converted to coke with nitrogen as the carrier gas is 70 per cent; with hydrogen the per cent is decreased to 53 per cent. Hollings and Cobb[20] found that when a mixture of hydrogen and methane, saturated with benzene vapor, was passed through a heated tube, benzene was not decomposed below 800°C. No doubt the reversibility of the decomposition as well as the high dilution of benzene in coke-oven gas and short contacts at these high temperatures account for the escape of benzene from nearly complete annihilation in the coke oven.

TABLE 1. PER CENT OF CARBON OF BENZENE CONVERTED TO COKE[23]

Temperature (°C)	% Carbon Converted to Coke in Contact with Coke Packing Contact Time in Seconds			
	2	10	20	40
800	1	3	6	8
900	3	19	33	39
1000	35	59	69	73
1100	80	91	94	96

The depression of the rate of formation of carbon by the presence of hydrogen may also be used as proof that the mechanism by which carbon is formed involves condensation of benzene nuclei with evolution of hydrogen rather than rupture of the carbon ring, which, in the presence of hydrogen, should give all manner of reaction products. Since only small amounts of methane and traces of acetylene are the main gaseous decomposition products in addition to hydrogen, it does not seem probable that the benzene nucleus is ruptured in appreciable amounts. The coke or carbon produced still retains hydrogen presumably attached to the periphery of the condensed molecules, and no doubt the latter shifts into the graphite-like structure characteristic of carbons when the molecular size becomes great enough to permit the association of the carbon planes in the graphitic manner. To dissociate hydrogen completely and produce a crystalline graphite, temperatures of 2500 to 3000°C are required.

The kinetics of the pyrolysis of benzene indicate that the reaction is a bimolecular surface reaction strongly retarded by products. Thus, Mead and Burk[26] report kinetic data that are best represented by the equation:

$$\frac{dx}{dt} = \frac{k(a-x)^2}{x}$$

At temperatures above 800°C, the rate of condensation to carbon becomes important, and since carbon has been shown to catalyze the decomposition of benzene, as well as other surfaces—which soon become coated with carbon—the kinetics of the reaction are complex. However, the reaction appears to be of second order and proceeds through adsorption on the contact surface. In an empty tube, carbon is not only deposited in a firmly adhering coat on the tube walls, but also is formed in the vapor stream and falls to the bottom of the tube as a soft voluminous deposit. In this connection Iley and Riley[22] describe three forms of carbon deposited in the pyrolysis of hydrocarbons, including benzene, at 800 to 1300°C. The three forms are vitreous, soft black, and filamentous, and are arranged zonally from the hotter to cooler ends of the tube, respectively. Presumably temperature affects, therefore, the growth characteristics of the condensing carbon structures as well as the quantity formed.

In the range of 800 to 1100°C, small quantities of methane and traces of acetylene are observed in the pyrolyses of benzene. The amount of methane produced is of the order of that obtained when carbons are heated with hydrogen, and it seems likely that this reaction is a major source of the methane accompanying the decomposition of benzene at high temperatures. It is interesting that the so-called "amorphous" carbons, when heated with hydrogen, do not yield aromatic hydrocarbons but instead form methane, by reacting no doubt at the edges of the graphitic crystallites. The traces of acetylene formed in the pyrolysis of benzene at high temperatures may be accounted for, in turn, by a secondary decomposition of methane, rather than the direct dissociation of benzene to acetylene. However, the latter reaction is believed by some[4] to occur, but is difficult to prove. Acetylene is almost completely decomposed at 750°C, the products being aromatic hydrocarbons of which benzene is a substantial component, coke, and gases of which hydrogen, methane, and ethylene, in that order,[10] constitute the main components. Since ethylene appears as an important decomposition product of acetylene, but is not an important product of the pyrolysis of benzene, it seems that the decomposition of benzene to acetylene is not an important reaction of this hydrocarbon. On the other hand, when benzene is irradiated with light of wavelengths of less than 2000 Å, acetylene, in addition to hydrogen, is formed,[47] and it is suggested that benzene is partly dissociated into acetylene. Consequently, if light energy is capable of disrupting the benzene ring, a suitable application of thermal energy should produce a similar effect. At the temperature of the electric arc, benzene, like other hydrocarbons, yields gaseous mixtures containing hydrogen, acetylene, methane, ethane, and related products.

Catalytic decomposition of benzene has been reported, but such reactions are actually hydrogenolyses. For example, benzene mixed with hydrogen is extensively "decomposed" to methane in contact with finely divided nickel at 300°C. Under these conditions benzene is first hydrogenated to cyclohexane, which then undergoes hydrogenolysis to methane. Cyclohexane, under the same conditions, is even more readily converted to methane.

Biphenyl. The thermal stability of biphenyl is a little greater than that of benzene. This would be expected because biphenyl is stabilized by 8 Calories of resonance energy in addition to that involved in two separate benzene molecules. Tilicheev[45] found that the velocity constant of the cracking of biphenyl at 500°C was twenty times that of naphthalene, and that the stability of benzene approached that of biphenyl. Greensfelder *et al.*[14] reported that practically no decomposition of biphenyl occurred in contact with a silica-zirconia-alumina catalyst at 550°C. Meyer and Hofmann[27] found that at a still higher temperature 4,4'-diphenyl-biphenyl was produced.

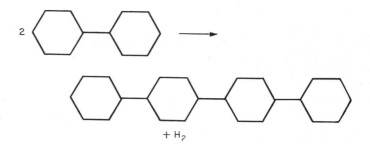

Naphthalene. The free energy of formation of naphthalene is, like that of benzene, positive at all temperatures.[39]

$$\Delta F° = 28,600 + 66T$$

Consequently, naphthalene is also unstable in respect to its elements. The resonance energy of naphthalene is 75 Calories per mole and may be related to that of benzene on the basis of the relative number of aromatic bonds, that is 11 to 6. At moderate temperatures naphthalene appears to be more stable than benzene. Thus at 500°C, Tilicheev[45] found that the rate of cracking of benzene was 20 times that of naphthalene, whereas that of phenanthrene and anthracene were 94 and 34,800, respectively. Foxwell[12] found that the relative rates of coke formation from naphthalene, phenanthrene, and anthracene in the range of 800 to 900°C were 1:78:10,800.

There is also considerable tendency for the naphthalene-ring system to form at high temperature. For example, naphthalene has been identified when decane containing 38 per cent decene was passed over a chromia-alumina catalyst at 475°C. Butylbenzene gave as much as 55 per cent naphthalene at 500°C with the same catalyst. Cyclohexene, passed over a silica-alumina-thoria catalyst at 400°C, undergoes an interesting reaction to produce 2,6-dimethylnaphthalene.

The mechanism of the decomposition of naphthalene is similar to that of benzene, forming binaphthyl. Both 1,1'- and 2,2'-binaphthyl have been identified, and probably the 1,2'-isomer as well. At higher temperatures perylene has been isolated, presumably by the further condensation of the 1,1'-isomer.

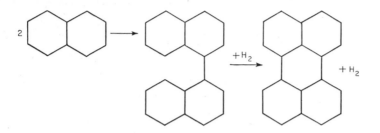

No benzene derivatives are formed by the pyrolysis of naphthalene. However, tetralin does yield benzene derivatives, so that reactions involving hydrogenolysis of naphthalene under suitable conditions yield benzene derivatives.

The decomposition of naphthalene at high temperatures yields coke or carbon, as does benzene, and at a higher rate, as will be seen in Table 2.

TABLE 2. PER CENT OF CARBON OF NAPHTHALENE CONVERTED TO COKE[23]

Temperature (°C)	% Carbon Converted to Coke in Contact with Coke Packing			
	Contact Time in Seconds			
	2	10	20	40
800°	0	2	4	7
900°	11	43	52	60
1000°	38	76	83	90

At 800°C the percentage of carbon of naphthalene deposited as carbon is about the same as with benzene—within experimental error. But at 900 and 1000°C a noticeably higher rate of decomposition is apparent. This is in contradiction to the statement of Tilicheev, but it is probable that at these high temperatures the rates of decomposition no longer depend on naphthalene and benzene as such, but rather on higher condensation products. The decomposition of naphthalene in this range is catalyzed by contact material including coke or carbon.

Tricyclic Aromatics. Of the two tricyclic aromatics, anthracene and phenanthrene, phenanthrene is the more thermally stable and is always present in larger amounts in tars and similar pyrolytic products. This greater stability of phenanthrene is reflected in the greater resonance energy of 110 Calories per mole compared with 104.7 for anthracene. The appearance of these hydrocarbons in cracked petroleum tar and coal tars may be the result of the pyrolysis of related structures such as tricyclic naphthenes, but they are also formed under thermal conditions which suggest the possibility that they may be synthesized from decomposition products resulting from the cracking of petroleum or the coking of coal. For example, Ferko[11] obtained the two hydrocarbons by pyrolyzing toluene, ethylbenzene, or a mixture of benzene and ethylene in a gas-fired iron tube. On the other hand, a mixture of toluene and ethylene gave only anthracene, whereas naphthalene and ethylene gave only phenanthrene.

In recent years the use of catalysts in cracking operations has shown that certain catalysts affect the condensation of aromatics. Thus, Mattox and Grosse[25] found that toluene, passed over a chromia-alumina catalyst at 550°C, gave a 1 per cent yield of anthracene per pass, which was 16 per cent of the toluene decomposed, and that no phenanthrene was formed. The thermal cracking of bibenzyl gives anthracene, but in contact with the chromia-alumina catalyst, stilbene, toluene and benzene were obtained, and no anthracene. However, a large carbon deposit of 14.5 per cent showed that aromatic condensation of the usual type did occur.

Meyer and Hofmann[27] proposed the following mechanism for the condensation of bibenzyl to anthracene.

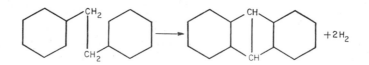

Consequently, it is possible that toluene could condense to bibenzyl, which, in turn, could produce anthracene. However, in the presence of chromia-alumina catalyst, bibenzyl appears not to be converted to anthracene. Therefore, the following mechanism is suggested, based on the characteristic dehydrogenating action of this catalyst.

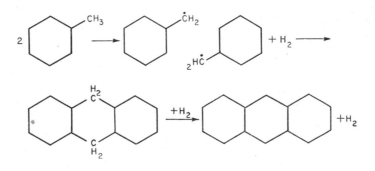

Platinized charcoal, on the other hand, favors the formation of phenanthrene, and not only bibenzyl and 1,2-dicyclohexylethane give this hydrocarbon, but stilbene gives a quantitative yield at only 300°C, according to Zelinsky and Titz.[48] The latter reaction is all the more remarkable because of the requirement that the *trans* configuration of stilbene shift into the *cis* during condensation.

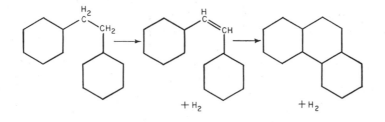

Phenanthrene is also obtained by the pyrolysis of o,o'-bitolyl.

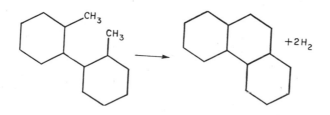

A very remarkable condensation has been reported, in which tetradecane yields both anthracene and phenanthrene when cracked on a chromia-alumina catalyst at 475°C. Although the yields are small, the complexity of processes that would result in tricyclic aromatic structures is quite notable. No doubt several reaction mechanisms are involved because p-dibutylbenzene, for example, gives an 18 per cent yield of phenanthrene, under the same conditions, but no anthracene.

Anthracene and phenanthrene are not normally isomerizable by thermal means. However, Prokopetz et al.[38] found that partial hydrogenation of either hydrocarbon over molybdenum sulfide at 350°C gave a mixture of hydroanthracene and hydrophenanthrene. Unfortunately nothing is known about the structures that undergo isomerization.

Condensations may also be obtained by the elimination of methane as well as hydrogen. This is shown in the following reaction, which results in the formation of the anthracene ring system.

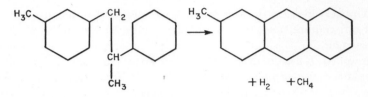

Anthracene. The thermal decomposition of anthracene proceeds readily at temperatures as low as 475°C. Thus Sachanen and Tilicheev[41] found that at this temperature the pressure within the autoclave rose to 70 atmospheres in $2\frac{1}{2}$ hours, indicating decomposition to gaseous products. The residue was a cokelike mass, 59 per cent insoluble in hot benzene.

The rate of decomposition was given by Tilicheev[45] as 370 times as fast as its isomer phenanthrene. The first product of decomposition seems to be bianthryl,[27] probably the 9,9'-isomer, but no meso-naphthodianthrene, which should result from the further condensation of this primary product, has been reported.

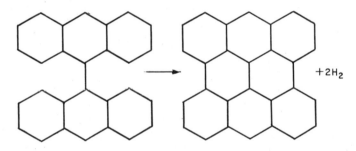

In the range of 800 to 1000°C, anthracene is rapidly decomposed to carbon, as Table 3 shows. The decomposition is, as usual, surface-

TABLE 3. PER CENT OF CARBON OF ANTHRACENE CONVERTED TO COKE[23]

Temperature (°C)	% Carbon Converted to Coke in Contact with Coke Packing			
	Contact Time in Seconds			
	2	10	20	40
800	21	67	83	90
900	32	79	89	95
1000	72	96	98	99

catalyzed. In contact with metallurgical coke packing the surface of the packing is not only coated with hard shiny firmly adhering carbon, but the interstices are also filled with a soft dull black variety of carbon, which implies that vapor-phase decomposition occurred as well as surface reaction. However, with a molecule as large as anthracene it probably would not require many condensations before the coke or carbon stage was reached.

The uncatalyzed hydrogenation of anthracene at 485°C and 250 atmospheres pressure results in tetrahydroanthracene, lower-boiling hydrocarbons derived from this intermediate, and condensation to pitch.

Phenanthrene. The rate of cracking of phenanthrene at 500°C is 370 times slower than that of anthracene, as measured by gas formation, but 94 times faster than that of naphthalene.[45] The relative rates of coke formation at the same temperature are 1:78:10,800 for naphthalene, phenanthrene, and anthracene. The cracking of phenanthrene at high temperatures, in the region of 700 to 1000°C, has not been reported, and no comparison with anthracene can be made. On hydrogenation at temperatures up to 485°C, tetrahydrophenanthrene and low-boiling products, no doubt resulting from the cracking of naphthenic rings, were obtained. No high-boiling tar was produced, as with naphthalene and anthracene.

Tetracyclic Aromatics. The five tetracyclic aromatic hydrocarbons, naphthacene, 1.2-benzanthracene, chrysene, triphenylene and pyrene have all been isolated from coal tar and, no doubt, exist as such, or as derivatives in petroleum tars and pitches. Chrysene has been obtained by the pyrolysis of indene and has been extracted from soil. The conversion of indene to chrysene is of interest in connection with the many reactions of indene, including the dehydropolymerization to truxene.

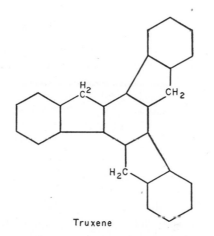

Truxene

Chrysene has been claimed among the pyrolytic products of benzene but this has also been denied. On the other hand, there seems to be no doubt but that triphenylene is formed from benzene. Pyrene is obtained by the pyrolysis of tetramethylbiphenyl.

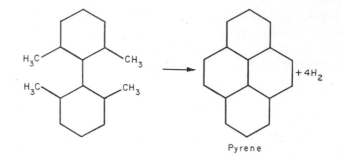

Pyrene

Both chrysene and pyrene have been pyrolyzed at 800 to 1000°C and were extensively condensed to coke and hydrogen. The per cent of carbon of the hydrocarbons deposited as coke is shown in Tables 4 and 5. The

TABLE 4. PER CENT OF CARBON OF CHRYSENE CONVERTED TO COKE[23]

	% Carbon Converted to Coke in Contact with Coke Packing			
Temperature (°C)	Contact Time in Seconds			
	2	10	20	40
800	4	13	20	25
900	30	65	77	84
1000	76	88	93	98

TABLE 5. PER CENT OF CARBON OF PYRENE CONVERTED TO COKE[23]

	% Carbon Converted to Coke in Contact with Coke Packing			
Temperature (°C)	Contact Time in Seconds			
	2	10	20	40
800	4	15	23	30
900	21	57	66	73
1000	70	90	100	100

rate of decomposition of both chrysene and pyrene was less than that of anthracene, but greater than that of naphthalene. Gaseous products in addition to hydrogen were methane and traces of acetylene.

Higher Aromatics. Many higher aromatics with five and more rings have been isolated from coal tar or have been synthesized. Many of these, such as picene and coronene, can be distilled undecomposed at normal pressures at temperatures well over 500°C. Such stability is truly remarkable and is all the more remarkable considering the tendency for aromatics to condense at such temperatures, with the elimination of hydrogen. This region between the truly aromatic hydrocarbons, on the one hand, and the carbon-like molecules of the so-called "amorphous" carbons has never been explored extensively or satisfactorily.

Thermal Behavior of the Mixed Aliphatic-Aromatic Hydrocarbons

Alkylated Aromatics. The thermal behavior of the alkylated aromatics is complicated by a multitude of reactions, all of which are affected by temperature, pressure, catalysts, the presence of hydrogen or of other aromatics that may act as hydrogen acceptors, and of olefins or other decomposition products. For example, the pyrolysis of toluene has been reported to yield benzene, bibenzyl, stilbene, bitolyl, phenyltolyl, phenyltolylmethane, ditolylmethane, biphenyl, styrene, naphthalene, anthracene, and phenanthrene. Longer side-chains or multiple substitutions increase the reaction possibilities; but, despite the complexity of the products obtained, one point stands out clearly, and that is the stability of the aromatic ring systems, which retain their identity through a great variety of pyrolytic reactions. There is one reaction, however, that destroys the aromatic structure, namely, pyrolysis in the presence of hydrogen, particularly in contact with a catalyst that may serve as a hydrogenating catalyst. Under these conditions aromatic rings are hydrogenated and then cracked. The heating of alkylaromatics with hydrogen, especially in the presence of catalysts, frequently results in the formation of the unsubstituted aromatic, which may then undergo hydrogenolysis.

Because of the large number of pyrolytic reactions given by alkylaromatics, discussion of their thermal behavior has been subdivided according to the following outline.

(1) Dealkylation at the aromatic ring

(2) Cracking in the aliphatic side chain

(3) Dehydrogenation reactions of the side chain

(4) Condensation reactions

(5) Isomerization of alkylaromatics

(6) Disproportionation of methyl groups between aromatics

Discussion of important individual hydrocarbons is given as examples under each subdivision.

Dealkylation at the Aromatic Ring. The dealkylation of aromatics is of particular interest for the production of increased quantities of benzene, toluene, naphthalene and similar useful aromatics. Dealkylation reactions are simply the reverse of alkylation and, since the latter reactions are favored by negative free energies of formation up to about 540°C and then become positive, relatively high temperatures are usually required for the satisfactory dealkylation of most aromatics.

Normal alkyl groups are eliminated with the greatest difficulty, followed by secondary and tertiary radicals, in that order. Of the normal groups, methyl is the most difficult to remove. The reason for this may be found in the tendency for hydrogen to dissociate from the methyl group. The multiplicity of products, a part of which are obviously the result of reactions of benzyl radicals or benzyl carbonium ions, has already been mentioned.

Herndon and Reid[19] have found that methyl-, ethyl- and t-butylbenzene and 1,1-diphenylethane are almost completely decomposed when heated at 525°C for 10 hours. Pease and Morton[35] arranged five simple benzene derivatives in the following order of thermal stability at 600°C, based on the relative gas volumes produced: o-xylene, toluene, benzene, m-xylene, ethylbenzene. In the range of 700 to 770°C, others have found that m-xylene is the most stable of the three xylenes and o-xylene gives the most condensation products.

Although normal alkyl groups are not readily split off by thermal means, this is the main reaction given by the silica-zirconia-alumina catalyst (U.O.P. type B) in the range of 500 to 550°C. Greensfelder et al.[14] found that ethyl-, n-propyl-, and n-butylbenzene were dealkylated almost exclusively to benzene, and with increasing ease as the length of the alkyl group increased. Thus at 500°C under fixed conditions, toluene was cracked to the extent of 1 per cent, ethylbenzene 11 per cent, and n-propylbenzene 43 per cent. At 400°C, n-butylbenzene was cracked 14 per cent at a rate of 12.5 moles per liter of catalyst per hour, and 28 per cent at one-half this rate.

Secondary and tertiary alkyl groups are removed with much greater ease. Thus, Greensfelder and co-workers, using the same catalyst, found that isopropylbenzene at 500°C was dealkylated to the extent of 80 per cent as compared with 43 per cent for n-propylbenzene; the butylbenzenes at 400°C were dealkylated as follows: normal 14 per cent, secondary 49 per cent, and tertiary 80 per cent. These results seem to be generally characteristic of the relative behavior of primary, secondary, and tertiary alkyl groups attached to aromatic rings.

Additional substitutions on aromatic rings have variable effects on the dealkylation of a more weakly attached group. Roberts and Good[37] made a comparison of substituted cumenes (isopropylbenzene) at 450°C with the silica-zirconia-alumina catalyst, as follows:

Cumene Derivative	% Decomposition
2,4-dimethyl	77
4-methyl	60
3,5-dimethyl	57
cumene	39
4-chloro	25
x,x,x-trichloro	8

These authors state that "this order of reactivity correlates well with activation energies for electophilic displacement of isopropyl by hydrogen calculated by an approximate molecular orbital method," and for this reason believe that the dealkylation reaction proceeds through the formation of a polar intermediate complex with an acidic center on the catalyst, proposed earlier by Thomas[44] and Greensfelder et al.[15] Thomas described the mechanism by means of the following three steps, in which HA represents the acid cracking catalyst.

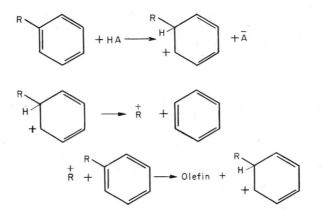

Greensfelder et al.[14] initiated this type of mechanism with a somewhat more simplified form.

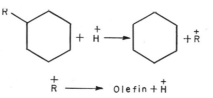

Another type of dealkylation occurs readily when two or more aromatic nuclei are attached to the same carbon atom of an aliphatic chain of two or more carbon atoms in length. Thus 1,1-diphenylethane is readily decomposed to benzene and styrene at 600°C over an acid clay catalyst.

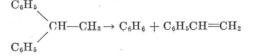

The methylnaphthalenes, like toluene, are resistant to demethylation. When α-methylnaphthalene is passed over silica-zirconia-alumina catalyst at 500°C, 87 per cent is decomposed to lower-boiling products, mainly naphthalene, but benzene derivatives may also be present, 5 per cent coke, 1 per cent gas and 3 per cent loss. The α-isomer is less stable than the β-isomer and at 450°C cracks 4 to 5 times as fast. At 500°C, catalytic cracking is estimated to be 100 times faster. Products are generally about equally distributed between naphthalene and higher-boiling condensation products.

tert.-Butylnaphthalene is readily split into naphthalene and a mixture of isobutene and isobutane at 500°C with the silica-zirconia-alumina catalyst. The formation of isobutane may be accounted for by saturation of isobutene by the hydrogen liberated during condensation to produce 9.2 per cent of coke. Amylnaphthalenes are also cracked to naphthalene and amylenes at 500°C.

Cracking in the Aliphatic Side-Chain. When alkylated aromatics are thermally cracked in the absence of active catalysts, primary and secondary alkyl groups undergo extensive cracking within the side-chain, but tertiary groups undergo the dealkylation reaction for the most part. Dobryansky and co-workers[8] heated ethyl-, isopropyl-, *n*-butyl-, and *t*-butylbenzene to 600 to 650°C, and from the products devised the following rules, which are generally applicable to the thermal decomposition of alkylated aromatics.

Type of Alkyl Group   Type of Products

(1) Primary $C_6H_5-CH_3 + CH_2=CH-R$

$C_6H_5-CH_2-CH_2-CH_2-R$

                                   $C_6H_5-CH=CH_2 + CH_3-R$

(2) Secondary

$$C_6H_5-\overset{\overset{\displaystyle R}{\displaystyle |}}{C}H-CH_3 \qquad \rightarrow C_6H_5-CH=CH_2 + R-H$$

(3) Tertiary
$C_6H_5-C(CH_3)_3 \qquad\qquad \rightarrow C_6H_6 + CH_2=C(CH_3)_2$

Sachanen and Hansford[40] cracked a 150 to 250°C petroleum fraction (sp gr 0.865), composed largely of propyl-, amyl-, and heptylbenzenes, at 482°C and 50 atmospheres pressure for 40 minutes, and obtained:

43% almost unchanged
25% largely cracked to toluene and xylenes
23% liquid condensation products (sp gr 1.04) (polynuclear aromatics)
 5% solid condensation products (asphalt and coke)
 4% gas and low-boiling hydrocarbons

The formation of toluene and xylenes would be expected on the basis of Dobryansky's rules, but not the relatively large amount of condensation to polynuclear aromatics (high specific gravity), asphalt, and coke. The condensation of alkylbenzenes to bicyclic aromatics has been demonstrated in the case of butylbenzene, which gave naphthalene in a 55 per cent yield over a chromia-alumina catalyst at 500°C. Although the cyclodehydration reaction probably proceeds faster in contact with the chromia catalyst, the above static time of 40 minutes may compensate for the lack of catalyst.

Dehydrogenation of the Side-Chain. An important example of this reaction is the conversion of ethylbenzene, manufactured by the alkylation of benzene with ethylene, to styrene. Thermally the reaction proceeds in the range of 650 to 700°C, but at much lower temperatures in contact with suitable catalysts. Thus Oblad *et al.*[30] found that in contact with chromia it proceeded at 480°C. The styrene produced for the manufacture of synthetic rubber during World War II was largely made by the Dow process,[16] using a ferric oxide on magnesia catalyst promoted with potassium carbonate and stabilized with copper oxide. The temperature was held at 600 to 660°C. Steam in the amount of 2.6 pounds per pound of ethylbenzene was used to remove the carbon as deposited on the catalyst. However, the use of a diluent, such as benzene, or low pressures aided the dehydrogenation reaction. Yields of 35 per cent per pass were obtained and ultimate yields of 90 per cent. The catalyst life was a year or more.

Webb and Corson[46] obtained thermal yields in the range of 700 to 800°C, with ultimate yields of 60 per cent. The distribution of products is given in Table 6 at two different contact times. The amount of carbon

TABLE 6. PYROLYSIS OF ETHYLBENZENE

Products	% Yields Contact Times, seconds	
	0.1	0.4
ethylbenzene	37	12
styrene	30	28
toluene	11	8
benzene	8	5
gas	7	13
high-boiling residue	7	34

produced varied between 0.01 per cent and 0.05 per cent of the carbon of the feed.

Isopropylbenzene, when pyrolyzed, yields α-methylstyrene.

$$C_6H_5\!-\!\underset{\underset{CH_3}{|}}{CH}\!-\!CH_3 \rightarrow C_6H_5\!-\!\underset{\underset{CH_3}{|}}{C}\!=\!CH_2 + H_2$$

Nichols *et al.*[29] found that the best ultimate yield of 84 per cent was obtained at 600°C, with a magnesium-iron-potassium-copper oxide catalyst at a 0.5 hourly space velocity, using 10 moles of steam per mole of hydrocarbon. The conversion per pass was about 25 per cent.

Condensation Reactions. Dehydrogenation reactions also result in condensation reactions with the formation of additional aromatic rings. There are three main types of these reactions: (1) intramolecular condensation, (2) intermolecular condensation involving the alkyl groups, and (3) intermolecular condensation involving only the aromatic nucleus.

Examples of intramolecular condensation include the pyrolysis of *n*-butylbenzene and *o,o'*-bitolyl, which produce naphthalene and phenanthrene, respectively. The conversion of *p*-di-*n*-butylbenzene to phenanthrene is interesting because the rings are closed in only one way, with no trace of anthracene.

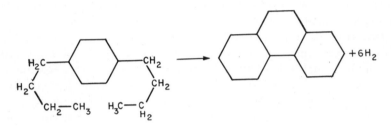

Although bibenzyl is thermally cracked to anthracene, in addition to stilbene and toluene, stilbene yields neither anthracene nor phenanthrene under similar conditions. However, Zelinsky and co-workers[48] found that stilbene as well as bibenzyl, and even dicyclohexylethane, give a quantitative yield of phenanthrene when passed over platinized charcoal

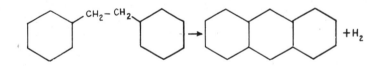

at 300°C. Diphenylmethane under the same conditions gives fluorene. Chrysene is obtained by the pyrolysis of 1-phenyl-2-α-naphthylethane. Picene is formed by heating 1,2-di-α-naphthylethylene.

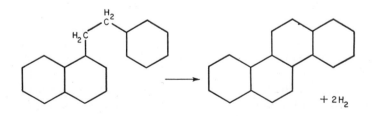

Examples of intermolecular condensation involving the alkyl groups include the pyrolysis of toluene, ethylbenzene, benzene plus ethylene, and the like, which produce polycyclic aromatics such as anthracene and phenanthrene. Actual yields are usually small.

The third type of condensation, intermolecular condensations involving the aromatic nucleus, has already been described as one of the most important thermal reactions of the unsubstituted aromatics, i.e., condensation. Similar condensations occur with the alkylated aromatics. Thus toluene yields bitolyl, among other products. In general this type of reaction requires higher temperatures than reactions involving the side-chains, and for this reason direct condensation of the nuclei of substituted aromatics is usually of lesser importance.

These three types of condensation reactions are in large measure responsible for the conversion of low-boiling, low-density petroleum fractions into high-boiling, high-density residues, the "dead oils," tars, pitches, and the like. These residues are not only difficult to crack, but when cracked give large deposits of coke, only a little light oil, and are generally uneconomical to process by simple thermal means. In addition, more attention must be paid to the carcinogenic hazards of residues boiling above 370°C, which creates an added difficulty to the disposal of these residues. Dietz *et al.*,[7] for example, give results of tests on various oil fractions and show (Table 7) how the multi-ring aromatics, which

TABLE 7. CHANGES IN COMPOSITION OF A GAS-OIL ON CATALYTIC CRACKING

Aromatic Ring Type	Weight % of Ring Type in Aromatic Fraction Boiling above 370°C	
	Fresh Feed	Clarified Oil (0% recycle)
benzenes	60	6
naphthalenes	14	5
anthracenes	1	1
phenanthrenes	15	22
pyrenes	3	21
benzanthracenes	0	4
chrysenes and benzphenanthrenes	3	24
five rings +	2	9
unknown to 1020°F	2	0
unknown above 1020°F	0	9

are the main carcinogenic offenders, increase when a 450 to 930°F gas-oil from a West Texas crude undergoes catalytic cracking. Thus it will be seen that, although over 90 per cent of the feed stock contains less than three aromatic rings, 67 per cent of the cracked oil contains four or more rings per molecule.

Because these condensation reactions are dehydrogenations, they may be avoided to a large degree by cracking under hydrogenating conditions and with hydrogenating catalysts. Or, if hydrocracking is not desirable in the first stages, as Sherwood[42] suggests, it should be used in the later stages to utilize better the residues that are being run to tar or coke (Skinner et al.[43]). The conversion of these residues to light oils by catalytic hydrogenolysis would be more economical than starting with raw coal, for example. That polynuclear aromatics can be hydrocracked has been shown (by Orlov and Lichachev)[31] by heating chrysene with hydrogen under pressure to about 450°C, with the formation of phenanthrenes, naphthalenes, and even benzene derivatives. This reaction proceeds by successive hydrogenation of the aromatic rings, alternating with cracking of the naphthenic rings as formed.

Isomerization of Alkylaromatics. Heating polyalkylaromatics leads to isomerization in certain cases. Apparently this reaction is limited to methyl groups because of the tendency of longer radicals to stabilize themselves by forming a double bond, with the dissociation of a hydrogen atom or by cracking. However, since aromatics are alkylated by olefins more or less readily, it is possible that higher polyalkylaromatics may be made to undergo a kind of pseudoisomerism, but little experimental evidence is available.

Methyl groups are known to shift from one aromatic ring to another, and it is not surprising that where one structure is relatively more stable than its isomers, that structure will be formed during pyrolytic treatment. Thus Dobryansky and Saprykin[9] found that *p*-xylene was readily isomerized into the meta-isomer by pyrolysis at 700 to 770°C, whereas *m*-xylene was transformed, to a smaller extent, to the para isomer. Greensfelder et al.[14] passed *p*-xylene over silica-zirconia-alumina catalyst at 550°C. In addition to disproportionation of methyl groups, 47 per cent of xylenes was recovered having the following composition as compared with theoretical values calculated by Pitzer and Scott.[36]

Isomer of *p*-xylene	Exp'l., %	Theor., %
para	28	21
meta	47	58
ortho	25	21

In this connection, the thermodynamic equilibrium between the C_8-aromatics has been calculated, and compared with their distribution in virgin petroleum and products of various cracking processes (Table 8).[17] The good agreement between the relative amounts of C_8-aromatics from the various sources indicates a fairly high degree of mobility of the alkyl groups and stability of the equilibrium mixture at about 450°C.

Disproportionation of Methyl Groups between Aromatics. Methyl groups also undergo shifts from one aromatic molecule to another when heated in contact with acid-type catalysts. Thus Natanson and Kagan[28] passed toluene over an aluminum silicate catalyst at 430°C and obtained a disproportionation of the methyl groups. The product contained 15.2 per cent benzene, 62.5 per cent toluene, and 13.4 per cent xylenes. Hansford, Meyers and Sachanen[18] passed a mixture of benzene and *m*-xylene over a silica-alumina catalyst at 540°C and obtained toluene, whereas *m*-xylene by itself gave toluene and trimethylbenzenes. Interestingly enough, α-methylnaphthalene did not give up its methyl to benzene when mixed with the latter compound, but when heated alone gave naphthalene and dimethylnaphthalene. Pseudocumene was converted to toluene, xylene, and polymethylbenzenes. Greensfelder *et al.*[14] found that when *p*-xylene was passed over a silica-zirconia-alumina catalyst at 550°C, 53 per cent was altered. Besides 24 per cent of chiefly toluene, 16 per cent of trimethylbenzenes was obtained. With mesitylene at 500°C, 6 per cent was converted to higher methylated derivatives, and with pseudocumene, 13 per cent to tetramethylbenzenes and higher.

TABLE 8. DISTRIBUTION OF C_8-AROMATICS FROM VARIOUS SOURCES

C_8-Hydro-Carbon	Thermodyn. Equil. at 420°C	Virgin Pet.	Cat. Crack. at 450°C	Platform.	Hydro-form. at 480–530°C
o-xylene	23	20	20	23	20
m-xylene	47	50	50	40	43
p-xylene	21	20	20	21	17
ethylbenzene	9	10	10	16	20

When aromatic derivatives containing larger alkyl groups are treated similarly, little evidence for a transfer of the groups intact has been found. It is likely that these groups are split off under the same conditions, but presumably they form the corresponding olefin by an electronic rearrangement and the elimination of hydrogen before the radical can react with another aromatic nucleus. No doubt the olefin molecule formed may alkylate aromatic nuclei, which would result in the same end product as though the group had been transferred intact, but the conditions employed for group transfer are not favorable to alkylation by olefins.

Naphthenic Aromatics. The pyrolytic behavior of the naphthenic derivatives of the aromatic hydrocarbons is generally closely related to the reactions of the open-chain alkylated aromatics. There are two main types of derivatives to consider: (1) naphthenic rings attached by single bonds to aromatic nuclei, and (2) naphthenic rings fused to aromatic nuclei.

Type (1) derivatives are characterized by a greater ease of thermal decomposition than type (2), and usually result in splitting at the bond between the rings, producing the parent aromatic and an unsaturated naphthene.

Where the temperature of cracking is sufficiently high to effect secondary reactions of the products, these may also be expected. Dehydrogenation catalysts, particularly platinized or palladinized charcoal or asbestos, nickel, and chromia catalysts, are especially effective in aromatizing the naphthenic ring. When the ring is not of the right size to produce an aromatic ring, dehydrogenation is more difficult and cracking of the ring usually results.

Fused aromatic-naphthenic ring hydrocarbons usually are thermally cracked in three directions: (1) Splitting of the naphthenic ring, forming aromatic derivatives; (2) Dehydrogenation of the naphthenic ring to an aromatic ring; and (3) Condensation reactions. Thus Sachanen and Tilicheev[41] found that tetralin, at 450°C for nearly 20 hours and at a final pressure of 100 atmospheres, was cracked to the extent of 86 per cent. Of the tetralin decomposed, 55 per cent yielded benzene derivatives resulting from the cracking of the naphthenic ring, 30 per cent was dehydrogenated to benzene, and 15 per cent was condensed to high-boiling products and coke. Later, reaction rates for the thermal cracking of tetralin at temperatures from 425 to 600°C were obtained, as shown in Table 9. From these data the activation energy was caclulated to be

TABLE 9. REACTION RATE CONSTANTS FOR THE CRACKING OF TETRALIN

T, °C	$k.$ sec^{-1}
425	3.4×10^6
450	1.7×10^5
500	3.2×10^5
550	4.2×10^3
575	1.3×10^2
600	4.1×10^2

65 Calories per mole, which is similar to values obtained for open-chain paraffins. By comparison, the five-membered ring of indan was found to be cracked only half as fast as tetralin, indicating a somewhat greater stability for the five-membered ring as compared with the six-membered ring. Decalin, under similar conditions, was even more readily decomposed than tetralin. At 500°C and about 7 atmospheres pressure, 95 per cent was decomposed in 1½ hours. The products included tetralin, naphthalene, benzene derivatives, and condensed products.

Tetralin is catalytically dehydrogenated to naphthalene over nickel at 300°C, whereas decalin is dehydrogenated to tetralin at 200°C. Adkins and Reid[2] found that tetralin is stable in contact with copper chromite at 350°C and a nitrogen pressure of 60 atmospheres, but undergoes dehydrogenation to naphthalene with Raney nickel, under these conditions, to the extent of 78 per cent. At 300°C, only 40 per cent naphthalene is obtained. Greensfelder *et al.*[15] found that activated carbon was 200 times more effective in dehydrogenating decalin to naphthalene at 500°C than the acidic silica-zirconia-alumina-type catalyst. Linstead *et al.*[24] also report these hydroaromatics and their methyl derivatives are quantitatively dehydrogenated in contact with platinum or palladium at 300°C to the corresponding aromatic. Even at the boiling point of tetralin there is a rapid evolution of hydrogen when the liquid is boiling vigorously. Cooke and Gulland[6] found that an aqueous solution of palladous chloride brought about the decomposition to naphthalene. Thus after boiling 33 hours, the weight of metallic palladium produced accounted for 98 per cent of the oxidation.

Bloch and Thomas[3] pyrolyzed tetralin over silica-alumina-zirconia catalyst at 400 to 500°C and obtained naphthalene, benzene, toluene, xylenes, and possibly ethylbenzene. Higher alkylbenzenes were also obtained but no alkenylbenzenes. Greensfelder *et al.*[14] obtained similar results with indan, except that no naphthalene was reported. Although indan cracked less rapidly than tetralin, more carbon was condensed on the catalyst, 4.8 per cent as compared with 1.9 per cent.

Even under hydrogenating conditions over a cupra*-alumina catalyst at 325°C, large deposits of carbon were observed. Under these conditions 60 per cent of the indan was decomposed to 57 mole-per cent toluene, 33 mole-per cent *n*-propylbenzene, 3 mole-per cent benzene, and the remainder cyclohexane derivatives and carbon. Adkins and Davis[1] found that tetralin and similar hydroaromatics were smoothly dehydrogenated when heated with nickel catalysts, with benzene as a hydrogen acceptor. Sulfur compounds effectively aided the transfer of hydrogen.

* Copper oxide.

References

1. Adkins, H., and Davis, J. W., *J. Am. Chem. Soc.*, **71**, 2955 (1949).
2. Adkins, H., and Reid, W. A., *Ibid.*, **63**, 741 (1941).
3. Bloch, H. S., and Thomas, C. L., *Ibid.*, **66**, 1589 (1944).
4. Bolton, K., Cullingworth, J. E., Ghosh, B. P., and Cobb, J. W., *J. Chem. Soc.*, **1942**, 252.
5. Brooks, B. T., *Ind. Eng. Chem.*, **18**, 521 (1926).
6. Cooke, G. W., and Gulland, J. M., *J. Chem. Soc.*, **1939**, 872.
7. Dietz, W. A., King, W. H., Priestley, W., and Rehner, J., *Ind. Eng. Chem.*, **44**, 1818 (1952).
8. Dobryansky, A. F., Kanep, E. K., and Katsman, S. V., *Chem. Abs.* **31**, 5334[2] (1937).
9. Dobryansky, A. F., and Saprykin, F. Y., *Oil Gas J.*, **39**, Aug. 8, p. 48 (1940).
10. Egloff, G., "The Reactions of Pure Hydrocarbons," p. 405, New York, Reinhold Publishing Corp., 1937.

11. Ferko, P., *Ber.*, **20**, 660 (1887).
12. Foxwell, G. E., *Coke Smokeless—Fuel Age*, **4**, 151 (1942).
13. Glockler, G., *J. Chem. Phys.*, **21**, 1249 (1953).
14. Greensfelder, B. S., Voge, H. H., and Good, G. M., *Ind. Eng. Chem.*, **37**, 1168 (1945).
15. Greensfelder, B. S., Voge, H. H., and Good, G. M., *Ibid.*, **41**, 2573 (1949).
16. Haensel, V., and Sterba, M. J., *Ibid.*, **40**, 1660 (1948).
17. Haensel, V., and Sterba, M. J., *Ibid.*, **43**, 2021 (1951).
18. Hansford, R. C., Meyers, C. G., and Sachanen, A. N., *Ibid.*, **37**, 671 (1945).
19. Herndon, L. R., and Reid, E. E., *J. Am. Chem. Soc.*, **50**, 3066 (1928).
20. Hollings, H., and Cobb, J. W., *Gas World*, **60**, 879 (1914).
21. Hurd, C. D., "The Pyrolysis of Carbon Compounds," p. 15, New York, The Chemical Catalog Co., 1929.
22. Iley, R., and Riley, H. L., *J. Chem. Soc.*, **1948**, 1362.
23. Kinney, C. R., and DelBel, E., *Ind. Eng. Chem.*, **46**, 548 (1954).
24. Linstead, R. P., and Michaelis, K. O. A., *J. Chem. Soc.*, **1940**, 1134.
25. Mattox, W. J., and Grosse, A. V., *J. Am. Chem. Soc.*, **67**, 84 (1945).
26. Mead, F. C., and Burk, R. E., *Ind. Eng. Chem.*, **27**, 299 (1935).
27. Meyer, H., and Hofmann, A., *Monatsh.*, **37**, 681 (1916).
28. Natanson, G. L., and Kagan, M. Y., *J. Phys. Chem. (U.S.S.R.)*, **17**, 381 (1943).
29. Nichols, J. E., Webb, G. A., Heintzelman, W., and Corson, B. B., *Ind. Eng. Chem.*, **41**, 563 (1949).
30. Oblad, A. G., Marschner, R. E., and Heard, L., *J. Am. Chem. Soc.*, **62**, 2066 (1940).
31. Orlov, N. A., and Lichachev, N. D., *Ber.*, **62B**, 719 (1929).
32. Pauling, L., "Organic Chemistry," 2nd ed., p. 1970, H. Gilman, editor, New York, John Wiley and Sons, Inc., 1943.
33. Pauling, L., and Brockway, L. O., *J. Am. Chem. Soc.*, **59**, 1223 (1937).
34. Pauling, L., and Wilson, E. B., "Introduction to Quantum Mechanics with Applications to Chemistry," New York, McGraw-Hill Book Co., Inc., 1935.
35. Pease, R. N., and Morton, J. M., *J. Am. Chem. Soc.*, **55**, 3190 (1933).
36. Pitzer, K. S., and Scott, D. W., *Ibid.*, **65**, 803 (1943).
37. Roberts, R. M., and Good, G. M., *Ibid.*, **73**, 1320 (1951).
38. Prokopets, E. I., *et al.*, *J. Applied Chem. (U.S.S.R.)*, **11**, 823; 840 (1938).
39. Sachanen, A. N., "Conversion of Petroleum," 2nd ed., p. 93, New York, Reinhold Publishing Corp., 1948.
40. Sachanen, A. N., and Hansford, R. C., U. S. Patent 2,223,133 (Nov. 26, 1940).
41. Sachanen, A. N., and Tilicheev, M. D., *Ber.*, **62B**, 658 (1929).
42. Sherwood, P. W., *Petroleum Refiner*, **29**, No. 8, 107 (1950).
43. Skinner, L. C., Donath, E. E., Shappert, H. C., and Frese, E., *Ibid.*, **29**, No. 7, 83 (1950).
44. Thomas, C. L., *Ind. Eng. Chem.*, **41**, 2564 (1949).
45. Tilicheev, M. D., *J. Applied Chem. (U.S.S.R.)*, **12**, 740 (1939).
46. Webb, G. A., and Corson, B. B., *Ind. Eng. Chem.*, **39**, 1153 (1947).
47. Wilson, J. E., and Noyes, Jr., W. A., *J. Am. Chem. Soc.*, **63**, 3025 (1941).
48. Zelinsky, N. D., and Titz, J. N., *Ber.*, **62B**, 2869 (1929).

CHAPTER 27

THEORY OF CATALYTIC CRACKING

B. S. Greensfelder

Shell Development Company, Emeryville, California

The catalytic cracking of hydrocarbons over acidic catalysts represents an accelerated severance of carbon-to-carbon bonds, compared with the thermal reaction under the same physical conditions. The carbon skeletons of aromatic rings remain essentially intact in catalytic cracking, so that the carbon-carbon bond ruptures to be considered are as follows: (a) aliphatic-aliphatic, (b) aliphatic-alicyclic, (c) alicyclic-alicyclic, (d) aliphatic-aromatic, and (e) alicyclic-aromatic.

A great amount of evidence is now available, in the form of product distribution data, for the catalytic and thermal cracking of pure hydrocarbons. From the two distinctively different sets of fragmentation patterns, it is concluded that basically different modes of carbon-carbon bond rupture are at work. As will be seen, catalytic cracking is typified by an ionic (carbonium ion), heterolytic split of the C—C bond, electronically represented as:

$$(1) \qquad\qquad C:C \rightarrow C \;\vdash\; :C$$

In contrast, thermal cracking is typified by a free-radical, homolytic split of the C—C bond, electronically represented as:

$$(2) \qquad\qquad C:C \rightarrow C\cdot \;+\; \cdot C$$

To reach the electronic energy state necessary to produce these ruptures, definite conditions must be fulfilled prior to the act of separation of the carbon atoms in each of the two cases. Although the details of the mechanisms proposed will be reserved for development later in this text, basically it can be stated that in catalytic cracking the essential reaction intermediate is a structure containing one less hydrogen atom than the parent molecule in the case of paraffins and naphthenes, and one more hydrogen atom than the parent molecule in the case of olefins and substituted aromatics. This intermediate fulfills the customary definition of a hydrocarbon carbonium ion, represented by the empirical formulas $C_nH_{2n+1}^+$ for aliphatics, $C_nH_{2n-1}^+$ for monocyclic naphthenes, and $C_nH_{2n-5}^+$ for monocyclic aromatics.

In thermal free-radical cracking, the reaction intermediate usually contains one less hydrogen atom than the parent molecule. Therefore, in both kinds of systems, the intermediate hydrocarbon structure always contains an odd number of hydrogen atoms. In catalytic cracking it assumes an ionic form, but in thermal cracking it appears as a free radical. It will be seen later that some ambiguity resides in our knowledge of the mechanism of cracking of substituted aromatics with respect to the exact nature of the intermediate; this ambiguity does not affect, however, the fundamental significance of the proposed concepts.

Proof for the two basic mechanisms, (a) acid-catalyzed ionic cracking and (b) thermal cracking via free radicals (in the absence of any catalysts) consists primarily of circumstantial evidence. In the case of catalytic cracking, the postulated ionic reactions are mechanistically the reverse of those obtained in acid-catalyzed low-temperature (0 to 100°C) association reactions, namely, polymerization of olefins, alkylation of aromatics with olefins, and alkylation of olefins with isoparaffins. The low-temperature acid-catalyzed reactions, all of which entail the participation of olefins, have been studied extensively, and the consensus of copious literature (see Ref.[34] for a recent summary) is that their mechanisms are characterized by the creation of carbonium ions as reaction intermediates.

As already indicated, the formation of carbonium ions requires either the subtraction of a hydrogen atom via the rupture of a carbon-hydrogen bond, or the addition of a hydrogen atom to form a new carbon-hydrogen bond. It is therefore of importance to the theory of these mechanisms that the accumulated experimental data show tertiary carbon-hydrogen bonds to be far more reactive than secondary C—H bonds, and these in turn to be much more reactive than primary C—H bonds in the ionic type of dissociation (cracking) and association reactions. The corresponding relative reactivities of tertiary-to-secondary and secondary-to-primary carbon-hydrogen bonds in thermal, free-radical reactions are much less. For this reason, tertiary and secondary structures will be seen to play a particularly dominant role in ionic reaction mechanisms. The first-named reactivity relationship is reflected by the data derived from mass spectrometric measurement of the appearance potentials of various alkyl ions. The alkyl-ion appearance potentials, combined with appropriate thermodynamic and bond-dissociation energy data for hydrocarbons, give energy values for the production of alkyl ions from their parent hydrocarbons that may be correlated qualitatively with the relative reactivities of primary, secondary, and tertiary hydrocarbon structures both in the low-temperature association, and high-temperature dissociation, ionic processes. Furthermore, free-radical C—H bond dissociation energies[37,39] reflect the lesser reactivity differences found in thermal, free-radical reactions among C—H bond types, so that a clear parallelism exists between the experimental data of catalytic and thermal cracking and the energetics of the proposed mechanisms.

Catalytic and Thermal Cracking

To compare the reaction characteristics of the catalytic cracking process with those of thermal cracking, a number of the more significant types of hydrocarbon dissociations and transformations encountered in these reaction systems are summarized in Table 1 similarly to Ref.,[19] Table A. These comparisons between catalytic and thermal modes of cracking, and between hydrocarbon classes, refer primarily to compounds having the same numbers of carbon atoms.

TABLE 1. COMPARATIVE SUMMARY OF CATALYTIC AND THERMAL CRACKING CHARACTERISTICS OF PURE HYDROCARBONS
(Temperature range, 400–550°C; pressure, about atmospheric)

Hydrocarbon	Catalytic Cracking	Thermal Cracking
n-Paraffins	Extensive breakdown to C_3 and larger fragments. Product largely in C_3 to C_6 range and contains many branched aliphatics. Few normal α-olefins above C_4.	Extensive breakdown to C_2 fragments, with much C_1 and C_3. Prominent amounts of C_4 to C_{n-1} normal α-olefins. Aliphatics largely unbranched.
Isoparaffins	Cracking rate relative to *n*-paraffins increased considerably by presence of tertiary carbon atoms.	Cracking rate increased to a relatively small degree by presence of tertiary carbon atoms.
Naphthenes	Crack at about same rate as those paraffins with similar numbers of tertiary carbon atoms. Aromatics produced, with much hydrogen transfer to unsaturates.	Crack at lower rate than normal paraffins. Aromatics produced with little hydrogen transfer to unsaturates.
Unsubstituted Aromatics	Little reaction; some condensation to biaryls.	Little reaction; some condensation to biaryls.
Alkyl Aromatics (substituents C_3 or larger)	Entire alkyl group cracked next to ring and removed as olefin. Crack at much higher rate than paraffins.	Alkyl group cracked to leave one or two carbon atoms attached to ring. Crack at lower rate than paraffins.
n-Olefins	Product similar to that from *n*-paraffins, but more olefinic.	Product similar to that from *n*-paraffins, but more olefinic.
All Olefins	Hydrogen transfer is an important reaction, especially with tertiary olefins. Crack at much higher rate than corresponding paraffins.	Hydrogen transfer is a minor reaction, with little preference for tertiary olefins. Crack at about same rate as corresponding paraffins.

It should be pointed out that thermal cracking commonly is regarded as a noncatalytic process. However, it is possible that an appreciable number of hydrocarbon molecules lose or gain a hydrogen atom at the wall of the reaction space, which then plays the part of a catalyst in producing free radicals. To retain the distinction between catalytic-cracking and thermal-cracking systems as generally understood, it may be stated that in the former, acidic or ionic catalysts are essential;[19,21,22] in the latter, catalysts are not needed, and any agents which may be operative as catalysts are definitely nonionic. There are indeed examples of accelerated or "catalyzed" free-radical-type thermal cracking which confirm this distinction, such as cracking over activated coconut charcoal.[19]

The free-radical theory of thermal cracking has been set forth by Rice and co-workers.[26,31-33] Its applicability to large paraffins has been shown by Voge and Good,[40] and its extension to other classes of petroleum hydrocarbons has been discussed by Greensfelder, Voge and Good.[19] The literature is now replete with evidence of free-radical mechanisms entering into many organic reactions. Although capable of improvement in detail, it is believed that the Rice-Kossiakoff theory constitutes the most satisfactory available explanation of the thermal cracking of hydrocarbons.

As a starting point for developing a detailed theory of catalytic cracking of specific hydrocarbons, we may write generalized simple stoichiometric equations for the decomposition of three major types of hydrocarbons found in petroleum as follows:

$$\text{Paraffin} \rightarrow \text{olefin} + \text{paraffin}$$
$$\text{Alkyl naphthene} \rightarrow \text{olefins or olefin} + \text{naphthene}$$
$$\text{Alkyl aromatic} \rightarrow \text{olefin} + \text{aromatic}$$

It is evident that in each of these cracking reactions, aliphatic olefins appear as primary products. Furthermore, the principal cracking reaction of aliphatic olefins is simply:

$$\text{Olefin} \rightarrow 2 \text{ or more olefins}$$

Both stoichiometrically and mechanistically, the cracking of alkyl naphthenes to cycloolefins, of alkyl aromatics to alkenyl aromatics, and of olefins to diolefins (all with simultaneous production of paraffins) also may occur. Diolefins and alkenyl aromatics are extremely reactive and are, therefore, difficult to isolate; their presence usually results in increased formation of coke on the cracking catalyst.

The common appearance of olefins in these primary, stoichiometric dissociation reactions provides an approach to the concept of an important reaction intermediate, identical with that postulated for the low-temperature, acid-catalyzed association reactions, namely, a carbonium ion formed by the simple addition of a proton, H^+, to an olefin. Therefore the mechanism and energetics of the reaction,

olefin + proton → alkyl carbonium ion

will be considered next.

Energetics of Ionic Reactions of Hydrocarbons

Recent data of Stevenson[36,37] for the ionization potentials of alkyl radicals (to alkyl carbonium ions) have been combined with basic thermochemical values (see Table 6) to give the proton affinities, shown in Table 2, of the most important olefins pertinent to the mechanism of

TABLE 2. PROTON AFFINITIES OF OLEFINS
Olefin + Proton → Alkyl Carbonium Ion
$C_nH_{2n}(g) + H^+(g) \rightarrow C_nH_{2n+1}^+(g)$; $\Delta H°_{298}$, Kcal/mole

Olefin	Carbonium Ion	Proton Affinity*
C_2H_4	$C_2H_5^+$	-153
C_3H_6	$n\text{-}C_3H_7^+$	-165
C_3H_6	$s\text{-}C_3H_7^+$	-181
$1\text{-}C_4H_8$	$n\text{-}C_4H_9^+$	-163
$1\text{-}C_4H_8$	$s\text{-}C_4H_9^+$	-189
$2\text{-}cis\text{-}C_4H_8$	$s\text{-}C_4H_9^+$	$\left.\begin{array}{c} \\ \end{array}\right\} -187$
$2\text{-}trans\text{-}C_4H_8$	$s\text{-}C_4H_9^+$	
$iso\text{-}C_4H_8$	$iso\text{-}C_4H_9^+$	-166
$iso\text{-}C_4H_8$	$t\text{-}C_4H_9^+$	-196
†$1\text{-}C_nH_{2n}$	$n\text{-}C_nH_{(2n+1)}^+$	-165
$1\text{-}C_nH_{2n}$	$s\text{-}C_nH_{(2n+1)}^+$	-190
$m\text{-}cis\text{-}C_nH_{2n}$	$m\text{-}C_nH_{(2n+1)}^+$	$\left.\begin{array}{c} \\ \end{array}\right\} -188$
$m\text{-}trans\text{-}C_nH_{2n}$	$m\text{-}C_nH_{(2n+1)}^+$	
$2\text{-}Me\text{-}1\text{-}C_nH_{2n}$	$2\text{-}Me\text{-}1\text{-}C_nH_{(2n+1)}^+$	-166
$2\text{-}Me\text{-}1\text{-}C_nH_{2n}$	$2\text{-}Me\text{-}2\text{-}C_nH_{(2n+1)}^+$	-201
$2\text{-}Me\text{-}2\text{-}C_nH_{2n}$	$2\text{-}Me\text{-}2\text{-}C_nH_{(2n+1)}^+$	-200
$2\text{-}Me\text{-}2\text{-}C_nH_{2n}$	$2\text{-}Me\text{-}3\text{-}C_nH_{(2n+1)}^+$	-190

* Values rounded to nearest whole number.
† For this section of table, n is equal to or greater than 5.

catalytic cracking. It is to be borne in mind that such values relating to normal and isobutyl ions, and to all C_5 and higher ions, have been extrapolated from experimental data on other ions and radicals by semi-empirical methods employing applicable information on related structures. It is believed that the extrapolated values are reliable to ± 3 or 4 Kcal/mole.

These and subsequent energy data as applied in this chapter all relate to heat of reaction, $\Delta H°_{298}$. The lack of entropy data precludes the systematic establishment of free energies, $\Delta F°_{298} = \Delta H°_{298} - T\Delta S°_{298}$, which are the truly desired values. The many remarkable parallelisms between $\Delta H°_{298}$ values and rates and modes of reactions provide the justification for their use. Similarly, all heat values relate to gaseous ions; their energies (and entropies) of solvation, or fixation on a catalyst, are not taken into account. It is to be understood that the strongly polarized nature of carbonium ions, their large energies of separation into an olefin and a proton, and their large energies of combination with a hydride ion lead to the view that their negative partners must reside in their close vicinity even at the moment of reaction.

From the data in Table 2, it is evident that large differences exist in the heats of reaction to form different carbonium ions from the same olefin, thus:

Olefin	Carbonium Ion	$\Delta H°_{298}$, Kcal/mole
Propene	n-Propyl	-165
	sec-Propyl	-181
Butene-1	n-Butyl	-163
	sec-Butyl	-189
Isobutylene	Isobutyl	-166
	$tert$-Butyl	-196
2-Methylbutene-2	sec-Isoamyl	-190
	$tert$-Amyl	-200

Such energy values indicate the preferred formation of secondary versus normal ions by margins of 15 to 25 Kcal/mole, and of tertiary versus secondary ions (from the same structure) by about 10 Kcal/mole. These values, combined where necessary with the heats of formation of the parent olefins, lead to useful information on the heats of isomerization of carbonium ions, as shown in Table 3. These energy values remain

TABLE 3. ENERGIES OF ISOMERIZATION OF CARBONIUM IONS
(For $C_nH_{2n+1}^+(g)$)

Isomerization Reaction	$\Delta H°_{298}$, Kcal/mole*
n-$C_3H_7^+ \rightarrow s$-$C_3H_7^+$	-16.0
n-$C_4H_9^+ \rightarrow s$-$C_4H_9^+$	-26.0
n-$C_4H_9^+ \rightarrow t$-$C_4H_9^+$	-36.5
n-$C_4H_9^+ \rightarrow i$-$C_4H_9^+$	$-\ 6.5$
i-$C_4H_9^+ \rightarrow t$-$C_4H_9^+$	-30.0
s-$C_4H_9^+ \rightarrow t$-$C_4H_9^+$	-10.5
i-$C_4H_9^+ \rightarrow s$-$C_4H_9^+$	-19.5
n-$C_5H_{11}^+ \rightarrow s$-$C_5H_{11}^+$	-25.0
n-$C_5H_{11}^+ \rightarrow t$-$C_5H_{11}^+$	-39.5
n-$C_5H_{11}^+ \rightarrow i$-$C_5H_{11}^+$	$-\ 4.5$
i-$C_5H_{11}^+ \rightarrow t$-$C_5H_{11}^+$	-35.0
s-$C_5H_{11}^+ \rightarrow t$-$C_5H_{11}^+$	-14.5
i-$C_5H_{11}^+ \rightarrow s$-$C_5H_{11}^+$	-20.5

* Values rounded to nearest 0.5 Kcal/mole.

The energy values shown above for C_5 carbonium ions apply rather closely to larger ions of equivalent structures.

about the same for increasingly large olefins and carbonium ions, namely, those above C_4 or C_5 as indicated in Tables 2 and 3. Hence, a large olefin such as *n*-hexadecene-1 (cetene) would tend to add a proton almost exclusively at the terminal carbon atom to yield a secondary hexadecyl ion.

Assessing these groups of data as a whole, it is seen that: (1) a large driving force exists for the immediate production of secondary rather than primary carbonium ions from straight-chain alpha olefins; (2) tertiary carbonium ions are especially favored over primary ions in the case of branched olefins of suitable structure; and (3) primary ions will isomerize to secondary or tertiary, and secondary ions to tertiary wherever possible.

Since these energy differences are much less marked in free-radical reactions, the influence of the specific structure of the parent molecule generally is greater in catalytic than in thermal cracking, in terms of both rate and mode of the initial decomposition into primary fragments. However, in viewing broadly catalytic and thermal cracking in this latter respect, the extensive secondary reactions of olefins in ionic systems may be taken into account, in anticipation of later discussion. So many rearrangements of product olefins occur in catalytic cracking that the net result is to superimpose an equilibrium mixture of the products of reactions of olefins upon the primary products of the cracking reactions. This makes the final hydrocarbon mixture to a considerable degree independent of the structure of the parent molecules. Thus, the presence of large amounts of olefin from the cracking of any of the major petroleum hydrocarbon classes, as previously postulated, provides a reservoir of material that can and does react in such a manner as to obscure at least partially the original effects of structure that control the primary decomposition steps. The secondary reactions of olefins are much less marked in free-radical systems, so that a seeming paradox is observed, namely, that the final products of catalytic cracking, especially those derived from petroleum fractions, frequently appear to be less dependent upon the nature of the original structures in the parent material than do those of thermal cracking.

In exact parallelism with the mechanism of proton addition to olefins, a carbonium ion may unite with an olefin to form a new, larger carbonium ion, thus:

$$R^+ + H_2C{=}CH_2 \rightarrow R{-}CH_2{-}CH_2{}^+$$

This type of reaction is an essential step in the low-temperature acid-catalyzed polymerization of olefins and alkylation of olefins with paraffins. In accordance with the energy differences between isomeric forms of carbonium ions, shown in Table 3, the product ion shown above appears to isomerize immediately, usually via a simple proton shift, to a secondary ion, as follows:

$$R—CH_2—CH_2{}^+ \rightarrow R—\underset{+}{CH}—CH_3$$

Therefore, the over-all reaction may be written

$$R^+ + H_2C{=}CH_2 \rightarrow R—\underset{+}{CH}—CH_3$$

Under more intense catalytic conditions, isomerization of the carbon skeleton may take place, leading to a tertiary carbonium ion.

For the present purpose of developing a theory of catalytic cracking, the simple addition of a carbonium ion to a C_3 or larger olefin to form directly a larger, secondary carbonium ion represents a fundamental mechanistic step; the reverse reaction of separating a large carbonium ion into an olefin and a smaller carbonium ion is the critical reaction step in the catalytic cracking of both paraffins and olefins.

TABLE 4. CARBONIUM ION AFFINITIES OF OLEFINS
$R_1{}^+ + \text{olefin} \rightarrow R_2{}^+; \Delta H°_{298}, \text{Kcal/mole}*$

Olefin, C_nH_{2n}	Carbonium Ion, R^+						
	$CH_3{}^+$	$C_2H_5{}^+$	$n\text{-}C_3H_7{}^+$	$s\text{-}C_3H_7{}^+$	$n\text{-}C_4H_9{}^+$	$s\text{-}C_4H_9{}^+$	$tert\text{-}C_4H_9{}^+$
C_2H_4, Reaction 1	-69.5	-35.0	-22.5	-8.5	-25.0	0.0	$+7.5$
C_2H_4, Reaction 2	-85.5	-61.0	-47.5	-33.5	-50.0	-25.0	-17.5
C_3H_6, Reaction 3	-90.5	-59.5	-45.0	-30.5	-47.0	-22.0	-14.5
1-C_4H_8, Reaction 4	-92.0	-60.0	-45.0	-31.0	-47.5	-22.0	-14.5
i-C_4H_8, Reaction 5	-103.0	-71.0	-56.0	-42.0	-58.5	-33.0	-24.0

Reaction 1: $R^+ + C_2H_4 \rightarrow R—CH_2—CH_2{}^+$

Reaction 2: $R^+ + C_2H_4 \rightarrow R—\underset{+}{CH}—CH_3$

Reaction 3: $R^+ + C_3H_6 \rightarrow R—CH_2—\underset{+}{CH}—CH_3$

Reaction 4: $R^+ + 1\text{-}C_4H_8 \rightarrow R—CH_2—\underset{+}{CH}—CH_2—CH_3$

Reaction 5: $R^+ + i\text{-}C_4H_8 \rightarrow R—CH_2—\underset{+}{\overset{\overset{\displaystyle CH_3}{|}}{C}}—CH_3$

Values for Reaction 4 may be applied generally to higher normal alpha-olefins reacting with carbonium ions according to the equation:

$$R^+ + 1\text{-}C_nH_{2n} \rightarrow R—CH_2—\underset{+}{CH}—(CH_2)_{n-3}—CH_3$$

* Values rounded to nearest 0.5 Kcal/mole.

To portray the energy values associated with this type of reaction, the carbonium-ion affinities of several important olefins with respect to a series of carbonium ions are shown in Table 4. These figures were calculated from the fundamental data given in Tables 2, 5, and 6. The energy values corresponding to the reverse reactions, representing catalytic cracking, are obtained by reversal of the algebraic signs in Table 4 (reaction 2 excepted, since an additional isomerization step is included therein).

Mechanism of Catalytic Cracking

With these considerations set forth, it is appropriate to examine more closely the fundamental reaction of catalytic cracking, namely, the severance of a single carbon-carbon bond, $C:C$, according to the ionic split,

$$C:C \rightarrow C: + C$$

Specifically, the cracking of simple normal alpha-olefins will be exemplified by that of n-hexadecene-1. In the presence of an acidic cracking catalyst (see Ref.[22] for a recent summary of cracking catalyst chemistry), the first step will be the addition of a proton to the terminal carbon atom to form a secondary alkyl ion,

$$\begin{array}{c} H \quad H \quad H \quad H \quad H \\ HC-C-C-C-C(CH_2)_{10}CH_3, \qquad \text{or,} \qquad 2\text{-}C_{16}H_{33}{}^+ \\ H \quad + \quad H \quad H \end{array}$$

It is seen from the abbreviated structural formula that the simplest possible carbon-carbon bond scission must be

$$\begin{array}{c} H \quad H \quad H \quad H \quad H \\ HC-C-C-C-C(CH_2)_{10}CH_3 \rightarrow \end{array} \quad \begin{array}{c} H \quad H \quad H \\ HC-C=C \end{array} + \begin{array}{c} H \quad H \\ HC-C(CH_2)_{10}CH_3, \end{array}$$

since no C—H bonds need be broken, and a stable molecule of propene is formed. It also conforms to the reaction,

$$C:C \rightarrow C: + C$$

since the two electrons become attached to the left carbon atom and then move into the C_mH_{2m} fragment to form an ethylenic double bond. The right carbon atom, carrying a positive charge, becomes the terminal carbon atom of the new carbonium ion, n-$C_{13}H_{27}{}^+$. It will be noted that carbon-carbon bond severance takes place in the beta-position relative to the positively charged carbon atom. This important mode of reaction is generally termed "beta fission."

The energy required for this step of the cracking reaction is equal to the heat of combination of the primary tridecyl ion, n-$C_{13}H_{27}{}^+$, with propene. From Table 4, this amounts to $+47$ Kcal/mole, using the value for n-$C_4H_9^+$ in combination with C_3H_6 and reversing the sign. Finally, the primary tridecyl ion should isomerize rapidly to a secondary ion with a reaction heat of -25 Kcal/mole, as shown in Table 3 for n-C_5 $\rightarrow$ s-C_5. The net heat required for these two steps of the cracking reaction is $+22$ Kcal/mole. The subsequent successive fragmentations of the tridecyl ion, $C_{13}H_{27}^+$, determines the product distribution pattern of the cracking of normal olefins. This series of reactions will be presented below as part of the description of the general cracking pattern of all normal aliphatic molecules.

TABLE 5. FORMATION OF CARBONIUM IONS FROM PARAFFINS, WITH SUPPLEMENTARY DATA

(All energy values in Kcal/mole, $\Delta H°_{298}$)

Parent Paraffins C_nH_{2n+2}	Corresponding Olefins C_nH_{2n}		Heat of Reaction:[†] $C_nH_{2n+2} \rightarrow C_nH_{2n+1}^+ + H^-$		
	Structure	Heat of Hydrogenation[35]	Type of Carbonium Ion		
			Primary	Secondary	Tertiary
CH_4	—	—	315.5	—	—
C_2H_6	C=C	-32.732	280.5	—	—
C_3H_8	C=C—C	-29.699	265.5	249.5	—
n-C_4H_{10}	C=C—C—C	-30.092	268.0	241.5	—
	c-C—C=C—C	-28.450	—	}241.5	—
	t-C—C=C—C	-27.407	—		—
i-C_4H_{10}	C=C—C (with C branch)	-28.109	263.0	—	233.0
n-C_5H_{12}	C=C—C—C—C	-30.00	266.0	241.0	—
	c-C—C=C—C—C	-28.29	—	}241.0	—
	t-C—C=C—C—C	-27.41	—		—
i-C_5H_{12}	C=C—C—C (with C branch)	-28.24	263.0	—	228.0
	C—C=C—C (with C branch)	-26.75	—	237.5	227.5
n-C_6H_{14}	C=C—C—C—C—C	-30.00	266.0	241.0	—
	c-C—C=C—C—C—C	-28.40	—	}241.0	—
	t-C—C=C—C—C—C	-27.40	—		—
	c-C—C—C=C—C—C	-28.40	—	}241.0	—
	t-C—C—C=C—C—C	-27.40	—		—
2-MeC_5H_{11}	C=C—C—C—C (with C branch)	-28.10	263.0	—	228.0

Note: Values shown for production of primary, secondary and tertiary carbonium ions from n-hexane and 2-methylpentane may be applied to all higher paraffins, excepting highly branched structures containing quaternary carbon atoms.

† Values derived from Table 2 via Equation (12), Table 6, and rounded to nearest 0.5 Kcal/mole.

The cracking of normal paraffins will be considered next, using the specific example of n-hexadecane. As has been stated, the reaction intermediate should be an ion containing one less hydrogen atom than the parent paraffin; therefore, the intermediate will have the empirical formula $C_{16}H_{33}^+$, which is identical with that noted for the corresponding olefin, n-hexadecene-1. Here, however, the intermediate cannot be generated by simple addition of a proton to a double bond; rather, it is necessary to remove a hydride ion, H^-, from the parent paraffin according to the general equation,

$$C_nH_{2n+2} \rightarrow C_nH_{2n+1}^+ + H^-$$

or, specifically,

$$C_{16}H_{34} \rightarrow C_{16}H_{33}^+ + H^-$$

The energies required for this type of reaction are shown in Table 5, under the heading "Heat of Reaction," and have been computed from the fundamental thermodynamic data shown in Tables 5 and 6 and the

TABLE 6. BASIC THERMOCHEMICAL VALUES; $\Delta H°_{298}$

(1) 1 electron-volt/molecule = 23.06 kcal/mole

(2) H_2 (g) $\rightarrow$ 2H (g); 4.48 e.v. = 103.3 kcal/mole

(3) H (g) $\rightarrow$ H^+ (g) + e; 13.60 e.v. = 313.6 kcal/mole

(4) H (g) + $e \rightarrow$ H^- (g); −0.7 e.v. = −16.1 kcal/mole

(5) H_2 (g) = H^+ (g) + H^- (g); 17.38 e.v. = 400.8 kcal/mole = (2) + (3) + (4)

(6) $nC + nH_2 \rightarrow C_nH_{2n}$; heat of formation of olefin[35]

(7) $nC + (n + 1)H_2 \rightarrow C_nH_{2n+2}$; heat of formation of paraffin[35]

(8) $C_nH_{2n} + H_2 \rightarrow C_nH_{2n+2}$; heat of hydrogenation of olefin = (7) − (6)

(9) $C_nH_{2n+2} \rightarrow C_nH_{2n+1} + H$; dissociation energy of paraffin

(10) $C_nH_{2n+1} \rightarrow C_nH_{2n+1}^+ + e$; ionization potential of alkyl radical

(11) $C_nH_{2n} + H^+ \rightarrow C_nH_{2n+1}^+$; proton affinity of olefin =
$$(8) + (9) + (10) - (2) - (3)$$

(12) $C_nH_{2n+1}^+ + H^- \rightarrow C_nH_{2n+2}$; hydride ion affinity of carbonium ion =
$$(8) - (5) - (11)$$

(13) $nC + (n + \frac{1}{2})H_2 \rightarrow C_nH_{2n+1}^+ + e$; heat of formation of carbonium ion =
$$\frac{1}{2}(2) + (3) + (6) + (11)$$

(14) $C_mH_{2m} + C_nH_{2n+1}^+ \rightarrow C_{m+n}H_{2(m+n+\frac{1}{2})}^+$; carbonium ion affinity of olefin
$$= (13)_{m+n} - (6)_m - (13)_n$$

Note: All energy values relate to gaseous state, assuming "perfect gas" laws.

proton affinities of olefins given in Table 2. It will be noted that 241.0 Kcal/mole must be supplied to sever a hydride ion from any secondary position in n-hexadecane. This energy requirement is so high that the hydride ion transfer reaction,

$$R^+ + C_nH_{2n+2} \rightarrow RH + C_nH_{2n+1}^+$$

must be invoked by way of explanation. Assuming the availability of a small alkyl ion such as s-propyl ion in the system, we may write,

$$s\text{-}C_3H_7^+ + n\text{-}C_{16}H_{34} \rightarrow C_3H_8 + s\text{-}C_{16}H_{33}^+$$

From the heats of reaction in Table 5, it is seen that this reaction will proceed with a driving force of 249.5 − 241.0 or 8.5 Kcal/mole. It is evident from Table 5 that a primary hexadecyl ion is not likely to be formed in this example of hydride-ion transfer, since this would require an endothermic heat of reaction of 266.0 − 249.5 or 16.5 Kcal/mole.

The presence of an available alkyl ion, such as s-propyl, must be explained next. In general, it seems reasonable to assume that a small amount of thermal cracking or oxidation may take place in a cracking system initially containing only saturates, thus leading to the formation of olefins. These, in turn, will rapidly react with the acidic cracking catalyst to form carbonium ions, R^+, which will then initiate the hydride-ion transfer reaction shown above, thereby producing the required carbonium ions from paraffins. Proof for the hydride-ion transfer mechanism between tertiary structures in low-temperature acid-catalyzed systems can be found in the work of Bartlett.[1] Brewer and Greensfelder[5] have established the exchange of secondary hydride ion for tertiary halide ion in similar systems, thus extending the mechanism to include important structures such as normal paraffins and the unsubstituted naphthenes, cyclopentane and cyclohexane. Additional evidence is provided by experiments upon acid-catalyzed hydrogen-deuterium interchange- and isomerization reactions of small paraffins by Beeck,[2,3,29,30,38,42] Oblad,[24] and Hansford.[23]

Cracking of Paraffins and Olefins. Upon these foundations, a detailed mechanism for the catalytic cracking of a representative normal paraffin, such as n-hexadecane, may be proposed. Exactly the same mechanism applies to the cracking of a normal olefin, such as n-hexadecene-1, except that the initial step comprises proton addition instead of hydride-ion transfer.

Step 1. n-Hexadecane, $C_{16}H_{34}$, reacts with a small carbonium ion, R^+, at the catalyst surface to give sec-hexadecyl carbonium ion, $s\text{-}C_{16}H_{33}^+$. In the case of n-hexadecene-1, proton addition to the terminal carbon atom would yield the same intermediate, $s\text{-}C_{16}H_{33}^+$. Furthermore, there are seven equivalent forms of $s\text{-}C_{16}H_{33}^+$, differing only in the location of the hydrogen atoms; all these forms should exist in rather even distribution, since their energy differences are relatively small.

Step 2. Cracking then takes place as shown already for n-hexadecene-1; thus, in the case of one of the seven $s\text{-}C_{16}H_{33}^+$ ions:

$$CH_3\text{—}\overset{+}{CH}\text{—}CH_2\text{—}CH_2\text{—}CH_2(CH_2)_{10}CH_3$$

$$\rightarrow CH_3\text{—}CH{=}CH_2 + \overset{+}{CH_2}\text{—}CH_2(CH_2)_{10}CH_3$$

Taking into account the much lower energies and the resulting preponderance of secondary ions in comparison with those of primary ions, we are led to the conclusion that the smallest *olefinic* fragments to be expected in catalytic cracking are propene molecules, since the beta fission of a secondary ion can produce no smaller olefin.

Step 3. The primary tridecyl ion produced in Step 2 will isomerize to a secondary tridecyl ion, thus:

$$\underset{+}{CH_2}CH_2(CH_2)_{10}CH_3 \rightarrow \underset{+}{CH_3}CH(CH_2)_{10}CH_3$$

This *s*-tridecyl ion, $C_{13}H_{27}^+$, will crack similarly to the ion $C_{16}H_{33}^+$, as shown in Step 2.

Step 4. The new, smaller ion obtained from $C_{13}H_{27}^+$ will repeat Steps 2 and 3 until a carbonium ion of so small a size is produced that it cannot yield two fragments of three or more carbon atoms each in size.

The reason has been given for considering propene to be the smallest expected olefin, but no comparable rule has been expressed with respect to the minimum size of the ionic fragment. Now, suppose that 2-amyl ion, $\underset{+}{CH_3}-CH-CH_2-CH_2-CH_3$, is the result of successive Steps 2 and 3. This ion can crack only to propene, C_3H_6, and ethyl ion, $C_2H_5^+$. Table 4, reaction 3, shows that the energy required to separate $C_2H_5^+$ from propene exceeds that required to separate *s*-$C_3H_7^+$ from propene by $59.5 - 30.5$ or 29.0 Kcal/mole. (Here, it is assumed that the isomerization of *n*-propyl ion, generated as a component of an activated complex, is so rapid that its isomerization energy may be included in the over-all energy requirement.) Therefore, it appears that under the usually imposed conditions of catalytic cracking, sufficient energy is provided to separate 2-hexyl ion into propene and *s*-$C_3H_7^+$, but not to separate 2-amyl ion into propene and $C_2H_5^+$. The *n*-propyl ion, which must first appear in the activated complex from 2-hexyl ion, would tend to recombine directly with coproduced propene unless isomerization to *s*-propyl ion occurred meanwhile to lower the energy of recombination from 45.0 to 30.5 Kcal/mole.

In summary, Table 4 shows the energies of separation of methyl and ethyl ions from olefins to be much larger than those of the secondary (and tertiary) forms of the higher ions. It is readily seen that the rule of largely excluding the formation in catalytic cracking of ionic fragments smaller than three carbon atoms has a fundamental energetic significance. Furthermore, it is clear that the over-all rule for the preferential production of C_3 or larger fragments in catalytic cracking stems from separate reasons that have been applied respectively to the olefinic and ionic fragments of the carbonium ion undergoing the cracking reaction.

Step 5. In a system comprising paraffins, the final small and relatively noncrackable carbonium ion undergoes hydride-ion transfer, as in Step 1, to yield a small paraffin and a new large carbonium ion. In the cracking of olefins, the final small carbonium ion may return a proton to the catalyst or transfer a proton to a large olefin to create a new large carbonium ion, becoming itself a small olefin in either case. This last reaction,

$$C_nH_{2n+1}{}^+ + C_mH_{2m} \rightarrow C_nH_{2n} + C_mH_{2m+1}{}^+$$

is governed by the proton affinities shown in Table 2, and may be considered to be a rather general ion-transfer reaction occurring between carbonium ions and olefins during intermediate stages of the catalytic-cracking process as well.

To illustrate the application of the proposed mechanism to the cracking of *n*-hexadecane, the experimental and calculated product distributions by carbon number are shown in Figure 1. It is to be expected that

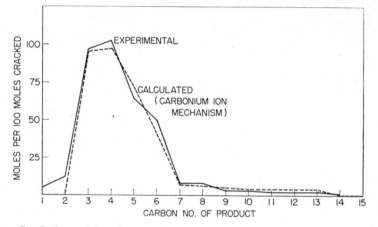

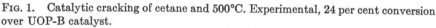

FIG. 1.   Catalytic cracking of cetane and 500°C. Experimental, 24 per cent conversion over UOP-B catalyst.

about half the original product olefins will recrack in accordance with the carbonium-ion mechanism under the applied experimental conditions; the calculated curve is based on this assumption.[19]

It has been emphasized that primary ions will isomerize to secondary or tertiary ions, and secondary ions will isomerize to tertiary ions wherever possible, in compliance with the energy relationships given in Table 3. For simplicity, the isomerization of parent or intermediate ions to tertiary ions during cracking was omitted in describing the stepwise mechanism. It is, however, an important reaction, since some 50 or 60 moles of isobutane and isobutene, aside from other isoaliphatics, are formed per 100 moles of *n*-hexadecane cracked (Ref.,[19] Table XI, Runs C-614, C-579, C-578).

This isomerization phenomenon strengthens the argument that the smallest olefinic fragments from catalytic cracking should be C_3 or larger. For example, the smallest olefin obtainable from a tertiary carbonium ion is isobutylene, thus:

$$\underset{+}{C-\overset{\overset{\displaystyle C}{|}}{C}}-C-C-C-C \rightarrow C-\overset{\overset{\displaystyle C}{|}}{C}=C + \underset{+}{C-C-C}$$

If the point of branching is one carbon atom further along the chain, the smallest olefin obtainable then becomes 2-methylbutene, thus:

$$C-\underset{+}{\overset{\overset{\displaystyle C}{|}}{C}}-C-C-C-C \rightarrow C=\overset{\overset{\displaystyle C}{|}}{C}-C-C + \underset{+}{C-C-C}$$

In fact, some 30 to 40 moles of iso-C_5-structures are found per 100 moles of n-hexadecane cracked,[19] and examination of the curves of Figure 1 shows the great predominance of C_3, C_4 and C_5 products.

Another interesting point is the already suggested isomerization of the *ionic fragment* during cracking, thus:

$$\underset{+}{C-C}-C-C-C-C-C \rightarrow (C-C=C + \underset{+}{C}-C-C-C)$$

$$\rightarrow (C-C=C + C-\underset{+}{C}-C-C) \rightarrow C-C=C + C-\overset{\overset{\displaystyle C}{|}}{\underset{+}{C}}-C$$

where the brackets indicate the components of successive forms of an "activated complex." From Table 4, the energies of separation of the two partners in the two activated complexes and the final reaction products as shown are $+47.0$, $+22.0$ and $+14.5$ Kcal/mole, respectively. Therefore, together with the energy release engendered by the isomerization of the ionic fragment, the final separation of the olefinic and ionic fragments also is assisted. In fact, the i/n butane and i/n pentane ratios are about 2 in the cracking of n-hexadecane under conditions[19] leading to little "hydrogen transfer" (discussed later), suggesting that much isomerization of the ionic fragments did occur. Theoretical equilibrium iso/normal ratios at 500°C are 0.49 and 1.97 for the butanes and pentanes, respectively. The corresponding C_4 and C_5 olefins are both close to thermodynamic equilibrium values. This behavior leads to the speculation that simple splitting of a straight-chain carbonium ion to olefinic and ionic fragments typified by

$$C-C=C \quad \text{and} \quad \underset{+}{C}-C-C-C$$

may result generally in recombination to regenerate the parent ion, whereas isomerization of the ionic fragment to

$$\underset{+}{C}-\underset{+}{C}-C-C \quad \text{or} \quad C-\underset{\underset{+}{|}}{\overset{\overset{C}{|}}{C}}-C$$

will lead generally to a permanent separation of the fragments. This view is in accord with the fact that no isomers of parent paraffins are found ordinarily in the catalytic cracking of paraffins.

In contrast to this behavior, straight-chain olefins can be converted readily to isomers of the parent molecule in the presence of a cracking catalyst, presumably through the same intermediate ionic form as that obtained from an equivalent paraffin by removal of a hydride ion. Since the intermediates are identical, a seemingly paradoxical situation arises in catalytic-cracking systems wherein parent olefins are isomerized[9,16] but parent paraffins are not.[15]

Qualitatively, it can be said that, in general, olefins can be isomerized extensively over weaker acid-type catalysts or under much milder conditions than those required for either the isomerization or cracking of paraffins. Of much importance, the experimental data show that olefins exposed to the higher temperatures and longer residence times required for paraffin cracking will crack rather than isomerize.[9,16] It is concluded that the high degree of activation required for the production of carbonium ions from normal paraffins, together with the high temperatures usually imposed, lead to a specific rate-ratio of reactions which greatly favors cracking over isomerization. Recently, Oblad and co-workers[28] have examined two normal paraffins and several isoparaffins in these respects at rather low temperatures, namely, 100 to 250°C. Under conditions giving little or no reaction for the normal compounds, paraffins with tertiary carbon atoms isomerize and crack extensively, the ratios of these reactions varying widely according to molecular weight and structure. These results demonstrate a special case of paraffin isomerization under greatly altered conditions.

This outline of the relationship of isomerization and cracking reactions illustrates a set of characteristics of the catalytic cracking system which offers an opportunity for much interesting research to elucidate the several factors responsible for the observed behavior. A close relationship between the isomerization and cracking of paraffins also has been observed in numerous studies of low-temperature, acid-catalyzed reactions, using strong catalytic agents such as aluminum chloride or bromide.[8]

Cracking of Naphthenes. The cracking of naphthenes can be viewed in much the same way as the cracking of paraffins, insofar as the initiatory step is concerned, since both types of hydrocarbons are saturated. However, it is interesting to observe that nearly all naphthenes found in petroleum necessarily contain tertiary carbon atoms because of alkyl substitution on the naphthene ring. From Table 5 it is seen that some 13.0 Kcal/mole less energy is required to remove a tertiary compared with a secondary hydride ion from C_5 and higher paraffins. Consequently, substituted naphthenes might be expected to crack more readily than normal paraffins, which they do.[17,18] If equivalent chain branching is introduced into the paraffinic molecule, the cracking rates of paraffins and naphthenes of equal carbon number become similar, as in the case of decahydronaphthalene and 2,7-dimethyloctane.[13]

Substituted naphthenes may crack either in the side chain or the ring. Several combinations of products may occur as the result of one fragmentation of a monocyclic alkyl naphthene, principally (a) two olefins, (b) an olefin and a naphthene, (c) a paraffin and a cycloolefin, and (d) a paraffin and an alkenyl naphthene. The products of cracking bicyclic polyalkyl naphthenes, which are expected to be important constituents of petroleum fractions suitable for catalytic-cracking operations, are more complex because of the double-ring structure, especially in the case of condensed rings.

Cracking of Aromatics. The catalytic cracking of aromatic hydrocarbons proceeds with a high degree of specificity. The aromatic nucleus itself is virtually inert to fragmentation, so that the cracking reaction, in terms of carbon-carbon bond breaking, is confined almost entirely to substituted alkyl and cycloalkyl groups and to saturated (polymethylenic) rings condensed with the aromatic ring system.

The outstanding characteristic of the cracking of substituted aromatics is that the primary point of cleavage is at the point of attachment of the substituent to the ring, thus:

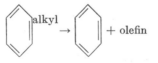

This reaction is exactly the reverse of the "alkylation" of aromatics with olefins, a well-known low-temperature acid-catalyzed reaction, which is now the subject of renewed interest with respect to mechanism, especially with Friedel-Crafts catalysts.[6] Indeed, the general theory of substitution of aromatics in acidic environment is related mechanistically to the catalytic cracking of aromatic hydrocarbons.

In light of this relationship, it follows that the same dilemmas as to mechanism of the aromatic-olefin alkylation and aromatic substitution reactions are met with in catalytic cracking. Briefly, the two most favored mechanisms based on experimental cracking results and circumstantial evidence drawn by analogy from other systems are:

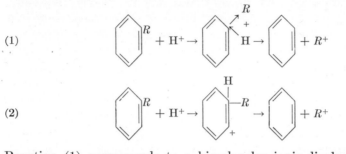

(1)

(2)

Reaction (1) corresponds to a bimolecular ionic-displacement reaction and reaction (2) corresponds formalistically to the mechanism of cracking of an olefin. Because of the unique properties of the benzene ring, perhaps best expressed as strong mutual interaction, within the coplanar ring, of all six carbon atoms and six pi electrons to create a molecular structure exceptional amongst hydrocarbons, it may be unwise to force exclusively upon the cracking of aromatics a pattern (2) derived from the behavior of aliphatic structures. In summary, it may be stated that reaction (1) represents a simple competition of proton and carbonium ion for a place on the aromatic ring, whereas reaction (2) expresses the view that a strong proton-aromatic (or catalyst-aromatic) complex is formed prior to splitting off the carbonium ion.

The difference between catalytic and thermal cracking, or, more specifically, between ionic and thermal mechanisms, is illustrated most strikingly in the case of aromatics. Indeed, it has been pointed out[19] that the catalytic and thermal mechanisms of the cracking of aliphatics bear a certain formalistic resemblance to each other, a prime distinction residing in the isomerization of the ionic intermediate. This is not the case in the cracking of alkyl aromatics, wherein the chief point of bond breaking is next to the ring in catalytic cracking and at least one carbon atom removed from the ring in thermal cracking, as shown below for *n*-propylbenzene.

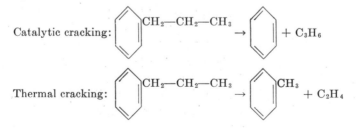

Catalytic cracking:

Thermal cracking:

Data have been provided by Szwarc[39] on the energies of the several bonds in substituted aromatics, and for the case of *n*-propylbenzene the bond-dissociation energies are as follows, in Kcal/mole.

$$\underset{\alpha}{\overset{88^*}{|}} CH_2 \underset{\beta}{\overset{62}{—}} CH_2 \underset{\gamma}{\overset{79^*}{—}} CH_3$$

The thermal cracking of *n*-propylbenzene very likely is represented by free-radical removal of a hydrogen atom from the methyl group, followed by "beta" cracking to benzyl radical and ethylene, with chain propagation sponsored by attack of benzyl on the parent structure to give toluene and a new radical. Parenthetically, the thermal-cracking possibilities of aromatics bear much resemblance energetically to those of certain aliphatics if the benzyl radical be viewed as an energetic analog of the allyl radical in the structure represented below, using data from Ref.[39]

$$CH_2 = CH \underset{\alpha}{\overset{87^*}{—}} CH_2 \underset{\beta}{\overset{60.5}{—}} CH_2 \underset{\gamma}{\overset{79^*}{—}} CH_3$$

The catalytic-cracking behavior is entirely different and that of aromatics appears to depend upon the unique electronic properties of the benzene ring and their exceptional response to an ionic environment, since the low homolytic bond-dissociation energy of the beta-bond has no perceptible influence on the catalytic cracking of alkyl-substituted aromatics.

The results of cracking catalytically representative hydrocarbons of the more important hydrocarbon classes have been reported extensively in the literature (see[13-19,41] and further references cited therein) and need not be repeated here. Excellent summarizing reviews by Haensel[20] and Hansford[21] have also appeared, with extensive bibliographies, to which the reader may be directed.

Before proceeding to consider some of the important secondary (non-cracking) reactions encountered in catalytic-cracking systems, a summary of the fragmentation patterns of the important hydrocarbon classes with respect to the important gas components[14] is presented in Table 7. These gaseous products range from 12 to 86 per cent weight of the total feeds reacted. The clean-cut severance of substituents from the benzene ring is portrayed especially well by the results with the two butylbenzenes. Of the nonaromatic types, olefins are cracked the most readily; simple normal olefins, free from structural complexities, show the highest selectivity of cracking to C_3 and C_4 gas components. Normal paraffins, which are much more resistant to cracking than olefins, and naphthenes, which

* Estimated.

TABLE 7. COMPOSITION OF GAS FROM CATALYTIC CRACKING OF PURE HYDROCARBONS

	Gaseous Components, Wt %* by Carbon Number			
	C_1	C_2	C_3	C_4
n-Paraffins				
Heptane	5	16	42	37
Dodecane	9	9	42	40
Hexadecane	2	6	45	47
Tetracosane	5	5	40	50
n-Olefins				
Octenes	1	2	30	67
Hexadecene-1	5	2	29	64
Naphthenes				
Isopropylcyclohexane	8	5	35	52
Amylcyclohexanes	10	7	36	47
Triethylcyclohexanes	4	11	37	48
Amyldecalins	9	8	36	47
Aromatics				
Isopropylbenzene	4	4	88	4
sec-Butylbenzene	—	1	7	92
tert-Butylbenzene	—	1	4	95

* Hydrogen-free basis.

Conditions: One atmosphere; silica-alumina-zirconia catalyst, Universal Oil Products Co., Type B; one-hour process period, except last two. n-Paraffins and naphthenes, 500°C and 13 to 14 moles/liter/hour; n-olefins, 400°C and ca 7 moles/liter/hour. Aromatics 12 to 14 moles/liter/hour; isopropylbenzene 500°C, others at 400°C and ¾-hour process period.

generally have many alternative paths of cracking, show definitely less selectivity under the applied conditions.

Secondary Reactions in Catalytic Cracking

A number of important reactions occur in most catalytic-cracking systems, aside from the primary cracking reactions requiring the severance of carbon-carbon bonds as the essential step. The more important secondary reactions are listed below and are divided into two principal classes, (1) those requiring carbon-hydrogen bond reactions alone, and

Reacting Bonds	Secondary Reactions	Amenable Hydrocarbon Types
C—H	Double-bond shift	Olefins
	Double-bond geometrical isomerization	Olefins
	Hydrogen transfer	To olefins, from divers donors
	Dehydrogenation to aromatics	Cyclohexane naphthenes
	Self-saturation	Olefins
Both C—C and C—H	Polymerization	Olefins
	Condensation	Aromatics
	Aromatization	Olefins
	Skeletal isomerization	Olefins; bicyclic naphthenes and naphthene-aromatics

(2) those in which both carbon-hydrogen and carbon-carbon bonds participate. The chief hydrocarbon types amenable to the several secondary reactions are specified.

The mechanisms of these secondary reactions are described below, together with some discussion of interesting interrelationships.

(1) *Double-Bond Shift.*

$$C=C-C-C + H^+ \rightarrow C-\underset{+}{C}-C-C \rightarrow C-C=C-C + H^+$$

(2) *Double-Bond Geometrical Isomerization.*

$$\underset{}{\overset{H \quad H}{C-C=C-C}} + H^+ \rightarrow \underset{+ \quad H}{\overset{H \quad H}{C-C-C-C}} \rightarrow \underset{}{\overset{H}{C-C=C-C}} + H^+$$

(3) *Hydrogen Transfer.* Hydrogen transfer is simply the summation of two reactions discussed extensively earlier in the chapter, namely, (1) capture of a proton by an olefin, to produce a carbonium ion, followed by (2) hydride-ion transfer from any neutral hydrocarbon molecule, to produce the paraffin corresponding to the original olefin.

In general, hydrogen transfer may be represented as follows:

$$\overset{CH_3}{\underset{}{H_3C-\overset{|}{C}=CH_2}} + H^+ \rightarrow \overset{CH_3}{\underset{+}{H_3C-\overset{|}{C}-CH_3}}$$

$$\overset{CH_3}{\underset{+}{H_3C-\overset{|}{C}-CH_3}} + R H \rightarrow \overset{CH_3}{\underset{H}{H_3C-\overset{|}{C}-CH_3}} + R^+$$

The fate of the carbonium ion, R^+, derived from RH as above, merits special attention. Clearly, since a proton was supplied by the system, a proton must be returned ultimately to it. Several notable alternatives should be considered as follows:

(1) If RH is a small paraffin, R^+ will split to a small olefin and a proton.

(2) If RH is a large paraffin, R^+ will crack to yield finally a small carbonium ion, R^+, which can split to a small olefin and a proton.

(3) If RH is an olefin, R^+ will split to a diolefin and a proton. The diolefin will react on the catalyst to yield considerable coke. This reaction is very likely one source of the copious amounts of coke which may accompany the "self-saturation" reaction of olefins.

(4) If RH is a naphthene, R^+ may crack in analogy to (2). More interestingly, it may return a proton to the system and become a cyclo-olefin. If this process be repeated twice more, six atoms of hydrogen will have been lost, and the naphthene will then have become an aromatic.

However, this is generally observed only in the case of C_9 or higher naphthenes, so that such reaction to aromatics may be concomitant with simple cracking of side chains. The necessary isomerization, if the parent naphthene was a substituted cyclopentane, is easily possible after it reaches the cycloolefinic state. A variant of this reaction is the conversion of tetrahydronaphthalene or methylindan to naphthalene by loss of four hydrogen atoms via successive hydrogen-transfer reactions.

(5) If RH is an aromatic, an interesting application of carbonium-ion chemistry comes to view. According to Hustrulid, Kusch and Tate,[25] no more than 318 Kcal/mole are demanded for the reaction

$$C_6H_6 \rightarrow C_6H_5^+ + H^-$$

Only methyl carbonium ion, CH_3^+, has a comparable affinity for hydride ion, namely, 315.5 Kcal/mole; ethyl ion can only supply 280.5 Kcal/mole. Therefore any carbonium ion directly formed from an olefin cannot enter readily into hydride-ion exchange with benzene. However, there do seem to be interaromatic condensations occurring in the presence of cracking catalysts when either polymethylbenzenes or naphthalene homologs are supplied to the reactor; the presence of methyl substitution on the aromatic ring leads to a product gas rich in methane.[18] A speculative reaction sequence is presented as follows:

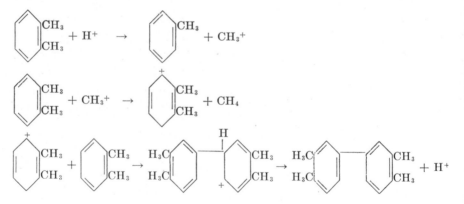

However, data of Franklin and Lumpkin[10] on the formation of benzyl carbonium ion, together with values from Table 5 and Ref.[39], lead to -40 Kcal/mole for the reaction:

Therefore an alternative and energetically preferred reaction sequence may be proposed that involves no direct attack of methyl carbonium ion on the aromatic ring to yield the observed methane.

In summary, the mechanism of hydrogen transfer explains not only the simple passage of hydrogen from a saturate to an unsaturate, but also accounts for other secondary reactions found in catalytic cracking systems and usually listed under other headings, namely:

(a) Dehydrogenation of cyclohexane naphthenes to aromatics

(b) Aromatization of cyclopentane naphthenes

(c) Self-saturation of olefins

(d) As a conjecture, the condensation of aromatics in certain cases, wherein hydrogen is eliminated as methane.

Polymerization of Olefins. As discussed earlier in connection with the energies of reaction shown in Table 4, the critical mechanistic step in the polymerization of an olefin is the addition of a carbonium ion derived from the combination of a proton and an olefin. The new carbonium ion may continue to react with monomer to form polymers until the reaction is terminated by splitting out a proton. For propene, the mechanism is:

$$H_3C-\overset{\overset{\displaystyle H}{|}}{C}=CH_2 + H^+ \rightarrow H_3C-\overset{\overset{\displaystyle H}{|}}{\underset{+}{C}}-CH_3$$

$$H_3C-\overset{\overset{\displaystyle H}{|}}{\underset{+}{C}}-CH_3 + H_3C-\overset{\overset{\displaystyle H}{|}}{C}=CH_2 \rightarrow H_3C-\overset{\overset{\displaystyle CH_3}{|}}{C}-CH_2-\overset{\overset{\displaystyle H}{|}}{\underset{+}{C}}-CH_3$$

$$\rightarrow H_3C-\overset{\overset{\displaystyle CH_3}{|}}{\underset{\underset{\displaystyle H}{|}}{C}}-CH=C-CH_3 + H^+$$

At cracking temperatures, polymerization is considerably restricted thermodynamically. Nevertheless, it can provide a mechanism by which olefins can associate and then recrack, leading to an apparent "disproportionation" and simultaneous isomerization of olefins. At temperatures between 200 and 300°C, the polymerization of butene-1 can be readily demonstrated.[41]

Aromatization. Aromatization, viewed as the conversion of hydrocarbons *other* than cyclohexane-type naphthenes to aromatics, can be observed in the case of olefins and cyclopentane-type naphthenes. In studies of the catalytic cracking of pure hydrocarbons, it was found that the high-boiling products from the cracking of various types of olefins had, as a rule, refractive indexes sufficiently high to indicate the presence of aromatics.[16] Special experiments[41] have shown that aromatics are readily produced from normal butenes. Therefore, it may be expected that aromatics may arise from the cracking of many different types of hydrocarbons, since small olefins, including butenes, are favored primary products. This is indeed the case; aromatics are found in the cracking products of paraffins such as *n*-dodecane and *n*-hexadecane,[15] olefins such as triisobutenes and cyclopentene,[16] and naphthenes such as methylcyclopentane.[17]

From this discussion, it follows that "aromatization," a significant contributor to the high octane level of catalytically cracked gasoline, may be characterized as a secondary reaction, proceeding through the polymerization or condensation of olefins produced in the cracking of a variety of parent compounds. The simple C_5 and C_6 cycloolefins, cyclopentene and cyclohexene,[16] give much aromatic material, but of relatively high boiling-range; this may be the result of the rapid polymerization or condensation of such olefins, followed by appropriate ring isomerization, hydrogen transfer, and cracking reactions.

This phase of catalytic cracking has not been given sufficient detailed study to provide a really adequate explanation of the mechanism of aromatization, even in the case of normal butenes.

Skeletal Isomerization. Isomerization (rearrangement) of the carbon atom skeleton of a hydrocarbon is a reaction of unusual interest in its relation to the cracking of a carbon skeleton. In cracking, at least one carbon-carbon bond is severed permanently; in skeletal rearrangement, a carbon-carbon bond is broken and one of the two carbon atoms involved enters into the formation of a new carbon-carbon bond. It can be shown in various ways (simple analysis of products,[41] experiments with labelled carbon atoms[2, 29]) that isomerization will proceed preponderantly intramolecularly; that is, the product molecules are composed of the very same carbon atoms as their parents. It follows that the two fragments of the parent molecule undergoing catalytic isomerization must remain, during reaction, either within each other's force fields or within the field of the catalyst, or both. Therefore, skeletal isomerization must be conducted under at least one of these two restrictive conditions. Since the reaction may be looked upon as an incipient cracking of a carbon-carbon bond, it is not surprising to find isomerization and cracking occurring side by side in many cases. If the specified conditions are not established satisfactorily, substantially only cracking and no isomerization of the parent molecule will take place, as stated earlier in the discussion of the catalytic cracking of paraffins and olefins.

In general, paraffins and many naphthenes will crack without isomerization of the parent molecule, whereas olefins will isomerize or crack in varying proportions according to conditions and molecular structure. Unsaturated naphthenes and partly hydrogenated aromatics that possess ethylenic double bonds are to be classed as olefins in this discussion and their ethylenic portions will tend to isomerize, as do those of their aliphatic relatives, subject to modification by their different molecular geometry.

However, certain saturates, such as condensed polycyclic naphthenes, have an inherent structure that imposes in an unusual manner the restriction of fragment contiguity stated above whenever one ring is cracked open. Here, the two fragments are tied to the second ring and can readily recombine to effect ring isomerization from a cyclohexane- to a cyclopentane-type ring or the reverse, as shown below.

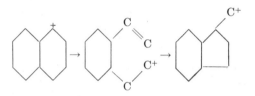

This reaction has been well demonstrated for decahydronaphthalene.[4] Condensed, partly hydrogenated aromatics without ethylenic double bonds present a similar and even simpler case, since the aromatic rings remain quite intact in catalytic-cracking systems. Here, molecules such as tetrahydronaphthalene may isomerize readily to methylindans.[4]

The Carbonium-Ion Concept

The concept of organic carbon compounds reacting by ionic mechanisms was sponsored vigorously by Whitmore[43] and has been given extensive support by many British chemists. Because of the nonionic character of most hydrocarbons and their relative inertness to electrochemical action, there has been understandable reluctance to accept the viewpoint that a hydrocarbon can split into fragments, one of which carries a positive charge, in the course of a chemical reaction.

As stated early in this chapter, the basic concept is indeed simple. A single carbon-carbon bond is comprised of two electrons. A hydrocarbon participating in any skeletal transformation must sever at least one such bond, and at that moment either the two electrons are divided evenly, or one carbon atom gets both and the other none. The energy relationships, however, are vastly different, since only 76 Kcal[39] are required to separate n-hexane into two n-propyl radicals, whereas about 260 Kcal[37] would be required to divide n-hexane into two n-propyl ions, one positive and the other negative. However, the systems discussed here do not require the large amount of energy seen to be needed to produce such a pair of ions, one positive and one negative, because the mechanism involves a preliminary step of positive-ion formation, involving proton- or hydride-ion transfer, induced by an appropriate ionic catalytic agent. Therefore, the critical step of carbon-carbon bond division results in the formation of a positive *ionic fragment* and a neutral olefinic or aromatic *molecule* from a parent carbonium ion, as shown in the divers mechanisms suggested; the data in Table 4 demonstrate the much smaller severance energy requirements for many carbonium ions in partnership with olefins than that indicated above for the disunion of *n*-hexane into a propyl ion pair.

In addition to the demonstration that ionic mechanisms are in harmony with a definite pattern of energy values, it has been stated that the existence of carbonium ions, protons and hydride ions in a free state, such as that met with in a mass spectrometer, is not contemplated in the carbonium-ion theory of organic reactions. Rather, the charged fragments are assumed to be in the close vicinity of their partners or the catalyst, or both.

Because of this close association of carbonium ions with olefins or with anions supplied by the catalyst, their mere existence is indeed difficult to establish by physical means. In the past, cryoscopic and ultraviolet spectroscopic techniques have been used to indicate the generation of carbonium ions from aromatic carbinols, as done by Newman and Deno.[27] More recently Gold and co-workers[11,12] have dissolved olefinic aromatics and polycyclic aromatics directly in 100 per cent sulfuric acid and obtained ultraviolet spectra completely different from those of the same compounds dissolved in nonionic solvents such as cyclohexane and in acetic acid, the latter being too weak to transfer a proton to the hydrocarbons tested. The ultraviolet absorption spectra of the hydrocarbons, 1,1-diphenylethylene, triphenylethylene and anthracene, dissolved in 100 per cent sulfuric acid were all closely similar. This similarity is attributed to the formation of a common ionic component in each of these molecules, namely, a diphenylmethyl carbonium ion.

Matsen and co-workers[7] reported comparable studies of 1-octene, but in this case a number of proton-donating acids were investigated with respect to a single hydrocarbon; in every case concordant ultraviolet absorption maxima were reported.

Strong evidence for the existence of ionic reaction mechanisms in hydrocarbon chemistry comes from the experimental work of Beeck and co-workers.[3,30,38,42] The interchangeability of isotopic hydrogen between sulfuric acid and isoparaffins can hardly be explained on any basis except that of interchange of catalyst deuterons and hydrocarbon protons. Furthermore, the unique part played by tertiary hydrogen, in these hydrocarbon-catalyst systems, as the seat of carbonium-ion propagation leads to the conclusion that hydride-ion transfer between carbonium ions and hydrocarbons is to be viewed as an essential step in these reaction mechanisms.

In summary, the ionic mechanism of catalytic cracking rests squarely upon the foundation laid by Whitmore in his extensive work upon the carbonium-ion reactions of olefins. Much additional support has been provided by many British chemists in their extensive study of ionic mechanisms in organic reactions; by the work of Schmerling and Bartlett relating to the alkylation of olefins with isoparaffins; by the recent publications of Brown on the Friedel-Crafts alkylation of aromatics with alkyl and aryl halides; and by the cited research of Beeck and co-workers. Physical data have been supplied through spectroscopic studies of hydrocarbon solutions in acids that were believed to generate carbonium ions and through the determination of appearance potentials of hydrocarbon ions, especially alkyl ions, in the mass spectrometer. The latter results have led to important thermodynamic data, which may be employed in a descriptive way to account for some of the unique properties of carbonium ions.

References

1. Bartlett, P. D., Condon, F. E., Schneider, A., *J. Am. Chem. Soc.*, **66,** 1531 (1944).
2. Beeck, O., Otvos, J. W., Stevenson, D. P., and Wagner, C. D., *J. Chem. Phys.*, **16,** 255 (1948).
3. Beeck, O., Otvos, J. W., Stevenson, D. P., and Wagner, C. D., *J. Chem. Phys.*, **17,** 418 (1949).
4. Bloch, H. S., and Thomas, C. L., *J. Am. Chem. Soc.*, **66,** 1589 (1944).
5. Brewer, C. P., and Greensfelder, B. S., *J. Am. Chem. Soc.*, **73,** 2257 (1951).
6. Brown, H. C., Pearsall, H. W., Eddy, L. P., Wallace, W. J., Grayson, M., and Nelson, K., *Ind. Eng. Chem.*, **45,** 1462 (1953).
7. *Chem. Eng. News*, **28,** 4552 (1950).
8. Egloff, G., Hulla, G., and Komarewsky, V. I., "Isomerization of Pure Hydrocarbons," New York, Reinhold Publishing Corp., 1942.
9. Egloff, G., Morrell, J. C., Thomas, C. L., and Bloch, H. S., *J. Am. Chem. Soc.*, **61,** 3571 (1939).
10. Franklin, J. L., and Lumpkin, H. E., *J. Chem. Phys.*, **19,** 1073 (1951).
11. Gold, V., Hawes, B. W., and Tye, F. L., *J. Chem. Soc.*, **1952,** 2167.
12. Gold, V., and Tye, F. L., *J. Chem. Soc.*, **1952,** 2172, 2181, 2184.
13. Good, G. M., Voge, H. H., and Greensfelder, B. S., *Ind. Eng. Chem.*, **39,** 1032 (1947).
14. Greensfelder, B. S., "Advances in Chemistry Series," **5,** 3 (1951).
15. Greensfelder, B. S., and Voge, H. H., *Ind. Eng. Chem.*, **37,** 514 (1945).
16. Greensfelder, B. S., and Voge, H. H., *Ind. Eng. Chem.*, **37,** 983 (1945).
17. Greensfelder, B. S., and Voge, H. H., *Ind. Eng. Chem.*, **37,** 1038 (1945).
18. Greensfelder, B. S., Voge, H. H., and Good, G. M., *Ind. Eng. Chem.*, **37,** 1168 (1945).
19. Greensfelder, B. S., Voge, H. H., and Good, G. M., *Ind. Eng. Chem.*, **41,** 2573 (1949).

20. Haensel, V., Chapter in "Advances in Catalysis and Related Subjects," Edited by W. G. Frankenburg, V. I. Komarewsky, and E. K. Rideal, Vol. 3, pp. 179–197, New York, Academic Press, Inc., 1951.
21. Hansford, R. C., Chapter in "Physical Chemistry of the Hydrocarbons," Edited by A. Farkas, Vol. II, p. 187, New York, Academic Press, Inc., 1953.
22. Hansford, R. C., Chapter in "Advances in Catalysis and Related Subjects," Edited by W. G. Frankenburg, V. I. Komarewsky, and E. K. Rideal, Vol. 4, pp. 1–30, New York, Academic Press, Inc., 1952.
23. Hansford, R. C., Waldo, P. G., Drake, L. C., and Honig, R. E., *Ind. Eng. Chem.*, **44**, 1108 (1952).
24. Hindin, S. G., Mills, G. A., and Oblad, A. G., *J. Am. Chem. Soc.*, **73**, 278 (1951).
25. Hustrulid, A., Kusch, P., and Tate, J. T., *Phys. Rev.*, **54**, 1037 (1938).
26. Kossiakoff, A., and Rice, F. O., *J. Am. Chem. Soc.*, **65**, 590 (1943).
27. Newman, M. S., and Deno, N. C., *J. Am. Chem. Soc.*, **73**, 3644 (1951).
28. Oblad, A. G., Hindin, S. G., and Mills, G. A., Division of Petroleum Chemistry, 123rd American Chemical Society Meeting, Los Angeles, California, March 1953.
29. Otvos, J. W., Stevenson, D. P., Wagner, C. D., and Beeck, O., *J. Chem. Phys.*, **16**, 745 (1948).
30. Otvos, J. W., Stevenson, D. P., Wagner, C. D., and Beeck, O., *J. Am. Chem. Soc.*, **73**, 5741 (1951).
31. Rice, F. O., *J. Am. Chem. Soc.*, **55**, 3035 (1933).
32. Rice, F. O., and Rice, K. K., "The Aliphatic Free Radicals," Baltimore, Johns Hopkins Press, 1935.
33. Rice, F. O., and Teller, E., *J. Chem. Phys.*, **6**, 489 (1938); **7**, 199 (1939).
34. Schmerling, L., *Ind. Eng. Chem.*, **45**, 1447 (1953).
35. "Selected Values of Properties of Hydrocarbons"; Circular of the National Bureau of Standards, C-461, U. S. Government Printing Office, Washington, D. C., 1947.
36. Stevenson, D. P., "Faraday Society Discussions on Hydrocarbons," **10**, 35 (1951).
37. Stevenson, D. P., *Trans. Faraday Soc.*, **49**, 867 (1953).
38. Stevenson, D. P., Wagner, C. D., Beeck, O., and Otvos, J. W., *J. Am. Chem. Soc.*, **74**, 3269 (1952).
39. Szwarc, M., *Chem. Rev.*, **47**, 171 (1950).
40. Voge, H. H., and Good, G. M., *J. Am. Chem. Soc.*, **71**, 593 (1949).
41. Voge, H. H., Good, G. M., and Greensfelder, B. S., *Ind. Eng. Chem.*, **38**, 1033 (1946).
42. Wagner, C. D., Beeck, O., Otvos, J. W., and Stevenson, D. P., *J. Chem. Phys.*, **17**, 419 (1949).
43. Whitmore, F. C., *Chem. Eng. News*, **26**, 668 (1948).

CHAPTER 28

THE EFFECTS OF THE VARIABLES IN CATALYTIC CRACKING

A. G. OBLAD, T. H. MILLIKEN, AND G. A. MILLS

Houdry Process Corporation, Linwood, Pennsylvania

This chapter discusses the process aspects of catalytic cracking from a chemical point of view. No attempt will be made to describe the commercial features of the cracking process, as that has been done adequately in other publications.[2,6,13] From the viewpoint of a chemist, the various catalytic cracking processes are all mechanical variations of the means for carrying out the same chemical reactions. Charge stocks, catalysts, and reaction conditions are generally similar in all processes. Consequently, products are similar and depend upon the important variables of the reactions involved, and only to a small degree on the apparatus in which the process is carried out in pilot-plant or commercial scale.

In catalytic cracking, heavy hydrocarbons are contacted with a catalyst at elevated temperatures and approximately atmospheric pressure. During this contact certain reactions occur to the oil vapors and to the catalyst. The purpose of this chapter will be to discuss what happens to the oil and the catalyst.

The cracking "reaction" is affected by the following variables: (1) temperature, (2) pressure, (3) contact time of oil (space velocity), and (4) contact time of catalyst (catalyst/oil ratio). Furthermore, the reactions occurring are affected by the nature of the catalyst, and the nature of the feed stock.

It is not possible to cover all possible permutations of these six important factors affecting catalytic cracking reactions in this limited discussion. Moreover, all the data required to do this are not available. Therefore, it will be necessary to hold some of these factors constant and discuss the effects of a smaller number of only the more important factors. For the most part, the discussion will be limited to a few charge stocks and one or two commercial catalysts. Later in the discussion, some effort will be made to show the major effect of changing the feed stock and changing the nature of the catalyst.

The term, catalytic cracking, describes a group of complex chemical reactions which go on simultaneously and consecutively, among which are carbon-carbon bond scission involving a heterolytic split of the molecule, isomerization (including skeletal isomerization and double-bond shifting), hydrogen transfer, dehydrogenation, cyclization, polymerization, ring fusion, etc. The principal reactions that differentiate catalytic cracking from thermal cracking are isomerization, cyclization, and hydrogen transfer. As a result of these latter three reactions, catalytic cracking produces a much more desirable gasoline product than thermal cracking.

It thus appears that catalysts important in cracking do not fulfill the classical definition of a catalyst; i.e., to speed up reactions normally occurring without a catalyst and to appear in the end unchanged. This is only an apparent anomaly, however. All the reactions that occur in catalytic cracking are obviously favorable from a free-energy standpoint. The products distribution, therefore, is largely a kinetic phenomenon and subject to the limitation of rates of reaction. Some of the possible reactions just do not occur in simple thermal cracking because the rates of reaction are too low. In bringing about these new reactions the catalyst thus performs its classical function in speeding up reactions that proceed slowly thermally. Thus, the distribution of products is a matter of the relative rates of the various reactions in the two processes. The advantage of catalytic cracking over the thermal process is that certain desirable reactions are greatly accelerated and, because of the much milder reaction conditions obtaining in the catalytic process, undesirable reactions normally occurring in thermal cracking are minimized. As a result of these factors a much better distribution of usable products is obtained. In summary, catalytic cracking shows the following advantages over thermal cracking:

(1) Lower yield of methane and ethane

(2) Larger yield of C_3- and C_4-hydrocarbons

(3) Larger yield of branched olefins and paraffins

(4) Larger yield of aromatics

(5) Lower yield of diolefins

(6) Greater range of charge stocks can be made into high quality products. Cycle stock quality is superior.

The practical results of these advantages of catalytic cracking are that:

(1) High yields of high-octane gasoline of low sulfur content and good stability are made available for automotive and aviation use.

(2) The high yields of C_3 unsaturate and C_4 unsaturates and saturates are available for polymerization and alkylation reactions to supplement gasoline yields. Likewise, the C_4-fraction can be utilized to produce butadiene or be used as blending agents to regulate gasoline volatility.

(3) High yields of aromatics are potentially available for the many chemical uses of these materials.

(4) Kerosene, light and heavy gas-oils, and reduced crudes are converted into more useful and valuable products.

Thermal Versus Catalytic Cracking of the Same Feed Stock

Until recently, thermal cracking had been the dominant means (volume-wise) for producing light hydrocarbons (C_3 and C_4) and gasoline from heavy fractions of crude oil. This process played an important role in improving not only the yield but the quality of gasoline and has, therefore, in effect greatly extended our petroleum resources. More efficient engines were designed to utilize the better fuels produced. Even more efficient engines have required higher octane fuels, and these trends, started some 30 years ago, have continued. Demand for high-octane aviation gasoline became acute at the start of World War II. Thermal cracking finally became a limitation on the quality of the gasoline produced. This limitation was foreseen in the early '30's, and by 1936 the Houdry catalytic cracking process was introduced commercially. This new process was not only competitive with the thermal process in ultimate gasoline yield, but had a very distinct advantage over thermal cracking in product quality. Large quantities of high-octane gasoline were thus potentially available. Following 1936, catalytic cracking capacity began to grow rapidly, and this growth has continued until today it has superseded thermal cracking as a means of making gasoline. It is predicted that by 1960[4] catalytic cracking will have completely replaced thermal cracking. A comparison of a typical thermal cracking result shows very clearly why this tremendous change is now taking place in the petroleum industry. Table 1 shows results on a Mid-Continent gas-oil for both thermal and catalytic cracking. This comparison was not made at the same conditions, but represents rather ultimate yields achieved at average commercial operating conditions for each process. (It is rather difficult to compare the two processes since thermal cracking is conducted in a great many different ways.) The heavy fuel product of the thermal cracking run is actually a reject tar. Thermal cracking yields 56.1 volume per cent of gasoline having a 70.0 octane number. Catalytic cracking, on the other hand, yields 58.8 volume per cent gasoline having 91.5 octane number. The data show that the ultimate gasoline yields are about the same for the two processes. The principal difference is in the distribution of the other products and the gasoline quality. The light-hydrocarbon cut in the catalytically cracked product shows the relatively large yields of C_4-hydrocarbons which are characteristic of the process. The absolute amount of butylenes produced in the catalytic

TABLE 1. COMPARISON OF THERMAL AND CATALYTIC CRACKING CHARGE STOCK: 28.5° API MID-CONTINENT GAS-OIL

	Thermal		Catalytic	
Catalyst	—		Silica-alumina bead	
Total feed/fresh feed ratio	3.0		2.0	
	Vol %	Wt %	Vol %	Wt %
C_3 and lighter		12.5		14.3
i-Butane	1.4	0.9	13.2	8.4
Butylenes	3.4	2.3	8.7	6.0
n-Butane	4.2	2.8	3.8	2.5
Debut. 400°F E.P. gasoline	56.1	48.1	58.8	49.9
Light fuel	—	—	5.0	5.3
Heavy fuel (tar)	29.1	33.4	5.0	5.9
Coke	—	—		7.7
C_5^+ gasoline				
RVP	5.6		6.5	
F-2 octane no. clear	63.0		80.5	
+3 cc TEL	64.5		86.0	
F-1 octane no. clear	70.0		91.5	
+3 cc TEL	72.5		97.5	

cracking run is much larger than in the thermal run, and likewise, in catalytic cracking the C_4-paraffin is largely isobutane. Isobutane and C_3- and C_4-olefins lend themselves readily to alkylation and polymerization reactions, which further increase the yields of motor and aviation gasoline. Also, high yields of the *n*-butenes are made available through catalytic cracking for use in the production of butadiene and petrochemicals. Further comparisons of thermal and catalytic cracking have been made in greater detail on pure compounds.[9] Though the compositions of the two gasolines are not available, the greater octane number of catalytic gasoline indicates a distinctly different composition for it when compared with thermal gasoline.

Table 2[3] compares the composition of thermal and catalytic gasolines prepared from a similar gas-oil, though not the same gas-oil as that represented in Table 1.

TABLE 2. COMPOSITION OF GASOLINE

	Vol % of Gasoline (50–347°F)			
	Paraffins	Naphthenes	Olefins	Aromatics
Catalytic gasoline	56	19	9	16
Thermal gasoline	53	14	30	3

In addition to a larger naphthene and aromatic content, catalytic gasoline has a higher content of isoparaffins. The characteristic evident in the

i-C$_4$/n-C$_4$ ratio of catalytic products given in Table 1 is continued into the higher paraffin. Table 3 gives the composition of the hexane cut of the two gasolines.

TABLE 3. COMPOSITION OF HEXANE CUT OF THERMAL AND CATALYTIC GASOLINES

	Catalytic Gasoline Vol %	Thermal Gasoline Vol %
n-Hexane	9	63
3-Methylpentane	48	18
2-Methylpentane	27	16
2,3-Dimethylpentane	13	3
2,2-Dimethylpentane	3	—

It is of interest that the relative amounts of the isoparaffins are greater than are predicted for equilibrium. The relative yields of the paraffin products must be a kinetically controlled effect rather than an equilibrium effect.

The higher octane of catalytic gasoline compared with thermal is brought about by the greater concentration of aromatic and isoparaffinic hydrocarbons.

Variables in Catalytic Cracking

The principal variables of catalytic cracking have previously been listed. With such a large number of variables affecting the reaction, catalytic cracking can and does have great flexibility. A refiner is able to operate on a wide variety of charge stocks, and by selective adjustment of reaction conditions, including the catalyst, he can produce the volume and quality of products he requires. All the variables affect product distribution, product quality, and conversion level. The important products in catalytic cracking are grouped together as follows: dry gas which includes hydrogen and C$_1$–C$_3$, C$_4$'s, C$_5^+$ gasoline, material boiling above gasoline, and a hydrocarbonaceous residue remaining on the catalyst (coke). The variables in cracking affect the relative quantities of these products. Product quality ordinarily consists of (1) degree of unsaturation in the C$_3$-fraction, (2) degree of unsaturation and the ratio of iso/normal in the C$_4$-fraction, (3) octane number, susceptibility to tetraethyl lead, boiling range, and stability of the C$_5^+$ gasoline, and (4) cracking characteristics or the fuel oil quality of the material boiling above gasoline. Not much is known regarding the effect of the process variable on the quality of the coke deposit.

Conversion in catalytic cracking is affected by all the variables enumerated. It is usually defined as 100 minus the volume per cent of material boiling above 400°F. It is a convenient index of the extent of cracking from the standpoint of pilot-plant and commercial operation. It does not, however, measure the complete effect of the catalyst upon the charge stock. The primary products of the reaction are subjected to additional effects of the catalyst and the material boiling above gasoline is not the same as virgin stock. In some instances where the charge stock contains relatively high concentrations of nitrogen compounds, sulfur compounds, or heavy metals, the recycle stock may be of better quality than the virgin stock in that a large part of this undesirable substance may have been removed in the first pass over the catalyst. In general, however, the recycle stock is not as good a charge stock as the virgin material with respect to yield of gasoline. The latter fact indicates that the materials boiling above gasoline have been "converted," even though such conversion does not figure into the extent of conversion as defined above.

A common way to evaluate the effect of the operating variables on product distribution and quality is to compare the experimental results at constant conversion. Where the data are available, this expedient has been used.

Effect of Temperature

In Tables 4 and 5 the effects of temperature on the results of catalytic cracking are shown (see Figure 1). The data in Table 4 were obtained at

TABLE 4. EFFECT OF TEMPERATURE
Charge: East-Texas Heavy Gas-Oil
Catalyst: 33 A. I. Silica-Alumina Bead*
L. H. S. V.: 1.0 Vol/Vol/Hr
Catalyst/Oil Ratio: 1.5 (approx)

Avg. reactor temperature, °F		780	845	895	955
Conversion,	wt %	40.8	47.4	54.9	70.2
H_2	"	0.01	0.05	0.05	0.1
CH_4	"	0.2	0.62	1.19	3.2
C_2H_4	"	0.2	0.23	0.72	3.5
C_2H_6	"	0.2	0.54	1.03	3.1
C_3H_6	"	0.9	2.16	3.17	4.7
C_3H_8	"	0.8	1.59	2.18	3.2 vol %
C_4H_8	"	1.0	2.41	4.19	4.42 (6.3)
$i\text{-}C_4H_{10}$	"	3.1	3.83	4.12	3.84 (6.0)
C_4H_{10}	"	0.9 vol %	1.25 vol %	1.10	1.19 (1.8)
C_5^+ gasoline	"	—	35.0	30.72 35.71	32.45 37.42(39.8)
10# RVP gasoline	"	—	37.6	32.20 37.96	33.7 39.42(42.2)
Light fuel	"	—	29.2 ⎫	53.3 52.60	46.30 28.1	(19.0)
Heavy fuel	"	—	30.0 ⎭			(10.8)
Coke	"	3.2	3.30	3.50	6.6
C_5^+ gasoline, F-1 octane no.					
clear		84.1	91.7	93.7	94.4
+3 cc TEL		93.0	98.2	98.2	98.5
10# RVP gasoline, °API		—	57.6	57.7	55.4
Gas-oil product, °API		27.7	27.1	25.6	19.1

* A. I. = Activity Index (see section on "Effect of Catalyst Activity").

TABLE 5. ONCE-THROUGH MOVING BED CRACKING EFFECT OF TEMPERATURE
Charge: 28.9 °API East-Texas Heavy Gas-Oil, 56–77% Crude
Catalyst: 33 A.I. Silica-Alumina Bead
Catalyst/Oil Ratio: 2.0

Space velocity		0.8	1.3	2.0
Avg reactor temperature, °F		850	900	950
Conversion, wt %		55.1	55.1	55.1
H_2	"	0.04	0.05	0.06
CH_4	"	0.71	0.85	1.29
C_2H_4	"	0.4	0.55	0.75
C_2H_6	"	0.6	0.75	1.05
C_3H_6	"	2.4	3.35	4.4
C_3H_8	"	2.1	2.15	2.15
$i\text{-}C_4H_{10}$	"	5.1	4.2	3.35
C_4H_8	"	2.9	4.0	5.0
$n\text{-}C_4H_{10}$	"	1.4	1.3	1.25
C_5^+ gasoline	"	34.6	33.5	32.2
Light fuel	"	15.8	13.8	12.4
Heavy fuel	"	29.1	31.1	32.5
Coke	"	4.85	4.2	3.7
C_5^+ gasoline				
Gravity, °API		56.9	55.2	53.5
10# RVP gasoline, F-1 octane no. clear		91.2	94.0	95.0
+3 cc TEL		97.6	98.6	99.0
RVP		7.2	7.3	7.4

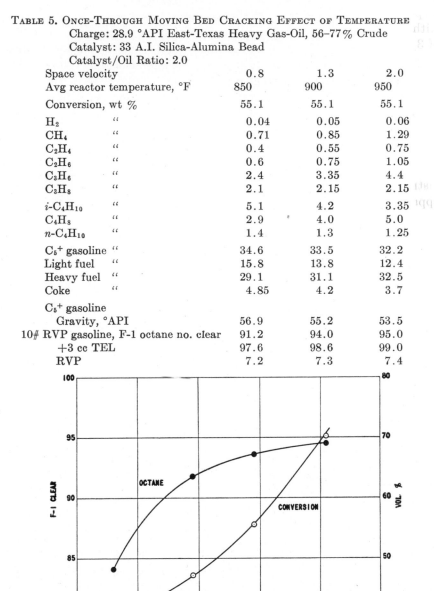

FIG. 1. Effect of temperature in catalytic cracking. Charge: East Texas Heavy gas-oil, 56–77 percent crude; CATALYST: Synthetic Silica-Alumina; CATALYST/ OIL Ratio: 1.5.

constant space velocity (volume of oil/60°F charged per hour per volume of catalyst in the reactor) and catalyst/oil ratio (weight). Conversion of the East Texas heavy gas-oil varies from 40.8 per cent at 780°F to 70.2 per cent at 955°F. Quantities of all the gases from C_1 through C_4 increase as the temperature increases. The increase of the amount of propylene and butylenes with temperature is especially great. Although the quantity of gasoline increases with temperature, the relative amount decreases. At temperatures higher than those shown in the tables, a point is reached when the product is largely C_1 and C_4 and the amount of gasoline is correspondingly small. The octane number of the gasoline increases markedly with an increase in temperature of cracking; however, after the addition of 3 cc of TEL per gallon, the octane numbers of the resulting gasolines show a much smaller effect of temperature. The gasoline and fuel oil products increase slightly in gravity with temperature. This indicates an increase in aromaticity. Comparison of the gravity of the charge with the fuel-oil product shows that the charge has become more aromatic after being subjected to catalytic cracking. Formation of large quantities of C_4 and lighter gases and saturated molecules in the gasoline leaves the fuel oil relatively poorer in hydrogen. The fuel oil product, therefore, is a poorer catalytic cracking charge stock than the fresh material.

Table 5 contains data showing the effect of temperature on products distribution and quality at constant conversion. The same trends are apparent as in the previous table. Brought out emphatically is the finding that at constant conversion the yield of C_5^+ gasoline decreases as the reaction temperature increases. In summary, reaction temperature is found to have a profound effect on conversion, products distribution, and product quality.

Effect of Pressure

Commercial catalytic cracking operations are run at pressures just slightly above atmospheric pressure. Furthermore, the reaction is carried out normally in the presence of steam so that the partial pressure of the oil charge is somewhat less than the total pressure. The reasons for carrying out the reaction at low pressure can be ascertained in the data given in Tables 6 and 7. Raising the pressure increases the amount of coke and lowers the octane number of the gasoline (see Figure 2). At low pressures a large amount of gas is formed which is highly unsaturated. The olefin content of the gasoline is likewise high. As pressure is increased, the bromine number of the gasoline drops steadily, indicating a loss of olefinic hydrocarbons. The loss of olefins will not account for the loss in octane observed. Therefore, as indicated in Table 6, part of the loss of octane must be associated with a decrease in the amount of aromatics and possibly with a lower relative amount of isoparaffins.

TABLE 6. EFFECT OF PRESSURE
Temperature, °F: 900
Charge: Light East-Texas Gas-Oil
L.H.S.V.: ca 1
Catalyst: Synthetic Silica-Alumina

Pressure		100 mm	15 psig
Conversion, wt %		46.6	56.4
H_2	"	0.08	0.03
CH_4	"	0.57	0.5
C_2H_4	"	0.38	0.3
C_2H_6	"	0.22	0.5
C_3H_6	"	4.87	} 4.3
C_3H_8	"	0.69	
C_4H_8	"	3.07	3.8 vol %
i-C_4H_{10}	"	2.86	8.2 vol %
n-C_4H_{10}	"	0.44	2.4 vol %
C_5^+	"	32.10	41.6 vol %
Gas-oil	"	53.4	43.6 vol %
Coke	"	1.3	3.8
C_5^+ gasoline, F-1 octane no. clear		95.5	88.0
+3 cc TEL		—	96.3
Gasoline			
paraffins, vol %		27.3	(50)
naphthenes "		9.9	(20)
aromatics "		29.1	(18)
olefins "		33.7	(12)
Gas-oil product, °API			31.9
Gasoline			56.7

TABLE 7. EFFECT OF PRESSURE
Temperature, °F: 825
L.H.S.V.: 1.25
Charge: Light East-Texas Gas-Oil, 34.1°API
Catalyst: Synthetic Silica-Alumina (35.4 A.I.)

Pressure, psia	6.4	10.8	16.2	30	45
Conversion					
Wet gas, wt %	5.9	6.0	8.1	8.1	10.2
C_5^+ gasoline, vol%	22.8	27.5	34.2	40.4	45.1
Coke, wt %	1.0	1.6	2.0	3.3	3.9
Bromine no., gasoline	55.1	38.9	31.7	22.7	14.5
F-1 Octane no., clear	92.0	91.0	89.4	86.0	84.2
C_5^+ gasoline, vol %/wt % coke	22.8	17.2	17.1	12.2	11.5

The effect of pressure on the extent of conversion cannot be evaluated from the data of Table 7, since superimposed on the effect of pressure is the effect of contact time. It will be noted that the runs given in Table 7 were made at constant space velocity and under these conditions the contact time is directly related to the pressure. The increase in the gas shown in Table 7, therefore, probably represents merely an increase in the con-

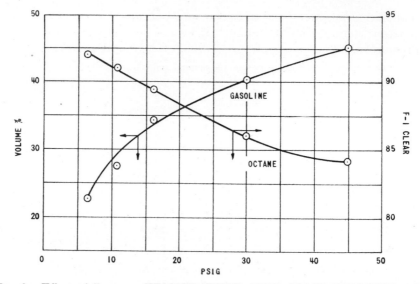

FIG. 2.   Effect of Pressure. TEMPERATURE: 825°F; SPACE VELOCITY: 1.25; CATALYST: Synthetic Silica-Alumina; CHARGE: East Texas light gas-oil.

TABLE 8. EFFECT OF CONTACT TIME
Average Reactor Temperature, °F: 845
Charge: East-Texas Heavy Gas-Oil
Catalyst: Silica-Alumina Bead, 33 A.I.
Pressure: 10 psig
Catalyst/Oil Ratio: 1.25

		0.1		0.5		1.0		2.0	
L.H.S.V., vol/vol/hr		0.1		0.5		1.0		2.0	
Conversion,	vol %	78.4		54.3		45.4		36.0	
H_2	wt. %	0.16		0.08		0.04		0.03	
CH_4	"	2.5		1.1		0.5		0.3	
C_2H_4	"	0.6		0.4		0.3		0.2	
C_2H_6	"	2.0		1.0		0.5		0.3	
C_3H_6	"	4.4		2.4		2.1		1.9	
C_3H_8	"	1.5		2.1		1.5		0.9	
C_4H_8	"	1.8		2.6		2.7		2.0	
i-C_4H_{10}	"	7.9		4.2		3.5		2.5	
C_4H_{10}	"	2.0	vol %	1.8	vol %	0.8	vol %	0.8	vol %
C_5^+	"	43.2	51.4	33.7	39.5	30.4	35.2	25.0	29.0
10# RVP gasoline	"	—		35.4	42.0	31.7	37.2	26.2	30.9
Gas-oil	"	23.0		46.7		55.2		64.3	
Coke	"	11.0		3.9		2.5		1.8	
C_5^+ gasoline, F-1 octane no.									
clear		86.2		90.6		92.0		91.1	
+ 3 cc TEL		94.9		97.7		97.0		97.6	
10# RVP gasoline, °API		57.7		58.6		58.6		57.0	
Gas-oil, °API		18.9		25.9		27.3		28.4	

version and is not directly related to an effect of pressure. It is likely that at constant contact time the amount of gas should decrease as a function of pressure. Commercially, the production of coke is the limiting factor

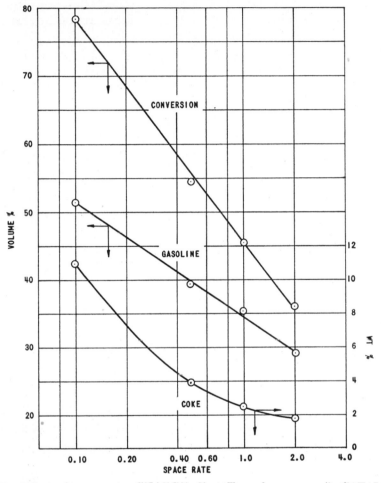

Fig. 3. Effect of space rate. CHARGE: East Texas heavy gas-oil; CATALYST: Synthetic Silica-Alumina; REACTOR TEMPERATURE: 845°F; PRESSURE: 10 psig; CATALYST/OIL RATIO: 1.5.

in the process, and since this increases with an increase in pressure, a limit is quickly reached for a practical operating pressure.

Effect of Contact Time

Contact time is varied in catalytic cracking by changing the amount of oil charged to a given amount of catalyst in unit time. Such a scheme gives a relative measure of true contact time. The latter will, of course, vary according to whether the charge is truly vaporized or only partly so. In Table 8 the effect of space velocity on product distribution and quality is shown at constant temperature, pressure, and catalyst/oil ratio. The conversion varies indirectly with space rate (hr^{-1}). In keeping with the change in conversion, the amounts of gas, gasoline, and coke decrease as the space velocity is increased (see Figure 3). At the long contact times the gasoline octane number is lower. This is not believed to be real, but is believed due to experimental difficulties. The recycle gas-oil is seriously down-graded at the longer contact times.

Effect of Catalyst/Oil Weight Ratio

The amount of catalyst used to contact a given amount of oil is an important variable in catalytic cracking. Data for this variable are given in Table 9. In a fixed bed this variable is related not only to the space velocity, but is also related to the total time that the bed is in contact with oil. In a moving bed, catalyst/oil ratio is determined by the oil and the catalyst charge rates.

TABLE 9. EFFECT OF CATALYST/OIL RATIO
Charge: East-Texas Heavy Gas-Oil, 56–77% Crude
Average Reactor Temperature: 845°F
Catalyst: Silica-Alumina Bead, 33 A.I.
Pressure: 10 psig
Liquid Hourly Space Velocity, V/V/Hr: 1.00

		1.25		2.5		5.0		10.0	
Catalyst/oil radio		1.25		2.5		5.0		10.0	
Conversion		45.4		50.2		61.8		66.1	
H_2	wt %	0.04		0.04		0.04		0.05	
CH_4	"	0.54		0.50		0.78		0.56	
C_2H_4	"	0.30		0.36		0.58		0.53	
C_2H_6	"	0.45		0.45		0.87		0.53	
C_3H_6	"	2.11		2.62		2.68		3.40	
C_3H_8	"	1.46		1.47		2.20		2.28	
C_4H_8	"	2.68		2.95		2.98		3.75	
$i\text{-}C_4H_{10}$	"	3.53		4.66		5.82		6.96	
C_4H_{10}	"	0.82	vol %	1.40	vol %	1.50	vol %	1.52	vol %
$C_5{}^+$	"	30.37	35.23	31.55	36.96	37.55	44.11	38.22	45.03
10# RVP gasoline	"	31.68	37.21	32.80	38.85	39.10	46.47	39.41	46.84
Gas-oil	"	55.20		50.50		39.40		34.90	
Coke	"	2.50		3.50		5.60		7.30	
10# RVP gasoline									
F-1 octane no, clear		92.0		91.6		91.5		92.2	
+3 cc TEL		97.0		97.5		97.7		98.3	
10# RVP gasoline, °API		58.6		58.5		59.8		60.3	
Gas-oil, °API		27.3		27.3		23.9		24.6	
Gasoline/coke wt ratio		12.2		9.0		6.7		5.25	

The fact that such a variable exists allows one to conclude immediately that practical catalysis is far removed from the idealized classical definition of a catalyst. According to the latter, a catalyst merely speeds up a reaction and in this action it is not changed itself. In catalytic cracking the catalyst is rapidly changed, not permanently but temporarily, by the growth of a coke deposit which is an integral part of the reaction. This

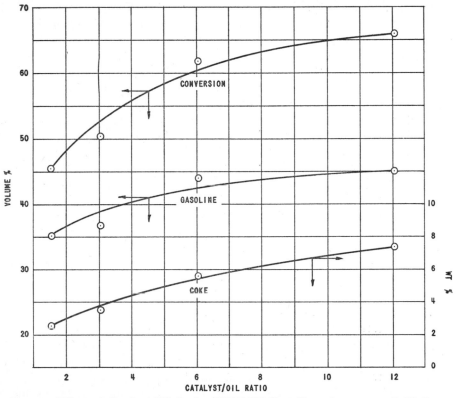

FIG. 4. Effect of Catalyst/Oil Ratio. CHARGE East Texas heavy gas-oil, 56–77% crude; SPACE RATE: 1.00; REACTOR TEMPERATURE: 845°F; PRESSURE: 10 psig; CATALST: Synthetic Silica-Alumina.

change decreases the conversion and alters the products distribution somewhat. When the catalyst is fresh; i.e., when little oil has been passed over it (the catalyst/oil ratio is high), the conversion is very high and coke production is relatively high. Products of dry gas and C_4's follow the same trend. Fresh catalyst, therefore, tends to over-crack, giving high gas and coke yields and low gasoline yields. As coke builds up on the catalyst it becomes attenuated, and there is apparently less secondary attack on the primary products of cracking. The buildup of coke continues throughout the run, and if contact is continued long enough the catalyst eventually is completely poisoned. However, this condition is reached only after 30 to 40 per cent by weight of coke is built up on the catalyst. The octane number of the gasoline produced is not affected by catalyst/oil ratios which are within practical limits. The recycle stock shows high aromaticity at high catalyst/oil ratios. This again is characteristic of high conversion. Generally, catalyst/oil ratio has the same general effects on product distribution and quality that space velocity shows (see Figure 4). These two variables are, therefore, for all practical purposes interchangeable. Thus, in effect, the coking of the catalyst changes the space velocity of the oil with respect to the concentration of active centers on the catalyst surface.

As is well known, the catalyst is reactivated after contacting with the charge by an air treatment. The hydrocarbonaceous residue is burned off in the regeneration step. The amount of coke laid down on the catalyst is limited by the regeneration equipment in a commercial unit and is not limited by the loss in activity accompanying coke deposition.

Effect of Catalyst Activity

Commercial cracking catalysts are all composed of silica and alumina. Active catalysts have been made which consist of silica-zirconia and of silica-magnesia. However, these catalysts have not met with commercial acceptance for various reasons. Initially catalysts were made exclusively from clays. Later synthetic catalysts were introduced and now constitute the bulk of catalyst used (70 per cent). Early in the development of the cracking process it was found that the effectiveness of the different catalysts varied widely. Standard methods for the empirical evaluation of catalysts were developed. These tests not only brought under control the manufacture of catalysts but also served in the development of new and better catalysts. In these tests[1,7,15] the activity of the catalyst is arbitrarily determined under a standard set of reaction conditions which approximate conditions obtaining in commercial operation.

The gasoline (C_5^+, 400°F E.P.), gas (wt %), and amount of residue remaining on the catalyst are usually determined in the various tests. The amount of gasoline, the conversion level, or some modification of these two obtained in the standard tests is taken as a measure of the intrinsic "activity" of the catalyst. Such a test is highly arbitrary and may or may not be directly related to the true activity of a catalyst. In the CAT-A test[1] the activity index of a catalyst is taken as the amount of gasoline produced by a catalyst under standard conditions of pressure, temperature, contact time, catalyst/oil ratio, and feed stock. Varying the catalyst activity affects the quantity of products obtained and also, to a certain extent, the quality. This can be seen by referring to Table 10. Here three catalysts whose composition is the same but whose "activity" has been adjusted by steam and high-temperature treatment are compared. It is seen that an increase in activity (greater concentration of active centers per volume of catalyst) causes not only an increase in all yields, but a marked decrease in the relative olefin content of the gas and gasoline. There is a corresponding increase in the amount of paraffins produced in the gasoline. The gasoline aromatics and naphthenes are constant. The change in composition of the liquid products appearing as a function of change of catalyst activity reflects itself in a corresponding change in the octane level of the C_5^+ gasoline product.

TABLE 10. EFFECT OF CATALYST ACTIVITY

Charge: Light East-Texas Gas-Oil
Liquid Hourly Space Velocity: 1.5
Temperature, °F: 800
Pressure: Atmospheric
Charge: Synthetic Silica-Alumina Catalyst (12.5 Wt % Al_2O_3–87.5 Wt % SiO_2)

CAT-A Activity Index		20		26		40	
Conversion		19.0		27.3		44.4	
H_2	wt %	0.01		0.03		0.04	
CH_4	"	0.04		0.07		0.14	
C_2H_4	"	0.08		0.17		0.34	
C_2H_6	"	0.04		0.06		0.13	
C_3H_6	"	0.39		0.86		1.41	
C_3H_8	"	0.04		0.34		0.78	
C_4H_8	"	0.36		0.54		0.86	
i-C_4H_{10}	"	0.40		1.24		2.64	
n-C_4H_{10}	"	0.05	vol %	0.14	vol %	0.32	vol %
C_5^+ gasoline	"	16.8	19.5	22.3	25.9	34.8	40.4
Gas-oil	"	81.0		72.7		55.6	
Coke	"	0.7		1.2		2.2	
C_5^+ gasoline, F-1 octane no, clear		84.4		83.6		81.3	
C_5^+ gasoline							
paraffins, %		29		41		50	
naphthenes, %		18		19		20	
aromatics, %		16		19		18	
olefins, %		37		21		12	

Catalyst activity is an independent variable and, like temperature, pressure, and contact time, has a major effect on conversion. Thus, to some extent catalyst activity can be employed to adjust for the effects of these other variables. Catalysts of 50 to 70 Activity Index have been made and could be made commercially. However, commercial catalysts today possess operating activities in the 22 to 32 A.I. range. Use of the more active catalysts would allow cracking to be carried out at milder conditions. However, because of the rigorous conditions existing in commercial catalytic cracking, the more active catalysts of the silica-alumina type are not stable. Their activity soon declines to a normal level and in some cases even to a lower activity, depending on the composition and method of manufacture. Very active catalysts produce a high level of coke at operable temperatures. Control of the coking tendency and removal of the coke are important problems in the design of commercial units. An abnormal replacement of catalyst adds significantly to the cost of the process.

Catalyst activity has been found to be closely related to the composition of the catalyst and its method of manufacture. A vast amount of work has been done on this subject. Only recently has any detailed information been brought to light on the exact seat of catalyst activity.[5,10,16,17]

Effect of Catalyst Type

The cracking process places stringent requirements on the properties of the catalyst. Not only must the catalyst give the desired quantity of products, but the quality of the products must be right. Also, the catalyst must be able to withstand the temperature effects in regeneration and the attrition in both cracking and regeneration parts of the cracking operation. Thus, the catalyst must possess unusual combination of particular chemical and physical properties. These desired properties place a limit on the kinds of material that can be used in the process. A large variety of catalysts have been investigated but only very few have been found to possess the qualities mentioned and which, in addition, are inexpensive to manufacture. From the standpoint of raw materials, catalysts fall into two classes—natural and synthetic. Natural catalysts can be made from bentonitic clays,[11,12] such as montmorillonite and other natural aluminum silicates as kaolin and halloysite. Synthetic catalysts can be made from silica in combination with alumina, zirconia, or magnesia. In both classes of catalysts the chemistry of manufacture is very complex and will not be discussed here. For the most part, the different catalysts that are of most interest to catalytic cracking vary principally in activity and stability, there being only minor differences in products distribution and quality at comparable activities. A synthetic silica-alumina bead catalyst, two types of natural catalysts made from clay, and a synthetic silica-magnesia catalyst are compared in Table 11.

In general, at constant conversion the clay catalysts produce more coke, less gas, less C_4-hydrocarbons (particularly isobutane), and more gasoline than synthetic silica-alumina catalyst. Houdry Type 1 catalyst is especially effective in producing high yields of gasoline. The gasoline produced by synthetic catalyst is usually a little higher in octane number than that produced by the natural catalysts. Silica-magnesia possesses a high intrinsic activity, but its gasoline, although large in volume, has a relatively poor octane number. The differences in the catalyst are largely

TABLE 11. EFFECT OF CATALYST TYPE
Once-Through Yields from Catalytic Cracking
Heavy East-Texas Gas-Oil
Charge: 56–77 Vol % East-Texas Crude
Cracking temperature, °F: 900
Conversion: 55 Vol %

Catalyst Type		28 A.I. Natural Clay	32 A.I. Synthetic Silica-Alumina	46 A.I. Silica Magnesia	30 A.I. Type 1
Yields					
H_2	wt %	0.03	0.03	0.05	0.02
CH_4	"	0.8	0.8	0.7	0.5
C_2H_4	"	0.3	0.6	0.2	0.3
C_2H_6	"	0.6	0.6	0.6	0.5
C_3H_6	"	2.8	3.5	1.7	2.6
C_3H_8	"	1.2	2.0	1.0	1.1
C_4H_8	vol %	5.9	6.0	3.8	5.6
i-C_4H_{10}	"	4.8	7.6	3.1	5.3
n-C_4H_{10}	"	1.4	1.5	1.2	1.1
C_5^+ gasoline, (385°F @ 90% evap.)	"	41.4	38.2	48.0	44.6
Gas-oil, vol %		45.0	45.0	45.0	45.0
Coke, wt %		4.8	3.8	2.2	2.8
C_5^+ gasoline F-1 octane no (~385°F @ 90% evap) clear		89.3	92.8	84.8	89.4
+3 cc TEL		96.3	98.4	93.9	96.5

chemical in nature. However, the differences in physical properties do play a minor part in the over-all effectiveness of the catalyst.

Effect of Feed Stock Type

Catalytic cracking has the outstanding characteristic of being able to produce high-quality gasoline from almost any crude oil. In Table 12, the gas-oils of like boiling range from the various crude oils are represented. These crude oils can be classified as follows:

Crude Oil	Type
West Edmond East Texas	paraffinic
Conroe	naphthenic
Refugio	aromatic
Abquaiq	high sulfur
Los Angeles Basin	high nitrogen

As might be expected, the naphthenic and aromatic gas-oils give gasoline of higher octane numbers. The presence of sulfur and nitrogen compounds in catalytic cracking charge appears to affect the product quality

TABLE 12. EFFECT OF FEED-STOCK TYPE

Once-Through Yields from Catalytic Cracking with Synthetic Bead Catalyst at 900°F and 55 Vol % Conversion

Feed Stock		West Edmond Gas-Oil	East Texas Gas-Oil	Conroe Gas-Oil	Heavy Refugio Gas-Oil	Abqaiq Gas-Oil	Los Angeles Basin Gas-Oil
Position in crude,		54.5–	56.0–	56.7–	31.6–	57.7–	—
vol %		90.5	77.0	91.8	83.6	89.9	
Characterization							
factor		12.2	12.1	11.9	11.3	12.0	11.5
Boiling range, °F		536–1006	539–928	484–870	426–864	473–1058	425–880
Chemical analysis							
paraffins, vol %		60	54	49	24	—	—
aromatics +							
olefins	"	14	18	28	40	—	—
naphthenes	"	26	28	23	36	—	—
S	wt %	0.17	0.38	—	—	2.14	0.70
N_2	"	—	0.05	—	—	0.07	0.25
Yields							
H_2S,	"	—	—	—	—	0.9	0.3
H_2	"	0.05	0.03	0.02	0.03	0.05	0.1
CH_4	"	0.7	0.8	0.7	0.6	0.8	1.2
C_2H_4	"	0.6	0.6	0.6	0.6	0.4	0.5
C_2H_6	"	0.6	0.6	0.6	0.5	0.8	1.0
C_3H_6	"	3.8	3.5	3.7	3.0	2.6	1.9
C_3H_8	"	1.6	2.0	1.9	1.3	2.4	1.8
i-C_4H_{10}	vol %	7.2	7.6	8.5	7.7	7.1	5.3
n-C_4H_{10}	"	1.7	1.5	1.9	1.1	1.8	1.7
C_4H_8	"	6.9	6.0	5.7	5.0	3.6	3.6
C_5^+ gasoline	"						
(385°F @ 90% evap)		39.3	38.2	36.7	41.4	39.3	38.7
Gas-oil,	vol %	45.0	45.0	45.0	45.0	45.0	45.0
Coke,	wt %	3.1	3.8	4.3	3.8	6.5	8.0
C_5^+ gasoline (~385°F @ 90% evap) F-1 octane							
no, clear		93.0	92.8	94.5	97.2	89.8	92.6
+3 cc TEL		99.1	98.4	98.8	99.4	95.8	97.0

but does not necessarily affect the products distribution,[14] except that part of the basic nitrogen compounds are chemisorbed on the catalyst and become part of the coke deposited on the catalyst. In this case the amount of coke produced may be proportionately larger. The quality of the gasoline is affected because of the presence of larger amounts of nitrogen and sulfur compounds than normal. Removal of nitrogen and sulfur constituents by standard treatments gives normal gasolines. Thus, the products distribution and quality are intrinsically a function of the hydrocarbon composition of the gas-oil charged and are not necessarily related to the presence of either nitrogen or sulfur compounds.

The presence of basic nitrogen compounds in catalytic cracking charge stock does depress the effective activity of the catalyst and, therefore, the conversion level at a fixed set of conditions.[5,14]

The distribution of sulfur in catalytically cracked products has been investigated. The sulfur distribution varies considerably with the charge stocks and cracking conditions, although the following distribution is common: of the total sulfur in feed, 35 to 55 per cent is in cycle stock, 35 to 25 per cent is in C_4 and lighter (mainly as H_2S), 20 to 10 per cent is in coke, with less than 10 per cent being in C_5^+ gasoline.

The boiling range of the charge stock also may be considered a variable in cracking. For given conditions, this variable affects principally the extent of conversion and the quality of the gasoline produced. In general, an increase in mid-boiling point favors the production of unsaturated hydrocarbons in the gasoline and lighter products.[3] Stocks of higher boiling point are more easily cracked. Overlap between the distilling range of the gasoline product and virgin charge stock brings about a lowering of gasoline quality, particularly octane number. The inclusion of low octane number, uncracked heavy naphtha in the higher boiling fraction of the gasoline product lowers the octane number of the gasoline in a serious way. The virgin heavy naphtha contained in this type of charge stock is more refractory than higher molecular-weight constituents of the charge and is substantially unaffected during a normal catalytic cracking processing step.

The Heat Effects in Cracking and Regeneration

The heat effects in catalytic cracking are not of prime importance to a chemist in gaining a knowledge of the chemistry of the reactions involved. However, in the case of the design and operation of a commercial plant, heat supply and removal are of paramount importance. It turns out that the heat of the cracking reaction is endothermic and the removal of the coke by combustion with air is exothermic. A desirable feature of a commercial design is to utilize part of the heat generated in the regeneration step to supply the heat of vaporization of the charge and the heat of cracking. This is done to a greater or lesser degree in most commercial units. The most important limitation is that of controlling the rise in temperature of the catalyst during regeneration. As little as 1 per cent coke on the catalyst is sufficient to raise the catalyst temperature 600°F under adiabatic conditions. Present catalysts cannot stand such a temperature rise above the cracking temperature so various means are utilized to keep this under control. As one might expect, a commercial catalytic cracking unit is in essence a very large device for controlled burning of coke.

For proper design of commercial plants a detailed knowledge of the heat of reaction for cracking and regeneration is, therefore, necessary. The

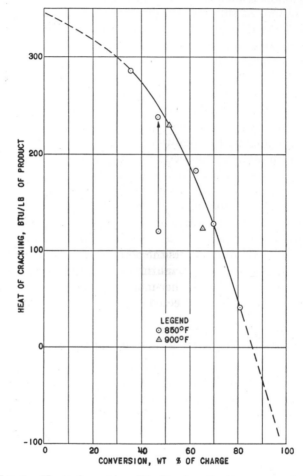

FIG. 5.   Heat of cracking, Btu/lb of product vs. conversion.

heat of cracking has been determined[8] by a calorimetric method. Within the temperature range employed in commercial operation, the endothermic heat of reaction has been found to vary from about 300 BTU/lb of products at 30 per cent conversion to about 40 BTU/lb of products at 80 per cent conversion. Figure 5 shows the relationship between the heat of cracking and conversion.

Catalytic cracking, as has been pointed out, is a composite of a large number of different chemical reactions. Some of these individual reactions are endothermic and others are exothermic. Since the heat of cracking changes sharply as conversion is increased, the relative importance of the predominant reactions must be changing. At low conversions such highly endothermic reactions as dealkylation must predominate, whereas at high conversions production of low-molecular-weight paraffins, aromatics, and coke is the most important characteristic of the reaction.

The heat of regeneration has been estimated for coked catalyst.[8] In order to use the data in the reference it is necessary to know the H/C ratio of the coke. Undoubtedly the heat of combustion of the coke will change as a function of the H/C ratio, just as it does in free hydrocarbons. The correlation in reference[8] is based on data of free hydrocarbons; the heat of absorption of coke is not known. The relative production of carbon monoxide and carbon dioxide is important in setting the heat of coke removal. Likewise, hydration effects of the clay catalyst complicate not only the heat of regeneration but also the heat of cracking. Some allowance must be made for these hydration effects in making heat balance for catalytic cracking.

The Nature of the Hydrocarbonaceous Residue

Not much is known about the exact nature of the coke remaining on the catalyst. Undoubtedly its character changes as a function of the process variables, particularly temperature and nature of the charge stock. At a temperature of 500°F and using isobutylene as a charge in polymerization reaction, the catalyst deposit appears to be a long-chain polymer of approximately 2/1 H/C atom ratio. At higher temperatures the deposit left by a gas oil has H/C ratio of less than 1/1. The latter indicates that the coke must be highly aromatic and of polycyclic structure. Voge, Good, and Greensfelder[18] have studied the production of coke under a standard set of cracking conditions as a function of the charge stock composition. Aromatics, and in particular bicyclic and tricyclic aromatics, produced

TABLE 13. EFFECT OF AROMATIC STRUCTURE ON COKE FORMATION
Temperature: 500°F
Catalyst: Silica-Alumina
Pressure: 1 Atmosphere
Feed Rate: 2.4 Moles/Liter/Hour

Aromatic Cpd Charge	Coke (wt % charge)
Benzene	0.6
Naphthalene	32.5
Anthracene	66.4
Biphenyl	8.7
Terphenyl	34.8

TABLE 14. EFFECT OF AMOUNT OF COKE ON CATALYST ON H/C RATIO

Amount of Coke (wt %)	H/C Ratio (wt)
0.643	0.1
1.51	0.074
2.71	0.074
2.96	0.052

the most coke. Table 13 shows the data of these authors. Table 14 shows the effect of amount of coke on the catalyst on the H/C ratio of the coke. The data in these tables are strong evidence for the conclusion that coke is a highly aromatic residue strongly adsorbed on the catalyst. Raising the temperature of a coked catalyst will remove part of the residue as light hydrocarbon gases (principally methane) and hydrogen. In this process the residue becomes even more carbonaceous. The end product of long heating at high temperature is probably graphite, since some graphite is found on catalysts which have been used in commercial units over extended periods of time.

Effects of Process Conditions on the Catalyst

Process conditions are also important because they control the rate and kind of changes which occur to the catalyst in use. These catalyst changes, in turn, cause marked changes in the products of cracking. The process conditions most important in affecting the catalyst are: temperature (particularly in the regeneration step), gas atmosphere to which the catalyst is exposed, length of time at each condition, and impurities brought in the petroleum and deposited on the catalyst.

The conditions mentioned above affect both the general activity level of the catalyst, that is the general ability to convert the charge into other products, and also the catalyst selectivity, that is the ability to form a desirable distribution of the products—gasoline, gas, and coke.

During the course of a single run, loss of activity occurs because of coke deposition. This is a temporary effect, activity being regained by burning off the coke. However, permanent catalyst changes occur at a slow rate so that after months of operation the catalyst is substantially different from new catalyst. For example, "equilibrium activity" catalyst is about one-half as active as fresh catalyst.

The most important agent in causing loss of activity usually is steam. Loss of activity occurs much more rapidly in steam than in a dry atmosphere at a given temperature. A corresponding loss of area is observed. The effect of lower catalyst activity has been discussed previously in this chapter.

Loss of selectivity occurs because of the presence of heavy metals in the cracking catalyst. These metals act to cause the hydrocarbons to form relatively large coke deposits on the catalyst. Because of the coke, the activity for production of gasoline is lowered. A substantial increase in the hydrogen production is observed. The metals come from two different sources. Crude oil charge contains metals, present in part as porphyrins, which are carried onto the catalyst. The most important here are vanadium, nickel, and copper. Some entrainment occurs but also some of these organometallic compounds are volatile. Even one part per million of metal in the oil can be harmful when brought continually into the catalyst where it tends to accumulate. An accumulation of 0.01 per cent metal is significant. A second method of metal "poisoning" occurs through the activation of iron in clay catalyst (often present to 1 per cent) through the action of the sulfur compounds which drive the iron from the clay lattice to form iron sulfide. The harmful effect of iron in clay in the cracking operation can be greatly minimized by utilizing steam in a prehydration technique.

Examples of metals addition and activation of iron in clay catalyst are shown in the following table:

Catalyst	Gasoline Vol %	Coke Wt %	Gas Wt %	Gas Grav Air = 1.0
Clay—New	32.9	2.4	3.3	1.40
Clay—After use with a sulfur stock, no prehydration	23.6	3.5	5.1	0.67
Synthetic—New	38.5	2.7	6.7	1.54
Synthetic—Containing Ni + V = 0.04% added with petroleum	34.9	2.5	7.9	1.23

Control of the process variables, charge composition and, with clays, the amount of steam determine the presence and activity of metals in the catalyst. Metals can cause coke production to increase greatly and at the same time cause a decline in gasoline production. This obviously has a very limiting effect on the reaction from a catalytic and commercial viewpoint. Also, as pointed out earlier, over-all catalyst activity is affected by overheating, particularly in the presence of steam. Therefore, control of process conditions is of paramount importance from the viewpoint of their effect on the catalyst. Only proper control can prevent alteration of the catalyst which would yield much less favorable products.

References

1. Alexander, J., and Shimp, H. G., *Nat'l Pet. News*, No. 9, R-537 (1944).
2. Ardern, D. B., Dart, J. C., and Lassiat, R. C., "Progress in Petroleum Technology," p. 13, *Advances in Chemistry*, Series No. 5, Am. Chem. Soc., 1951.
3. Bates, J. R., Rose, F. W., Jr., Kurtz, S. S., Jr., and Mills, I. W., *Ind. Eng. Chem.*, **34**, 147 (1942).
4. Bland, W. F., *Petroleum Processing*, **4**, No. 9, 933 (1950).

5. Boedeker, E. R., Mills, G. A., and Oblad, A. G., *J. Am. Chem. Soc.*, **72,** 1554 (1950).
6. Burtis, T. A., Dart, J. C., Kirkbride, C. G., and Peavy, C. C., *Chem. Eng. Progress*, **45,** 97 (1949).
7. Conn, M. E., and Connolly, G. C., *Ind. Eng. Chem.*, **39,** 1138 (1947).
8. Dart, J. C., and Oblad, A. G., *Chem. Eng. Progress*, **45,** 110 (1949).
9. Greensfelder, B. S., and Voge, H. H., *Ind. Eng. Chem.*, **37,** 514 (1945).
10. Milliken, T. H., Mills, G. A., and Oblad, A. G., "Heterogeneous Catalysis," *Trans. Faraday Soc.*, 279 (1950).
11. Milliken, T. H., Oblad, A. G., and Mills, G. A., National Conference on Clays and Clay Technology, Berkeley, Calif., July 1952.
12. Mills, G. A., Holmes, J., and Cornelius, E. B., *J. Phys. & Coll. Chem.*, **54,** 1170 (1950).
13. Murphree, E. V., "Progress in Petroleum Technology," p. 30, *Advances in Chemistry*, Series No. 5, Am. Chem. Soc. (1951).
14. Schall, J. W., and Dart, J. C., *Proc. 3rd World Petr. Congr. The Hague*, Section 4, p. 106 (1951).
15. Shankland, R. V., and Schmitkins, G. E., *Proc. Am. Petr. Inst.*, **27,** (3), 57 (1947).
16. Tamele, M. W., "Heterogeneous Catalysis," *Trans. Faraday Soc.*, p. 270 (1950).
17. Thomas, C. L., *Ind. Eng. Chem.*, **41,** 1485 (1949).
18. Voge, H. H., Good, G. M., and Greensfelder, B. S., *Proc. 3rd World Petr. Congr. The Hague*, Section 4, 124 (1951).

CHAPTER 29

AROMATIZATION, HYDROFORMING AND PLATFORMING

Vladimir Haensel

Universal Oil Products Company, Riverside, Illinois

Catalytic reforming of straight run gasolines has been the subject of extensive research and development for the last twenty years. Prior to the widespread use of catalysts, the concentration of effort had been on thermal processing, similar to the thermal cracking operations which had been well established by that time. There are several reasons for attempting to utilize catalytic methods for upgrading straight run gasolines. The application of heat and pressure, as done in thermal reforming, is a wasteful operation due to substantial loss of charging stock to gaseous products. The ultimate octane numbers realized by thermal reforming are relatively low, except in those cases where nearly half of the liquid feed is converted into gaseous products. It is true that, with the advent of catalytic polymerization of refinery gases, a certain portion of the gaseous product resulting from thermal reforming is converted to a liquid fuel, thereby recovering some of the losses incurred during the thermal reforming. It was well realized, even at the time when thermal reforming capacity was rapidly expanding, that thermal reforming was, at best, a marginal operation which a refiner had to carry out in order to dispose of the low octane straight-run gasoline stocks. In many instances thermal reforming was looked upon as an unprofitable operation because the margin between the value the refiner assigned to the straight-run charge and the price of the finished gasoline was insufficient to overcome the substantial yield loss incurred during thermal reforming.

Before going into an extensive discussion of the reactions involved in thermal and catalytic reforming it is necessary to discuss the composition of straight-run gasolines and naphthas. In the early days of reforming, very little was known about the raw materials available for processing. The stocks were usually described as being more or less naphthenic. For example, the California stocks were considered to be highly naphthenic while the Pennsylvania and Michigan stocks were believed to be highly paraffinic. The Midcontinent and Gulf Coast stocks were thought to be somewhere in-between these two extremes. Even at the present time, our knowledge of the various straight run stocks is still meager but it is considerably greater than the information available twenty years ago. A large amount of information has been obtained on the composition of the lower boiling fractions of straight-run gasolines. The work of Rossini and associates has been of tremendous help because they have established clearly the composition patterns for a large number of lower boiling fractions. The following tables show the composition of the 140–185°F and 185–220°F fractions from various straight-run gasolines.

TABLE 1. COMPOSITION OF 140–185°F. FRACTIONS FROM VARIOUS STRAIGHT-RUN GASOLINES[10]

	Source						
Hydrocarbon, Vol. %	Ponca Okla.	East Texas	Bradford Pa.	Greendale Mich.	Winkler Texas	Midway Calif.	Conroe Texas
2-Methylpentane	9	15	22	7	17	14	11
3-Methylpentane	8	12	13	5	42	10	8
n-Hexane	41	31	37	63	11	16	17
2,2 & 2,4-Dimethylpentane	2	6	6	2	8	4	3
Methylcyclopentane	20	23	9	9	15	34	21
Cyclohexane	16	12	12	11	6	21	31
Benzene	4	1	1	3	1	1	9
Total naphthenes	36	35	21	20	21	55	52
% of 140–185°F fraction based on C$_5$–360°F. Gasoline	13	16	15	18	10	12	14

TABLE 2. COMPOSITION OF 185–220°F FRACTIONS FROM VARIOUS STRAIGHT-RUN GASOLINES[*,10]

	Source						
Hydrocarbon, Vol. %	Ponca Okla.	East Texas	Bradford Pa.	Greendale Mich.	Winkler Texas	Midway Calif.	Conroe Texas
2,3-Dimethylpentane ⎱ 2-Methylhexane ⎰	14	14	15	8	31	11	9
3-Methylhexane	4	5	6	2	25	3	2
n-Heptane	29	19	31	56	9	6	12
1,1-Dimethylcyclopentane	2	2	2	2	4	3	2
tr 1,3-Dimethylcyclopentane	15	16	6	3	10	26	6
tr 1,2-Dimethylcyclopentane	5	6	6	1	8	10	1
Methylcyclohexane	21	27	24	18	10	30	36
Ethylcyclopentane (est.)	(3)	(4)	(4)	(3)	(1)	(5)	(5)
Toluene	7	7	6	7	2	6	27
Total naphthenes	46	55	42	27	33	74	50
% of 185–220°F fraction based on C$_5$–360°F. Gasoline	23	25	24	23	15	20	27

* Including all the natural toluene, part of which tends to appear in this fraction because of a tendency to be more volatile in the presence of other hydrocarbons.

The data shown in Tables 1 and 2 indicate that there is a very substantial variation in the composition of stocks obtained from different parts of the United States. It should be realized that the two fractions shown in these tables represent about 40% of the total C_5 to 360°F gasoline. The composition of the higher boiling 60% of the straight-run gasoline is, in a great many cases, quite unknown. In these instances, however, we have established the composition by hydrocarbon types, that is, paraffins, naphthenes and aromatics. This is of considerable help in judging the results of catalytic reforming studies. Furthermore, it is believed that the composition exhibited by low boiling fractions should be a reasonable guide to the composition of the higher boiling fractions, thus making it possible to interpret the results obtained with a considerably greater degree of accuracy.

The available information indicates that the patterns exhibited by the 140–185°F fraction are, in general, carried over into the 185–220°F fraction, thus making it fairly reasonable that still higher boiling fractions will continue to exhibit a similar pattern. There is a very substantial variation in the naphthene content of the fractions studied. For example, it will be noted that the 140–185°F fraction from the Michigan area contains only 20% naphthenes, while the same fraction from a California straight-run gasoline contains 55% naphthenes. In the 185–220°F fraction, the naphthene content from the same two sources is 27 and 74 respectively. Furthermore, stocks which contain a small amount of naphthenes exhibit a very high ratio of straight chain paraffins to branched paraffins, while in stocks with a high naphthene content, the ratio of straight chain to branched paraffins is quite low. Thus, it becomes apparent that a generally useful catalytic reforming process must be suitable for stocks that are low in naphthenes and high in normal paraffins as well as for stocks that are rich in naphthenes and low in normal paraffins.

The primary purpose of catalytic reforming is to increase the octane number of the stock without incurring substantial losses. With the advent of higher compression ratio engines the trend toward high octane number fuels has made it impossible to put a ceiling on octane numbers. Thus, in catalytic reforming work the tendency has always been to exceed the currently required octane numbers by a substantial margin. At the present time, the aim of catalytic reforming is to produce fuels having clear research octane numbers of the order of 90 to 95 with a minimum loss of charging stock.

Keeping in mind the variability of charging stocks and the demands for high octane numbers and yields, let us review the reactions of hydrocarbons which lead to an octane number improvement. The work is therefore subdivided into reactions of paraffins, naphthenes and aromatics. Actually, the amount of aromatic hydrocarbons present in straight-run gasolines is relatively small. It varies from about 5 to 15%

and, in view of the high octane number of aromatics and their great stability in catalytic reforming, there has been no need for conversion of natural aromatics. Thus, we are primarily concerned with the conversion of paraffins and naphthenes. At a later point in this chapter we shall discuss the reactions of thermally cracked gasolines which also require upgrading for octane number and other purposes.

Reactions of Paraffins and Naphthenes

A great deal of work has been done on methods of upgrading paraffin hydrocarbons boiling in the gasoline range. The reactions which can lead to an octane number improvement are isomerization, dehydrogenation to olefins, dehydrocyclization to aromatics and hydrocracking to lower paraffins. In the case of naphthenes, the primary octane number improving reaction is the conversion to aromatics. Since both five and six membered ring naphthenes are present in variable quantities, depending upon the source of the crude, the workers in the field of catalytic reforming have had to devise means for converting both types of naphthenes into aromatics.

Isomerization. The isomerization of pentane is a well established catalytic operation. Similarly the isomerization of hexane has been practiced on a commercial scale. The isomerization of both C_5 and C_6 hydrocarbons has very little bearing upon catalytic reforming from the standpoint of motor fuel production, since in most cases the octane numbers of the C_5 and C_6 fractions are sufficiently high so that they do not require catalytic reforming. In addition to that the lead susceptibility of these two fractions is substantial, thus providing another reason for not including these two fractions in the reforming charging stock. For aromatic production, however, and specifically benzene from the C_6 cut the simultaneous isomerization of the C_6 paraffins is important. The isomerization of the C_7 paraffins has been the subject of extensive study. The work has not materialized in a commercial operation although it appears to be a theoretically reasonable way of upgrading C_7 paraffins. The main advantage is, of course, the exceedingly high theoretical yield of high octane isomers. In practice, however, the presence of naphthenic and aromatic hydrocarbons, as well as the tendency to obtain substantial disproportionation into high and low boiling products, has made the operation very difficult from the standpoint of commercial utilization. The C_7 paraffin fraction is probably the highest boiling fraction that can be considered useable in isomerization since the C_8, C_9 and C_{10} paraffins, upon isomerization to equilibrium even at the low temperatures utilized with the Friedel-Crafts type catalysts, will not produce a sufficiently high octane number for present day requirements.

Since the extent of branching is reduced as the temperature is increased, the octane number improvement will be less at higher temperatures. For example, the data of Frost[11] indicate that at a reasonable catalytic reforming temperature of about 450°C the C_7 equilibrium isomerization product will have a motor method octane number of about 59, while it is about 55 for the C_8 equilibrium product. The data of Mavity[33] indicate a motor method octane number of 68 for the C_7 equilibrium product and 43 for the C_8 equilibrium product. Thus, it is apparent that if one assumes a catalytic reforming temperature of about 450–500°C the reaction of isomerization of paraffins above heptane does not yield a satisfactory octane number improvement.

The picture is only slightly brighter for stocks which contain a substantial amount of naphthenes. It is known that the five membered ring naphthenes have a higher octane number than the corresponding six membered ring naphthenes. In addition, the equilibrium relationship at higher temperature is in favor of five membered ring naphthenes. Thus, some octane number gain should be realized in the isomerization of naphthenes boiling in the gasoline range. However, stocks that are rich in naphthenes, such as from the California fields, already have a high ratio of five membered ring naphthenes to six membered ring naphthenes so that the net improvement would be small. In an average Midcontinent field with about 40% naphthenes, of which about one-half is five-membered ring naphthenes, the maximum improvement by isomerization of the naphthenic component does not exceed 2–3 octane numbers.

The overall conclusion is that the isomerization of paraffins and naphthenes as a single reaction is of little value in catalytic reforming. The main utility of the isomerization reaction would be, therefore, as a supporting reaction along with other reactions, since in catalytic reforming the upgrading of a part of the gasoline from an octane number of 10–20 to 50–60 is very important although the 50–60 still falls short of the desired 90–95 octane number. The finished gasoline can contain a reasonable concentration of the 50–60 octane number components and still meet the desired octane number specification, while components having octane numbers of the order of 10–20 can be present in only very small concentration.

Dehydrogenation to Olefins. Similar to the situation existing with isomerization of paraffins, a very substantial amount of work has been done on the dehydrogenation of lower paraffins. In the early work on the catalytic dehydrogenation of gaseous paraffins, Grosse and Ipatieff[14] point out that carbon-to-carbon cleavages are favored over the carbon to hydrogen cleavages on the basis of bond energy values. This is further complicated by the fact that high temperatures are required (500–750°C)

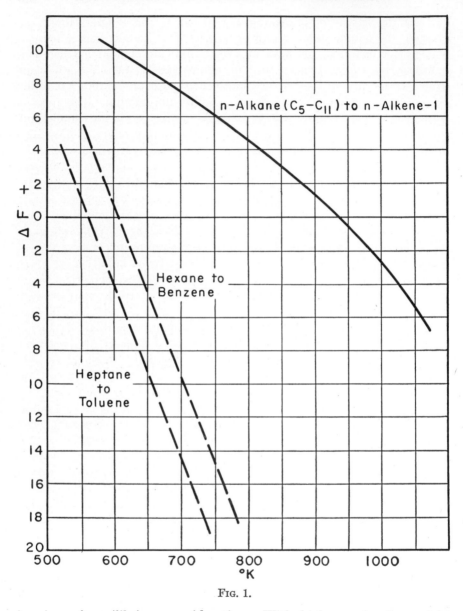

Fig. 1.

in view of equilibrium considerations. With higher molecular weight hydrocarbons a competing reaction of cyclization comes into the picture. The above graph, No. 1, shows the free energy values[43] for the conversion of C_5–C_{11} n-alkanes to n-alkenes-1 as well as the values for the conversion of n-hexane and n-heptane to benzene and toluene respectively. On the basis of these data it would appear that cyclization should be by far the preferred reaction. However, the pressure effect is very pronounced in the case of cyclization, as compared to dehydrogenation to olefins. Furthermore, a number of olefins can be formed from a C_6 or C_7 alkane as compared to the single species of aromatic derived from the same alkanes. Thus, accounting for both of these effects[4] and assuming an operating pressure of about 10 atmospheres it appears that equal conversions to an aromatic and a mixture of three equally probable olefins would be possible at 800°K if the ΔF differential for the two reactions were of the order of 8 K calories. Actually, the difference at 800°K is nearer 25 K calories, thus indicating that in the presence of a material which could catalyze both reactions the aromatic formation would still predominate.

A further consideration in connection with the production of olefins is the octane number and lead susceptibility. Although there is a substantial change in the octane number of an olefin as the double bond is shifted from the end position toward the center, the average octane number of an olefinic product is still low. The lead susceptibility of an olefinic gasoline is also relatively low. In addition, unless the gasoline is inhibited, its storage characteristics are rather poor. The overall conclusion reached is that from the standpoint of gasoline production by catalytic reforming, the reaction of dehydrogenation to olefins is not particularly promising.

Dehydrocyclization to Aromatics. The conversion of paraffins to aromatics is one of the most important and interesting reactions in catalytic reforming. The reaction has been known for less than twenty years[15,29,36] and during this period of time a large number of investigators have participated in developing better catalysts and better understanding of the mechanism of the reaction.

The utility of dehydrocyclization of paraffins to aromatics is exceedingly great in catalytic reforming since this reaction converts some of the lowest octane number components into aromatics having very high octane numbers. The reaction involves a substantial change in the density of the hydrocarbon feed, the theoretical volumetric yields range from 68 per cent for the conversion of n-hexane to benzene to 75–76 per cent for the conversion of n-octane to a mixture of xylenes and ethylbenzene. Thus, the loss of 4 moles of hydrogen from a paraffin is small compared to the loss incurred due to the density shift in going from a paraffin to an aromatic. Nevertheless, the dehydrocyclization reaction provides an efficient upgrading method since paraffins which have octane numbers of about 10 are converted into aromatics with average blending octane numbers of 130.

In their early work on dehydrocyclization of paraffins, Grosse, Morrell and Mattox[15] utilized chromia on alumina as well as mixtures of oxides of chromium, vanadium and molybdenum on alumina as catalysts. It was found that supported catalysts exhibited considerably longer life due primarily to greater ruggedness in regeneration.

Once through yields amounting to about 60 per cent toluene based on n-heptane were obtained at atmospheric pressure, 550°C and liquid hourly space velocities ranging from 0.03 to 0.5 using a chromia on alumina catalyst (6 atomic % Cr). An analysis of the total product obtained at 500°C, atmospheric pressure and 3.6 space velocity showed that the conversion proceeded to give on a weight basis: 12.1% toluene, 11.5% heptenes, 74.0% unreacted n-heptane, 0.17% carbon and 1.7% dry gas (97.1% hydrogen). The cracking to lower boiling hydrocarbons amounted to only 0.5% of the feed.

According to the work of Moldavsky, Kamusher and Kobylskaya[36] normal octane is cyclized, using an unsupported chromium oxide catalyst, at 460°C, atmospheric pressure and space velocities of 0.2–2 to give a liquid product containing 94–21% aromatics and 3 to 10% olefins.

The above quoted results are only a small part of the work done on a variety of pure compounds, wherein both olefins and paraffins, as well as alkylaromatics (such as butylbenzene) were subjected to cyclization.[29,36]

Similarly, a large number of catalysts were tested. The list given below shows some of the catalysts employed for the dehydrocyclization reaction:

Catalyst	Support	Reference
Oxides of Cr	—	36
" " Cr	Al_2O_3	12, 15
" " Cr and V	"	15
" " Cr and Mo	"	15
" " V and Mo	"	15
" " Cr, V and Mo	"	15
Platinum	Carbon	29
Oxides of Mo	Al_2O_3	12, 25, 44
" " "	Cr_2O_3	25
Ammonium alumino-molybdate (6 acid)	—	25
Ammonium thorio-molybdate (12 acid)	—	25
Phospho-molybdic acid	—	25
Ammonium chromo-molybdate (6 acid)	—	25
Ammonium ferro-molybdate (6 acid)	—	25
Ammonium cobalto-molybdate (6 acid)	—	25
Ammonium nickelo-molybdate (6 acid)	—	25
Ammonium phospho-vanado-molybdate	—	25
Ammonium vanado-molybdate	—	25
Oxides of chromium, cerium and potassium	Alumina	1
Oxides of chromium and antimony	Alumina	9

The above list of catalysts indicates that oxides of group VI metals have been the most widely used materials in conjunction with alumina as a carrier. Other ingredients can be looked upon as promoting or stabilizing agents. Since chromia-alumina and molybdena-alumina have been extensively utilized as dehydrocyclization catalysts it is of interest to compare their behavior in the conversion of normal heptane. Greensfelder, Archibald and Fuller[12] found that chromia-alumina gives a high conversion to toluene at atmospheric pressure and no toluene at 20 atmospheres, while molybdena-alumina gives a very similar conversion at both conditions, the average value being about 25% toluene. At the same time it was found that the molybdena-alumina catalyst is capable of isomerizing normal paraffins while in the presence of chromia-alumina no isomerization took place.

The dehydrocyclization reaction is not confined to paraffins containing a straight chain structure of at least six carbon atoms. For example, considerable work has been done on the conversion of 2,2,4-trimethylpentane,[25,39] wherein para-xylene is the principal aromatic produced. The product analysis obtained in cyclization of various pure paraffins has led to the development of the mechanism theory of cyclization.

In order to be able to evaluate the merits of a mechanism theory, it is well to consider the experimental results first. Extensive work by Hoog, Verheus and Zuiderweg[27] led to the following conclusions:

"(a) Under the given conditions aromatization increases in the order of the series:

> paraffin
> corresponding aliphatic olefin
> corresponding six ring naphthene
> corresponding cycloölefin

(b) Within each of these hydrocarbon groups aromatization increases with the number of carbon atoms.

(c) Branching of the carbon chain may either diminish or increase the suitability for aromatization.

(d) In the aromatization of olefins the position of the double bond may be of great influence on the amount of conversion obtained."

The above conclusions are based on the conversion of various hydrocarbons over a specially prepared pilled chromium oxide catalyst at 465°C, atmospheric pressure and an hourly weight space velocity of about 0.22. The conversion of the various classes in the C_6–C_8 series were as follows:

Hydrocarbon	% Aromatic
Hexane	19.5
Hexene-1	31
Hexene-2	18
Cyclohexane	40
Cyclohexene	73
Heptane	36
Heptene-1	69
Heptene-2	65
Octane	46
Octene-2	57
Ethylcyclohexane	84
3-Methylheptane	35
2,5-Dimethylhexane	52

A number of alternative mechanisms have been proposed. Agreement has been reached by a number of investigators that, as stated by Hoog, Verheus and Zuiderweg:[27] "The cyclization of a paraffin largely proceeds through the dehydrogenation to a corresponding aliphatic olefin." Of particular interest is the mechanism proposed by Twigg[46] on the basis of the results shown above and two alternative mechanisms suggested by Pitkethly and Steiner.[41] According to Twigg, heptane proceeds through the following intermediates:

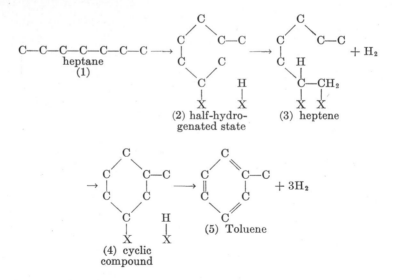

It is interesting to note that throughout the whole process the molecule remains attached to the surface. The conversion from heptene to the cyclic compound proceeds in the same way as the exchange reaction between ethylene and deuterium:

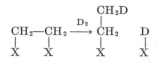

In the cyclization step the CH_2 group takes the place of the D_2 molecule.

The mechanism shown above appeared to be sufficiently plausible to have survived the test of time and other work. It did need, however, two modifications or expansions. The first one involves an explanation of the conversion of substituted paraffins, which lack a six-membered chain, such as 2,2,4-trimethylpentane, into aromatics. The second concerns a clarification of the preponderance of some aromatic species over others in the cyclization reaction.

The answer to both questions was furnished by the excellent work of Herrington and Rideal.[25] These investigators showed that statistical considerations govern the yield of aromatics from paraffins. They also showed that aromatics produced from substituted pentanes are formed through an isomerization of a five-six carbon atom ring system. In most cases, the calculated product distribution of aromatics from paraffins was shown to be in excellent agreement with the observed results. In the case of n-octane, the statistical method, based on diagrammatic representation of solid forms, predicts 33% ethylbenzene, 33% o-xylene, 28% m-xylene and 6% p-xylene. The observed results show 33% ethylbenzene, 33% o-xylene, 27% m-xylene and 7% p-xylene.

In the case of substituted five-carbon atom molecules such as 2,3,4-trimethylpentane, a similar diagrammatic treatment predicts only para- and ortho-xylenes upon cyclization. In this case, as illustrated by Herrington and Rideal, a five membered ring is formed and broken as follows:

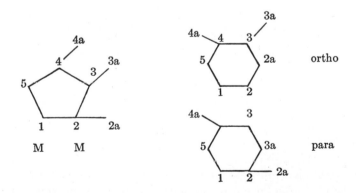

In this simplified case the breaking of the 2–3 bond is preceded by the formation of the 5–1 bond. The subsequent entry into the ring of carbon

2a or 3a leads to the formation of either ortho- or para-xylene upon dehydrogenation. The observed product distribution is 60% ortho and 40% para. The authors calculated a product distribution of 50:50 ortho:para, based on ring opening between the 2–3 position which is adjacent to the point of attachment to the catalyst. If a further postulate is made that ring opening and expansion can occur at any carbon to carbon bond, where at least one carbon atom is substituted and except where the carbon atoms are attached to the catalyst, the calculated product distribution will be 3 ortho to 2 para products, or a 60:40 ratio. If, in addition, ring opening and expansion is permitted to occur between the two carbon atoms attached to the catalyst the calculated product distribution will be 4 ortho and 2 para or a 67:33 ratio.

The complete mechanism of cyclization of 2,3,4-trimethylpentane, as proposed by Herrington and Rideal, involves, after the formation of the five-membered ring and simultaneous liberation of a hydrogen atom, a rotation of the ring and interaction with the chemisorbed hydrogen atom which opens the ring and permits one of the two methyl groups to go into the ring. This particular mechanism explains the greater rate of aromatization of substituted pentanes as compared to substituted cyclopentanes, since a hydrogen atom is liberated in the right position for the cracking reaction when substituted pentanes are cyclized, while the substituted cyclopentanes, already cyclized, do not have that hydrogen atom readily available.

Dehydrogenation of Naphthenes to Aromatics. As pointed out earlier in this chapter, the dehydrogenation of naphthenes to aromatics is the primary octane number improving reaction. The net gain in octane number in this case, however, is not as extensive as it is in the case of the dehydrocyclization of paraffins, since the clear research octane number of most naphthenes is in the range of 65–80. At the same time, the average density shift in the conversion of naphthenes to aromatics is smaller than the case of the conversion of paraffins to aromatics, thus resulting in a somewhat higher yield of reformate. It should be noted that, except in cases of exceedingly high naphthene content stocks, the conversion of naphthenes to aromatics as the sole reaction does not provide sufficient octane number improvement for present day requirements. This is easily seen from a simplified example wherein a stock consisting of 45% naphthenes, 45% paraffins and 10% aromatics is reacted to convert all of the naphthenes to aromatics. The following calculation can then be made, assuming linear blending characteristics, but correcting for a higher blending value of aromatics at low concentrations than at high concentrations:

	Volumes	Charge Octane No. Contribution	Volumes	Product Octane No. Contribution
Paraffins	45	(.45 × 10) = 4.5	45	.45 × 10 = 4.5
Naphthenes	45	(.45 × 70) = 31.5	0	0
Aromatics	10	(.10 × 140) = 14.0	10 + 38.2	.482 × 120 = 57.9
Total Vol.	100		91.2	
Octane Number		50		$\dfrac{4.5 + 57.9}{91.2} = 68$

Thus, it can be clearly seen that the dehydrogenation of naphthenes cannot be the only sustaining reaction in catalytic reforming, since the low octane number paraffins, unless converted at the same time, drastically depress the overall octane number. However, as pointed out earlier, in order to attain the desired result of catalytic reforming, the dehydrogenation of naphthenes has to be an important participating reaction. It should be emphasized that the dehydrogenation of naphthenes during catalytic reforming includes the conversion of both the six- and five-membered ring compounds. If the dehydrogenation were restricted to six-membered ring naphthenes, the net effect would be quite small for some stocks.

The conversion of cyclohexane to benzene over platinum or palladium was discovered by Zelinski[48] in 1911 and since then the reaction has been the subject of numerous investigations. The mechanism of the reaction, particularly from the standpoint of the geometry of the catalytic structure, has also been studied extensively. The work of Balandin[2,3] is notable in this respect, not only from the standpoint of presenting an explanation of heterogeneous reactions in geometric terms, but also on the basis of stimulating a great deal of further work by other investigators. A discussion of such studies is outside of the scope of this chapter, however, one should refer to the excellent critical review "Balandin Contribution to Heterogeneous Catalysis" by Trapnell.[45]

As mentioned above, catalytic reforming involves the conversion of five-membered ring naphthenes in addition to the dehydrogenation of cyclohexane derivatives. In its simplest case, this reaction involves the transformation of methylcyclopentane to benzene:

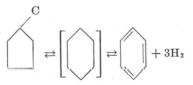

As shown by the equation the intermediate formation of a cyclohexane species appears to be a necessary part of the reaction sequence. Assuming for the present that cyclohexane is an intermediate, the picture becomes more complicated by the fact that at temperatures required for catalytic reforming, that is 475–525°C, the methylcyclopentane-cyclohexane equilibrium is directed to about 95% methylcyclopentane. Thus, unless the operating conditions are such that nearly all of the cyclohexane is permitted to be converted to benzene, a very substantial amount of methylcyclopentane would remain unconverted.

The presently accepted carbonium ion theory of methylcyclopentane-cyclohexane conversion postulates the following steps:

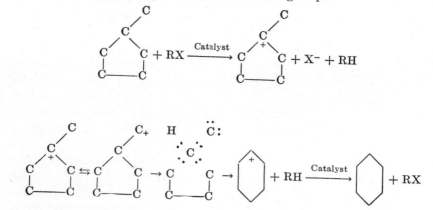

It can be easily seen that the conversion of the primary methylcyclopentane carbonium ion could actually proceed in two directions, one leading to the formation of the cyclohexyl carbonium ion, while the other to the normal hexenyl carbonium ion with subsequent isomerization to produce branched chain hexenes:

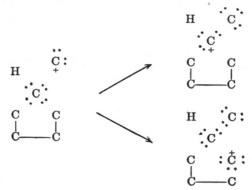

In the presence of hydrogen and a hydrogenation catalyst the overall result of the reaction would be the formation of cyclohexane and hexanes. Thus, depending upon the operating conditions and catalyst, methylcyclopentane can be converted into branched hexanes rather than benzene. The entire system can be looked upon as existing in a dynamic equilibrium, with variable ratios of benzene and hexanes appearing in the product.

From the standpoint of octane number improvement, the conversion of naphthenes to slightly branched paraffins would be undesirable. It should be noted that the above discussion, although directed primarily to methylcyclopentane, applies also to the more substituted cyclopentane derivatives. However, the higher homologs have a more favorable equilibrium relationship between the aromatic and the cyclohexyl hydrocarbons, thus permitting the reaction to proceed more in the desired direction of aromatics rather than paraffins.

The literature contains appreciable information on the conversion of methylcyclopentane and higher five-membered ring naphthenes in the presence of various catalysts. Greensfelder and Fuller[13] have shown that methylcyclopentane is converted to benzene in the presence of a molybdena-alumina catalyst. The percentage conversion diminishes rapidly with the length of the process period. Added hydrogen exerts a beneficial effect in prolonging the process time. The authors believe that isomerization and dehydrogenation occur simultaneously. On the other hand, the considerable work done by Kazansky and co-workers[30] indicates that, at lower temperatures (300–350°C) and atmospheric pressure and in the presence of platinized carbon, methylcyclopentane yields branched hexanes

The overall conclusion in the conversion of naphthenes to aromatics is: (1) The six-membered ring compounds are easily converted with high yields of aromatics. (2) The five-membered ring compounds are more difficult to convert and, in view of side reactions producing paraffins, the yield of aromatics is lower.

Hydrocracking. The term hydrocracking is defined as the interaction of a hydrocarbon with hydrogen which results in a cleavage of a carbon to carbon bond. One hydrogen molecule then adds across the bond which is broken. Examples of such reactions are:

$$C-C-C-C-C + H_2 \rightarrow C-C-C + C-C$$

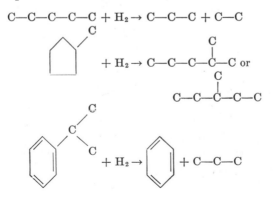

The course of the reaction and the position of cleavage are governed to a large extent by the selection of catalyst and operating conditions. For example, as shown by Haensel, Linn and Ipatieff[22] with a nickel on kieselguhr catalyst the hydrocracking reaction is directed toward splitting off methane to the virtual exclusion of other reactions. For example, cetane is converted to n-C_{15}, n-C_{14}, n-C_{13} etc., and methane, with less than 2 per cent of the product being formed by hydrocracking at positions other than at the end of the chain. The demethylation is favored by lack of branching, thus making it possible to convert neohexane to neopentane with only traces of isopentane being formed.[21] The demethylation reaction has been extended to the conversion of alkylcyclohexanes and alkylaromatics to produce the corresponding hydrocarbons with one carbon atom less than the parent molecule. In the case of alkylcyclopentanes the reaction appears to proceed in the direction of ring opening rather than demethylation, in line with the previously described results of Kazansky and co-workers.[30]

The above results were obtained with a supported nickel catalyst, wherein the support, kieselguhr, does not appear to possess any appreciable acidity to promote carbonium ion type reactions. An entirely different picture is obtained when the hydrogenation component is supported on an acidic material. Data are available on the conversion of a mixture of 66% 2,2,3-trimethylpentane and 34% 2,3,4-trimethylpentane over nickel on kieselguhr, silica-alumina-nickel and silica-alumina catalysts.[17] The experiments were made at pressures ranging from 300–400 psig., 1.5 to 2 space velocity and hydrogen to hydrocarbon ratios of 4 to 5. With the nickel on kieselguhr catalyst at 300°C the conversion to C_7 hydrocarbons (mostly 2,2,3-trimethylbutane and 2,3-dimethylpentane) was 33%, the reaction being primarily one of demethylation. With silica-alumina-nickel at 325°C, 31% of the product was a mixture of C_3–C_5 hydrocarbons, of which isobutane was the major component (86%). The extent of demethylation was very small. With the silica-alumina catalyst at 365°C no reactions of hydrocracking or demethylation were observed.

The results point out that the hydrogenation component by itself catalyzes one type of hydrocracking, and that is demethylation. When an acid acting support alone is used as a catalyst, no reaction takes place even at considerably higher temperatures, while a small amount of hydrogenation component added to the acid acting support induces the reaction to proceed in the direction of splitting off fragments of C_3 and larger. The manner of splitting is in accordance with the carbonium ion mechanism of catalytic cracking which is discussed in detail in a separate chapter of this treatise.

Extensive work by Ciapetta and Hunter[6,7] shows that in the presence of the silica-alumina-nickel catalyst and hydrogen the conversion of normal paraffins leads to the formation of branched hydrocarbons in the products of hydrocracking and isomerization of the parent hydrocarbon. For example, at 348°C, 24.8 atmospheres pressure, 1 space velocity and a hydrogen to hydrocarbon ratio of 4, 100 mols of normal octane give 11 mols C_3H_8, 18 mols isobutane, 12 mols normal butane, 10 mols isopentane, 2.5 mols normal pentane and 70 mols of branched chain octanes, mostly of the monomethyl structure. The authors also indicate that in the absence of hydrogen a nickel-silica-alumina catalyst does not induce isomerization, as shown by experiments using nitrogen and n-hexane.

Since hydrocracking produces lower boiling hydrocarbons which have higher octane numbers and lower densities than the parent hydrocarbons, the reaction should be considered from the standpoint of utility in catalytic reforming. With lower boiling constituents, that is, C_6–C_8 hydrocarbons, hydrocracking does not appear to be desirable since at least one, if not both, of the products of hydrocracking, are butanes or lighter:

$$\text{Primary Products}$$
$$C_6H_{14} \xrightarrow{H_2} 2C_3H_8$$
$$C_7H_{16} \xrightarrow{H_2} C_3H_8 + iC_4H_{10}$$
$$2C_8H_{18} \xrightarrow{2H_2} iC_4H_{10} + nC_4H_{10} + iC_5H_{12} + C_3H_8$$

With higher boiling constituents, that is C_9–C_{12} hydrocarbons, hydrocracking can be an efficient reaction from the standpoint of increasing the octane number without an appreciable loss in yield. In the absence of data, only rough calculations can be made which would give an approximate picture of the yield-octane relationship for hydrocracking of a C_9–C_{12} paraffinic feedstock. For example, one can start with an equimolar mixture of C_9–C_{12} paraffins and permit hydrocracking to occur equally to all hydrocarbons present. It must be assumed that no methane or ethane would be formed and all the remaining bonds would be equally susceptible to hydrocracking. The isomer distribution among the products of hydrocracking can be assumed to be that of equilibrium, although in some instances it has been demonstrated that the iso concentration exceeds the equilibrium value. Using these assumptions the calculated yield of C_4–C_9 hydrocarbons is about 102% by volume of the charge, despite the formation of a substantial amount of propane. The C_4–C_9 product has a calculated clear F-1 octane number of about 70 and a leaded value of about 90. The charging stock has a clear octane of appreciably below zero, thus illustrating that there is a considerable overall octane improvement. If hydrocracking were the only reaction taking place, its utility would be rather limited because of the limit on octane number and the excessive production of C_4 and C_5 hydrocarbons. This would result in the formation of a gasoline having too high a vapor pressure.

On the other hand, hydrocracking, as a supporting reaction, can be very useful when operating primarily on higher boiling paraffins. This is particularly true where it is permitted to take place in conjunction with dehydrogenation of naphthenes and dehydrocyclization of paraffins. It provides for the production of a full boiling range gasoline having a relatively uniform octane number throughout the boiling range. The reaction is especially useful in cases where the octane number requirement is not too high.

The conversion of naphthenes into paraffins by hydrocracking is not a desirable reaction in catalytic reforming since it would tend to reduce the potential yield of aromatics.

Commercial Operations

In the earlier sections of this chapter it was attempted to show how individual classes and types of hydrocarbons present in a naphtha can react to produce an increase in octane number. The resulting yield octane relationship was also indicated. The present section deals with commercial operations in the field of catalytic reforming.

Historical. The first large scale catalytic reforming operation was hydroforming. Four units were put into operation just before 1941 and four additional units were built during the war years. These units were utilized for the production of toluene and aviation gasoline blending components during the war. Later, most of these units were converted to the production of motor gasoline.

No new commercial catalytic reforming units were installed during the four year period following World War II. In 1949 the first commercial U.O.P. Platforming unit was put into operation. This process for the conversion of straight run stocks into premium gasoline found wide acceptance by the petroleum industry and by the end of 1953 some 36 units, with a combined capacity of 113,900 barrels per day, were in operation. A number of these units are used for the production of aromatic hydrocarbons, i.e., benzene, toluene and xylenes.

The first commercial Catforming unit for the production of gasoline was put into operation in 1952 and by the end of 1953 three additional units went on stream.[40] A fluid hydroforming unit was in operation in 1953.[40] Very recently a Houdriforming unit for the production of aromatics was also started.[5]

Hydroforming. An excellent review of the hydroforming operations has been presented by Hill, Vincent and Everett.[26] The process is carried out in the presence of a molybdena-alumina catalyst at temperatures of

900–1000°F, a liquid hourly space velocity of about 0.5 and pressures of 150–300 psig with a high partial pressure of hydrogen in the reaction zone. The operation is cyclical in nature in that two of the four catalyst cases are on regeneration while the other two are on process cycle. The complete cycle involves an elaborate electric time cycle control mechanism to accommodate some nine procedures. For a nine-hour complete cycle these are:

	Time Hours	Minutes
(1) Reaction	4	30
(2) Recycle gas purge		15
(3) Flue gas purge		16½
(4) Downflow burning	2	15
(5) Upflow burning	1	01
(6) Depressuring		07
(7) Recycle gas purge		15
(8) Repressuring		10
(9) Valve changes		10½
Total	9	00

The regeneration step removes the carbonaceous matter from the catalyst, and, in addition, it reoxidizes the catalyst which otherwise loses activity by partial reduction and sulfiding, particularly when high sulfur naphthas are used as charging stocks. As can be seen from the above description of the cycle of operation, the regeneration is carried out under pressure (usually 250–275 psig) and the units are equipped with safety devices to prevent internal explosions.

The reaction products are recovered and fractionated in a four-tower fractionating system to give: (1) a hydrogen rich gas, (2) a depropanized 400°F end point gasoline and (3) an aromatic "polymer" boiling above 400°F.

In a typical operation on a 218–402°F Mid-Continent virgin naphtha at 225 psig, an hourly liquid space velocity of 0.65 and using 3000 cu. ft. of recycle gas (STP) per barrel of charge, the following yield structure was obtained.

	Yield		
	Wt. % of Feed	Vol. % of Feed	Std. cu. ft./bbl. Charge
Debutanized Gasoline	74.4	71.4	
Butanes	4.6	6.1	76
Polymer	2.2	1.7	—
C₄-free gas	16.8	—	1241
Carbon	2.0	—	—

Octane Numbers of Debutanized Gasoline:

Motor Method, clear	77.8
" " +3 cc. TEL	87.3
Research Method, clear (app.)	84
" " +3 cc. TEL (app.)	94

The C_4-free gas contains 53% hydrogen, 22% methane, 14% ethane and 11% propane by volume.

It is of interest to compare these values with those normally obtained in thermal reforming of Midcontinent naphtha:

	Hydroforming[26]		Thermal Reforming
Octane No. M.M. clear, 10# RVP gasoline	79.7	71.5	71–72
Gas Production, cu. ft./bbl. charge			
Hydrogen	659	409	18
Methane	268	150	130
Ethane	176	91	165
Propane	138	53	233
Butane and Butenes	76	60 (app.)	153

These results, particularly where the octane numbers of the gasolines are equal, emphasize the difference between two ways of processing to obtain a product having the same antiknock characteristics. In thermal reforming, a major part of the octane gain is produced by cracking off smaller fragments from a hydrocarbon molecule. In hydroforming a large part of the gain in octane number is achieved by removing hydrogen from a hydrocarbon molecule, thus reducing the need for cracking. This is quite apparent since the production of C_2–C_4 hydrocarbons in hydroforming is considerably less than in thermal reforming. However, the methane production is greater in hydroforming than in thermal reforming, which would indicate that the catalytic action involves not only dehydrogenation but also demethylation. Since methane formation represents an important factor in the yield-octane picture, it has to be reduced very appreciably when higher octane number fuels are to be considered.

In view of the close relationship between fixed bed hydroforming and fluid hydroforming, it is well to consider the latter at this time. A number of papers have been presented on this subject.[31,32,37] As indicated by the authors, the advantages of the fluid hydroforming operation over the fixed bed hydroforming process reside in an improved yield-octane relationship obtained by increasing the recycle gas rate, by reducing thermal cracking in the preheater and by operating at lower temperatures and low pressure. According to McGrath and Hill[32] the fluid hydroforming operation produces yields that are about 2% higher at the same octane number as compared to fixed bed hydroforming.

Platforming.

Introduction. The development of the Platforming process is based upon the idea that a successful catalytic reforming process must meet the following requirements:

(1) The process must be essentially free from undesirable thermal reactions.
(2) Since gasolines contain different hydrocarbon classes and each class requires a different chemical reaction, the process has to be made up of a number of chemical reactions.
(3) The process must be inherently simple, particularly from the standpoint of eliminating non-productive sections of the equipment, such as regeneration.

Description of the Process.[16,28,38] The process is carried out at pressures of 200 to 1000 psig., temperatures ranging from 850 to 980°F and space

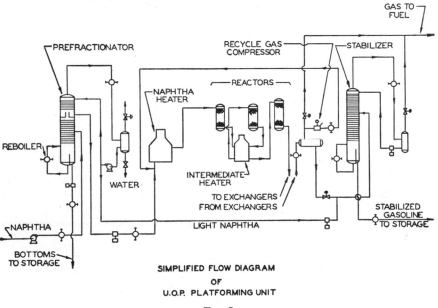

SIMPLIFIED FLOW DIAGRAM
OF
U.O.P. PLATFORMING UNIT

Fig. 2.

velocities of 1 to 6. A hydrogen rich gas is separated from the liquid product and a part of the gas is recycled to contact the fresh feed as it enters the reaction zone. The ratio of hydrogen to hydrocarbon on a molar basis varies from about 3 to 10. The catalyst consists of very small amounts of platinum supported on an acid acting base.

A flow diagram of the process is shown in Figure 2. It will be observed that the fresh feed is first subjected to a prefractionation step to remove a light overhead product and a small amount of bottoms. In a number of units the prefractionation has been eliminated and the material is taken directly from the crude unit. The charge is then preheated, mixed with the hydrogen rich recycle gas and passed through a series of reactors containing the Platforming catalyst. The number of reactors used depends upon the nature of the feedstock and the desired quality of the product. The overall reaction is endothermic and the effluent from the first reactor is reheated to a suitable reaction temperature prior to entering the second reactor. A substantial temperature drop occurs in the upper part of the first reactor and, in order to eliminate long contact of the stock at low temperatures where the reaction rate is relatively low, the usual practice is to make the first and second reactor smaller than the third. After leaving the last reactor the effluent is cooled by heat exchange with the charging stock and the gas is separated from the liquid product. The liquid product is subjected to stabilization to remove propane and hydrogen sulfide as overhead and a stabilized Platformate as a bottoms product.

Reactions. The major reactions taking place in Platforming are:[16]
(1) Dehydrogenation of naphthenes
(2) Hydrocracking of paraffins
(3) Isomerization of paraffins
(4) Dehydrocyclization of paraffins
(5) Desulfurization

In a study of the reactions of pure hydrocarbons over the Platforming catalyst,[19] Haensel and Donaldson have found that at 500 psig., 459°C, a liquid hourly space velocity of 2 and a hydrogen to hydrocarbon ratio of 3.3 n-heptane produces the following yield structure:

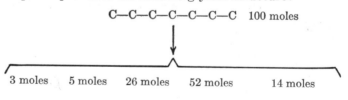

$$C-C-C-C-C-C-C \quad \text{100 moles}$$

| 3 moles | 5 moles | 26 moles | 52 moles | 14 moles |

$$C_1 + C_6 \qquad C_2 + C_5 \qquad C_3 + C_4 \qquad C_7 \text{ isomers} \qquad \text{n-}C_7 \text{ unconverted}$$

These data show a pronounced tendency to produce large fragments which is indicative of a carbonium ion mechanism. However, it is thought that the reaction is somewhat different due to the very rapid quenching by hydrogen of the ions formed, thus eliminating secondary decomposition. The good agreement in the yields of methane and hexane, ethane and pentanes, and, finally, propane and butanes is indicative that the fragments formed do not undergo further hydrocracking.

The composition of the C_7 fraction is of interest from the standpoint of approach to equilibrium. This comparison is shown in the following tabulation:

	Observed	Equilibrium[42]
2,2,3-Trimethylbutane	2.1	3
2,2-Dimethylpentane	2.5	5
3,3-Dimethylpentane	2.8	7
2,4-Dimethylpentane	2.5	5
2,3-Dimethylpentane	9.4	23
2-Methylhexane	29.6	17
3-Methylhexane	31.7	24
3-Ethylpentane	—	3
n-Heptane	19.4	13

The results indicate a fair approach to equilibrium, particularly when it is considered that some of the more reactive isomers may be removed by the hydrocracking reaction.

At the experimental conditions used the conversion of normal heptane to toluene is about 2%. At the same conditions, the conversion to aromatics of a 100% paraffinic C_8–C_{10} fraction (hydrogenated Fischer Tropsch Product) is about 25%.[8] A lower operating pressure produces a still higher yield of aromatics by dehydrocyclization.

The study of hydrocracking and isomerization has been extended to the investigation of the behavior of branched chain alkylaromatics. Isopropylbenzene, for example, when processed over the Platforming catalyst at the same conditions as those used for normal heptane, produces the following yield structure:

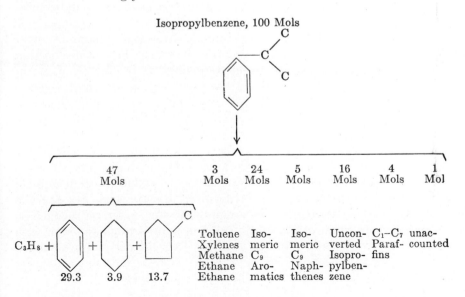

The selective hydrocracking reaction producing propane and benzene is noteworthy. Of particular interest is the fact that the benzene formed during the hydrocracking reaction undergoes hydrogenation and subsequent isomerization into methylcyclopentane. There is also an extensive rearrangement of the isopropylbenzene to produce trimethylbenzenes and ethyltoluenes.

The conversion of methylcyclohexane to toluene was also investigated under conditions of normal operation where the conversion to toluene is not restricted and under conditions of high pressure where the formation of toluene is restricted by equilibrium. At normal operating conditions the product consists of 91.5% toluene, 7.6% unconverted methylcyclohexane and 0.9% unidentified. Under restricted conditions of dehydrogenation 94% of the methylcyclohexane undergoes reaction to give 56% toluene, 33% isomeric alkylcyclopentanes, 4% C_1–C_6 paraffins and 1% unidentified material. The major isomerization product was found to be 1,3-dimethylcyclopentane.

A considerable amount of work has been done on the effect of composition of naphthas upon the yield octane structure.[20] A highly paraffinic Kuwait naphtha and a low paraffin content Venezuela stock having the same boiling range were processed at various severities. Data were obtained over the conversion range of 73 to 99 F-1 (research) clear octane number of the debutanized Platformate. The results obtained indicate that the paraffin hydrocarbons in the low naphthene content feed undergo extensive dehydrocyclization and thereby contribute substantially to the upgrading of the charge. The observed yield differential between low and high paraffin content naphthas at the 95 F-1 clear octane number level was 8.5 volume per cent of the charge. Of this, about 5 volume per cent can be charged to the lower octane number of the highly paraffinic stock which requires more aromatic formation to reach the specified octane number. The balance of the yield differential is associated with the inherently greater volumetric yield losses in the case of dehydrocyclization of paraffins as compared with dehydrogenation of naphthenes to produce aromatics and the greater extent of hydrocracking that accompanies dehydrocyclization.

A comparison of Platforming and thermal reforming has been described by Haensel and Sterba.[23] The work was done using a Pennsylvania straight run gasoline and it was shown that at an F-1 clear octane number of 80 the yield of debutanized Platformate is 88%, while the thermal reformate yield at the same octane number is 66% based on the charge. When polymerization of the C_3–C_4 fraction is used in conjunction with thermal reforming the yield of gasoline having an octane number of 80 increases to 77%.

Of particular interest is the hydrocarbon class analysis of the charging stock, thermal reformate and Platformate. These are shown in graphical form (Figure 3). It will be observed that in the charge stock, with a boiling range of 140–390°F, the naphthene content is quite uniform in the range of 20–100% of the material. The aromatics are also fairly uniformly distributed in the region of 40–100% of the gasoline. In the case of the thermal reformate the formation of olefins and cycloölefins is an important reaction. At the same time, there is some loss of naphthenes and a slight gain in aromatics. Actually, based on the feed, the net aromatic production is very small and the increase in aromatic concentration shown in the product is the result of the destruction of the nonaromatic material. An analysis of the Platformate indicates a large gain in aromatics and a corresponding loss of naphthenes. The general shift in the direction of a parafinic lower boiling fraction and an aromatic higher boiling fraction is due to the fact that as paraffins are isomerized and hydrocracked the average boiling point is lowered, while as naphthenes are converted into aromatics the average boiling point increases.

The following information has been obtained in commercial operation on a Midcontinent charge stock:

Analysis:	Reactor Charge	Platformate
API Gravity @ 60°F	56.1	56.3
Specific Gravity @ 60°F	0.7543	0.7535
Engler Distillation IBP °F	192	102
10%	231	149
30	256	206
50	277	249
70	299	283
90	325	324
E.P.	362	376
Octane Number		
F-1 Clear	44.1	83.9
F-1 + 3 cc TEL/gal.	67.2	94.7
Reid Vapor Pressure	1.4	9.2
% Sulfur	0.025	0.0021
% Paraffins	43.8	53.0
% Naphthenes	47.5	10.3
% Aromatics	7.6	35.8
% Olefins	1.1	0.9

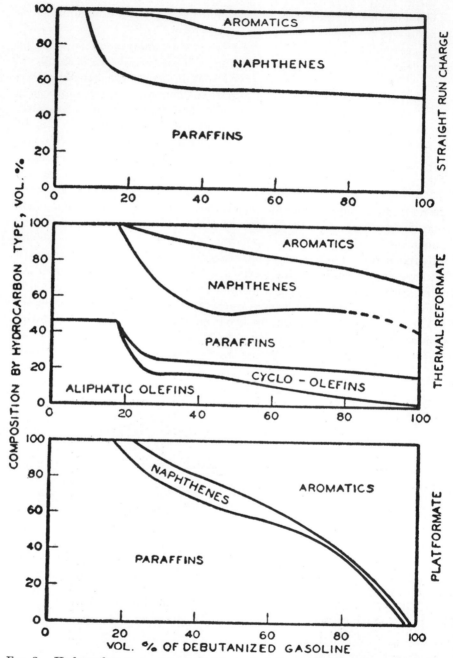

Fig. 3.　Hydrocarbon-type content of debutanized Pennsylvania straight-run gasoline, platformate, and thermal reformate.

The yield structure, based on the feed, is as follows:

Component Yields	Weight %	Volume %	Std. Cu. Ft./Bbl.
Hydrogen	1.11	—	551
Methane	0.46	—	29
Ethane	1.12	—	37
Propane	3.32	—	75
Butanes	4.09	5.4	
Pentanes	6.96	8.4	
C_6^+	82.94	80.5	
Total	100.00		
C_5^+ yield, volume % of feed		88.9	
C_4^+ yield, volume % of feed		94.3	

The above results indicate a good selectivity of reaction, particularly from the standpoint of the relatively small production of methane and ethane.

Catforming. The operation of a 750 b/d Catforming unit has been described by Milner.[35] The process is a continuous fixed bed operation with reactor temperatures ranging from 875–975°F, a reactor pressure of 500 psig., a gas recycle to naphtha ratio of 10 and a weight space velocity of 3. It is also stated that the catalyst may be occasionally subjected to regeneration to remove the carbonaceous deposits.

The results obtained in processing two different stocks are shown below:

Stock	I		II	
	Feed	Reformate	Feed	Reformate
API Gravity	56.3	56.6	62.7	64.7
Reid Vapor Pressure	3.4	7.3	5.0	6.6
IBP °F	126	98	116	100
10%	200	146	198	140
30	239	196	240	178
50	267	235	275	218
70	297	270	303	258
90	340	320	341	310
E.P.	379	392	382	378
F-1 Cl. Octane No.	56	79.3	30.8	64.0
% Paraffins	50.6	49.6	74.8	74.8
% Naphthenes	36.5	15.3	20.2	8.1
% Aromatics	12.9	35.1	5.2	17.1

As shown by the author the yields of hydrogen for stock I is 0.6 weight % of feed, while the yield of C_1–C_3 gases is 4.5%. For stock II the hydrogen yield is 0.2 weight % of feed, while the C_1–C_3 yield is 4.6%. This would indicate a yield of C_4^+ product of about 95% by volume of the feed for both stocks.

Houdriforming. The conversion of various pure hydrocarbons over the Houdriforming catalyst have been investigated by Heinemann, Mills, Hattman and Kirsch.[24] The authors define the catalyst as consisting of special preparations of precious metals of group VIII of the Periodic Table on an acid support. It was found that in the conversion of cyclohexane at 950°F, 300 psig., a liquid space velocity of 3 and hydrogen to hydrocarbon ratio of 4 the yield of debutanized product was 82.4%, of which 91.5% was benzene. The residual material is reported to be a mixture of C_6 and C_7 paraffins. In the work on methylcyclopentane at 300 psig., 6 space velocity and a hydrogen to hydrocarbon ratio of 4, the conversion to benzene amounts to about one-half of the total methylcyclopentane reacted. This particular ratio does not change with temperature over the range of 900 to 975°F. The major products, in addition to benzene, are C_6 paraffins and smaller amounts of butane and lighter gases. The authors have found, in studying the isomerization of n-heptane, that the cracking reaction can be inhibited by the introduction of 15% benzene based on the feed.

In another paper dealing with Houdriforming, Mills, Heinemann, Milliken and Oblad[34] postulate the catalytic mechanism. The authors believe that methylcyclopentane may undergo dehydrogenation to methylcyclopentene, the olefin then leaves the dehydrogenation site and moves to an isomerization site and at that point an equilibrium is established between methylcyclopentene and cyclohexene. Although the equilibrium is stronger in favor of methylcyclopentene, cyclohexene undergoes rapid dehydrogenation, thus converting more methylcyclopentene to cyclohexene. In the time that the shifting takes place from one site to another, the intermediates are quite vulnerable to other reactions, thus producing ring opening and further hydrocracking. The authors also propose that it is not essential that all 6-hydrogen atoms be removed simultaneously from cyclohexane, as postulated by Balandin, but suggest that the cyclohexane to benzene conversion may proceed stepwise through an olefin and diolefin during a single residence period on the catalyst surface.

Production of Aromatics. Since the formation of aromatic hydrocarbons is one of the major reactions in catalytic reforming, it is logical that this method of processing should be applicable for the production of specific aromatic hydrocarbons. Indeed, this has been the case, and at the present time substantial amounts of benzene, toluene and xylenes are produced from petroleum.

A number of Platforming units are used to produce benzene and toluene in conjunction with gasoline in a blocked-out type of operation. Others are designed specifically for the production of benzene, toluene and xylenes. In general, the production of aromatics is carried out at lower pressures than the production of gasoline. The recovery of pure aromatic hydrocarbons is normally carried out by extraction, such as the Udex process, or by extractive distillation.

The successful production of benzene from a C_6 fraction depends upon the conversion of both methylcyclopentane and cyclohexane to benzene. Methylcyclopentane, as shown in an earlier section of this chapter, can undergo hydrocracking readily to form hexanes, therefore conditions of operation must be selected to produce minimum side reactions. This is particularly true in cases where the methylcyclopentane concentration exceeds that of cyclohexane. As shown by Haensel and Berger,[18] a C_6–C_7 cut containing methylcyclopentane and cyclohexane in a ratio of 3 to 1 can be converted to benzene over the Platforming catalyst in yields of 92% of the theoretical conversion.

Catalytic Reforming of Cracked Gasolines. In many instances it is desirable to desulfurize, saturate and increase the octane number of cracked gasolines. Since thermally cracked gasolines rely primarily upon the olefin content for their octane number, the saturation of the olefins would markedly reduce the octane number. Thus, it is necessary to induce other reactions, such as aromatization, isomerization and hydrocracking, to raise the octane number to the desired level. The following table gives the results obtained in Platforming a blend of 70% Santa Maria coker distillate and 30% Los Angeles Basin straight-run naphtha.

TABLE III. PLATFORMING OF BLEND OF COKER DISTILLATE AND STRAIGHT-RUN NAPHTHA

Inspections	Feed	Debutanized Platformate
Gravity, Deg. API	52.2	52.1
Reid Vapor Pressure, lb.	—	2.8
Sulfur, % by Wt.	1.75	0.0007
Bromine Number	50.0	1.8
Octane Numbers:		
F-1 Clear	68.3	85.0
F-1 + 2 cc TEL	74.6	94.2
ASTM Distillation, Deg. F		
IBP	166	130
50%	272	250
E.P.	360	394
Yields, based on feed		
Dry Gas, % by Wt.	7.4	
Butanes, % by Vol.	4.0	
10-lb. RVP Platformate, % by Vol.	99.2	
Outside Butane, % by Vol.	6.3	

It will be observed that the elimination of sulfur from the charge is virtually complete along with a substantial increase in octane number and saturation of olefins.

The upgrading of cracked gasolines represents an important link in the production of high octane number fuels from crude.

References

1. Archibald, R. C., and Greensfelder, B. S., *Ind. Eng. Chem.*, **37**, 356 (1945).
2. Balandin, A. A., *J. Phys. Chem.*, (U.S.S.R.) **B2**, 289 (1929).
3. Balandin, A. A., *J. Phys. Chem.*, (U.S.S.R.) **B3**, 167 (1929).
4. Berger, C. V., Universal Oil Products Co., Unpublished data.
5. *Chem. Eng. News*, **31**, 5174 (1953).
6. Ciapetta, F. G., and Hunter, J. B., *Ind. Eng. Chem.*, **45**, 147 (1953).
7. Ciapetta, F. G., and Hunter, J. B., *Ind. Eng. Chem.*, **45**, 155 (1953).
8. Donaldson, G. R., Pasik, L. F., and Haensel, V., Paper presented before the National Meeting of the American Chemical Society, New York, September, 1954.
9. Fisher, F. E., Watts, H. C., Harris, G. E., and Hollenbeck, C. M., *Ind. Eng. Chem.*, **38**, 61 (1946).
10. Forziati, A. F., Willingham, C. B., Mair, B. J., and Rossini, F. D., *Petroleum Refiner*, **22**, No. 11, 109 (1943).
11. Frost, A. V., *Oil Gas J.*, **43**, No. 12, 165 (1944).
12. Greensfelder, B. S., Archibald, R. C., and Fuller, D. L., *Chem. Eng. Progr.*, **43**, 561 (1947).
13. Greensfelder, B. S., and Fuller, D. L., *J. Am. Chem. Soc.*, **67**, 2171 (1945).
14. Grosse, A. V., and Ipatieff, V. N., *Ind. Eng. Chem.*, **32**, 268 (1940).
15. Grosse, A. V., Morrell, J. C., and Mattox, W. J., *Ind. Eng. Chem.*, **32**, 528 (1940).
16. Haensel, V., Paper presented before the Western Petroleum Refiners Assn., San Antonio, Texas, March 28, 1950.
17. Haensel, V., Universal Oil Products Co., Unpublished data.
18. Haensel, V., and Berger, C. V., *Petroleum Processing*, **6**, 265 (1951).
19. Haensel, V., and Donaldson, G. R., *Ind. Eng. Chem.*, **43**, 2102 (1951).
20. Haensel, V., and Donaldson, G. R., *Petroleum Processing*, **8**, 236 (1953).
21. Haensel, V., and Ipatieff, V. N., *J. Am. Chem. Soc.*, **68**, 345 (1946).
22. Haensel, V., Linn, C. B., and Ipatieff, V. N., Paper presented before the Shreveport Section of the American Chemical Society, December 12, 1948.
23. Haensel, V., and Sterba, M. J., *Am. Chem. Soc.*, Adv. in Chem. Series, No. 5, p. 60, 1951.
24. Heinemann, H., Mills, G. A., Hattman, J. B., and Kirsch, F. W., *Ind. Eng. Chem.*, **45**, 130 (1953).
25. Herrington, E. F. G., and Rideal, E. K., *Proc. Roy. Soc.*, (London) A., **434**, 447 (1945).
26. Hill, L. R., Vincent, G. A., and Everett, E. F., *Trans. Am. Inst. Chem. Engrs.*, **42**, No. 4, 611 (1946).
27. Hoog, H., Verheus, J., and Zuiderweg, F. J., *Trans. Faraday Soc.*, **35**, 993 (1939).
28. Kastens, M. L., and Sutherland, R., *Ind. Eng. Chem.*, **42**, 582 (1950).
29. Kazansky, B. A., and Plate, A. F., *Ber.*, **69**, 1862 (1936).
30. Kazansky, B. A., Rumayuzer, Z. A., and Batnev, M. I., *Bull. acad. sci.*, (U.R.S.S.) **5**, 473, 483 (1947).

31. McGrath, H. G., *Petroleum Refiner*, **30**, No. 12, 102 (1951).
32. McGrath, H. G., and Hill, L. R., *Am. Chem. Soc.*, Adv. in Chem. Series, No. 5, p. 39, 1951.
33. Mavity, J. M., Universal Oil Products Co., Unpublished data.
34. Mills, G. A., Heinemann, H., Milliken, T. H., and Oblad, A. G., *Ind. Eng. Chem.*, **45**, 134 (1953).
35. Milner, B. E., *World Petroleum*, **24**, No. 1, 50 (1953).
36. Moldavsky, B. L., Kamusher, G. D., and Kobylskaya, M. V., *J. Gen. Chem.*, (U.S.S.R.) **7**, 169, 1835 (1937).
37. Murphree, E. V., *Petroleum Refiner*, **30**, No. 12, 97 (1951).
38. Nelson, E. F., *Oil Gas J.*, **47**, No. 49, 95, (1949).
39. Obolentsev, R. D., and Usov, Yu. M., *J. Gen. Chem.*, (U.S.S.R.) **16**, 933 (1946).
40. *Petroleum Refiner*, **32**, No. 9, 98 (1953).
41. Pitkethly, R. C., and Steiner, H., *Trans. Faraday Soc.*, **35**, 979 (1939).
42. Rossini, F. D., in "Physical Chemistry of Hydrocarbons," edited by A. Farkas, Vol. I, p. 363, New York, Academic Press Inc., 1950.
43. Rossini, F. D., et al, "Selected Values of Properties of Hydrocarbons," Circular of The National Bureau of Standards, C461, U. S. Government, 1947.
44. Russell, A. S., and Stokes, J. J., Jr., *Ind. Eng. Chem.*, **38**, 1071 (1946).
45. Trapnell, B. M. W., in "Advances in Catalysis," **3**, p. 1, New York, Academic Press Inc.
46. Twigg, G. H., *Trans. Faraday Soc.*, **35**, 1006 (1939).
47. Weinert, P. C., Sterba, M. J., Haensel, V., and Grote, H. W., Paper presented before the 17th Mid-Year Meeting of the American Petroleum Institute's Division of Refining, San Francisco, California, May 14, 1952.
48. Zelinski, N. D., *Ber.*, **44**, 3121 (1911).

CHAPTER 30

CATALYTIC DEHYDROGENATION

K. Kearby

Esso Laboratories—Chemical Division, Standard Oil Development Company, Linden, N. J.

Processes for making olefins and diolefins by catalytic dehydrogenation were first applied extensively in the United States during World War II. Methods of making olefins had been available for several years, as a result of intensive research carried out by the petroleum industry in the period 1930 to 1940. However, these processes had been too costly to make olefins for existing requirements at that time. Also, the need for gaseous olefins was relatively low because of the abundant supply that became available from catalytic cracking. During the war the requirements of olefins and diolefins for alkylate gasoline and synthetic rubber led to the installation of numerous dehydrogenation plants.

Prior to the increased demands brought on by the Synthetic Rubber program, styrene was being made on a small scale by dehydrogenating ethyl benzene. The petroleum industry was beginning to install plants to produce some butadiene by the high-temperature thermal cracking of naphthas and gas-oils. The thermal cracking process also produced other useful diolefins such as isoprene and cyclopentadiene, but the yields of butadiene were only 2 to 5 per cent on feed. The use of thermal cracking was expanded to some extent at the outset of World War II in order to provide so-called "quickie" butadiene. However, the largest share of butadiene production was allotted to a process based on the dehydrogenation of butenes. Only a small proportion of the program utilized butane as a feedstock. The more expensive process of converting ethyl alcohol into butadiene was also used extensively, but the German process of making butadiene from acetylene was not adopted as a part of the U. S. Synthetic Rubber program. After considering all factors, the government allocated butadiene production as shown in Table 1.

The largest share of the butadiene program was allocated to a new butene dehydrogenation process which became known as the "Jersey Process" because it had been developed by the Standard Oil Development Company, a subsidiary of Standard Oil Co., N. J.[72] This process was relatively simple from an engineering viewpoint, and plants were designed on the basis of laboratory data without the usual preliminary large pilot-plant program. It is commendable that these plants met design capacity; and, with subsequent catalyst improvements, the dehydrogenation sections were able to exceed design capacity. The butene dehydrogenation catalysts also proved superior to existing catalysts for dehydrogenating ethyl benzene to styrene and were used extensively in these plants as well.

TABLE 1

| | Capacity, Short Tons/Year | |
Process	Orig. Allocation	1953 Capacity*
Butene dehydrogenation	350,000†	⎫
Butane dehydrogenation	75,000	⎬ 539,000
Thermal cracking	67,000	⎭
Alcohol	220,000	215,000

* Installed and under construction.[81]
† Includes 45,000 ton/yr of butenes made from butane.

Catalytic dehydrogenation has thus been applied to the production of olefins, diolefins and styrenes. Some of the more important aspects of these three reactions are discussed in this chapter. Another important dehydrogenation reaction, the formation of aromatic hydrocarbons, is dealt with in Chapter 29.

Thermodynamic Equilibria in Dehydrogenation

Typical dehydrogenation reactions are illustrated by the following equations:

(1) $$CH_3—CH_2—CH_2—CH_3 \xrightarrow{\text{catalyst}} CH_3—CH_2—CH{=}CH_2 + H_2$$
$n\text{-}butane$ $1\text{-}butene$

(2) $$CH_3—CH_2—CH_2—CH_3 \xrightarrow{\text{catalyst}} CH_2{=}CH—CH{=}CH_2 + 2H_2$$
$n\text{-}butane$ $1,3\text{-}butadiene$

(3) $$CH_2{=}CH—CH_2—CH_3 \xrightarrow{\text{catalyst}} CH_2{=}CH—CH{=}CH_2 + H_2$$
$1\text{-}butene$ $1,3\text{-}butadiene$

(4)

$ethylbenzene$ $styrene$

The first and third reactions consist of splitting out a hydrogen molecule from butane and butene, respectively. Two hydrogen molecules are removed in reaction (2) which is probably a stepwise combination of reactions (1) and (3). The fourth reaction, the dehydrogenation of an alkyl group on an aromatic ring, forms a double bond in conjugation with an aromatic ring rather than with an olefinic bond. It resembles reaction (3) closely in requiring similar catalysts and reaction conditions.

The extent of dehydrogenation at equilibrium in the above reactions increases with increasing temperature and decreasing pressure. The effect

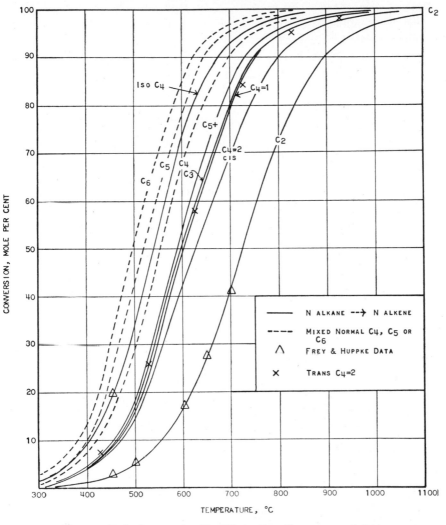

FIG. 1.   Dehydrogenation Equilibria, Paraffins ———— olefins.

of temperature on the dehydrogenation equilibrium of paraffins to olefins is shown in Figure 1 and in Table 2. It is apparent that C_3 and higher paraffins can give a 50 per cent conversion to alpha-olefins at about 600°C. Isobutane can be 50 per cent dehydrogenated at only 540°C, but ethane requires a temperature of 725°C. Although the equilibrium yields of normal, alpha-unsaturated olefins from normal paraffins are very little affected by increasing molecular weight above C_3, the yields of total normal olefins do increase. This is because the number of isomeric cis and trans, internally unsaturated isomers increases with the molecular weight. For example, as shown in Figure 1, a 50 per cent yield of mixed normal hexenes is thermodynamically possible at a temperature of only 495°C, as compared with 555°C for mixed normal butenes and 595°C for propylene.

TABLE 2. DEHYDROGENATION EQUILIBRIA
Temperatures, °C, required for given conversions
(Paraffin → Olefin + H_2)

Conversion Mole %	C_2	C_3	C_{4-1}	C_{4-2} cis	C_{4-2} trans	Normal Mixed	Iso-butene	Pentenes C_{5-1}*	Pentenes Normal Mixed	Hexenes Normal Mixed
5	500	410	415	415	405	375	360	405	360	335
10	555	456	460	470	450	420	405	450	410	380
20	615	510	515	525	505	470	435	505	440	425
30	660	540	545	555	540	505	490	535	465	445
40	695	570	575	590	572	530	515	560	490	470
50	725	595	600	625	598	555	540	585	520	495
60	755	625	630	660	630	580	560	615	545	520
70	790	660	670	700	640	610	590	650	575	550
80	830	700	705	740	710	645	625	685	605	585
90	900	750	753	800	760	700	680	730	650	625
95	960	815	815	860	820	745	730	790	695	670

* Same values hold for C_{6-1} and higher olefins.

TABLE 3. EQUILIBRIUM BETWEEN n-BUTANE, n-BUTENES, AND 1,3-BUTADIENE

	Mol %. Conversion of n-Butane at 1.0 Atm Pressure; Temperature, °C						
	550	600	650	700	750	800	850
To 1,3-butadiene	—	6.0	14	27.5	45	61.5	74
To total n-butenes	—	62.5	69	64.5	54	37.5	23
1-Butene	—	22.5	27	26	22.5	17	10
2-Butene-*cis*	—	16	17	16	13	9	4.5
2-Butene-*trans*	—	24	25	23	18	12.5	6.0

	Mol % Conversion of n-Butane at 0.167 Atm; Temperature, °C						
	550	600	650	700	750	800	850
To 1,3-butadiene	11.5	27.5	48.5	69	82	—	—
To total n-butenes	68.5	64.5	48.5	31.5	17.5	—	—
1-Butene	23.5	23	19	13	7.5	—	—
2-Butene-*cis*	18	16.5	12	7.5	4	—	—
2-Butene-*trans*	27	25	17.5	11	6	—	—

With increasing molecular weight, the paraffins are less stable to cracking, and the indicated higher yields of olefins are therefore not readily formed.   In addition to cracking, paraffins having six or more carbon atoms in a straight chain cyclize to form aromatics, and this also makes it difficult to obtain the high yields of olefins indicated as being thermodynamically possible.

The data in Figure 1 and Table 2 are for the formation of olefins in the absence of diolefin formation. At temperatures above 600°C, buta-

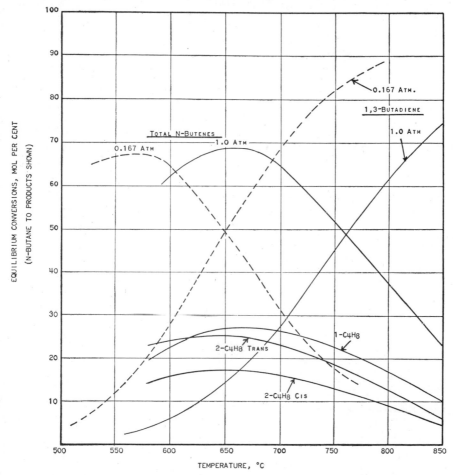

Fɪɢ. 2.   Equilibrium between paraffin, olefins and diolefin (N-butane $\rightleftarrows$ N-butenes $\rightleftarrows$ 1,3-butadiene.)

diene also forms from n-butane. Equilibrium data at 1.0 and 0.167 atmospheres pressure for the simultaneous formation of mixed normal butenes and 1,3 butadiene from n-butane are shown in Figure 2 and are summarized in Table 3.*

* Unpublished calculations kindly contributed by D. W. Wood, Standard Oil Development Company.

The effect of pressure on the equilibrium yields of butenes from *n*-butane at 527°C is illustrated in Table 4, which is not corrected for simultaneous formation of butadiene.

TABLE 4

	Pressure, atm				
	0.01	0.1	1.0	10	100
Conv. to butenes, %	97	80	38.5	13	4

By using low pressures and low temperatures, it is possible to obtain increased dehydrogenation with less degradation to cracked products. In commercial processes for making butadiene and styrene, reduced pressures are usually obtained by using steam as a diluent.

Data for various paraffin-olefin and olefin-diolefin equilibrium relationships are shown in Figures 1 to 4 and in Tables 2, 3 and 5. These values have been calculated from the data of Rossini, Pitzer, *et al.*,[69] and are considered the best presently available.

It should be remembered that equilibrium yields are not necessarily obtained in practice.

Dehydrogenation of Paraffins to Olefins

Catalysts. Although the conversion of paraffins to corresponding mono-olefins was investigated by a number of investigators during the period from 1919 to 1930, no really satisfactory catalyst was found. The choice of chromia catalysts by Frey and Huppke[17] for their studies of the equilibria involved in these reactions was a major factor in the development of a satisfactory catalyst. Their work showed that equilibrium could be closely approached in dehydrogenations to form ethylene, propylene, isobutylene, and normal butenes. Some of their results, as shown in Figure 1, are seen to be in good agreement with presently accepted values.

Frey and Huppke showed that selective dehydrogenation could be obtained at suitable operating conditions, but excessive temperatures or contact times caused cracking reactions to occur. These reactions generally resulted in more hydrogen being produced than olefin, but, in the case of isobutane, considerable methane was formed, giving a lower production of hydrogen. The chromia-gel catalysts used in the early work of Frey and Huppke proved to have rather poor life. A more stable catalyst consisting of chromia containing alumina as a stabilizer was patented by them.[17] Since then, numerous modifications of alumina-chromia catalysts have been reported, and these two components still constitute the best catalysts known for converting butane to either butenes or butadiene.

TABLE 5. TEMPERATURES REQUIRED FOR VARIOUS EQUILIBRIUM CONVERSIONS

% Conv.	n-Butane to 1-Butene		n-Butane to 1,3-C$_4$H$_6$		1-Butene to 1,3-C$_4$H$_6$		cis-2-Butene to 1,3-C$_4$H$_6$	trans-2-Butene to 1,3-C$_4$H$_6$	1-Pentene to 1,3-C$_5$H$_8$ Cis	Trans	Mixed	2-Methyl-1-Butene to Isoprene	Ethyl Benzene to Styrene		i-Propyl Benzene to Me-Styrene
	1.0 Atm	0.1 Atm	1.0 Atm	0.1 Atm	1.0 Atm	0.1 Atm	1.0 Atm	1.0 Atm	1.0 Atm	1.0 Atm	1.0 Atm	1.0 Atm	1.0 Atm	0.1 Atm	1.0 Atm
5	415	350	500	420	435	370	430	450	350	365	335	430	415	350	340
10	460	390	540	440	485	405	480	495	400	410	380	480	465	390	380
20	515	430	585	475	550	445	540	560	455	460	430	545	525	430	420
30	545	455	615	505	595	480	580	600	495	500	460	590	565	455	450
40	575	480	640	525	630	510	610	630	530	535	495	615	595	480	475
50	600	500	660	545	665	540	635	655	560	570	525	650	620	505	500
60	630	525	680	565	700	570	665	685	595	600	555	680	645	535	530
70	670	555	700	585	730	600	695	720	625	630	590	715	675	565	560
80	705	585	715	605	780	625	735	760	665	670	625	760	715	595	595
90	753	625	740	620	855	675	805	825	730	745	680	830	780	630	640
95	815	670	775	630	925	725	855	885	805	825	750	890	845	670	690

Alumina itself has only mild activity, which is greatly enhanced by very small amounts of chromium oxide. Burgin and Groll[9] showed that as little as 2 per cent chromium resulted in a marked improvement, and 15 per cent resulted in further improvement.

TABLE 6. EFFECT OF CHROMIA ON ACTIVATED ALUMINA
1200 Space Velocity, Propane, n-Butane or Isobutane Feed

Catalyst	Alumina		Al_2O_3 + 2% Cr		Al_2O_3 + 12–15% Cr	
Period, Hrs	3		1.5		1.0	
Temperature, °C	650		625		550–575	
Olefin						
	% Yield	Ratio*	% Yield	Ratio*	% Yield	Ratio*
Propene	23.6	0.87	37.4	0.95	25.8	0.95 (575°C)
n-Butenes	—	—	22	0.60	30.1	0.97 (550°C)
Isobutene	31	0.74	35.5	0.78	37	0.83 (550°C)

* Ratio dehydrogenated olefin to total olefins.

Alumina-chromia compositions ranging from as low as 3 per cent to as high as 60 per cent Cr_2O_3 are effective catalysts for dehydrogenating paraffins to olefins. Compositions containing about 20 per cent Cr_2O_3 are probably in most general use. These compositions are more active than magnesia-chromia and give higher yields of olefins than do alumina-molybdena catalysts.

Early studies by the Universal Oil Co.[22] used a catalyst containing only 3 to 4 per cent Cr_2O_3. In Germany, an 8 per cent Cr_2O_3 catalyst has been used. A publication by Howard[32] indicates that the Kellogg Co. considered $90Al_2O_3$-$10Cr_2O_3$ a suitable composition. The Phillips Co. have indicated that their commercial process was improved by increasing the Cr_2O_3 content of the catalyst.[28] The improved composition may be the 17 to 19 per cent Cr_2O_3 catalyst described as a "Commercial Catalyst" by Pitzer.[62] Pitzer has also indicated advantage for a $40Cr_2O_3$-$10BeO$-$50Al_2O_3$ composition made by digestion with three times its weight of 70 per cent nitric acid followed by drying and calcining. A further study of this type of catalyst produced good results with $60Cr_2O_3$-$5BeO$-$35Al_2O_3$ and $40Cr_2O_3$-$0.75KOH$-$59Al_2O_3$ catalysts, digested with either nitric acid or ammonium nitrate solutions.[63] Owen also used an 18 per cent Cr_2O_3 catalyst and increased the selectivity from 76 to 80 per cent, at a 35 to 40 per cent conversion level, by putting the Cr_2O_3 only on the outer surface of alumina pills.[57]

Riesz et al.[68] claimed advantages for a $75Al_2O_3$-$25Cr_2O_3$ composition made by coprecipitation rather than by impregnation of active alumina. Equilibrium yields could be obtained at 500°C. The use of alkali or alkaline earth promoters to reduce carbon formation has been described by several investigators.[11,23,29,59] The use of about 1 per cent added K_2O

appears to be described most frequently. It is also possible to improve the selectivity of alumina-chromia catalysts by calcining them at high temperatures to reduce their carbon-forming tendencies.

Regenerated alumina-chromia catalysts usually contain some hexavalent chromium oxides; and catalysts containing only 3 to 5 per cent Cr_2O_3 are yellow in color rather than green. Activity can sometimes be restored to alumina-chromia catalysts by oxidation at high temperatures to increase the hexavalent chromium content. Alkalis in the catalyst appear to promote the maintenance of the higher oxidation state. Only meager data have been published on the effect of oxidation and reduction on this type of catalyst.[1,42]

Effect of Operating Conditions. The importance of choosing optimum operating conditions for the dehydrogenation of paraffins to monoolefins is illustrated by the results of Grosse and Ipatieff.[22] At optimum conditions they obtained ultimate recycle yields of olefins as high as 90 per cent, with a product gas containing 90 per cent hydrogen. However, at a given temperature, a fairly critical choice of feed rate was required to obtain maximum selectivity to olefins, as shown by the following data for a $97Al_2O_3$-$3Cr_2O_3$ catalyst.

TABLE 7

Contact Time, seconds	Volume % Olefins in Product Gas				
	n-Butane		Isobutane		
	500°C	600°C	500°C	550°C	600°C
1	—	24.5	—	9.5	25
2	11	30	—	16	31
4	20	24.5	7.5	22	33
8	18.5	—	12	24.5	22
20	14.5	—	18	22.5	—
100	—	—	13	—	—

Maximum olefin contents of exit gas were 21, 30 and 33 per cent for propane, n-butane, and isobutane feeds, respectively. Their data also illustrate the advantages of catalytic over thermal dehydrogenation.

TABLE 8

Feed	Exit Gas Composition % Olefin		Production Rate V olefin/V reactor/hr	
	Catalytic	Thermal	Catalytic	Thermal
Isobutane	31	18	156	24
n-Butane	30	4	152	40

The data of Grosse and Ipatieff show little advantage for isobutane as a feedstock as compared with n-butane, although its thermodynamic equilibrium is more favorable. As shown above, Burgin and Groll obtained higher olefin yields with isobutane, and their results are more typical of numerous other investigators. For example, Perkins[60] shows

yields of 80 per cent from isobutane, as compared with 74 per cent from
n-butane and 89 per cent from propane. Ethane requires such high
temperatures that catalytic dehydrogenation has thus far shown no advantage over thermal dehydrogenation. The conversion of ethane and
propane to ethylene by catalytic, thermal, and partial oxidation processes
has been described by numerous investigators.[58,64,71,75]

Hanson and Hays[28] have shown the effect of operating conditions on
butane dehydrogenation in tests carried out by the Phillips Petroleum
Co. at the Plains plant. Data showing the effect of space velocity and
catalyst age are given in Table 9.

TABLE 9

Space Velocity V/V/hr	Catalyst 1.25 days old			Catalyst 61.5 days old		
	Conv. %	Select. to Olefin %	Carbon Wt % on Feed	Conv. %	Select. to Olefin %	Carbon Wt % on Feed
500	47.4	75.2	2.6	34.3	66	0.9
1000	31.8	81.4	1.4	25.2	72	0.4

However, a newer catalyst gave somewhat higher conversions and yields
of coke. Average values for 100 days of operation showed a 9 per cent
increase in conversion and an 8 per cent increase in selectivity for the
new catalyst (34.2 per cent conversion and 80.5 per cent selectivity).

Conversions increased and selectivities decreased with increasing temperature. For example, as the temperature of the flue gas heating the
catalyst tubes was increased from 1150 to 1250°F, the conversion increased from 26 to 37 per cent, and the selectivity decreased from 83 to
67 per cent.

Increased amounts of butenes in the recycle butane also decreased
conversions. For example, 8 per cent butenes in the feed decreased the
conversion and selectivity to 74 and 87 per cent of values without butene.
Carbon deposition was increased by 50 per cent, whereas butadiene was
increased only 11 per cent.

Product Distribution. The results given above indicated that
operating variables had a marked effect on formation of cracked products.
However, the proportions of butene isomers were relatively constant
(33.5 per cent 1-butene, 38 per cent trans-2-butene, 28.5 per cent cis-2-
butene). At conversion levels in the range of 20 to 30 per cent, it is
possible to obtain butene selectivities (or ultimate recycle yields) of 85
to 90 per cent. These selectivities usually decrease as the conversion level
increases and as the yield of olefin approaches equilibrium. They also
depend greatly on the particular catalyst used and on the choice of
operating conditions.

Dodd and Watson[13] have published results of a study of the kinetics
of butane dehydrogenation which led to rather optimistic predictions of

selectivities at high conversion levels, but agreed with their experimentally determined values at low conversion levels. Their results are compared in Table 10 with other experimental data.[76] The differences in the experimental results probably merely reflect differences in operating conditions.

TABLE 10. EFFECT OF CONVERSION LEVEL ON DEHYDROGENATION SELECTIVITY
n-Butane, Al_2O_3-Cr_2O_3 Catalysts

	Conversion, %				
	10	20	30	40	50
Selectivity to butenes					
Dodd *et al.* (calc'd)	93	92	91	87	72
Dodd *et al.* (expm.)	95	92	89	72	—
S.O.D. data[76]	—	—	84	77	66

The degradation of butane at higher conversion levels is primarily to cracked products that include methane, ethane, ethylene, propane and propylene. The amount of cracking can vary considerably, depending on the catalyst and the operating conditions used, as illustrated in Table 11.

TABLE 11. PRODUCT DISTRIBUTION FROM BUTANE DEHYDROGENATION[76]

Catalyst	$91Al_2O_3$-$9Cr_2O_3$			$60Al_2O_3$-$40Cr_2O_3$		
Temperature, °F	1010–1030			1075		
Butane Conversion, %	30	40	50	30	40	50
% Reacted butane to:*						
Butene	84	77	66	65	59	53
Butadiene	2.3	2.6	2.6	5.7	5.2	4.8
CH_4	1.9	3.4	5.8	5.3	6.8	8.5
$C_2H_4 + C_2H_6$	2.0	3.9	7.0	7.8	9.1	10.7
$C_3H_6 + C_3H_8$	3.2	5.1	7.9	10.2	11.4	12.6
Carbon	2.4	3.0	6.0	6.4	8.5	10.2

* Mol per cent selectivity based on carbon balance only.

The selectivities to isobutylene and C_5^+ products were only 1 to 3 per cent, respectively, and it is possible that the feed contained small amounts of these materials.

The ratio of olefins to parafins in the C_2 cut for the above tests was about 0.2 at 1020°F and 0.3 at 1075°F. The ratio of propylene to propane was about 1.0 at 1020°F and 2.0 at 1075°F. The lower content of ethylene may reflect the lower equilibrium value for ethylene, some of the ethylene formed by cracking being hydrogenated to ethane.

The selectivity of dehydrogenation decreased with increasing pressure as well as with increasing temperature. Comparative data on the $91Al_2O_3$-$9Cr_2O_3$ catalyst at a 30 per cent conversion level indicated a decrease from 82 to 68 per cent selectivity as the pressure was increased from 1 to 3 atmospheres. Subatmospheric pressures resulted in improved selectivity as compared with atmospheric pressure operation.

Commercial Processes for Dehydrogenating Butane. The dehydrogenation of butanes to butylenes is usually carried out at temperatures of 540 to 600°C and about one atmosphere pressure or lower. The endothermic reaction requires about 1000 BTU/lb of butane reacted, and commercial dehydrogenation plants have to provide this heat. Two types of catalytic butane dehydrogenation processes are in use in the United States. The Phillips Petroleum Company process supplies the heat of reaction by passing heated flue gas around two-inch tubes containing the catalyst, whereas the Houdry process operates on short cycles building up sufficient heat in the catalyst during regeneration to furnish the heat of reaction during dehydrogenation.

The Phillips process, which is similar to the Universal Oil Co. process,[27] gives butylene yields of 80 per cent, using an alumina-chromia catalyst in the form of eighth-inch pills. In this process the feed is dried over bauxite, since water is harmful to the catalyst. The process is described in detail by Hanson and Hays.[28] A plant is located at Borger, Texas.

The Houdry process[2,40,80,88] utilizes the heat capacity of the catalyst plus an inert diluent to supply the heat of reaction in butane dehydrogenation. An alumina-chromia catalyst, steamed for 10 hours at 1400°F and mixed with two parts of alundum, has been described.[30,31] Dehydrogenation cycles of only 7 to 15 minutes give a 50°F loss in temperature, and the temperature is then restored by burning carbon off the catalyst with undiluted air. By proper choice of operating conditions, a heat balance is realized between the heat of reaction and that of regeneration. The process can be operated for producing either butylenes or butadiene from n-butane. It is designed for operation at reduced pressures of about 5 inches of mercury, a necessary feature in obtaining good yields of butadiene. Operating temperatures are 1050 to 1100°F at feed rates of 0.8 to 2.0 liquid v/v/hr. In recent operations, the plant at El Segundo, California, has operated to maximize production of butenes, which are then converted to butadiene by the Jersey process (described later).

The I. G. Farbenindustrie dehydrogenated butanes to butylenes for use in making alkylate during World War II.[29] Their process utilized gas-fired catalyst tubes, with the catalyst moving downward through the tubes in a four-hour period. The catalyst was then regenerated in a separate system. Conversions of 20 to 25 per cent per pass, with ultimate yields of 85 per cent, were obtained. An alumina-base catalyst containing 8 per cent Cr_2O_3 and 1 to 2 per cent K_2O was used.

Present Status. It is probable that butane dehydrogenation is still too costly at present to be used as a source of motor gasoline and can only be used for producing more valuable materials. A survey made in 1946 by the M. W. Kellogg Co.[60] indicated that it would not be profitable to dehydrogenate propane or butanes to obtain olefins for alkylation or polymerization. Large amounts of gaseous olefins are produced by thermal and catalytic cracking processes and thus make their production by dehydrogenation processes less necessary. Processes for converting higher paraffins to olefins would probably be attractive if good yields could be obtained.

Formation of Butadiene by Dehydrogenation

Catalytic dehydrogenation is utilized in producing butadiene from both n-butane and n-butylenes. At a given temperature, within the operating range where cracking is not excessive, higher equilibrium yields are obtainable by dehydrogenating butylenes. For example, at 650°C and atmospheric pressure, conversions to butadiene of 47 to 57 per cent are possible from normal butylenes as compared with 14 per cent from n-butane. However, by reducing the pressure to 0.167 atmospheres, the n-butane equilibrium conversion to butadiene increases to 49 per cent, as was shown in Figure 2.

When the Rubber program was frozen, the Houdry process for making butadiene directly from n-butane was considered insufficiently developed to warrant large-scale inclusion in the Program.[70] However, an opportunity to demonstrate the process was afforded when the Government authorized construction of two Houdry plants, one operated by Standard Oil Co. of California at El Segundo, California, and the other, at Toledo, Ohio, by Sun Oil Co. These plants had considerable initial difficulty in meeting design capacity of 15,000 and 18,000 T/yr, producing about 9,000 T/yr each in 1945. However, subsequent operations were improved and design capacity was attained[50] in this type of plant.

The Houdry process was described in the previous section on production of monoolefins. In view of the fact that recent operations in the El Segundo plant maximize the production of butylenes, which are then converted to butadiene by the Jersey process, it appears that the Houdry process is most efficient for making butenes. This tandem operation is similar to that carried out by the Phillips Petroleum Co., which dehydrogenates butanes to butenes over alumina-chromia and then uses a steam-dilution process to convert the butylenes to butadiene. The Phillips steam-dilution process originally operated with a promoted bauxite catalyst but subsequently changed to the superior promoted iron catalysts described below. The design and present capacities of principal dehydrogenation plants producing butadiene are summarized in Table 12.

The process adopted by the government for producing 350,000 T/yr of butadiene, known as the "Jersey process,"[72] included three distinctive features: (1) the new catalyst which dehydrogenated butenes in the presence of diluent steam, (2) the separation methods for isolating butenes and butadiene, and (3) the engineering design of the equipment for carrying out all of the operations involved.

TABLE 12. PRINCIPAL BUTADIENE PLANTS

Operator	Location	Capacity Short Tons/Yr Orig. Design	1953[81]
Cities Service	Lake Charles, La.	55,000	60,000
Humble Oil and Ref.	Baytown, Tex.	30,000	49,000
Neches Butane	Port Neches, Tex.	100,000	197,000
Phillips Chemical	Borger, Texas	45,000	71,000
Sinclair Rubber	Houston, Tex.	50,000	78,000
Shell Chemical*	Los Angeles, Cal.	55,000	61,000

* Includes butadiene produced by Standard Oil (Cal.) and refined by Shell.

In the Jersey process,[39,52,72] a feed containing about 70 per cent normal butylenes at 1100°F is mixed with 10 to 20 volumes of 1300°F steam and passed through a 4- to 6-ft bed of catalyst in a 16-ft-diameter reactor. A feed rate of about 200 to 800 v/v/hr (STP) is used, and the products are quenched with steam or water. Butadiene is separated by extraction with cuprous ammonium acetate, and unreacted butenes are recycled.

The diluent steam prevents carbon from forming rapidly. In early operations it was customary to shut off the feed after about one hour and allow the steam to remove deposited carbon from the catalyst, although much longer periods could be used, especially when large ratios of steam to butene were employed. In later operations, different catalysts, known as Shell 105 and 205 catalysts, have been used, and the process can be operated with very infrequent regeneration-steaming periods. Operating periods between regenerations are reported to be one week for 105 catalyst and longer for 205 catalyst.[66] Recently a catalyst developed by the Dow Chemical Co. has been substituted in two plants, but this catalyst requires regeneration with steam and air after one hour dehydrogenation periods.[66] The differences between various catalysts are discussed below.

Butene Dehydrogenation Catalysts. Catalysts for dehydrogenating butenes to butadiene were investigated and patented over a period of thirty years before actual commercial use of the process was made. Mathews patented the use of metals like copper and various oxides and salts in 1912.[44] The I. G. Farbenindustrie patented a strontium uranate catalyst in 1926[73] and also disclosed the use of partial vacuum and of steam or carbon dioxide diluents. Russian investigators published extensive work in the field beginning about 1934.[5,6,16,87] The Russian investigators appeared to favor the use of carbon dioxide as a diluent. A patent filed in 1936[18] by the Standard Oil Development Company described dehydrogenation of butenes over an alumina-chromia catalyst using a partial vacuum (50 mm P). This process was later investigated by Grosse *et al.*,[24] and a special engineering modification of it is used in the Houdry butadiene process. The I. G. Farbenindustrie patented catalyst compositions such as porcelain, graphite, carbon and silver vanadate for dehydrogenating butenes in the presence of diluent steam.[33-36] On the basis of most extensive coverage, their best catalyst appears to have been a $72ZnO-9CaCrO_4-18Al_2O_3$ composition.[25] This catalyst was claimed to give a 70 per cent selectivity at 20 per cent conversion. As discussed below, a somewhat similar catalyst was used by the Germans for dehydrogenating ethyl benzene to styrene, but it does not appear that it was used for making butadiene.

When American industrial laboratories initiated intensive work on butene dehydrogenation about 1940, none of the earlier catalysts described for operation with diluent steam appeared to be satisfactory. By the time the Synthetic Rubber program was finalized, the Phillips Petroleum Co. had developed a promoted bauxite catalyst, and the Standard Oil Development Co., a promoted iron catalyst.

The Phillips catalyst was prepared by impregnating bauxite with 5 per cent barium hydroxide and probably owed its activity to the iron present in the bauxite. Because ultimate plant yields of butadiene of only 50 to 37 per cent were obtained, this catalyst was replaced by the promoted iron oxide catalysts discussed below.[74]

The Standard Oil Development Company catalyst, known as 1707 catalyst, had the composition $72.4MgO-18.4Fe_2O_3-4.6CuO-4.6K_2O$.[37] In laboratory tests this catalyst gave ultimate yields of butadiene from pure *n*-butenes of 85 per cent at 20 per cent conversion and 72 per cent at 40 per cent conversion. However, in plant tests with less pure butylene feeds, lower selectivities were obtained (70 to 80 per cent at 20 to 25 per cent conversion). The iron component is the active dehydrogenation component. The copper is thought to contribute somewhat to activity and to serve as a stabilizer. The potassium, which is probably present as K_2CO_3, serves as a promoter and assists the reaction of deposited carbon with steam. The use of the potassia promoter was a major contribution to the art, since it was greatly superior to soda, lithia, calcia, etc., used in some previous catalysts. Only the very expensive rubidium and cesium promoters gave results comparable to potassium. In use the catalyst becomes depleted in potassia, but this can be replenished by injecting K_2CO_3 solution with the feed or steam. Numerous variations of the 1707 composition have been described.[37] Laboratory tests indicated that fairly active catalysts could be made by using chromium, manganese or cobalt in place of iron; and zinc, beryllium or zirconium oxides in place of magnesium oxide. Zinc oxide promoted with K_2O is fairly active without added iron oxide.

The life of 1707 catalyst in butadiene plants was only a few months. Laboratory butene dehydrogenation tests in which K_2CO_3 in the catalyst was replenished continuously showed that there was no loss in activity or selectivity after seven months' use.

Iron oxide, when suitably promoted with potassium carbonate, can also be used without any support.[38] The Shell Development Co. carried out an extensive development program that produced a specific composition of unsupported iron oxide promoted with potassium carbonate. Shell introduced this to the industry and it became known as Shell 105 catalyst. It has a composition of about $90Fe_2O_3$-$4Cr_2O_3$-$6K_2CO_3$.[14,15] A later preparation, known as 205 catalyst, contains more K_2CO_3. This catalyst has better self-regenerating characteristics,[66] requiring less steam, but may be slightly inferior in selectivity. At high steam-dilution ratios, 105 catalyst operates continuously for a week or longer, and 205 catalyst, for several months. Catalyst 105 is currently used in most commercial plants. Catalyst 205 has received only limited use, as has the Dow nickel-calcium phosphate catalyst. Specific features of the 105 type catalysts are described in the patent literature.[26,61,74,85]

Britton and Dietzler of the Dow Chemical Co. developed a different type of butene dehydrogenation catalyst having the composition Ca_8Ni-$(PO_4)_6$ and containing about 2 per cent Cr_2O_3.[7,8] This catalyst gives higher selectivities to butadiene but is more expensive and requires periodic regeneration with air. The catalyst has proven successful in plants at Sarnia, Ontario, and in part of the Humble plant at Baytown, Texas. With high steam-dilution ratios, selectivities of about 90 at a 35 per cent conversion level can be obtained with this catalyst as compared with 69 to 72 per cent selectivity at a 27.5 per cent conversion level with Shell 105 catalyst. Steam consumption per ton of butadiene produced is about the same for the two catalysts.[55,66] The nickel operates at a feed rate of about 120 v/v/hr butenes, 2500 v/v/hr steam (STP), and at temperatures varying from about 1100 to 1200 as the catalyst ages over a seven-month life.

Reilly has summarized the advantages and disadvantages of the nickel-calcium phosphate catalyst, but it is not clear whether this catalyst will ultimately replace the iron-potassia-type catalysts or not. Its unquestioned ability to give higher yields of butadiene from a given quantity of butylenes is an important advantage which increases with decreasing availability or increasing cost of butylenes. However, the catalyst is less rugged and occasionally has shown a tendency to "go wild," forming large deposits of carbon and gas and causing the catalyst pellets to disintegrate. Also, additional plant investments would be required to convert existing "Jersey process" plants to use of the Dow catalyst and to pay the higher price for catalyst inventory. At the present time, it is difficult to predict the immediate future trend the industry will follow with regard to choice of catalyst and process. However, on a long-range basis one would expect the most selective catalyst to be adopted.

Products Formed in Butene Dehydrogenation. The conversion of butenes to butadiene increases with increasing temperature and decreasing feed rate. The selectivity to butadiene decreases with increasing conversion level, more cracked gases, oxides of carbon and coke being formed at higher conversion levels. Selectivity decreases more rapidly with increasing conversion level over 1707 and 105 catalysts than over nickel-calcium phosphate catalyst. However, since commercial processes have operated at 20 to 30 per cent conversion levels, comparisons of selectivity with the Dow catalyst should be made at this conversion level. Its greater selectivity at a conversion level of about 28 per cent is illustrated by the data in Table 13.[76]

TABLE 13

	1707 MgO-Fe$_2$O$_3$ CuO-K$_2$O		Shell 105 Fe$_2$O$_3$-Cr$_2$O$_2$ K$_2$O		Dow Type B NiCa Phosphate Cr$_2$O$_3$	
			Catalyst			
Dehydrog. Period, hrs	1.0		continuous		0.5	
Temp., °F	1165		1164		1171	
Butene v/v/hr	392		394		300	
Steam v/v/hr	3966		4011		6000	
Conversion, %	27.7		28.2		27.5	
Selectivity, %	73		72†		92	
Coke, %	0.2		—		0.2	
Product Gas						
H$_2$	26.7		29.6		23.3	
CO	⎱6.3		6.8		0.5	
CO$_2$	⎰				1.2	
C$_1$	2.6		2.8		1.3	
C$_2$	0.7	Feed	0.7	Feed	0.1*	Feed
C$_3$	2.2	(0.4)	2.3		1.7	(0.3)
C$_4$H$_{10}$	1.6	(1.8)	1.0	(1.8)	1.8	(2.3)
C$_5$ +	1.0	(1.1)	1.0	(1.1)	1.4	(1.4)
C$_4$H$_6$	12.8	(0)	12.3	(0)	17.6	(0.6)
C$_4$H$_8$	40.1	(96.7)	43.5	(96.7)	50.4	(95.4)

* Probably low. Reilly reports 0.8%.[66]
† About 75–76% at 6,000 v/v/hr steam.

It is apparent that the nickel-calcium phosphate catalyst is more selective and forms less cracked gases and oxides of carbon than the iron-type catalysts, which give very similar products. Part of the advantage in selectivity for the nickel-calcium phosphate catalyst is due to the higher steam-to-butene ratio used. For example, at a similar steam-to-butene

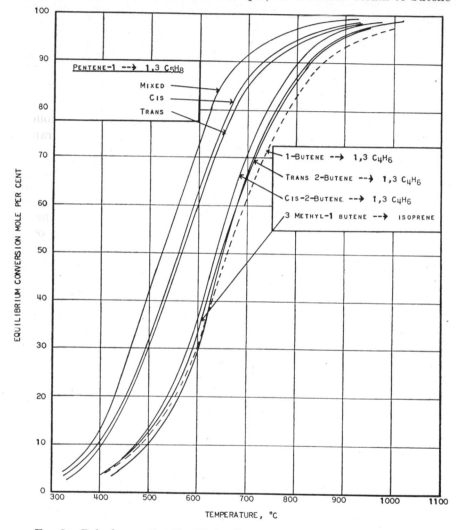

FIG. 3.   Dehydrogenation Equilibria. Comparison of butenes and pentenes.

ratio, the iron-type catalysts would be expected to have selectivities about 5 per cent higher than shown in Table 13.

Other differences in product formation between the two types of catalysts are noted with respect to production of acetylene- and carbonyl-type compounds. Reilly[66] reports that the Dow catalyst gives 4 per cent acetone and 1 per cent acetylenes, based on butadiene produced. With the iron-type catalysts, acetone production is negligible and the amount of acetylenes is only half that formed by the nickel-calcium phosphate catalyst. These products require special treatment to avoid difficulties in the product separation equipment.

Little difference has been observed in the dehydrogenation of 1-butene and 2-butenes. The reaction product from any one of these feeds usually contains all three isomeric normal-butenes, indicating that shifting of the double bond takes place readily. On the other hand the formation of isobutylene is usually negligible, and only very small amounts of butadiene are formed by the dehydrogenation of isobutylene. Paraffins like *n*-butane are not readily converted under the conditions used in the steam-dilution-type butene-dehydrogenation processes. However, in recycle processes neither isobutylene nor butanes build up to excessive concentrations, plant feeds normally containing about 70 per cent of *n*-butenes. Minor quantities of such compounds as allene, methylacetylene, vinylacetylene, ethylacetylene, 1,2-butadiene, diacetylene and dimethylacetylene may be formed in crude petroleum butadiene. Larger amounts of these products are present in butadiene produced by thermal cracking at high temperatures than in those made by catalytic dehydrogenation.

Production of Styrene by Dehydrogenation

Styrene can be obtained by dehydrogenating ethyl benzene in a manner similar to the production of butadiene from *n*-butenes. Similar catalysts and processes can be used for both hydrocarbons, and the dehydrogenation of ethyl benzene occurs more readily than that of butene. Because of this greater reactivity, dehydrogenation of ethyl benzene was possible over catalysts unsatisfactory for butenes, and plants for making styrene were in operation before suitable catalysts were available for making butadiene.

Prior to World War II, the Dow Chemical Co. operated a styrene plant at Midland, Michigan. During the War the Rubber Reserve Co. authorized the building of additional plants to produce 187,500 short tons per year of styrene by using the Dow process. These plants are listed in Table 14.

TABLE 14. STYRENE PLANTS

Operating Company	Location	Rated Capacity Short Tons/Yr
Carbide and Carbon	Institute, W. Va.	25,000
Dow Chemical Co.	Los Angeles, Cal.	25,000
Dow Chemical Co.	Velasco, Texas	50,000
Koppers Company	Kobuta, Pa.	37,500
Monsanto Chemical Co.	Texas City, Tex.	50,000

The U. S. plants produced styrene from ethyl benzene with 90 per cent selectivity at conversion levels of 35 to 40 per cent. These yields appear to be the same as those obtained in different-type plants, and with a different catalyst, in Germany.

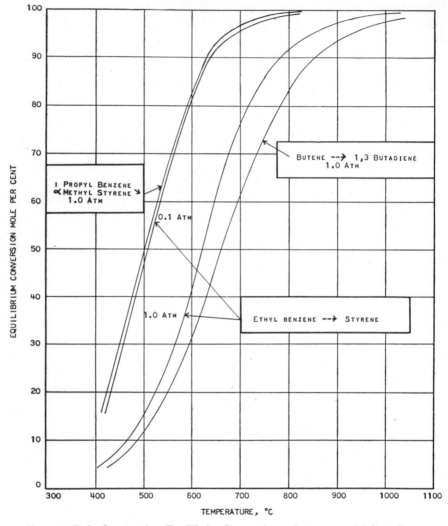

FIG. 4.   Dehydrogenation Equilibria. Comparison of styrenes with butadiene.

Description of Process. The U. S. process operates with contact times of about 0.5 second at temperatures that increase from 600 to 660°C as the catalyst age increases to one year or more.[48,70] Ethyl benzene feed is diluted with enough steam to reduce its partial pressure to about

0.1 atmosphere. The plants have a specially designed catalyst chamber in which a weighted ram automatically compensates for shrinkage of the catalyst. Nickel-containing alloys are considered harmful except in the steam preheat section. In order to avoid formation of insoluble polymers, it is necessary to have a feed containing no more than 0.04 per cent diethyl benzene. Feed specifications also limit benzene to 1.0 per cent and chlorine content to 0.05 per cent. Finished styrene of 99.7 per cent purity is produced, the remaining 0.3 per cent being mostly ethyl and isopropyl benzene.[48]

Werner and Dybdal[83] investigated the dehydrogenation of ethyl benzene without a diluent and with steam dilution, using unspecified catalysts. It seems probable that their work with undiluted feed was with alumina-chromia or possibly bauxite catalysts and that catalyst 1707 was used in the work with steam dilution. Their data are correlated for the purpose of predicting effects of operating conditions and designing reactors. Selectivities to styrene were about 90 per cent with steam dilution and only 72 per cent without diluent. Toluene exceeded benzene formation, but steam dilution inhibited the formation of both products, as well as of tar. Degradation to gas was mainly to ethane and carbon dioxide. Their data are summarized in Table 15.

TABLE 15. DEHYDROGENATION OF ETHYL BENZENE

Diluent	None	Steam			
Temperature, °C	673	625	626	634	671
Ethyl benzene v/v/hr	3.3	0.51	0.43	0.61	5.5
H_2O/Et B, Mol ratio	0	22.4	19.2	11.3	11.3
Inlet pressure, atm	1.15	1.4	1.3	1.3	1.3
Conversion, %	36.3	38.2	38.3	38.4	38.9
Selectivity, Mols/100 Mols Reacted					
To styrene	71.6	90.3	86.1	89.5	89.8
To benzene	12.1	2.4	3.7	2.8	3.1
To toluene	13.4	5.9	6.5	7.3	4.2
To tar*	3.6	0.11	0.10	0.19	0.19
To CH_4	—	2.2	4.9	3.2	1.1
To C_2H_4	—	0.66	0.73	0.32	0.75
To C_2H_6	—	2.8	5.1	3.9	5.4
To CO_2	—	10.2	23	7.3	14.6
To CO	—	0.2	0.0	0.1	0.3

* Basis of assumed molecular weight of 180.

In Germany a gas-fired tubular reactor was employed, using copper liners in stainless steel tubes. Ultimate yields of 90 per cent at 40 per cent conversion were obtained.

Catalysts for Dehydrogenating Ethyl Benzene. Ethyl benzene can be dehydrogenated thermally, but ultimate yields are only 45 to 55 per cent,[48,82] as compared with 90 per cent or better obtained over the best catalysts. Many materials were investigated as catalysts in the period from about 1920 to date.

Both Du Pont and I. G. Farbenindustrie filed patent applications in this field in 1929–1930.[21,43,79,86] These early patents recognized the importance of operating at reduced pressures and the feasibility of dehydrogenating homologous alkyl benzenes and naphthalenes. Wulff *et al.*[43,86] obtained the reduced pressures by use of diluent steam or CO_2 over catalysts containing iron, nickel or cobalt, as well as with a $50ZnO$-$40Al_2O_3$-$10CaO$ composition. They also disclosed the use of phosphates, borates, etc. to prevent nickel and iron from forming excessive carbon. It is interesting that these early patents disclosed some of the essential features of present processes. Apparently the $50ZnO$-$40Al_2O_3$-$10CaO$ catalyst was used in Germany until 1942, before the advantages of using a potassium promoted catalyst were recognized. A composition of $77.4ZnO$-$7.6Al_2O_3$-$4.7CaO$-$4.7MgO$-$2.8K_2CrO_4$-$2.8K_2SO_4$ was then used.[67]

The first commercial styrene in the United States was produced with an iron-containing bauxite catalyst.[84] Laboratory data on this catalyst show conversions up to 40 per cent, with selectivities of 90 to 95 after an induction period of lower activity. Activity then declined, requiring periodic regeneration. Side reactions included formation of about 2 per cent benzene and toluene and product gas containing 1 to 2 per cent each of methane, C_2, CO, and CO_2.

Dolomites containing CaO and MgO as well as iron oxide are also catalysts giving about 70 per cent selectivity to styrene. Other catalysts that have been investigated include V_2O_5 on MgO, Al_2O_3, SiO_2, etc.;[77,78] Al_2O_3-Cr_2O_3[19,20,46,56] and many others. The Dow nickel-calcium phosphate catalyst is reported to give 90 per cent selectivity but has not been used commercially.[55]

Two of the catalysts developed for butene dehydrogenation, 1707 and 105 (see section on butadiene) proved superior to the catalyst used in the original Dow styrene plant. Because of the greater ease of dehydrogenating ethyl benzene, the 105 catalyst offered less advantage in these plants than in butene dehydrogenation plants. The 1707 catalyst could also be used without frequent regeneration. However, after catalyst production for butadiene plants shifted from 1707 to 105 catalyst, the 105 catalyst was also used in the styrene plants.

Dehydrogenation of Other Alkyl-Aromatics. The dehydrogenation of hydrocarbons such as isopropyl benzene, ethyl naphthalene, etc., has been studied less extensively than that of ethyl benzene. However, it appears that most aromatics with 2 to 3 carbon-atom alkyl groups can be dehydrogenated readily. Isopropyl benzene dehydrogenates primarily to alpha-methyl styrene over 1707 catalyst.[49]

Nickels *et al.*[54] were unable to get good yields of styrene from isopropyl benzene. At relatively high selectivities to total styrenes of about 85 per cent, they obtained yields of only 1 per cent styrene and 20–25 per cent methyl styrene, using $85Al_2O_3$-$15Cr_2O_3$, $99Al_2O_3$-$1NiO$, and 1707 catalysts. At more severe conditions, they were able to get a seventh to a third of the total styrenes as styrene rather than methylstyrene.

The dehydrogenation of isopropyl benzene has also been investigated over vanadia catalysts on alumina and other carriers.[77] Butyl and dibutyl benzenes have given 71 to 74 and 68 per cent selectivities to corresponding styrenes.[3] Ethyl naphthalene was converted, with 90 per cent selectivity, to vinyl naphthalenes at reduced pressure over calcined magnesite catalyst, but gave only 82 per cent selectivity with diluent steam.[53] Ethyl naphthalene can be dehydrogenated in existing styrene plants using similar operating conditions. Corson reported selectivities to styrenes over a dolomite catalyst of 70 per cent for ethyl naphthalene, 71 per cent for ethyl benzene, 46 per cent for isopropyl benzene, and 62 per cent for diethyl benzene (41 per cent monovinyl and 21 per cent divinyl benzene).[12]

Although steam offers many operating advantages as a diluent, carbon dioxide can be used with good results.[4] Benzene is also reported to be a suitable diluent.[45,51] Sulfur has been patented as a feed additive effective in converting ethyl benzene to styrene.[47] At temperatures of 670 to 700°F, without a catalyst, a selectivity of 90 per cent at conversions of 30 to 45 per cent is claimed.

Present and Future Status

The production of butadiene and styrene by catalytic dehydrogenation appear to be established processes. While dependent on the total demand for rubber and the supply of natural rubber, it appears doubtful that future variations in these markets could cause a complete shut down of this industry. Following World War II production of GR-S decreased from 760,000 to 275,000 tons/yr, all alcohol butadiene production being stopped, and butene dehydrogenation somewhat reduced. The low production figure held when natural rubber sold for 18.3 cents/pound in January 1950. When this price rose to 73 cents/pound in November 1950, the production of synthetic rubber was increased, 530,000 T/yr being made in 1951.[65] Petroleum butadiene capacity, installed and under construction, is currently 637,000 tons/yr (1953), and alcohol butadiene, 215,000 tons per year.[81] It thus appears probable that catalytic dehydrogenation of butylenes and ethyl benzene will continue in use unless better methods of making butadiene and styrene are found.

The dehydrogenation of butane to butenes still appears to be a relatively expensive process for making motor gasoline, and will probably be used only for making more valuable products such as chemicals. Its use for this purpose will be limited to locations where butylenes are in short supply and butanes are available at low cost. However, the development of an improved or cheaper process of dehydrogenating butanes could result in more extensive application to the production of both mono- and diolefins.

References

1. Altmann, L. S., and Frost, A. V., *Khima Tverd. Topliva* **8**, No. 5, 490 (1937); *For. Lit. Serv. Abstract*, 37A.
2. Anon., *Petroleum Refiner*, Process Handbook Section, **26**, No. 4, (1947).
3. Balandin, A. A., Marukyan, G. M., and Seimovich, R. G., *Referaty* 1944 *of Acad. Sci. USSR Chem. Sect.*, **102**, U.S.S.R. Patent 64, 222 (1945).
4. Balandin, A. A., and Tolstopyatova, A. A., *Zh. Ob. Khim*, **17**, 2182 (1947).
5. Balandin, A. A., Zelinski, N. D., Bogdanova, O. K., and Shcheglova, A. P., *Zh. Prikl. Khim.*, **14**, 435 (1941); *For. Petr. Tech.*, **9**, No. 7, 265 (July 1941).
6. Batalin, V. S., Sekretareva, E. V., and Filikovskaya, N. N., *Sintet. Kauchuk*, **4**, 67 (1935).
7. Britton, E. C., Dietzler, A. J., and Noddings, C. R., *Ind. Eng. Chem.*, **43**, 2871 (1951).
8. Britton, E. C., and Dietzler, A. J., U. S. Patents 2,442,319; 2,442,320 (1948), 2,456,367; 2,456,368 (1948).
9. Burgin, J., and Groll, H., U. S. Patents 2,184,234–5 (1939); 2,217,865 (1940) and 2,270,165 (1942).
10. Cantzler, A., and Krekler, H., U. S. Patent 2,274,358 (1942).
11. Corson, B. B., and Maxutov, C. D., U. S. Patent 2,375,402 (1945).
12. Corson, B. B., and Webb, G. A., U. S. Patent 2,444,035 (1948).
13. Dodd, R. H., and Watson, K. M., *Trans. Am. Inst. Chem. Engrs.*, **42**, 263 (1946).
14. Eggertsen, F. T., and Vogue, H. H., U. S. Patent 2,414,585 (1947).
15. Eggertsen, F. T., and Davies, E. P., U. S. Patent 2,461,147 (1949).
16. Federov, B. P., Smirnova, A. I., and Semenov, P. A., Brit, C. A.-A:324 (March 1935); *J. Appl. Chem. Russ.*, **7**, 1166 (1934).
17. Frey, F. E., and Huppke, W. F., *Ind. Eng. Chem.*, **25**, 54 (1933); U. S. Patent 2,098,959 (1937), Reissue 21,911 (1941).
18. Gaylor, P. J., and Rosen, R., U. S. Patent 2,209,215 (1940).
19. Ghosh, J. C., Guha, S. R. D., and Roy, A. N., *Petroleum*, **10**, 127, 180, 236 (1947).
20. Ghosh, J. C., and Guha, S. R. D., *Petroleum* (London), **15**, 33 (1952).
21. Graves, G. D., U. S. Patent 2,036,410 (1936).
22. Grosse, A. V., and Ipatieff, V. N., *Ind. Eng. Chem.*, **32**, 268 (1940).
23. Grosse, A. V., U. S. Patent 2,172,534 (1939).
24. Grosse, A. V., Morrell, J. C., and Mavity, J. M., *Ind. Eng. Chem.*, **32**, 309 (1940); Petr. Div. A.C.S. Preprints, Sept. 11-15, 1939; see also U. S. Patents 2,178,584; 2,178,602; and 2,313,162.
25. Grosskinsky, O., Roh, N., and Hoffman, J., U. S. Patent 2,265,641 (1941); also French Patent 853,646, British Patent 535,329 and German Patent 743,372.

26. Gutzeit, C. L., U. S. Patents 2,408,139 (1946); 2,408,140 (1946); 2,449,295 (1948).
27. Haensel, V., and Sterba, M. J., *Ind. Eng. Chem.*, **40**, 1660 (1948).
28. Hanson, G. H., and Hays, H. L., *Chem. Eng. Prog.*, **44**, No. 6, 431 (1948).
29. Holroyd, R., "Report on Investigations of Fuels and Lubricant Teams," U. S. Bureau of Mines Information Circulars 7370 and 7375 (1946).
30. Houdry, E. J., U. S. Patent 2,419,997 (1947).
31. Houdry, E. J., and Shabaker, H. A., U. S. Patent 2,399,678 (1946).
32. Howard, E. W., Univ. of Ill. Bull. 48, No. 29, Circular 61 (1950).
33. I. G. Farbenindustrie, French Patent 840,519 (1939).
34. I. G. Farbenindustrie, French Patent 844,146 (1939).
35. I. G. Farbenindustrie, British Patent 508,764 (1939).
36. I. G. Farbenindustrie, French Patent 853,645 (1940).
37. Kearby, K., *Ind. Eng. Chem.*, **42**, 295 (1950). U. S. Patents 2,370,797; 2,370,798; 2,395,875; 2,395,876; 2,407,373; 2,408,146; 2,418,888; 2,418,889; 2,426,829; 2,442,131.
38. Kearby, K., U. S. Patent 2,426,829 (1947).
39. Kleiber, C. E., Campbell, D. L., Stines, D. L., and Nelson, C. C., U. S. Patent 2,414,816 (1947).
40. Lassait, R. C., and Parker, F. D., *Oil Gas J.*, **43**, No. 28,229 (1944).
41. Lyrbraskii, G. D., and Kagan, M. Ya. C. R., *Akad. Sci. USSR*, **29**, 575 (1940).
42. Malyanskii, G. N., and Bursian, N. R., *Zh. Ob. Khim*, **17**, No. 2,208 (1947).
43. Mark, H., and Wulff, C., U. S. Patent 2,110,833 (1938).
44. Mathews, F. E., and Perkin, W. H., British Patent 17235 (1912).
45. Mavity, J. M., Zetterholm, E. E., and Hervert, G., *Ind. Eng. Chem.*, **38**, 829 (1946).
46. Mavity, J. M., Zetterholm, E. E., and Hervert, G., *Trans. Am. Inst. Chem. Engrs.*, **41**, 519 (1945).
47. McCullough, C. R., and Gehrke, W. H., U. S. Patent 2,392,289 (1946).
48. Mitchel, J. E. Jr., *Trans. Am. Inst. Chem. Engrs.*, **42**, 293 (1946).
49. Morrell, C. E., and Slotterbeck, O. C., U. S. Patent 2,449,004 (1948).
50. Munster, W. N., Office of Synthetic Rubber, Private communication (August 22, 1952).
51. Naugatuck Chemical Co., German Patent 600,268 (Ptlb. **55**, 2036 (8/23/1934)).
52. Nicholson, E. W., Moise, J. E., Segura, M. A., and Kleiber, C. E., *Ind. Eng. Chem.*, **41**, 646 (1949).
53. Nickels, J. E., and Corson, B. B., *Ind. Eng. Chem.*, **43**, 1685 (1951); U. S. Patent 2,424,841 (1947).
54. Nickels, J. E., Webb, G. A., Heintzelman, W., and Corson, B. B., *Ind. Eng. Chem.*, **41**, 563 (1949).
55. Noddings, C. R., Heath, S. B., and Corey, J. W., Paper presented at National A.C.S. Meeting, Chicago, Sept. 1953.
56. Oblad, A. G., Marschner, R. F., and Heard, L., *J. Am. Chem. Soc.*, **62**, 2067 (1940).
57. Owen, J. R., U. S. Patent 2,606,159 (1952).
58. Pao-Teh-Wan, *J. Chem. Eng. China*, **16**, 32–55 (1949) (German); *Chem. Abs.*, **44**, 1398 (2-25-50).
59. Parker, R. L., and Huffman, H. C., U. S. Patent 2,518,714 (1950).
60. Perkins, M. M., *California Oil World*, **39**, 12 (1946).
61. Pine, P. R., and Ray, E. C., U. S. Patent 2,457,719 (1948).

62. Pitzer, E. W., U. S. Patent 2,586,377 (1952).
63. Pitzer, E. W., U. S. Patent 2,638,455 (1953); Paper before A.C.S. Meeting, Chicago, Sept. 1953.
64. Potolowskii, L. and Atal'yen, A., *Neft. Khoz.*, **19**, No. 4 (19–38); *For. Lit. Serv. Transl.* No. S-41A.
65. Reconstruction Finance Corp., 1951 Annual Report, p. 21.
66. Reilly, P. M., *Chemistry in Canada*, **5**, 41 March (1953).
67. Reimers, H. A., and Boeke, W. F. (Translators) I. G. Farben Report O.P.B. No. 13, 363, Report No. RM-302 (9/27/45).
68. Riesz, C. H., Pelican, T. L., and Komarewsky, V. I., *Oil Gas J.*, **43**, No. 10, 67 (1944).
69. Rossini, F. D., Pitzer, K. S., Arnutt, R. L., Braun, R. M., and Pimentel, G. C. Selected Values of Physical and Thermodynamic Properties of Hydrocarbons and Related Compounds, Carnegie Press (1953).
70. Rubber Reserve Co., Report on Rubber Program 1940–1945, Feb. 24, 1945, Supplement No. 1, April 8, 1946.
71. Ruhemann, M., and Steiner, H., *Intern. Chem. Eng. Process Ind.* **30**, 314 (1949).
72. Russell, R. P., Murphree, E. V., and Asbury, W. C., *Trans. Am. Inst. Chem. Engrs.*, **42**, 1–14 (1946).
73. Schmidt, O., Grosskinsky, O., and Niemann, G., U. S. Patent 1,732,381 (1929).
74. Schulze, W. A., Hillyer, J. C., and Drennan, H. E., U. S. Patents 2,367,620; 2,371,850; 2,380,876; 2,391,646; 2,485,927.
75. Shutt, H. C., *Chem. Eng. Prog.*, **43**, 102 (1947).
76. Standard Oil Development Co., Unpublished data.
77. Stanley, H. M., and Salt, F. E., U. S. Patent 2,342,980 (1939); British Patents 514,587 and 572,410.
78. Stanley, H. M., Salt, F. E., and Weir, T., French Patent 947,371 (1947).
79. Suida, H., U. S. Patent 1,985,844 (1934).
80. Thayer, C. H., Lassait, R. L., and Lederer, E. R., *Natl. Petr. News*, **34**, No. 39, R-305 (1942).
81. Tracy, O. V., *Chem. Eng. News*, **31**, 2667 (1953).
82. Webb, G. A., and Corson, B. B., *Ind. Eng. Chem.*, **39**, 1153 (1947).
83. Werner, R. R., and Dybdal, E. C., *Chem. Eng. Prog.*, **44**, 275 (1948).
84. Wood, W. H., and Capell, R. G., *Ind. Eng. Chem.*, **37**, 1148 (1945).
85. Wright, K. A., U. S. Patent 2,385,484 (1945).
86. Wulff, C., and Roell, E., U. S. Patent 1,986,241 (1935).
87. Yakubchik, A. I., *Sintet. Kauchuk.*, **4**, 60 (1935).
88. Ziegenhain, W. T., *Oil Gas J.*, **41**, No. 15, 30 (1942).

CHAPTER 31

MECHANISMS OF THE REACTIONS OF NONBENZENOID HYDROCARBONS

Louis Schmerling

Universal Oil Products Co., Riverside, Ill.

It is the object of this chapter to show that practically all of the reactions of the aliphatic and cycloaliphatic hydrocarbons can best be explained as occurring by way of either carbonium ion or free radical, usually chain, mechanisms. No attempts will be made to present a detailed discussion of the mass of evidence which has been accumulated in favor of the mechanisms, nor will the various alternative schemes be discussed. Instead, a unified, common basis for catalytic reactions of hydrocarbons, on the one hand, and for thermal reactions, on the other, will be developed by setting up certain generally accepted basic principles describing the behavior of carbonium ions and of free radicals. It will be demonstrated that it becomes possible to coordinate and integrate the large variety of otherwise apparently unrelated reactions (and side reactions) of hydrocarbons and show that they are inherent in the plausible, simplified (but not overly-simplified), theory which results. Detailed discussions of fine points and of any seemingly contrary observations are outside the scope of this necessarily brief chapter. Also, reactions resulting in the formation or scission of carbon-to-carbon bonds will be emphasized; the mechanisms of such reactions as hydrogenation, oxidation, halogenation, and nitration will not be considered here.

Carbonium ions are involved in reactions catalyzed by the so-called acid-type catalysts which include the protonic acids (e.g., sulfuric acid, phosphoric acid, and hydrogen fluoride), the Friedel-Crafts halides (e.g., aluminum chloride, zirconium chloride, and boron fluoride), and oxides (e.g., silica-alumina). The carbonium ions which are formed under the reaction conditions undergo one or more of the following changes before being converted to the reaction products:

Principle 1. The carbonium ion may add to an unsaturated molecule to yield a higher molecular weight carbonium ion.

$$R^+ + CH_2{=}CH_2 \rightleftharpoons R{-}CH_2{-}CH_2{}^+$$

Principle 2. The carbonium ion may decompose to another ion (e.g., a smaller carbonium ion or a proton) and an unsaturated compound.

$$R-CH_2-\overset{+}{C}H-R' \Big\langle \begin{array}{l} R^+ + CH_2{=}CH-R' \\ H^+ + R-CH{=}CH-R' \end{array}$$

Principle 3. The carbonium ion may isomerize via migration of hydrogen, alkyl, or aryl together with a pair of electrons.

$$\begin{array}{ccc} & H_3C & \\ & | & \\ R-\overset{|}{\underset{H_3C}{C}}-\overset{+}{C}H-R' & \rightleftharpoons & R-\overset{+}{\underset{H_3C}{C}}-\underset{CH_3}{\overset{|}{C}}H-R' \end{array}$$

Conversion of the final carbonium ion to the reaction product occurs by:

Principle 4. Elimination of a proton or other cation, a reaction which is analogous to that of Principle 2.

Principle 5. Abstraction of a hydride ion or other anion from another molecule.

$$R^+ + R'H \rightleftharpoons RH + R'^+$$
$$R^+ + R'Cl \rightleftharpoons RCl + R'^+$$

Principle 6. Disproportionation of two carbonium ions

$$2R-\overset{+}{C}H-CH_2-R' \rightarrow R-CH_2-CH_2-R' + R-CH{=}CH-R'$$

Free radicals which are the intermediates in thermal reactions or in peroxide-induced reactions undergo reactions which are similar to those of the carbonium ions:

Principle 1'. The free radical may add to an unsaturated molecule to yield a higher molecular weight free radical.

$$R\cdot + CH_2{=}CH_2 \rightleftharpoons R-CH_2-CH_2\cdot$$

Principle 2'. The free radical may decompose to yield a small radical (or a hydrogen atom) and an unsaturated compound.

$$R-CH_2-\overset{\cdot}{C}H-R' \Big\langle \begin{array}{l} R\cdot + CH_2{=}CH-R' \\ H\cdot + R-CH{=}CH-R' \end{array}$$

The final free radical is converted to the reaction product by:

Principle 4'. Elimination of a proton or a smaller free radical, a reaction which is analogous to Principle 2'.

Principle 5'. Abstraction of hydrogen atom or other atom from another molecule.

$$R\cdot + R'H \rightleftharpoons RH + R'\cdot$$
$$R\cdot + R'Cl \rightleftharpoons RCl + R'\cdot$$

Principle 6'. Disproportionation of two free radicals.

$$2R—\dot{C}H—CH_2—R' \rightarrow R—CH_2—CH_2—R' + R—CH=CH—R'$$

It will be noted that no reaction analogous to the isomerization reaction (Principle 3) of carbonium ions is listed for the free radicals since free radicals, unlike carbonium ions, rarely undergo rearrangement, a fact which accounts for the difference in products obtained in some thermal reactions as compared to the analogous catalytic reactions.

Formation of Carbonium Ions

All of the acid-type catalysts apparently owe their activity to the ability to form carbonium ions from one or more of the reactants under the reaction conditions. A number of the ways in which the ions may form will be summarized here.

From Olefins. The protonic acid catalysts convert olefins to carbonium ions by the addition of a proton from the acid to the extra electron pair in the double bond (the pi electrons):

$$R—CH=CH_2 + H^+OSO_3H^- \rightleftharpoons R—\overset{+}{C}H—CH_3\ OSO_3H^-$$

Protons may also be present on the surface of oxide catalysts such as the silica-alumina cracking catalyst; the activity of the catalyst is destroyed when the acidity is neutralized by the adsorption of both organic and inorganic basic compounds.[17,30,37,61,62,66] It has been suggested that the active constituent is $(HAlSiO_4)_x$.[62]

With catalysts of the Friedel-Crafts type, the proton is usually derived from the promoter, usually hydrogen halide. For example, formation of the carbonium ions in the presence of aluminum chloride promoted by hydrogen chloride may be expressed as follows:

$$R—CH=CH_2 + HCl + AlCl_3 \rightleftharpoons R—\overset{+}{C}H—CH_3\ AlCl_4^-$$

It has been established that hydrogen aluminum tetrachloride ($HAlCl_4$) is non-existent, even at $-120°$.[4,5] However, interaction of aluminum chloride and hydrogen chloride does occur in the presence of basic substances (electron donors) such as benzene and, presumably, olefins. Thus, $R^+AlCl_4^-$ represents the relatively stable ester of the unstable acid, $HAlCl_4$, just as $CO(OR)_2$ and $ClCOOR$ are stable esters of the nonexistent acids, $CO(OH)_2$ and $ClCOOH$.

Similarly, evidence has been presented to show that while HBF_4 is unstable, its complexes with aromatic hydrocarbons, $ArH_2^+BF_4^-$, are quite stable.[34]

Analogous conclusions may be made concerning aluminum bromide[15] and gallium chloride.[4]

With water as promoter, the proton is derived from the complex formed with the catalyst:

$$AlCl_3 + H_2O \rightleftharpoons H_2O:AlCl_3 \rightleftharpoons H^+ \ HOAlCl_3^-$$

Decomposition of the complex yields hydroxyaluminum dichloride and hydrogen chloride which are also sources of protons:

$$H_2O:AlCl_3 \rightleftharpoons HCl + HOAlCl_2$$

Boron fluoride monohydrate and boron fluoride dihydrate, on the other hand, are stable active catalysts:

$$H_2O:BF_3 \rightleftharpoons H^+ \ HOBF_3^-$$

$$H^+HOBF_3^- \overset{H_2O}{\rightleftharpoons} H_3O^+ \ HOBF_3^-$$

Evidence that esters of hydrogen aluminum tetrachloride are intermediates in Friedel-Crafts reactions may be found in the exchange of radioactive chlorine atoms for ordinary chlorine atoms which occurs when *t*-butyl chloride is treated with benzene in the presence of aluminum chloride containing radioactive chlorine atoms; radioactive hydrogen chloride is evolved.[13]

$$(CH_3)_3CCl + AlCl_3^* \rightleftharpoons (CH_3)_3C^+[AlCl_4^*]^-$$
$$(CH_3)_3C^+[AlCl_4^*]^- + C_6H_6 \rightleftharpoons (CH_3)_3CC_6H_5 + [HAlCl_4^*]$$
$$[HAlCl_4^*] \rightarrow HCl^* + AlCl_3^*$$
(Cl* is chlorine, part of which is radioactive.)

From Saturated Hydrocarbons. Paraffins and cycloparaffins are usually converted to carbonium ions by loss of a hydride ion to a carbonium ion (cf. Principle 5).[1] Hydride ions attached to tertiary carbon atoms are most readily abstracted. The resulting carbonium ion undergoes one or more of the various reactions outlined above before it, in turn, abstracts a hydride ion from another molecule of the saturated hydrocarbon. A chain reaction thus ensues, and the carbonium ion which initiates the reaction need be present in only trace amounts.

When writing equations involving carbonium ions, it is often convenient to consider the changes only of the carbonium ion, the negative portion of the ionic pair being neglected. Nevertheless, it must be remembered that the anion plays an essential, if lesser, role. It must also be noted that while it has become customary to consider the reactions of the carbonium ions as involving migration (or elimination) of an atom or group of atoms, (e.g., hydrogen or methyl) with (or in the case of elimination, without) the attached electron pair, it is useful and probably more accurate to consider the changes as involving migration or elimination of an electron pair with or without the attached atom or group of atoms.[67]

In the present discussion, the carbonium ion will be written with the classical structure: the electron-deficient carbon atom is considered to have only six electrons in the valence shell, the driving force for its reaction being the tendency to complete the octet. Such classical structures are quite satisfactory for almost all of the petroleum chemist's purposes. On the other hand, bridged structures which have recently been proposed for carbonium ions have the advantage of giving a better stereochemical picture of certain reactions. The following are examples of the non-classical structures which have been postulated.[72]

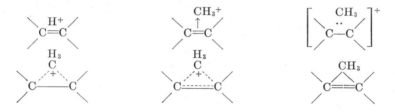

Formation of Free Radicals.

Homolytic scission of a carbon-carbon bond in hydrocarbons occurs at high temperatures, yielding free radicals:

$$
\begin{array}{ccccc}
\text{H} & \text{H} & & \text{H} & \text{H} \\
\text{..} & \text{..} & & \text{..} & \text{..} \\
R : \text{C} : \text{C} : \text{H} & \to & R : \text{C} \cdot + \text{H} : \text{C} \cdot \\
\text{..} & \text{..} & & \text{..} & \text{..} \\
\text{H} & \text{H} & & \text{H} & \text{H}
\end{array}
$$

A number of substances, particularly organic peroxides, decompose at relatively low temperatures yielding free radicals. Since free radical reactions of hydrocarbons, like the carbonium ion reactions, are usually chain reactions, the use of peroxides thus affords a convenient means for obtaining the free radicals necessary to induce the desired reaction.

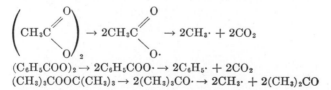

$(C_6H_5COO)_2 \to 2C_6H_5COO\cdot \to 2C_6H_5\cdot + 2CO_2$
$(CH_3)_3COOC(CH_3)_3 \to 2(CH_3)_3CO\cdot \to 2CH_3\cdot + 2(CH_3)_2CO$

The free radicals which initiate the reaction chain may also be formed by the illumination of substances which decompose on absorbing radiation in the ultraviolet or the visible range, e.g. acetone or bromotrichloromethane.

As may be inferred from the list of their basic reactions (p. 248), free radicals initiate reactions of paraffins by abstracting hydrogen atoms and of olefins either by adding to the double bond or by abstracting hydrogen atoms preferably from an allylic carbon atom.

Hydrogen-Halogen Exchange

Metal Halide-Catalyzed Reaction. Hydrogen-halogen exchange occurs when saturated hydrocarbons containing tertiary carbon atoms are treated with alkyl halides in the presence of aluminum chloride.[1] For example, the reaction of isopentane with t-butyl chloride in the presence of aluminum bromide at contact time of as little as 0.001 sec. results in the formation of t-pentyl bromide (50–70 per cent yield) and isobutane. This reaction may be taken as evidence that a carbonium ion can abstract a hydride ion as indicated in Principle 5. The mechanism of the exchange reaction may be written:

$$(CH_3)_3CCl + AlBr_3 \rightleftharpoons (CH_3)_3C^+AlBr_3Cl^-$$
$$(CH_3)_3C^+AlBr_3Cl^- + C_2H_5(CH_3)_2CH \rightleftharpoons (CH_3)_3CH + C_2H_5(CH_3)_2C^+AlBr_3Cl^-$$
$$C_2H_5(CH_3)_2C^+AlBr_3Cl^- \rightleftharpoons C_2H_5(CH_3)_2CBr + AlBr_2Cl$$

A chain reaction including the abstraction of halogen from t-alkyl halide by the intermediate carbonium ion may be involved under some conditions.[56]

$$C_2H_5(CH_3)_2C^+AlBr_3Cl^- + (CH_3)_3CCl \rightleftharpoons C_2H_5(CH_3)_2CCl + (CH_3)_3C^+AlBr_3Cl^-$$

Because tertiary alkyl cations are more stable than secondary ions, hydride ions are more readily abstracted from tertiary carbon atoms than from secondary carbon atoms; hence, isoparaffins and alkylcycloparaffins undergo the hydrogen-halogen exchange reaction more readily than do n-paraffins and unsubstituted cycloparaffins. However, there is evidence that even hydride ions attached to secondary carbon atoms can be abstracted. For example, the reaction of t-butyl bromide with propane in the presence of aluminum bromide at room temperature resulted in a 16 per cent yield of isopropyl bromide.[3] Similarly, the exchange reaction with n-butane produced secondary bromopentane in 9 per cent yield and t-pentyl bromide in 6 per cent yield, formation of the latter involving the intermediate rearrangement of a secondary pentyl ion to a t-pentyl ion (Principle 3; cf. mechanism of the isomerization of n-butane, page 269). The aluminum chloride-catalyzed reaction of cyclopentane or cyclohexane with t-butyl chloride resulted in up to 20 per cent yields of chlorocyclopentane and chlorocyclohexane, respectively. The fact that no 1-chloro-1-methylcyclopentane was obtained in the reaction with cyclohexane indicates that the intermediate cyclohexyl cation did not isomerize to methylcyclopentyl cation before being converted to chlorocyclohexane by abstraction of a chloride ion from the *t*-butyl chloride or by dissociation of the cyclohexyl tetrachloroaluminate. Abstraction of a secondary hydride ion is also involved in the formation of 2-chloro-bicyclo [2.2.1]-heptane in 22–26 per cent yield by the reaction of bicyclo-[2.2.1]heptane with *t*-butyl chloride in the presence of aluminum chloride at about 0°C.[46]

Attempts to obtain an exchange reaction with ethane and *t*-butyl bromide in the presence of aluminum bromide were unsuccessful, indicating that abstraction of hydride ions from primary carbon atoms is particularly difficult.[3]

A similar hydrogen-halogen exchange occurs with polyhaloalkanes. Chloroform is obtained when carbon tetrachloride is treated with saturated hydrocarbons and aluminum chloride.[29]

Peroxide-Induced Reactions. Carbon tetrachloride is also converted to chloroform when it is treated with a saturated hydrocarbon in the presence of a free radical forming substances such as a peroxide.[57] The presence of a tertiary carbon atom in the saturated hydrocarbon is not essential; the exchange reaction occurred about as readily with straight-chain paraffins containing at least three carbon atoms as with branched-chain paraffins and cycloparaffins. Thus, propane, *n*-heptane, isobutane and methylcyclohexane were converted chiefly to isopropyl chloride, *s*-heptyl chlorides, *t*-butyl chloride, and 1-chloro-1-methyl-cyclohexane, respectively, when heated at 130–140°C with carbon tetrachloride in the presence of di-*t*-butyl peroxide. The carbon tetrachloride was reduced to chloroform. The free radical formed by decomposition of the peroxide initiates the following chain reaction:

$$(CH_3)_3CO \cdot + (CH_3)_3CH \rightarrow (CH_3)_3COH + (CH_3)_3C \cdot$$
$$(CH_3)_3C \cdot + CCl_4 \rightarrow (CH_3)_3CCl + Cl_3C \cdot$$
$$Cl_3C \cdot + (CH_3)_3CH \rightarrow Cl_3CH + (CH_3)_3C \cdot$$

This exchange reaction may be taken as evidence that a radical can abstract a hydrogen atom from a saturated hydrocarbon (Principle 5′). The significance of the observation that free radicals abstract hydrogen atoms attached to secondary and tertiary carbon atoms equally readily while carbonium ions abstract very readily only those hydride ions attached to tertiary carbon atoms will become apparent in the discussion of the alkylation of paraffins.

Condensation of Alkyl and Cycloalkyl Halides with Olefins and Haloolefins

Metal Halide-Catalyzed Reaction. The condensation of olefins[47,48,49,55] and haloolefins[50,51] with alkyl halides containing at least three carbon atoms and with cycloalkyl halides in the presence of catalysts of the Friedel-Crafts type to yield higher molecular weight haloalkanes involves Principle 1 and, in some cases at least, Principle 5. The reaction of t-butyl chloride with ethylene in the presence of aluminum chloride results in a 75 per cent yield of 1-chloro-3,3-dimethylbutane:

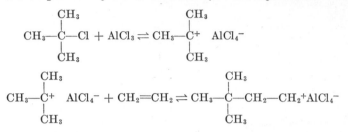

Part of the final product may be formed by dissociation of the complex:

$$\text{CH}_3\text{—}\overset{\overset{\text{CH}_3}{|}}{\underset{\underset{\text{CH}_3}{|}}{\text{C}}}\text{—CH}_2\text{—CH}_2{}^+\text{AlCl}_4{}^- \rightleftharpoons \text{CH}_3\text{—}\overset{\overset{\text{CH}_3}{|}}{\underset{\underset{\text{CH}_3}{|}}{\text{C}}}\text{—CH}_2\text{—CH}_2\text{Cl} + \text{AlCl}_3$$

Most of the product is formed by abstraction of a chloride ion from t-butyl chloride:[56]

$$\text{CH}_3\overset{\overset{\text{CH}_3}{|}}{\underset{\underset{\text{CH}_3}{|}}{\text{C}}}\text{—CH}_2\text{—CH}_2{}^+\text{AlCl}_4{}^- + \text{CH}_3\text{—}\overset{\overset{\text{CH}_3}{|}}{\underset{\underset{\text{CH}_3}{|}}{\text{C}}}\text{—Cl}$$

$$\rightarrow \text{CH}_3\text{—}\overset{\overset{\text{CH}_3}{|}}{\underset{\underset{\text{CH}_3}{|}}{\text{C}}}\text{—CH}_2\text{—CH}_2\text{Cl} + \text{CH}_3\text{—}\overset{\overset{\text{CH}_3}{|}}{\underset{\underset{\text{CH}_3}{|}}{\text{C}}}{}^+ \text{AlCl}_4{}^-$$

Evidence that both methods of formation are involved is found in the results of an experiment on the condensation of t-butyl chloride (1.03 moles) with ethylene in the presence of aluminum bromide (0.33 mole) at -40 to $-50°C$, 1-bromo- and 1-chloro-3,3-dimethylbutane were formed in 15 and 32 per cent yields, respectively.[56] The amount of bromohexane was thus approximately one-third of the condensation product rather than one-half as calculated on a statistical basis. Similarly, the reaction of t-butyl bromide (1.02 moles) with ethylene in presence of aluminum chloride (0.34 mole) under the same conditions resulted in a 58 per cent yield of 1-bromo-3,3-dimethylbutane and only 13 per cent of the 1-chloro-3,3-dimethylbutane formed by interaction with the catalyst.[56]

That carbonium ions can abstract halide ions from tertiary alkyl halides is confirmed by the observation that the reaction of 0.5 mole each of *t*-butyl bromide and *t*-pentyl chloride at −25 to −30°C in the presence of a catalytic amount (0.04 mole) of aluminum chloride produced 0.18 mole *t*-butyl chloride and 0.25 mole *t*-pentyl bromide.[56]

$$(CH_3)_3C^+AlCl_3Br^- + C_2H_5(CH_3)_2CCl \rightleftharpoons (CH_3)_3CCl + C_2H_5(CH_3)_2C^+AlCl_3Br^-$$
$$C_2H_5(CH_3)_2C^+AlCl_3Br^- + (CH_3)_3CBr \rightleftharpoons C_2H_5(CH_3)_2CBr + (CH_3)_3C^+AlCl_3Br^-$$

On the other hand, little or no halogen exchange occurred when *t*-butyl bromide was treated with 1-chloro-3,3-dimethylbutane at −45 to 0°C in the presence of aluminum chloride because the *t*-butyl cations (which form more readily than the primary hexyl cations) do not abstract halogen held by primary carbon atoms. This is analogous to the observation that the aluminum chloride-catalyzed exchange of halogen for hydrogen between alkyl halides and paraffins takes place very readily only with paraffins containing tertiary carbon atoms,[1] presumably because alkyl carbonium ions abstract hydride ions held by primary and secondary carbon atoms with relative difficulty. It may further be concluded that the formation of 1-chloro-3,3-dimethylbutane by the reaction of the 3,3-dimethylbutyl cation with *t*-butyl chloride is a substantially irreversible reaction.

When a secondary chloride (for example isopropyl chloride[47] or cyclohexyl chloride[49] is condensed with ethylene in the presence of aluminum chloride, the product which is isolated is that formed by interaction of one molecule of the chloride with two of the olefin. The primary reaction products (isopentyl chloride and 2-cyclohexylethyl chloride, respectively) contain tertiary carbon atoms and isomerization of the intermediate carbonium ions to tertiary carbonium ions occurs. Since tertiary carbonium ions add more readily to olefins than do secondary carbonium ions, these tertiary ions add more rapidly than do the original secondary ions (isopropyl and cyclohexyl). The final products are the same as those obtained by the condensation of ethylene with the corresponding tertiary chlorides and are 1-chloro-3,3-dimethylpentane and 1-(2-chloroethyl)-1-ethylcyclohexane, neither of which contain a tertiary carbon atom and are therefore the principal products.

Analogously,

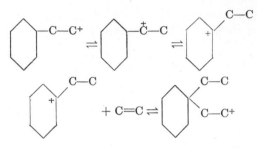

On the other hand, condensation of these secondary chlorides with vinyl chloride yields 1,1-dichloro-3-methylbutane[50] and (2,2-dichloroethyl)cyclohexane,[49] respectively. The presence of a chlorine atom on the positively charged carbon atom apparently prevents the isomerization of the carbonium ion prior to its conversion to the dichloride.

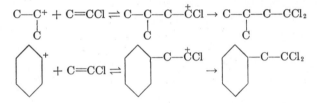

Condensation of *t*-butyl chloride with 1,2-dichloroethylene in the presence of aluminum chloride is of interest because it resulted in the production of 1,1,2-trichloro-3,3-dimethylbutane in up to 75 per cent yield when *cis*-dichloroethylene was used and in less than 2 per cent yield with the *trans* isomer.[50] Difficulty of addition of *t*-butyl cations to hindered double bonds is indicated.

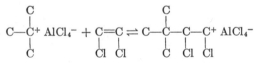

Dichloroalkanes in which at least one of the chlorine atoms is attached to a tertiary carbon atom may be condensed with ethylene and chloroethylene in the presence of Friedel-Crafts catalysts:[58]

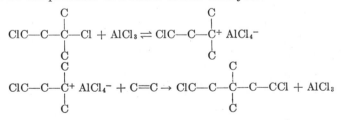

On the other hand, condensation of olefins with polyhaloalkanes containing two or more halogen atoms on a single carbon atom does not occur in the presence of these catalysts.[43] For example, the addition of carbon tetrachloride to ethylene does not take place in the presence of aluminum chloride, polymerization of the olefin occuring more rapidly than the condensation with the carbon tetrachloride. If a polychloroethylene[43] is used instead of ethylene, the desired addition to the double bond does take place; *sym*-heptachloropropane is obtained by the reaction of carbon tetrachloride (as $Cl_3C^+ AlCl_4^-$) with trichloroethylene:

$$CCl_4 + CH_2=CH_2 \xrightarrow{\quad\times\quad} Cl_3C—CH_2—CH_2Cl$$
$$CCl_4 + CHCl=CCl_2 \xrightarrow{\quad\quad} Cl_3C—CHCl—CCl_3$$

Peroxide-Induced Reaction. Carbon tetrachloride can be condensed with olefins under free radical rather than carbonium ion conditions. Thus, acetyl peroxide induces the reaction of carbon tetrachloride with 1-octene to yield 1,1,1,3-tetrachlorononane.[31,32] Trichloromethyl radicals act as chain carriers:

$$CH_3CO_2· + CCl_4 \rightarrow CH_3Cl + CO_2 + Cl_3C·$$

$$Cl_3C· + CH_2=CH—C_6H_{13} \rightarrow Cl_3C—CH_2—\overset{·}{C}H—C_6H_{13}$$

$$Cl_3C—CH_2—\overset{·}{C}H—C_6H_{13} + CCl_4 \rightarrow Cl_3C—CH_2—CHCl—C_6H_{13} + Cl_3C·$$

Polymerization of Olefins

Catalytic Dimerization of Olefins. The polymerization of isobutylene in the presence of dilute sulfuric acid results in a mixture of trimethylpentenes consisting of about four parts of 2,4,4,-trimethyl-1-pentene and one of 2,4,4-trimethyl-2-pentene.[35] The mechanism[68] involves Principles 1 and 4.

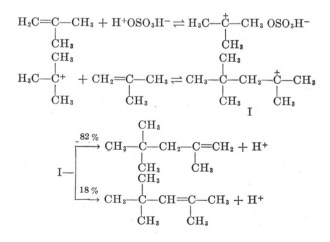

The 1-pentene derivative is formed in larger amount because elimination of one of the six protons on the two primary carbon atoms adjacent to the electron-deficient carbon atom takes place more readily than does loss of one of the two protons on the methylene carbon atom in the neopentyl group, a group which apparently loses protons with comparative difficulty.

An investigation of the action of 75 per cent sulfuric acid on 3-methyl-2-butanol at 90°C is of interest because it illustrates a number of features of the polymerization mechanism.[70] The major products were 3,5,5-trimethyl-2-heptene (V), 35 per cent yield, and 3,4,5,5-tetramethyl-2-hexene (IX), 45 per cent; minor products included 2-methyl-2-butene (II), 1 per cent; 3-methyl-2-pentene (VIII), 3 per cent; 3-methyl-2-butanone, 1 per cent; diisobutylenes, 1 per cent; 2,3,4,4-tetramethyl-1-pentene, 2 per cent; other nonenes, 1 per cent; polymers of higher molecular weight than decene, 5 per cent.

The major products are produced by polymerization of methylbutenes formed from the alcohol, the polymerization reaction involving not only Principles 1 and 4, but also Principles 2 and 3:

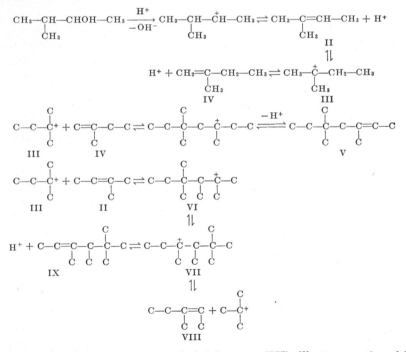

Formation of 3,4,5,5-tetramethyl-2-hexene (IX) illustrates the shift of a methyl group in accordance with Principle 3. Whether it occurs by a

1,3- shift of the methyl group as written or whether it actually involves a succession of 1,2- shifts is a moot question, further discussion of which is beyond the scope of this chapter.[6,7,38,71]

Production of 3,5,5-trimethyl-2-heptene (V) rather than the 3-heptene isomer and of 3,4,5,5-tetramethyl-2-hexene (IX) rather than the 3-hexene isomer are further illustrations of the relative difficulty with which a proton is eliminated from the neopentyl group.

Formation of 3-methyl-2-pentene (VIII) and *t*-butyl cation (hence, isobutylene), from the decyl ion (VII) is an example of Principle 2. It involves scission at the bond in beta-position to the electron-deficient carbon atom and is consequent to the shift of an electron pair from the adjacent carbon atom without the attached alkyl group. Such beta-scission occurs particularly readily within carbonium ions containing the grouping R_3C—C—C+.

The isobutylene resulting from the scission of VII polymerizes to yield diisobutylene and copolymerizes with 2-methyl-2-butene (II) and other pentenes to yield respectively, 2,3,4,4-tetramethyl-1-pentene and other nonenes.

Oxidation of the 3-methyl-2-butanol (accompanied by the formation of sulfur dioxide) accounts for the 3-methyl-2-butanone by-product.

The copolymerization of isobutylene with propene in the presence of phosphoric acid yields heptylene consisting principally of 2,2- and 2,3-dimethyl-*x*-pentene as shown by the fact that hydrogenation yields 2,2- and 2,3-dimethylpentane.[28] The reaction involves the addition of *t*-butyl cation to propene:

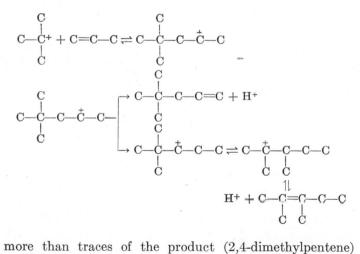

No more than traces of the product (2,4-dimethylpentene) which would be formed by the addition of isopropyl cation to isobutylene were

obtained because the addition of the isopropyl ion to the olefinic double bond takes place too slowly. This is analogous to the fact that *t*-butyl chloride adds more readily to ethylene in the presence of acid catalysts of the Friedel-Crafts type than does isopropyl chloride.[47]

Thermal Dimerization of Isobutylene. Polymerization of isobutylene at 370–460° and 36–360 atm. yields 1,1,3-trimethylcyclopentane rather than an octylene.[36] About 46 per cent of the total liquid product obtained at 400° and 36 atm. consisted of the cyclic dimer. Its formation involves a chain reaction initiated by a free radical which may be formed by decomposition of the isobutylene or by other means:

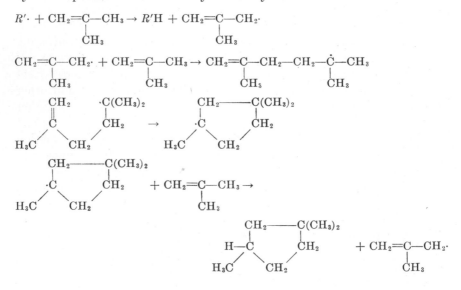

Conjunct Polymerization. Conjunct polymerization[23,25] of olefins (i.e., polymerization resulting in the formation of both saturated and unsaturated hydrocarbons) can be caused to take place with all olefins by proper choice of catalyst and reaction conditions.

With sulfuric acid, the type of polymerization depends on the concentration of the acid; conjunct polymerization occurs with acid of greater than about 90 per cent concentration while true polymerization occurs with more dilute acid.[26] With phosphoric acid, the type of polymer depends on the temperature, conjunct polymerization occurring at temperatures above about 250 to 300°C.[27] With aluminum chloride, true polymerization occurs only under very special conditions, as for example when aluminum metal is used as promoter.[18]

The mechanism of conjunct polymerization involves the abstraction of hydrogen from an olefin polymer by an alkyl carbonium ion to yield an olefinic carbonium ion and a paraffin.[1] Thus, the formation of the water-white, chiefly paraffinic, upper layer and the viscous dark red-brown lower layer which are obtained by the polymerization of ethylene in the presence of aluminum chloride promoted by hydrogen chloride may be illustrated by the following equations in which $RCH_2CH_2CH{=}CHR'$ represents a molecule of true polymer.

$$RCH_2{-}CH_2{-}CH{=}CHR' + HCl + AlCl_3 \rightleftharpoons R{-}CH_2{-}CH_2{-}\overset{+}{C}H{-}CH_2R'AlCl_4{}^-$$

$$RCH_2{-}CH_2{-}\overset{+}{C}H{-}CH_2R' + R{-}CH_2{-}CH_2{-}CH{=}CHR' \rightleftharpoons$$

$$RCH_2{-}CH_2{-}CH_2{-}CH_2R' + RCH_2{-}\overset{+}{C}H{-}CH{=}CHR'$$

$$RCH_2{-}\overset{+}{C}H{-}CH{=}CHR'AlCl_4{}^- \rightleftharpoons RCH{=}CH{-}CH{=}CHR' + AlCl_3 + HCl$$

The final products are paraffins and polyolefins. The latter form complexes with the aluminum chloride and make up the so-called lower layer.

The formation of isobutane (18.8 per cent by weight of the converted ethylene) together with a mixture of other paraffins as well as olefins, naphthenes, and aromatic hydrocarbons by the polymerization of ethylene at 330°C in the presence of 90 per cent phosphoric acid[27] may be explained in analogous manner. An n-butyl cation formed by dimerization of ethylene isomerizes to *t*-butyl cation which abstracts a hydride ion from another molecule, for example octene (ethylene tetramer) to form isobutane and an unsaturated carbonium ion which may lose a proton to yield a diene or may cyclize to yield an ethylcyclohexyl ion.

$$CH_2{=}CH_2 + PO(OH)_3 \rightleftharpoons CH_3CH_2{}^+ + OPO(OH)_2{}^-$$

$$CH_3CH_2{}^+ + CH_2{=}CH_2 \rightleftharpoons CH_3CH_2CH_2CH_2{}^+ \rightleftharpoons CH_3CH_2\overset{+}{C}HCH_3$$

$$CH_3\overset{+}{C}CH_3 + CH_3CH_2CH_2CH_2CH_2CH_2CH{=}CH_2 \rightleftharpoons$$
(with CH_3 below the charged carbon)

Aromatic compounds are formed by dehydrogenation (by way of reaction with carbonium ions) of the ethylcyclohexene and similar products or, less likely, by cyclization of a triolefinic carbonium ion.

Catalytic Macropolymerization of Isobutylene. The polymerization of isobutylene at temperatures below about $-70°C$ in the presence of Friedel-Crafts catalysts such as aluminum chloride, boron fluoride, and titanium tetrachloride leads to the formation of high molecular weight polymers having elastic properties.[63] For example, the addition of boron fluoride to liquid isobutylene at $-80°C$ results in an immediate, almost explosive, reaction; in contrast, polymerization at the boiling point of isobutylene $(-6°C)$ occurs after an induction period, yielding an oil. The molecular weight of the product decreases from 200,000 to 10,000 as the temperature is increased from $-90°$ to $-10°C$.

No reaction occurs when pure isobutylene in the vapor phase is contacted with pure boron fluoride.[9,10,11] There is instantaneous reaction when water or t-butyl alcohol is added to the mixture of olefin and catalyst; the boron fluoride is consumed in quantities approximately equivalent to the moles of promoter. On the other hand, the presence of a promoter did not seem to be necessary when the pure isobutylene was in the liquid phase.

The mechanism of macropolymerization is similar to that of true polymerization, the important difference being that growth of the polymer chain by addition of the carbonium ion to a molecule of isobutylene occurs more readily than does loss of a proton, the reaction which is predominant at higher temperatures. The chain is initiated by a t-butyl cation formed from isobutylene by the addition of a proton from the promoter.

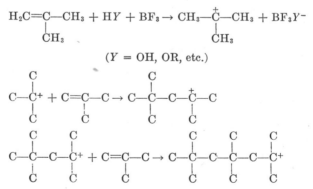

$$H_2C=\!\!\underset{\underset{CH_3}{|}}{C}\!\!-CH_3 + HY + BF_3 \rightarrow CH_3-\!\!\underset{\underset{CH_3}{|}}{\overset{+}{C}}\!\!-CH_3 + BF_3Y^-$$

$$(Y = OH, OR, etc.)$$

The polymer ion continues to grow by addition to isobutylene until its growth is terminated by one of the following reactions in which M represents monomer (isobutylene) and n is the number of molecules reacted:

$$M_nH^+ + F_3BY^- \rightarrow M_n + F_3BYH$$
$$M_nH^+ + F_3BY^- \rightarrow M_nHY + BF_3$$
$$M_nH^+ + M \rightarrow M_n + MH^+$$

At higher temperatures, the loss or transfer of a proton from the polymer ion occurs more rapidly than does the addition to isobutylene; hence, lower molecular weight products are obtained.

The higher polymer chain is propagated chiefly by head-to-tail addition, an observation which is explained on the basis of the heats of reaction of head-to-tail, tail-to-tail, and head-to-head addition of the tertiary carbonium ion to isobutylene.[11]

It has been suggested[19] that polymerization in the absence of a promoter involves a dipole formed by the addition of the catalyst to the pi electrons of the olefin:

$$F_3B + CH_2{=}C{-}CH_3 \rightarrow F_3B : \overset{..}{\underset{..}{C}} : \overset{+}{\underset{..}{C}} : CH_3$$

with the H above and $\overset{|}{CH_3}$ below on the left, and H CH_3 below on the right.

It was found that isobutylene polymers prepared in the presence of boron fluoride contained a noncombustible residue even after solution, filtration, and precipitation.

A similar complex "carbonium ion" was proposed[20] as the active agent in the polymerization of ethylene in the presence of aluminum chloride. The complex, which like the carbonium ion formed by the addition of a proton to an olefin contains an electron-deficient carbon atom, differs from such a true carbonium ion in that it is in itself electronically neutral. It has been suggested[69] that this difference is related to the fact that metal halide catalysts tend to yield much higher polymers than do the protonic acid catalysts. On the other hand, this postulation does not take into account the promoting effect of hydrogen halides, water, and other promoters in reactions effected in the presence of aluminum chloride and boron fluoride.

Peroxide-Induced Macropolymerization of Ethylene. A free-radical chain reaction mechanism seems to be involved in the polymerization of ethylene to very high molecular weight polymers by heating under high pressures in the presence of peroxide or oxygen.[14,42,60] The peroxide-induced reaction is initiated by free radicals formed by the decomposition of the peroxide. The oxygen-induced reaction may involve the intermediate formation of a peroxide or of a free radical olefin-oxygen addition product.

Polymerization at 110–120°C and 200–300 atm. pressure, for example, in the presence of a methanol solution of benzoyl peroxide yields a wax melting at 105–110°C, having a molecular weight of 2000–3000 and containing 0.7–1.3 per cent of oxygen. The initiation step may be indicated by

$$(C_6H_5COO)_2 \rightarrow 2C_6H_5COO\cdot \rightarrow 2C_6H_5\cdot + 2CO_2$$
$$C_6H_5COO\cdot + CH_3OH \rightarrow C_6H_5COOH + \cdot CH_2OH$$
$$C_6H_5\cdot + CH_3OH \rightarrow C_6H_6 + \cdot CH_2OH$$

The chain is propagated in accordance with Principle 1′:

$$R\cdot + CH_2{=}CH_2 \rightarrow RCH_2CH_2\cdot$$
$$RCH_2CH_2\cdot + (n+1)CH_2{=}CH_2 \rightarrow RCH_2CH_2(CH_2CH_2)_nCH_2CH_2\cdot$$

$R\cdot$ is hydroxymethyl, phenyl, or benzoyloxy. Its exact nature is relatively unimportant because it serves only to initiate the first cycle, the subsequent cycles being initiated by hydroxymethyl radicals formed by chain transfer with the solvent.

Chain transfer terminates the growing polymer chain by abstracting a hydrogen atom from the methanol solvent in accordance with Principle 5′ and at the same time yields a hydroxymethyl radical which starts a new cycle. The hydroxymethyl radical accounts for the oxygen present in the wax.

$$RCH_2CH_2(CH_2CH_2)_nCH_2CH_2\cdot + CH_3OH$$
$$\rightarrow RCH_2CH_2(CH_2CH_2)_nCH_2CH_3 + \cdot CH_2OH$$

Alternatively, and less probably, the growing chain may transfer hydrogen to the ethylene:

$$R\,CH_2CH_2(CH_2CH_2)_nCH_2CH_2\cdot + CH_2{=}CH_2 \rightarrow$$
$$RCH_2CH_2(CH_2CH_2)_nCH{=}CH_2 + CH_3CH_2.$$

The chain is terminated by coupling or disproportionation of two radicals which need not necessarily be alike:

$$2R(CH_2CH_2)_mCH_2CH_2\cdot \rightarrow R(CH_2CH_2)_mCH_2CH_2CH_2CH_2(CH_2CH_2)_mR$$
$$2R(CH_2CH_2)_mCH_2CH_2\cdot \rightarrow R(CH_2CH_2)_mCH{=}CH_2 + R(CH_2CH_2)_mCH_2CH_3$$

Alkylation of Paraffins and Cycloparaffins

Catalytic Alkylation. The catalytic alkylation of an isoparaffin with an olefin occurs by way of a chain mechanism involving the conversion of the isoparaffin to a t-alkyl cation which adds to the olefin (Principle 1) to yield a higher molecular weight cation which undergoes rearrangement (Principle 3) followed by abstraction of a hydride ion from the isoparaffin (Principle 5) to yield the alkylation product and a t-alkyl ion which starts a new cycle.[1,52]

The production of 2,3-dimethylbutane by the reaction of isobutane with ethylene in the presence of aluminum chloride promoted by hydrogen chloride is indicated by:

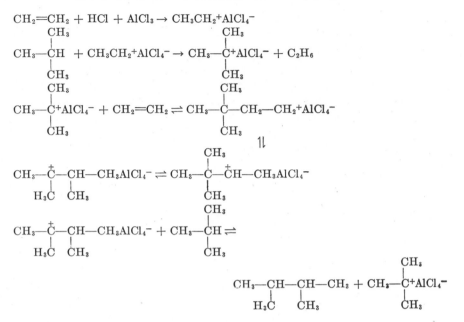

Because ethane is formed in the chain initiating only, the amount formed is relatively small.

In all alkylations of isobutane, 2,2,4-trimethylpentane is a by-product regardless of the olefin used. Its formation involves the secondary reaction of the *t*-butyl cation as shown in the following reactions which occur, for example, during the alkylation of isobutane with propene:

$$(\overset{\cdot}{C}H_3)_3CH + C_3H_6 + H^+ \rightarrow (CH_3)_3C^+ + C_3H_8$$
$$(CH_3)_3C^+ \rightleftharpoons (CH_3)_2C{=}CH_2 + H^+$$

$$(CH_3)_3C^+ + (CH_3)_3C{=}CH_2 \rightleftharpoons (CH_3)_3CCH_2\overset{+}{C}(CH_3)_2$$

$$(CH_3)_3CCH_2\overset{+}{C}(CH_3)_2 + (CH_3)_3CH \rightleftharpoons (CH_3)_3CCH_2CH(CH_3)_2 + (CH_3)_3C^+$$

The over-all reaction is

$$2(CH_3)_3CH + C_3H_6 \rightarrow (CH_3)_3CCH_2CH(CH_3)_2 + C_3H_8$$

It has been found that by-product trimethylpentane and a paraffin corresponding to the olefin used are formed in approximately equimolecular quantities.

Formation of other by-products in the catalytic alkylation of isoparaffin are also readily explained in terms of carbonium ion theory (see Chapter 54).

The alkylation of cycloparaffins often involves ring expansion and/or contraction.[40] For example, the ethylation of cyclohexane in the presence of aluminum chloride involves the addition of a methylcyclopentyl cation to ethylene to yield a 2-(1-methylcyclopentyl)ethyl cation which isomerizes to a 1,2-dimethylcyclohexyl ion which reacts with cyclohexane to produce 1,2-dimethylcyclohexane and a cyclohexyl cation, rearrangement of which forms the methylcyclopentyl cation.

Thermal Alkylation. The fact that the thermal alkylation of isobutane with ethylene at 500°C and 300 atm. pressure yields 2,2-dimethylbutane (neohexane) as the principal reaction product rather than 2,3-dimethylbutane (biisopropyl, diisopropyl) which is obtained in catalytic alkylation is inherent in the principles of free radical reactions. The tertiary butyl radical adds to ethylene to yield a hexyl radical (Principle 1′) which, unlike the corresponding hexyl cation, does not undergo rearrangement before abstracting a hydrogen atom from isobutane (Principle 5′).[16] As was pointed out in the outline of the general principles of free radical behavior, free radicals, unlike carbonium ions, do not undergo isomerizations involving alkyl group migration.

The reaction chain is initiated by free radicals formed, for example, by cracking of the isobutane.

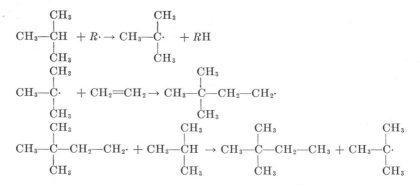

2,2-Dimethylbutane is the chief alkylation product. 2-Methylpentane is produced in minor amount by similar reactions involving isobutyl radicals formed by abstraction of a hydrogen atom attached to a primary carbon atom of isobutane; such hydrogen atoms are less reactive but more numerous than the hydrogen atom attached to the tertiary carbon atom.

Because free radicals, unlike carbonium ions, are able to abstract hydrogen from straight-chain as well as branched-chain paraffins under the alkylation conditions, thermal alkylation, but not catalytic alkylation, occurs readily with propane and other *n*-alkanes. Thus, alkylation of propane with ethylene yields a mixture of *n*- and isopentane which are formed via the addition of *n*-and isopropyl radicals to ethylene.[16]

Condensation of Paraffins with Chloroolefins

Metal Halide-Catalyzed Reaction. 1-Chloro-3,4-dimethylpentane and 1,2-dichloro-4,4-dimethylpentane are obtained in 35–40 per cent and 13–15 per cent yields, respectively, by the reaction of isobutane with allyl chloride at −10°C.[53] Formation of both these products is inherent in a chain mechanism which is analogous to the mechanism of the alkylation of isoparaffins with olefins. The chain-carrying steps may be presented as follows:

$$
\begin{array}{c}
\text{C} \\
|\\
\text{C}-\overset{+}{\text{C}}\text{AlCl}_4^- + \text{C}{=}\text{C}-\text{C}-\text{Cl} \rightleftharpoons \text{C}-\overset{\text{C}}{\underset{\text{C}}{\text{C}}}-\text{C}-\overset{+}{\text{C}}-\text{C}-\text{ClAlCl}_4^- \\
|\\
\text{C}
\end{array}
$$

$$
\begin{array}{c}
\text{C} \\
|\\
\text{C}-\text{C}-\overset{+}{\text{C}}-\text{CClAlCl}_4^- \rightleftharpoons \text{C}-\overset{\text{C}}{\text{C}}-\text{C}-\text{C}-\text{CCl} + \text{AlCl}_3 \\
|\qquad\qquad\qquad\qquad\qquad | \\
\text{C}\qquad\qquad\qquad\qquad\text{Cl}
\end{array}
$$

$$\Updownarrow$$

$$
\begin{array}{c}
\text{C} \\
|\\
\text{C}-\text{C}-\overset{+}{\text{C}}-\text{C}-\text{CCl} + \text{AlCl}_4^- \rightleftharpoons \text{C}-\overset{+}{\text{C}}-\text{C}-\text{C}-\text{CClAlCl}_4^- \\
|\qquad\qquad\qquad\qquad\qquad\qquad\qquad | \;\; | \\
\text{C}\qquad\qquad\qquad\qquad\qquad\qquad\text{C}\;\text{C}
\end{array}
$$

$$
\text{C}-\overset{+}{\text{C}}-\text{C}-\text{C}-\text{CClAlCl}_4^- + \text{C}-\overset{\text{C}}{\underset{\text{C}}{\text{C}}} \rightleftharpoons \text{C}-\text{C}-\text{C}-\text{C}-\text{CCl} + \text{C}-\overset{\text{C}}{\underset{\text{C}}{\overset{+}{\text{C}}}}\text{AlCl}_4^-
$$

Polychloroolefins react similarly. Of particular interest is the reaction of *cis-* and *trans-*dichloroethylene since 1,1,2-trichloro-3,3-dimethylbutane was obtained in 35 per cent yield with the *cis* isomer and in less than 5 per cent yield with the *trans* compound.[54] Difficulty of addition of *t*-butyl cations to hindered double bonds is again indicated (cf. page 256). The fact that no dichloro- or monochlorohexane was isolated indicates that the trichloride and the corresponding cations are relatively unreactive toward chlorine-hydrogen exchange with isobutane because two of the chlorine atoms are attached to a primary carbon atom and the third to a secondary atom in a neopentyl group. Any trichloride which does react is eventually reduced to hexane by means of a hydrogen-chlorine reaction because the intermediate di- and monochlorohexane are comparatively unstable since tertiary carbon atoms are formed during the exchange reaction. For example, the trichloride is probably converted to 1,1-dichloro-2,3-dimethylbutane which isomerizes to reactive 1,2-dichloro-2,3-dimethylbutane.

Peroxide-Induced Reactions. A free radical chain mechanism is involved in the condensation of saturated hydrocarbons (including propane) with polychloroethylenes in the presence of peroxides.[59] The products are chloroolefins containing one chlorine atom less than the chloroethylene used. Condensation of propane with 1,2-dichloroethylene, with trichloroethylene, and with tetrachloroethylene in the presence of di-*t*-butyl peroxide at 130–135°C yielded (as principal isomer in each case) 1-chloro-, 1,1-dichloro-, and 1,1,2-trichloro-3-methyl-1-butene, respectively, in 10, 31 and 27 per cent yields. The reaction of isobutane with *cis*- and with *trans*-dichloroethylene under the same conditions resulted in 35 and 38 per cent yields, respectively, of 1-chloro-3,3-dimethyl-1-butene.

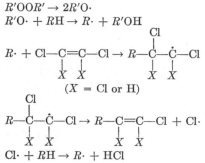

$$R'OOR' \rightarrow 2R'O\cdot$$
$$R'O\cdot + RH \rightarrow R\cdot + R'OH$$

The observation that *cis*- and *trans*-dichloroethylene show little difference in reactivity with isobutane in the peroxide-induced reaction while there is a marked difference in the aluminum chloride-catalyzed condensation indicates that there is a significant difference between the ease of addition of *t*-butyl radicals and *t*-butyl cations to hindered double bonds. The other differences between the peroxide-induced and the metal halide-catalyzed reactions (the fact that the peroxide-induced reaction gives good yields of unsaturated chlorides with both *n*- and isoparaffins while the aluminum-chloride-catalyzed reactions gives good yields of saturated chlorides but only with isoparaffins) are explained by the basic principles of free radical and carbonium ion behavior.

Isomerization of Paraffins and Cycloparaffins

Isomerization of saturated hydrocarbons in the presence of aluminum halides also may be explained by a carbonium ion chain mechanism involving Principles 3 and 5. Chain initiators are formed, for example, by the reaction of the catalyst with olefins present as such or formed by heating the reaction mixture to a sufficiently high temperature. When very carefully purified *n*-butane is treated under certain controlled conditions with pure aluminum chloride or pure aluminum bromide, no isomerization occurs.[41] There is little effect on the addition of hydrogen halide promoter in a small concentration unless the reaction mixture is heated to cause cracking. On the other hand, the addition of as little as 0.01 per cent of olefin, together with hydrogen halide, to the purified butane results in isomerization, the olefin acting as chain initiator by reacting with the catalyst ($AlX_3 + HX$). Other chain initiators include water,[64] hydrogen halide in sufficient amount to induce cracking (about 15 mole %) and oxygen.[65]

Isomerization of *n*-butane in the presence of aluminum chloride and hydrogen chloride may be indicated by:[2]

$$CH_3CH_2CH_2CH_3 + R^+ \rightleftharpoons CH_3\overset{+}{C}HCH_2CH_3 + RH$$

$$CH_3\overset{+}{C}HCH_2CH_3 \rightleftharpoons \underset{\underset{CH_3}{|}}{CH_3CHCH_2{}^+} \rightleftharpoons \underset{\underset{CH_3}{|}}{CH_3\overset{+}{C}CH_3}$$

$$\underset{\underset{CH_3}{|}}{CH_3\overset{+}{C}CH_3} + CH_3CH_2CH_2CH_3 \rightleftharpoons \underset{\underset{CH_3}{|}}{CH_3CHCH_3} + CH_3\overset{+}{C}HCH_2CH_3$$

Chain initiation by promoters is also involved in the isomerization of cycloparaffins:[39]

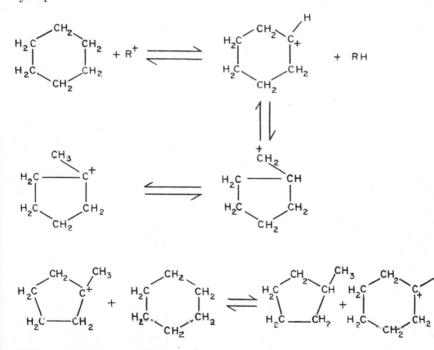

Isomerization of Olefins

Catalytic Isomerization. Acid-catalyzed isomerization of olefins involves migration of a pair of electrons together with either hydrogen or an alkyl group. The former rearrangement results in a double bond shift; the latter, in skeletal rearrangement. For example, the isomerization of 1-pentene to 2-pentene in the presence of activated alumina at 357°C[12] and to 2-methylbutenes in the presence of silica-alumina catalyst at 400°[8] may be described by applying Principles 3 and 4:

$$CH_3—CH_2—CH_2—CH=CH_2 + H^+ \rightleftharpoons CH_3—CH_2—CH_2—\overset{+}{C}H—CH_3$$

$$CH_3—CH_2—CH_2—\overset{+}{C}H—CH_3 —\left[\begin{matrix} \rightarrow CH_3—CH_2—CH=CH—CH_3 + H^+ \\ \rightarrow \overset{+}{C}H_2—CH—CH_2—CH_3 \\ \qquad\quad | \\ \qquad\quad CH_3 \end{matrix} \right.$$

$$CH_3—C=CH—CH_3 + H^+ \rightleftharpoons CH_3—\overset{+}{C}—CH_2—CH_3$$
$$\quad | \qquad\qquad\qquad\qquad\qquad | $$
$$\quad CH_3 \qquad\qquad\qquad\qquad\quad CH_3$$

Thermal Isomerization. It has already been pointed out that free radicals, unlike carbonium ions, rarely undergo rearrangement. This explains the fact that skeletal isomerization of olefins under thermal conditions has not been observed. On the other hand, isomerization involving the migration of hydrogen atoms apparently does occur under relatively drastic conditions. For example, 1-pentene is isomerized to 2-pentene at 550–600°C.[21,22] A chain mechanism involving allylic radicals is probably involved.

$$CH_3—CH_2—CH_2—CH=CH_2 + R· \rightleftharpoons CH_3—CH_2—\overset{.}{C}H—CH=CH_2 + RH$$

$$CH_3—CH_2—CH=CH—CH_2 \rightleftharpoons [CH_3—CH_2—\overset{.}{C}H—\overset{.}{C}H—\overset{.}{C}H_2]$$
$$CH_3—CH_2—CH=CH—\overset{.}{C}H_2 + CH_3—CH_2—CH_2—CH=CH_2 \rightleftharpoons$$
$$\qquad CH_3—CH_2—CH=CH—CH_3 + CH_3—CH_2—\overset{.}{C}H—CH=CH_2$$

Cracking of Paraffins and Cycloparaffins

The cracking of paraffins and cycloparaffins may be considered to be a dealkylation reaction and its mechanism can be written as the reverse of the mechanism of alkylation. Catalytic cracking involves the decomposition of a carbonium ion into a smaller carbonium ion and an olefin (Principle 2) while thermal cracking involves the decomposition of a free radical into a smaller radical and an olefin (Principle 2'). In both cases, the scission takes place at a bond in beta-position to the "trivalent" carbon atom. The basic differences in behavior of carbonium ions and of free radicals explain the fact that catalytic cracking yields products which are markedly different from those obtained by thermal cracking. For example,[17] cracking of hexadecanes in the presence of a silica-alumina cracking catalyst yields, as major products, branched-chain hydrocarbons boiling in the C_3 to C_6 range while thermal cracking of the hexadecane yields ethylene as the single major product, with little of the aliphatic product being branched-chain. Furthermore, catalytic cracking yields little straight-chain 1-alkene boiling above the C_4 range, while thermal cracking yields C_3 to C_{15} olefins consisting chiefly of straight-chain 1-alkenes.

It is generally agreed that silica-alumina cracking catalysts are acidic. For example, the catalysts may be titrated with potassium hydroxide or with organic bases such as quinoline. The acidity may be due to the presence of protons on the surface of the catalyst, the active constituent of which may be $(HAlSiO_4)_x$[62] or to electron-deficient aluminum atoms.[37,61] Discussion of the theories which have been proposed to explain the acidity is beyond the scope of this chapter. For present purposes, it is necessary only to assume that the carbonium ion, R^+, which initiates a chain reaction is produced by either (1) the reaction of the protonic acid catalyst with an olefin formed by incipient thermal cracking or dehydrogenation of the paraffin or (2) the abstraction of a hydride ion from the paraffin by the electron-deficient aluminum in the catalyst.

The mechanism of the cracking of hexadecane is illustrated by the following equations:[17,62]

$$C_{11}H_{23}(CH_2)_4CH_3 + R^+ \rightarrow C_{11}H_{23}(CH_2)_3\overset{+}{C}HCH_3 + RH$$

$$C_{11}H_{23}(CH_2)_3\overset{+}{C}HCH_3 \rightarrow C_{11}H_{23}CH_2CH_2^+ + CH_2{=}CHCH_3$$

$$C_{11}H_{23}CH_2CH_2^+ \rightleftharpoons \underset{(A)}{C_{10}H_{21}CH_2\overset{+}{C}HCH_3} \rightleftharpoons C_9H_{19}CH_2\overset{+}{C}HCH_2CH_3$$

$$\underset{(B)}{\underset{\underset{CH_3}{|}}{C_9H_{19}CH_2\overset{+}{C}CH_3}} \rightleftharpoons \underset{\underset{CH_3}{|}}{C_9H_{19}CH_2CHCH_2^+}$$

$$A \rightleftharpoons C_{10}H_{21}^+ + CH_2{=}CHCH_3$$

$$B \rightleftharpoons C_9H_{19}^+ + \underset{\underset{CH_3}{|}}{CH_2{=}CCH_3}$$

Any of the carbonium ions present in the reaction system can start a new cycle by abstracting a hydride ion from a hexadecane molecule.

Because primary alkyl ions readily isomerize to secondary and tertiary alkyl ions, the electron-deficient carbon atom does not remain at the end of a chain of atoms. Hence, beta-scission of the higher molecular weight ion yields fragments containing at least three carbon atoms; this explains why the major products of catalytic cracking boil in the C_3 or higher range. Furthermore, rearrangement of the carbonium ion (Principle 3) occurs very readily and branched compounds predominate.

The mechanism of the catalytic cracking of cycloparaffins may be outlined in analogous manner.

Cracking of paraffins in the presence of aluminum chloride promoted by hydrogen chloride yields a mixture of products of both higher and lower molecular weight than the charged paraffin. This reaction, which has been termed "auto-destructive" alkylation,[24] involves catalytic cracking accompanied by alkylation, the latter proceding via addition of a tertiary alkyl carbonium ion to an intermediate olefin.

Thermal Cracking. The thermal cracking of paraffins is best described as a free radical chain mechanism.[33,44,45] For example, the cracking of n-hexadecane is illustrated by[17]

$$C_9H_{19}CH_2CH_2CH_2C_4H_9 + R\cdot \rightarrow C_9H_{19}CH_2\dot{C}HCH_2C_4H_9 + RH$$

$$C_9H_{19}CH_2\dot{C}HCH_2C_4H_9 - \left[\begin{array}{l} \rightarrow C_9H_{19}CH_2CH{=}CH_2 + C_4H_9\cdot \\ \rightarrow C_9H_{19}\cdot + CH_2{=}CHCH_2C_4H_9 \end{array} \right.$$

$$CH_3CH_2CH_2CH_2\cdot \rightarrow CH_3CH_2\cdot + CH_2{=}CH_2$$
$$C_5H_{11}CH_2CH_2CH_2CH_2\cdot \rightarrow C_5H_{11}CH_2CH_2\cdot + CH_2{=}CH_2$$
$$C_3H_7CH_2CH_2CH_2CH_2\cdot \rightarrow C_3H_7CH_2CH_2\cdot + CH_2{=}CH_2$$
$$CH_3CH_2CH_2CH_2CH_2\cdot \rightarrow CH_3CH_2CH_2\cdot + CH_2{=}CH_2$$
$$CH_3CH_2CH_2\cdot \rightarrow CH_3\cdot + CH_2{=}CH_2$$
$$C_{16}H_{34} + CH_3\cdot \text{ (or } CH_3CH_2\cdot) \rightarrow C_{16}H_{33}\cdot + CH_4 \text{ (or } C_2H_6)$$

Because free radicals do not isomerize readily, the free radicals formed by beta-scission will usually remain primary free radicals; beta-scission of these primary free radicals yields ethylene and new primary free radicals. Hence, ethylene is a major product of the thermal cracking of straight chain paraffins.

The methyl and ethyl radicals start new cycles by abstracting hydrogen atoms attached to secondary carbon atoms yielding methane and ethane and secondary hexadecyl ions. Beta-scission of the latter yields 1-alkenes (1-heptene and 1-dodecene in the above example) and free radicals. Since seven different secondary straight-chain hexadecyl radicals are formed approximately equally readily and since all but one (the 1-methylpentadecyl radical) can undergo beta-scission at two points in the molecule, all the straight-chain 1-alkenes from propene to 1-pentadecene are produced.

The principle that free radicals do not readily isomerize also explains why the thermal cracking product contains few branched-chain compounds. On the other hand, it has been suggested[33] that a long-chain primary alkyl radical can undergo isomerization to a secondary radical by intramolecular abstraction of a hydrogen atom from a secondary carbon atom:

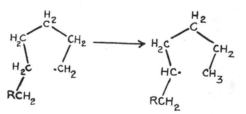

By assigning values for the relative ease of abstracting hydrogen at, tached to primary, secondary, and tertiary carbon atoms by free radicals-it becomes possible to predict the amount of the various products formed. In the earliest formulation of the free radical mechanism for the thermal cracking of hydrocarbons, it was proposed that these ratios are 1:2:10 for cracking at 600°C. More recent calculations based on consideration of the resonance of the radicals has resulted in the ratios 1:3.2:10.3.[33]

The thermal cracking of naphthenes takes place by a similar free radical chain mechanism with the added principle that dehydrogenation (by elimination or abstraction of hydrogen from radicals) to aromatic hydrocarbons occurs.

Cracking of Olefins

Olefins undergo catalytic cracking in the presence, for example, of silica-alumina catalyst at a much higher rate than do the corresponding paraffins; furthermore, hydrogen transfer is a major reaction and is selective for tertiary olefins.[17] On the other hand, the thermal cracking of olefins takes place at about the same rate as that of the paraffins; hydrogen transfer is a minor non-selective reaction.[17] These observations are inherent in the behavior of the carbonium ions and free radicals. The faster rate of catalytic cracking of olefins is due to the more ready formation of carbonium ions by the addition of a proton (from the catalyst) to the olefin. The hydrogen transfer, which involves the abstraction of a hydride ion from a molecule of olefin or of paraffin by a carbonium ion (Principle 5) occurs more rapidly with tertiary ions than with secondary ions and is therefore selective for tertiary olefins. The compounds furnishing the hydrogen for the hydrogen transfer are converted to diolefins, acetylenes, and aromatic hydrocarbons as well as to catalyst deposit.

Because the double bond is not directly involved in the formation of the free radicals which initiate the thermal cracking chain, olefins and paraffins will undergo thermal cracking at about the same rate. Furthermore, any primary and secondary alkyl radicals which may be formed abstract hydrogen atoms from the allyl position in the olefins about as readily as do tertiary alkyl radicals and any hydrogen transfer which occurs is therefore non-selective.

References

1. Bartlett, P. D., Condon, F. E., and Schneider, A , *J. Am. Chem. Soc.*, **66**, 1531 (1944).
2. Bloch, H. S., Pines, H., and Schmerling, L., *ibid*, **68**, 153 (1946).
3. Brewer, C. P., and Greensfelder, B. S., *ibid*, **73**, 2257 (1951).
4. Brown, H. C., and Pearsall, H., *ibid*, **73**, 4681 (1951).
5. Brown, H. C., Pearsall, H., and Eddy, L. P., *ibid*, **72**, 5347 (1950).

6. Cook, N. C., Ecke, G. C., and Whitmore, F. C., Paper before Organic Division, A.C.S., Atlantic City, September 1949.
7. Drake, N. L., Kline, G. M., and Rose, W. G., *J. Am. Chem. Soc.*, **56**, 2076 (1934).
8. Egloff, G., Morrell, J. C., Thomas, C. L., and Bloch, H. S., *ibid*, **61**, 3571 (1939).
9. Evans, A. G., Holden, D., Plesch, P. H., Polanyi, M., Skinner, H. A., and Weinberger, M. A., *Nature*, **157**, 102 (1946).
10. Evans, A. G., Meadows, G. W., and Polanyi, M., *ibid*, **158**, 94 (1946).
11. Evans, A. G., and Polanyi, M., *J. Chem. Soc.*, (1947), 52.
12. Ewell, R. H., and Hardy, P. E., Paper presented before Division of Petroleum Chemistry, A.C.S. Meeting, Atlantic City, Sept. 1941, P.231.
13. Fairbrother, F., *J. Chem. Soc.* (1937), 503; (1941), 293.
14. Flory, P. J., *J. Am. Chem. Soc.*, **59**, 241 (1937).
15. Fontana, C. M., and Herold, R. J., *ibid*, **70**, 2881 (1948).
16. Frey, F. E., and Hepp, H. J., *Ind. Eng. Chem.*, **28**, 1439 (1936).
17. Greensfelder, B. S., Voge, H. H., and Good, G. M., *ibid*, **41**, 2573 (1949).
18. Hall, F. C., and Nash, A. W., *J. Inst. Petroleum Technol.*, **23**, 679 (1933).
19. Houtman, J. P. W., *J. Soc. Chem. Ind.*, **66**, 102 (1947).
20. Hunter, W. H., and Yohe, R. V., *J. Am. Chem. Soc.*, **65**, 1248 (1933).
21. Hurd, C. D., *Ind. Eng. Chem.*, **26**, 59 (1934).
22. Hurd, C. D., Goodyear, G. H., and Goldsby, A. R., *J. Am. Chem. Soc.*, **55**, 235 (1936).
23. Ipatieff, V. N., and Grosse, A.V., *ibid*, **58**, 915 (1936).
24. Ipatieff, V. N., and Grosse, A. V., *Ind. Eng. Chem.*, **28**, 461 (1936).
25. Ipatieff, V. N., and Pines, H., *ibid*, **28**, 684 (1936).
26. Ipatieff, V. N., and Pines, H., *J. Org. Chem.*, **1**, 464 (1936).
27. Ipatieff, V. N., and Pines, H., *Ind. Eng. Chem.*, **27**, 1364 (1935).
28. Ipatieff, V. N., and Schaad, R. E., *ibid*, **37**, 362 (1945).
29. Ipatieff, V. N., and Schmerling, L., unpublished results.
30. Kazanskii, B. A., and Rozengart, M. I., *J. Gen. Chem.* U.S.S.R., **13**, 304 (1943).
31. Kharasch, M. S., Jensen, E. V., and Urry, W. H., *Science*, **102**, 128 (1945); *J. Am. Chem. Soc.*, **68**, 154 (1946).
32. Kharasch, M. S., Reinmuth, O., and Urry, W. H., *ibid*, **69**, 1105 (1947).
33. Kossiakoff, A., and Rice, F. O., *ibid*, **65**, 590 (1943).
34. McCaulay, D. A., and Lien, A. P., *ibid*, **73**, 2013 (1951).
35. McCubbin, R. J., and Adkins, H., *ibid*, **52**, 2547 (1930).
36. McKinley, J. B., Stevens, D. B., and Baldwin, W. E., *ibid*, **67**, 1455 (1945).
37. Milliken, T. H. Jr., Mills, G. A., and Oblad, A. G., *Faraday Soc. Discussions*, **8**, 279 (1950).
38. Mosher, W. A., and Cox, J. C. Jr., *J. Am. Chem. Soc.*, **72**, 3701 (1950).
39. Pines, H., Abraham, B. M., and Ipatieff, V. N., *ibid*, **70**, 1742 (1948).
40. Pines, H., and Ipatieff, V. N., *ibid*, **67**, 1631 (1945).
41. Pines, H., and Wackher, R. C., *ibid*, **68**, 595 (1946).
42. Price, C. C., Ann. N. Y. Acad. Sci., **44**, 351 (1943).
43. Prins, H. J., *Rec. trav. chim.*, **51**, 1078 (1932).
44. Rice, F. O., *J. Am. Chem. Soc.*, **55**, 3035 (1933).
45. Rice, F. O., and Teller, E. J., *J. Chem. Phys.*, **6**, 489 (1938).
46. Schmerling, L., *J. Am. Chem. Soc.*, **68**, 195 (1946).
47. Schmerling, L., *ibid*, **67**, 1152 (1945).
48. Schmerling, L., *ibid*, **69**, 1121 (1947).
49. Schmerling, L., *ibid*, **71**, 698 (1949).
50. Schmerling, L., *ibid*, **68**, 1650, 1655 (1946).

51. Schmerling, L., *ibid*, **71**, 701 (1949).
52. Schmerling, L., (a) *ibid*, **66**, 1422 (1944), (b) *ibid*, **67**, 1778 (1945), (c) *ibid*, **68**, 275 (1946).
53. Schmerling, L., *ibid*, **67**, 1438 (1945).
54. Schmerling, L., *ibid*, **70**, 379 (1948).
55. Schmerling, L., and Meisinger, E. E., *ibid*, **71**, 753 (1949).
56. Schmerling, L., and West, J. P., *ibid*, **74**, 3592 (1952).
57. Schmerling, L., and West, J. P., *ibid*, **72**, 3525 (1950).
58. Schmerling, L., and West, J. P., *ibid*, **74**, 2885 (1952).
59. Schmerling, L., and West, J. P., *ibid*, **71**, 2015 (1949).
60. Staudinger, H., *Trans. Faraday Soc.*, **32**, 97 (1936).
61. Tamele, M. W., *Faraday Soc. Discussions*, **8**, 270 (1950).
62. Thomas, C. L., *Ind. Eng. Chem.*, **41**, 2564 (1949).
63. Thomas, R. M., Sparks, W. J., Frolich, P. K., Otto, M., and Muller-Conradi, M., *J. Am. Chem. Soc.*, **62**, 276 (1942).
64. Wackher, R. C., and Pines, H., *ibid*, **68**, 1642 (1946).
65. Wackher, R. C., and Pines, H., *ibid*, **68**, 599 (1946).
66. Walling, C., *ibid*, **72**, 1164 (1950).
67. Whitmore, F. C., *Chem. Eng. News*, **26**, 668 (1948).
68. Whitmore, F. C., *Ind. Eng. Chem.*, **26**, 94 (1934).
69. Whitmore, F. C., and Meunier, P. L., *J. Am. Chem. Soc.*, **63**, 2197 (1941).
70. Whitmore, F. C., and Mosher, W. A., *ibid*, **63**, 1120 (1941).
71. Whitmore, F. C., and Mosher, W. A., *ibid*, **68**, 281 (1946).
72. Winstein, S., and Morse, B. K., *ibid*, **74**, 1133 (1952).

CHAPTER 32

GENERAL THEORY OF HYDROCARBON OXIDATION[*]

BERNARD LEWIS AND GUENTHER VON ELBE

Formerly with U. S. Bureau of Mines, Pittsburgh, Pa.; now with Combustion and Explosives Research, Inc., Pittsburgh, Pa.

It is not yet possible to discuss the mechanism of hydrocarbon oxidation with any degree of finality. However, considerable progress has been made in the last decade, and there exists today a large area of agreement between various investigators concerning the basic features of the reaction. In this chapter we shall discuss several problems that arise from critical study of the literature of the oxidation of methane and higher hydrocarbons.

Oxidation of Methane

The most conspicuous fact about the methane-oxygen reaction is the parallel increase of the reaction rate (rate of methane consumption) and the concentration of formaldehyde in the reacting mixture. This was first observed by Bone and Gardner.[6] The increase is at first exponential with time and then tapers off. This parallelism between reaction rate and formaldehyde concentration is understandable if a chain reaction is assumed in which (1) minute traces of formaldehyde are formed spontaneously from methane and oxygen, (2) chain carriers are formed by reaction of formaldehyde and oxygen, (3) formaldehyde is formed as a consequence of reaction between methane and chain carriers, and (4) formaldehyde is destroyed by reaction with chain carriers. In such a mechanism, the formaldehyde concentration increases at first exponentially with time ("induction period") and later attains a steady-state value at which the rates of formation and destruction are equal, and the reaction rate is at any instant proportional to the concentration of formaldehyde, since the latter determines the number of chains that are generated per second. The mechanism has been accepted by Norrish and co-workers[31] and by the present authors[22] as uniquely consistent

[*] Based on Chapter IV of "Combustion, Flames and Explosion of Gases," Academic Press Inc. New York, 1951.

with experimental facts. On the other hand, Chamberlain and Walsh,[7,58] though accepting assumptions (3) and (4), have attempted to replace assumptions (1) and (2) with the assumption that chain carriers are mainly formed by reaction between methane and oxygen. The experiments of Bone and Gardner are crucial in refuting this viewpoint; according to Chamberlain and Walsh's hypothesis, the formaldehyde concentration in the early stages of the reaction should increase linearly with time, whereas the experiments definitely show the increase to be exponential with time.

On the basis of the foregoing we consider chains to be initiated by the reaction,

$$HCHO + O_2 = CHOO + OH \qquad\qquad (I)$$

There are other conceivable formulations of this reaction, the essence being that the product formed by direct association of formaldehyde and oxygen is capable of splitting in such manner that a chemical bond is broken and two free valences are formed. A radical possessing a free valence is then supposed to react with methane, as:

$$OH + CH_4 = H_2O + CH_3 \qquad\qquad (II)$$

This is an inherently plausible reaction. The radical CH_3 is considered to react further with oxygen to yield formaldehyde,

$$CH_3 + O_2 = HCHO + OH \qquad\qquad (III)$$

The fourth reaction concerns the destruction of HCHO in collisions with free radicals:

$$OH + HCHO = H_2O + CHO \qquad\qquad (IV)$$

However, the four reactions provide only a part of the total reaction mechanism. Additional guidance for completion of the mechanism is chiefly provided by the data of Norrish and Foord[32] and Norrish and Reagh,[33] who investigated the dependence of the reaction rate on vessel diameter, pressure, and mixture composition. The data of these authors can be summarized by the following empirical equation for the steady-state rate following the induction period:

$$-\frac{d[CH_4]}{dt} = \frac{ad^2}{1 + bd^2} \qquad\qquad (1)$$

d is the vessel diameter, and a and b are functions of pressure and mixture composition. Coefficient a is proportional to the fourth power of the pressure, and coefficient b, as far as one can judge from the data, to the first power of the pressure, although the second power might be tolerated. Furthermore, a is proportional to the square of the mole fraction of methane and the first power of the mole fraction of oxygen; b appears to be independent of mixture composition, as far as the data permit judgment. Experiments with added nitrogen show that the rate increases with increasing partial pressure of inert gas; but the curve of reaction rate versus inert gas pressure has a declining slope, as is expected if both a and b increase with pressure. Figure 1 shows reaction rates as function of vessel diameter and pressure. The data of Norrish and Foord are seen to agree with those of Norrish and Reagh in smaller vessels, whereas in larger vessels Norrish and Reagh observed significantly larger rates. Curves fitting the data of Norrish and Reagh are obtained if a is taken to be equal to $0.228(P/300)^4$ mmHg/min^{-1}mm^{-2} and b equal to $0.00548(P/300)$. mm^{-2}. The discrepancy between the earlier data of Norrish and Foord and the later data of Norrish and Reagh may be ascribed to an erratic influence of the nature of the vessel surface[6,32] on the rate, which is not easily eliminated. Thus Norrish and Foord report that they obtain concordant and reproducible results only by carrying out a complete series of experiments without allowing the reaction vessel to cool and by pumping out the vessel for at least a half-hour between successive experiments. Previous admittance of air lowered the rate considerably. In Norrish and Reagh's experiments, the previous experience was fully utilized so that these data may be more representative of a trouble-free surface.

Another fact is that there exists a critical lower limit of vessel diameter below which reaction is not observed at all, and the methane-oxygen system appears to be stable for an indefinite period.

In order to accommodate the facts of the diameter and pressure dependence of the rate, at least qualitatively, we must introduce the reaction,

$$OH \xrightarrow{\text{wall}} \text{destruction} \qquad\qquad (V)$$

This formulation implies that the free radical OH which diffuses to the wall may on collision with the wall become adsorbed and ultimately destroyed by heterogeneous recombination with another free radical. The fact that inert gas accelerates the reaction rate is interpreted as being due to the decreased rate of diffusion of OH to the surface. According to the diffusion theory,[22] this implies further that the chain-breaking efficiency ϵ of the wall, i.e., the number of times a chain carrier must on the average collide with the wall before it is destroyed, is much larger than the ratio of the mean free path to the vessel diameter; the rate of reaction (V) is in this case inversely proportional to the pressure and to the square of the vessel diameter. Writing the rate of reaction (V) as being equal to the product of the average concentration of OH and a coefficient K_5, the dependence of the rate on pressure and vessel diameter is thus given by the equation,

$$K_5 = \frac{k_5}{[M]d^2}$$ (2)

where k_5 is a mild function of temperature and is insensitive to changes in the nature of the surface, and $[M]$ is the total concentration of all the molecules. With increasing vessel diameter K_5 becomes smaller, and the reaction rate therefore becomes larger. However, since the data show that, with increasing vessel diameter, the rate does not increase indefinitely but tends to taper off to a constant value, there must be another chain-breaking reaction that is independent of the vessel diameter and thus arrests the rise of reaction rate with increasing diameter. Reaction (IV) will serve in this role if it is assumed that the radical CHO does not continue the chain. We shall investigate the kinetic consequences of the latter assumption, specifying at present merely that CHO radicals disappear in some manner. The reaction scheme then becomes:

$$HCHO + O_2 \rightarrow \text{free radicals} \rightarrow OH \qquad \text{(I)}$$
$$OH + CH_4 = H_2O + CH_3 \qquad \text{(II)}$$
$$CH_3 + O_2 = HCHO + OH \qquad \text{(III)}$$
$$OH + HCHO = H_2O + CHO \qquad \text{(IV)}$$
$$OH \xrightarrow{\text{wall}} \text{destruction} \qquad \text{(V)}$$
$$CHO \rightarrow \text{destruction}$$

This scheme leads to the following equations for the steady-state concentrations of OH and formaldehyde:

$$[OH] = \frac{k_1[HCHO][O_2]}{K_5 + k_4[HCHO]}$$ (3)

$$[HCHO] = \frac{k_2[CH_4] - K_5}{2k_4}$$ (4)

The rate of methane consumption is $k_2[CH_4][OH]$, and on inserting equation (2) the steady-state reaction rate is given by:

$$-\frac{d[CH_4]}{dt} = \frac{k_1 k_2}{k_4} [CH_4][O_2] \frac{\frac{k_2}{k_5}[CH_4][M]d^2 - 1}{\frac{k_2}{k_5}[CH_4][M]d^2 + 1}$$ (5)

This equation is of the form,

$$-\frac{d[CH_4]}{dt} = a' \frac{b'd^2 - 1}{b'd^2 + 1}$$ (6)

where, at constant mixture composition, a' and b' are each proportional to the square of the total pressure. Equation (6) is qualitatively consistent with the observations of effects of vessel diameter, pressure, inert gas and mixture composition and shows that below a critical diameter the reaction rate drops to zero. It yields curves of a type similar to those in Figure 1 but does not lend itself to be fitted to the data as closely as empirical equation (1). Thus, if coefficients a' and b' are calculated from the values of the rates at 300 mm of pressure in the larger vessels, one calculates that the rate becomes zero in vessels of 7, 10 and 14 mm

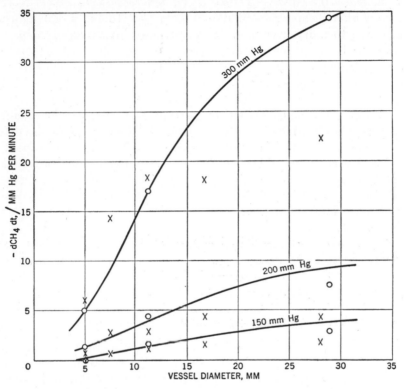

FIG. 1. Reaction rate of methane and oxygen as function of vessel diameter. 1CH$_4$ + 1O$_2$; 530°C.

⊙ Data of Norrish and Reagh. x Data of Norrish and Foord. Curves calculated from equation $-\dfrac{d[\mathrm{CH^4}]}{dt} = \dfrac{ad^2}{1 + bd^2};$

$a = 0.288\ (p/300)^4\mathrm{mm\ Hg\ min^{-1}\ mm^{-2}};\ b = 0.00548\ (p/300)\ \mathrm{mm^{-2}}.$

diameter for 300, 200 and 150 mm of Hg pressure, respectively. Actually, the rate remains measurable in a 5-mm vessel, except for 150 mm of Hg pressure. Furthermore, at a vessel diameter of 29 mm the calculated rates at 200 and 150 mm of Hg pressures are 13.3 and 6.0 mm of Hg per minute, respectively, compared to the experimental rates of 7.5 and 2.8 mm of Hg per minute.

In order to modify the scheme so that the rate equation takes the form of empirical equation (1), it is merely necessary to assume with Norrish[31] that the radicals CHO usually continue the chain and only occasionally disappear without chain continuation. This assumption changes theoretical equation (6) in the sense that the term $a'(b'd^2 - 1)/(b'd^2 + 1)$ now becomes $0.5a'(b'd^2 - 1)/(bd^2 + 1)$, where $b' \gg b$. Since Norrish and co-workers' experimental data require bd^2 to be of a magnitude comparable to unity over most of the range of investigation, it follows that $b'd^2 \gg 1$, except for very small vessel diameters, so that the term -1 in the numerator can be neglected and the empirical equation (1) results, coefficient a being identified as the product $0.5a'b'$. Thus, by means of a simple extension of the reaction scheme, agreement with the experimental information is obtained. Whether an altogether different mechanism can be postulated, which leads to the same result and is otherwise defensible on the basis of theoretical and experimental information, cannot be stated with certainty at this time, but it appears to be rather improbable.

Concerning the actual chain-terminating and chain-continuing reactions of CHO radicals, Norrish[31] proposes that CHO dissociates instantaneously into H and CO. The H atoms are then allowed to break the chain by the reaction,

$$H + O_2 + M = HO_2 + M \qquad\qquad (VI)$$

followed by

$$HO_2 \xrightarrow{\text{wall}} \text{destruction}$$

or to continue the chain by

$$H + O_2 + F = CO + H_2O + OH$$

The latter reaction is supposed to occur much more frequently than reaction (VI). Another proposal by Chamberlain and Walsh[7,58] similarly assumes that CHO decomposes instantly to H and CO, but H and O_2 are thought to react in a binary collision to form an excited $HO_2{}^*$. The latter is thought to survive long enough either to be deactivated by a collision (this terminates the chain as in reaction (VI) above) or to react with methane or formaldehyde according to

$$HO_2{}^* + CH_4 = CH_3 + 2OH,$$

or

$$HO_2{}^* + F = CO + H + 2OH$$

The two latter reactions are chain-branching reactions because three free radicals, each capable of forming a chain, replace the disappearing radical $HO_2{}^*$.

Kinetic development of either proposal leads to a rate equation of the form:

$$-\frac{d[\text{CH}_4]}{dt} = \frac{0.5a'(b'd^2 - 1)}{[0.5(b'd^2 - 1)\varphi + 1]}$$

φ is a numerical factor $\leqslant 1$. For $\varphi = 1$ the equation reduces to equation (6) and for $\varphi \ll 1$, to empirical equation (1), b being approximately $0.5b'\varphi$ since $b'd^2 \gg 1$, as explained above.

In Norrish's scheme,

$$\varphi = \frac{k'[M]}{(k'[M] + k''[\text{CH}_4])}$$

k' being the coefficient of the chain-breaking reaction, i.e., reaction (VI), and k'' the coefficient of the chain-continuing reaction. In Chamberlain and Walsh's scheme,

$$\varphi = \frac{1 - 3k''[\text{CH}_4]}{(k'[M] + k''[\text{CH}_4])}$$

k'' being the coefficient of the chain-branching reaction. In both schemes φ is independent of total pressure. The condition $\varphi \ll 1$ is fulfilled in Norrish's scheme if $k''[\text{CH}_4] \gg k'[M]$; this makes $\varphi \sim [M]/[\text{CH}_4]$. In Chamberlain and Walsh's scheme φ can be positive only if $k''[\text{CH}_4] < 0.5k'[M]$. In both schemes φ decreases with increasing percentage of methane; however, in Norrish's scheme the relation is a simple inverse proportionality, whereas in Chamberlain and Walsh's scheme it is an inverse relation of high order. The latter fact weighs against the scheme. Since b' is proportional to the product $[\text{CH}_4][M]$ (compare equations 5 and 6) and thus depends on the methane percentage only to the first order, the factor $b = 0.5b'\varphi$ would have a high-order inverse dependence on the methane percentage and might even become negative as the latter percentage is increased. This conflicts with the fact, reported earlier, that b seems to be independent of mixture composition, as far as one can judge from the data. On the other hand, in Norrish's scheme the factor b becomes indeed independent of mixture composition. It also becomes proportional to $[M]^2$, that is, the square of the total pressure, which might be tolerated, as previously stated, though the first power is preferable.

Although Norrish's scheme is satisfactory for the present kinetic development, it seems rather doubtful in other respects. Since reaction (VI) has little or no energy of activation and since formaldehyde is present only in a few tenths of a per cent, reaction (VI) is the preferred path unless the formaldehyde in the competing reaction has a collision probability far in excess of any other molecule. In particular, the collision probability should exceed even that of H_2O, which is 40 times as efficient as O_2, as a third body in reaction (VI).[54] Otherwise the accumulation of H_2O as the reaction progresses would inhibit the methane oxidation, for which there is no evidence.

With regard to Chamberlain and Walsh's scheme, apart from the objection raised above, the question arises whether binary collisions between H and O_2 to form HO_2^* are at all possible.

We favor the view that Norrish's concept is fundamentally correct but believe that another set of reactions should be selected. Unfortunately, the choice of reactions is very limited. It appears to us that the stability of the radical CHO has been underestimated. As is discussed elsewhere,[23] this radical is probably quite stable and it may be proposed that in the temperature range of methane oxidation, the reaction

$$CHO + O_2 = CO + HO_2 \tag{VII}$$

occurs as a comparatively rare event only, whereas more frequently the ternary reaction,

$$CHO + O_2 + M = CHO_3 + M \tag{VIII}$$

takes place in which the performyl radical CHO_3 is formed. It is further assumed that HO_2 does not continue the chain, while CHO_3 reacts with formaldehyde in preference to all other possible reactions by

$$CHO_3 + HCHO = 2CO + H_2O + OH \tag{IX}$$

The factor φ then becomes $k_7/(k_7 + k_8[M])$. This is not entirely satisfactory, as it leaves factor b dependent upon the methane concentration (see the corresponding discussion of Norrish's scheme above); however, it is not entirely certain that b is really independent of mixture composition, and alternative schemes seem to be even more difficult to accommodate to all the facts.

The empirical rate equation (1) is deficient because it does not state that there exists a critical vessel diameter below which the reaction rate drops to zero. The theoretical rate equation actually predicts this effect because of the term -1 in the numerator, as was pointed out in discussion of equation (6). However, in the subsequent modification of the theoretical equation the numerator term -1 has become rather insignificant and now predicts entirely too small values of the critical diameters. Another imperfection of the present theoretical equation is the fact that it does not predict the experimentally observed effect of the nature of the surface on the rate. None of the rate coefficients of the elementary reactions that have been introduced thus far is dependent on the nature of the surface. As mentioned, the coefficient K_5 is insensitive to this variable. Norrish considers K_5 to be of the form σ/Pd, where σ is a function of surface conditions, but on the basis of diffusion theory this is not admissible. It is therefore necessary to introduce a surface-dependent reaction, for which we choose, with Norrish,

$$F + O_2 \xrightarrow{\text{surface}} \text{destruction of } F \tag{X}$$

This reaction can account for erratic changes in the rate and for the comparatively large critical diameters.

Our complete tentative scheme is therefore:

$$F + O_2 = \text{free radicals} \rightarrow OH \tag{I}$$
$$OH + CH_4 = H_2O + CH_3 \tag{II}$$
$$CH_3 + O_2 = F + OH \tag{III}$$
$$OH + F = H_2O + CHO \tag{IV}$$
$$CHO + O_2 = CO + HO_2 \tag{VII}$$
$$CHO + O_2 + M = CHO_3 + M \tag{VIII}$$
$$CHO_3 + F = 2CO + H_2O + OH \tag{IX}$$
$$OH \xrightarrow{\text{wall}} \text{destruction} \tag{V}$$
$$HO_2 \xrightarrow{\text{wall}} \text{destruction} \tag{XI}$$
$$F + O_2 \xrightarrow{\text{wall}} \text{destruction of } F \tag{X}$$

The steady-state concentrations of OH and formaldehyde, assuming $k_7 \ll k_8[M]$, are given by:

$$[OH] = \frac{k_1[\text{HCHO}][O_2]}{K_5 + k_4 \dfrac{k_7[\text{HCHO}]}{k_8[M]}} \tag{7}$$

$$[\text{HCHO}] = \frac{k_2[CH_4] - K_5 \left(1 + \dfrac{K_{10}}{k_1}\right)}{k_4 \left(2 + \dfrac{k_7}{k_8[M]}\dfrac{K_{10}}{k_1}\right)} \tag{8}$$

The steady-state reaction rate is, with $K_{10} = k_{10}/d$,

$$- \frac{d[CH_4]}{dt} = \frac{k_1 k_2 [CH_4][O_2]}{2k_4} \frac{\dfrac{k_2}{k_5}[CH_4][M]d^2 - \dfrac{k_{10}}{k_1}\dfrac{1}{d} - 1}{\dfrac{1}{2}\dfrac{k_2 k_7}{k_5 k_8}[CH_4]d^2 + 1} \tag{9}$$

where k_{10} is dependent upon the nature of the surface. This equation reduces to the form of equation (1) if the two negative terms in the numerator are small compared to the d^2-term. Under the conditions of reproducibility that existed in Norrish and Reagh's experiments, reaction (X) may be considered negligible, so that equation (9) indeed reduces to the form of equation (1). The lower rates occasionally observed by Norrish and Foord are attributed to the surface sensitivity of reaction (X), which according to equation (9) can exert a profound effect on the rate.

Equation (9) shows correctly that the critical diameter at which reaction ceases should be a function of pressure and also of mixture composition.

The scheme is consistent with the results of chemical analysis of Bone and co-workers[6] which showed that the products of the reaction are initially H_2O and CO. The formation of CO_2 may be explained by the further reaction of CO with OH. Evidence for a concurrent CO reaction has been described by Vanpee.[53] The absence of peroxides is explained by the destruction of CHO_3 in reaction (IX) and the infrequent occurrence of reaction (VII) apart from the possibility of further destructive reaction of H_2O_2 formed from HO_2 radicals.

The reactions (VII) and (VIII), which have been introduced into the reaction mechanism for the purpose of obtaining the desired rate equation, are in themselves plausible, but the postulated nonoccurrence of gas-phase reactions of HO_2 on the one hand, and surface reactions of CHO_3 on the other, may be questioned. The choice represents the least implausible of a very limited number of possibilities. It is thus clear that the methane-oxygen system requires further experimental study. A larger body of data is desired on the effect of vessel diameter, pressure, mixture composition and inert gases, and temperature, efforts being concentrated on obtaining good reproducibility so that the obscuring effects of erratic surface reactions are eliminated.

Cool Flames and Two-Stage Ignition

From the preceding section it appears that the oxidation of methane can be described adequately by steady-state kinetics, which postulates that the concentration of intermediates, and hence the reaction rate, attains a steady state subject only to a gradual change that is caused by consumption of the reactants. For higher members of the homologous series we must abandon the steady-state concept, at least for the oxidation reaction at low temperatures, which is characterized by the phenomena of cool flames and two-stage ignition. They are common to all hydrocarbons or compounds of the hydrocarbon series, notably ethers and aldehydes, except methane, methyl alcohol, benzene, ethylene, glyoxal, and formaldehyde.

A clear phenomenological description of the subject is provided in a paper of Newitt and Thornes[30] on the oxidation of propane. Figure 2 typifies the critical temperature and pressure limits for cool flames and second-stage ignition as determined by these authors. Within the region bounded by the curve ABC and the ignition curve at the right, cool flames appear. On passing through the region along the isobar line DE, the following phenomena are observed:

Temperature range	Observations
275–285°C	After an induction period of several minutes, faint luminosity develops and remains until reaction is substantially complete.
290°C	Faint luminosity develops, followed by a pale-blue cool flame, which starts near the center of the vessel and spreads outward, giving rise to a slight pressure pulse; the luminosity persists for some seconds after the flame.

330–340°C   The initial luminosity observed immediately on filling the vessel is succeeded by four or five separate cool flames at intervals of several seconds. Each of these flames traverses the whole vessel before extinction.

340°C   Two cool flames only are formed.

345–385°C   Over this range, only one cool flame is observed.
The intensity of the cool flames increases as their number diminishes, and in all cases they are succeeded by an intense, uniform glow that persists for some seconds. Between 350° and 385°C the single cool flames diminish in intensity, whereas the general luminescence increases until eventually it becomes impossible to distinguish the flames.

380–425°C   Intense luminosity develops immediately on filling the vessel; at 425°C it is succeeded by a bright-blue flame, which, at a slightly higher temperature, changes to the characteristic yellow flame usually associated with true ignition. The narrow shaded strip adjacent to the ignition curve defines the region in which these blue flames are formed.
On traversing the isothermal line FH at 315°C, the observed phenomena are similar to those described above; the number of cool flames first increases from one at 180 mm Hg to four or five at 321 to 520 mm Hg and then diminishes. It is noteworthy that true ignition at about 530 mm Hg will sometimes occur after an interval of several seconds succeeding the passage of one or two separate cool flames and that under these experimental conditions it is usually accompanied by carbon formation in the cool-flame region.

Numerous reports in the literature indicate that other fuels containing aliphatic carbon chains exhibit very similar phenomena. The temperatures along an isobaric line at which the luminosity markedly increases, at which cool flames appear and vanish, and at which ignition occurs depend on various conditions. They are not greatly dependent on the ratio of fuel to air if the fuel is in excess; they shift markedly to lower values as one ascends in the series of *n*-paraffins; they shift to higher values when an olefin or naphthene is substituted for the corresponding paraffin, or an unsaturated cyclic compound like cyclohexene is substituted for the saturated compound cyclohexane. By this criterion, aromatic compounds are much more resistant to oxidation than paraffinic or naphthenic compounds. This order of reactivity is closely parallel to the knocking tendency of fuels established in engine tests. The behavior of alcohols, aldehydes, and ethers parallels that of the paraffins, with differences in the temperature thresholds. The temperatures are particularly low for ethyl ether.

Neumann and Aivazov[27] studied the pentane-oxygen system in a long, cylindrical quartz vessel, observing the luminosity effects visually and recording the pressure development by means of a sensitive glass diaphragm manometer. After the mixture had come to temperature equilibrium with the vessel, the pressure remained virtually constant for a while and then suddenly rose. Simultaneously, cool flames were observed to travel along the tube. The pressure passed through a maximum coincident with the disappearance of the cool flame but remained considerably above the original pressure. Following this, the pressure rose gradually with time. During the cool-flame period an increase in the number of

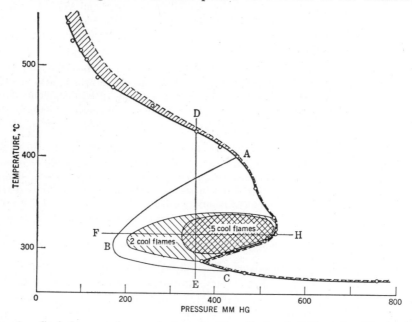

FIG. 2. Cool flame and second stage ignition limit of $C_3H_8 + O_2$ (Newitt and Thornes).

moles occurred and also some heat liberation. Occasionally more than one wave was observed with corresponding irregularities in the pressure record. On repeating a standardized experiment some twenty times, it became possible to collect products of the reaction formed at various stages of the pressure rise. They were identified as aldehydes, peroxides, acids, and carbon monoxide. The appearance of cool-flame waves characterized by a sudden rise and fall of pressure can, as shown in Figure 2, be suppressed by lowering the pressure below some critical value, all other conditions being the same; and at a higher critical pressure the reaction following the cool flame terminates in explosion, which in stronger mixtures is marked by considerable violence. An example of this is given in Table 1, which refers to an experiment of Neumann and

Aivazov with a mixture of $1C_5H_{12}$ and $4O_2$ at 340 mm of Hg and 318°C. The first row of figures denotes the time, in seconds, from the beginning of the experiment, and the second row, the pressure increase in mm of Hg.

TABLE 1. INCREASE OF PRESSURE DURING REACTION OF PENTANE AND OXYGEN

Seconds	0	8	8.2	8.4	8.6	8.8	9.0	9.2	9.21
Δp, mm Hg	0	0	2	35	48	52	54	57	explosion

This record typifies the phenomenon of two-stage ignition with its two separate induction periods, which we shall denote by τ_1 and τ_2. The induction period τ_1 from the beginning of the reaction to the appearance of cool flames is about 8.2 seconds, and the induction period τ_2 from the appearance of cool flames to the onset of violent explosion is about 1.01 seconds. We shall designate these as the τ_1 and τ_2 regimes. These regimes culminate in cool flames and second-stage ignition, respectively, if the pressures and temperatures exceed the critical limits. The τ_1 regime is very probably governed by chain-branching reactions, and the cool flames are of the nature of branched-chain explosions,[18] except that the reaction is arrested before a large part of the chemical enthalpy is liberated. The τ_2 regime concerns reaction in the chemically altered residual mixture after the branching reactions have subsided. On the low-temperature side of the cool-flame peninsula (Figure 2) the nonexplosive over-all reaction takes place almost entirely in the τ_1 regime, and the reaction is self-accelerating in accordance with the kinetic data of Prettre and of Aivazov and Neumann mentioned below. On the high temperature side of the cool-flame peninsula, the τ_1 regime is only weakly developed, and, according to the data of Norrish and Reagh,[33] the over-all reaction in the nonexplosive region resembles that of methane. The latter observations were made on ethane and propane and concerned particularly the diameter and pressure dependence, which was found to be very similar to that of methane. As with methane, the existence of a critical vessel diameter was noted below which reaction ceased. Accordingly, it may be surmised that the τ_2 regime consists of unbranched chains that are initiated by reaction of formaldehyde, and perhaps other aldehydes, with oxygen. Aldehydes, particularly formaldehyde, are always formed during the course of the preceding τ_1 regime, and the two regimes are linked in this manner as well as by the residue of peroxides. Under conditions such as Norrish and Reagh's, where the branching reaction characteristic of the τ_1 regime is largely suppressed, one might expect the reaction to develop to a steady state, because the aldehydes are both formed and destroyed by chain carriers. However, the systematic data of Newitt and Thornes on the change of concentration of the various molecular species with time show that consumption of the reactants strongly interferes with attainment of steady-state conditions. On the basis of these concepts, second-stage ignition is not of the branched-chain type but occurs as a result of unbalancing of thermal equilibrium. It leads to complete release of chemical enthalpy and to the final products.

Prettre[38] and Aivazov and Neumann[1] have succeeded in obtaining quantitative kinetic data on the induction period in the τ_1 regime. These data show the effect of pressure, mixture composition, temperature, and vessel factors. For the details of these difficult investigations we refer the reader to the original publications; the various quantitative relations are certainly an important contribution to the available kinetic information; but the complexity of the subject is such that these relations do not seem to be of immediate value for the establishment of the reaction mechanism.

Andreev[2] has studied both the τ_1 and τ_2 regimes by following the pressure increase of an equimolar mixture of butane and oxygen in a quartz vessel, using a glass-membrane manometer and a photographic recording system. In agreement with data of Aivazov and Neumann,[1] τ_1 is found to decrease continuously with increasing temperature. In striking contrast, τ_2 increases with temperature. Supplementary information obtained by Neumann and Tutakin[29] shows that τ_2 steadily decreases as the pressure of a given mixture is increased. This was also found by Kane,[20] who systematically studied the effect of pressure on the induction periods τ_1 and τ_2 in propane and propylene by means of a pressure-recording device operating at high pressures.

From the various investigations, two cardinal facts emerge that govern the predominance of one regime over another: With increasing temperature, τ_1 decreases, τ_2 increases; with increasing pressure, both τ_1 and τ_2 decrease.

Independent confirmation of these latter facts was obtained by Rögener.[41] This investigator was able to observe very short induction periods, τ_1 and τ_2, corresponding to high pressures and temperatures, by rapidly compressing fuel-air mixtures to a precisely determined fraction of the original volume, and recording the pressure developed in the subsequent chemical reaction by means of a piezo-electric gage in conjunction with a cathode-ray oscilloscope. The principle of rapid compression as a means of studying ignition lags at high pressures and temperatures was utilized originally by Tizard and Pye.[47] This work was later continued by Jost and Teichmann[18,19] and Scheuermeyer and Steigerwald,[43,44] who were able to observe very short induction periods but did not obtain clear-cut separations of the τ_1 and τ_2 regimes. The records obtained by Rögener, on the other hand, show this separation very clearly; illustrations of such records together with a description of the technically interesting apparatus are found in a paper by Jost.[18] The adiabatic-compression temperatures attained in Rögener's experiments range from approximately 400° to 500°C; pressures range from 5 to 40 atmospheres; and the observed induction periods from 10^{-1} to less than 10^{-3} second. The results are summarized by empirical equations for τ_1 and τ_2 in Table 2. Although no immediate kinetic significance

TABLE 2. EMPIRICAL EQUATIONS FOR τ_1 AND τ_2 (RÖGENER)
(Stoichiometric mixtures of fuel in air)

$$n\text{-heptane}\begin{cases}\tau_1 = 8.1 \times 10^{-12} \times p^{-.66} \times e^{15,100/T} \\ \tau_2 = 0.5 \times p^{-1.82} \times e^{-1,400/T}\end{cases}$$

$$n\text{-pentane}\begin{cases}\tau_1 = 2.7 \times 10^{-9} \times p^{-.69} \times e^{11,600/T} \\ \tau_2 = 4.5 \times p^{-1.54} \times e^{-3.030/T}\end{cases}$$

$$n\text{-butane}\begin{cases}\tau_1 = 5.8 \times 10^{-6} \times p^{-1.35} \times e^{8,330/T} \\ \tau_2 = 2.35 \times 10^4 \times p^{-2.96} \times e^{-5,220/T}\end{cases}$$

τ in seconds; p and T are pressure in atmospheres and temperature in degrees K at the end of compression and before occurrence of appreciable chemical reaction.

attaches to the "activation energies" and other numerical values in these equations, it is seen that τ_1 always decreases and τ_2 always increases with temperature, and both τ_1 and τ_2 decrease with pressure. Concerning the relative magnitudes of these effects, it is noted that the decrease of τ_1 with temperature is more rapid than the corresponding increase of τ_2, and that τ_2 decreases with pressure more rapidly than τ_1.

These relations indicate that the total induction period, $\tau = \tau_1 + \tau_2$, depends on temperature and pressure in a complex manner. This is illustrated further by the measurements of Scheuermeyer and Steigerwald[43] on n-heptane. In Figure 3 the induction period τ is plotted on a logarithmic scale against the reciprocal of the absolute temperature at the end of the compression calculated with the assumption of adiabatic conditions. Three curves are shown corresponding to end pressures of 9, 15, and 20 atmospheres. At low temperatures, each curve conforms rather well to a straight line; that is, τ decreases by the factor $e^{-\text{const}/T}$, indicating that τ_1 is predominant. Toward high temperatures the curve turns up, the more so the lower the pressure. This conforms to the trend of τ_2, which increases with increasing temperature but decreases with increasing pressure more rapidly than τ_1.

For a further understanding of the nature of the two τ regimes we refer to the previously stated view, expressed by almost every investigator of the subject, that the regimes represent different chain-reaction mechanisms and are linked to each other mainly in the sense that the τ_1 regime initiates the τ_2 regime. The two regimes compete for the supply of reactants, i.e., the fuel and the oxygen, and the available evidence indicates that at low temperatures (below approximately 400°C) the τ_1 reaction obtains most of the supply, whereas at higher temperatures most is obtained by the τ_2 reaction.

The transition from conditions of predominantly τ_1 regime to conditions of predominantly τ_2 regime becomes well-recognizable in Figure 4. In the lower part of the figure, average plots of the rates are plotted.[27] They represent the reciprocal of the half-time from the beginning of the reaction to the completion of the pressure rise at pressures below the ignition limits. In juxtaposition to these rate curves is a plot of critical

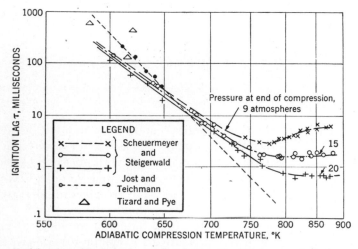

Fig. 3.   Ignition lags for stoichiometric mixture of n-heptane and air determined by rapid compression method (Scheuermeyer and Steigerwald).

pressures for cool flames and second-stage ignition,[50] the induction period $\tau = \tau_1 + \tau_2$ being indicated along the curve.* The composite figure shows that the temperature range of decreasing reaction rate, i.e., negative temperature coefficient, coincides with the temperature range of increasing critical pressures. The induction period $\tau = \tau_1 + \tau_2$ shows the expected trend; at low temperatures, τ_2 is vanishingly small and τ_1 decreases until it practically vanishes in the region of the negative temperature coefficient; as the temperature increases, τ_2 becomes more and more predominant. It is noted that the lower part of the figure refers to a mixture of pentane and oxygen and the upper part to a mixture of hexane and air. These differences of fuel and other constituents do not affect the temperature region of transition from the τ_1 to the τ_2

---

* The accuracy of observation of the induction period was not better than 1 second, so that a 1-second induction period might mean a much smaller value.

regime. This is generally true for all hydrocarbons and related compounds, as may be seen from the various figures of cool flames and ignition limits.

It is appropriate at this time to mention that the source of luminosity in the cool-flame region has been firmly established as emanating from excited formaldehyde molecules,[11,14] and that the number of light

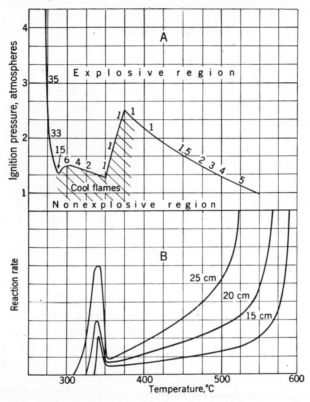

Fig. 4. (A) Ignition region of 3.1 per cent hexane in air mixture. Region of "cool flames" marked by shaded area. Induction periods, in seconds, indicated by numbers along curve (Townend, Cohen and Mandlekar). (B) Reaction rates of 11.1 per cent pentane in oxygen mixture at different pressures (Neumann and Aivazov).

quanta emitted is an extremely small fraction of the number of hydrocarbon molecules reacting.[9,48] The excitation energy of formaldehyde is at least 77 Kcal. This precludes the formation of excited aldehyde in normal reaction chains. In particular, the reaction:

$$CH_3 + O_2 = HCHO + OH \tag{10}$$

is exothermic by only 47 Kcal. Therefore, the excitation can be explained only by a reaction between two free radicals,[57] and this accounts for the rarity of emitted light quanta. Walsh[57] mentions that the reaction

$$RCH_2O + OH = ROH + HCHO \tag{11}$$

would be sufficiently exothermic (about 91 Kcal). Alternatively, one may suggest

$$CH_3 + HO_2 = HCHO + H_2O \tag{12}$$

and

$$CH_3 + CHO_3 = HCHO + H_2O + CO \tag{13}$$

both of which are amply exothermic (over 100 Kcal).

A number of observations have been reported on the effect of additives in the τ_1 and τ_2 regions. Of particular importance appears to be the effect of additives that are also intermediate products of the reaction, such as formaldehyde and acetaldehyde. With pentane-oxygen and hexane-oxygen, at temperatures slightly above 200°C, it was observed that moderate amounts of formaldehyde exert a powerful inhibitory effect.[8] Similarly, in the propane-oxygen mixtures, it was found that formaldehyde increases the induction period.[15] In contrast, observations on the effect of acetaldehyde on a mixture of $1C_5H_{12} + 2O_2$ at 329°C and 200 mm of Hg pressure (this is presumably in the τ_1 region) show that the induction period decreases on addition of acetaldehyde.[1] It is noteworthy, however, that in these experiments the induction period did not decrease to zero even with 5 per cent acetaldehyde, although, according to the data of the experimenters,[1] this corresponds approximately to the concentration of acetaldehyde at the end of the induction period under conditions where no acetaldehyde had been added to the mixture. Aivazov and Neumann concluded, therefore, that acetaldehyde alone cannot be the cause of instantaneous cool flame, and that peroxides, which they find in comparable amounts, must also play a role in the mechanism of cool flames. This probably is true, but it poses the question whether the peroxides that can be isolated from the reacting mixture are identical with the active peroxides that are responsible for the chain-branching reaction in the τ_1 regime. It appears that one should distinguish between at least two processes of peroxide formation. One is the oxidation of formaldehyde, which yields performic acid and probably also hydrogen peroxide, either of which reacts with formaldehyde or other aldehydes to form dioxydialkylperoxides, which are fairly stable[40] and can be isolated readily. The other is the formation of an alkyl hydroperoxide by reaction of a radical $ROO—$ with a saturated hydrocarbon to form $ROOH$ and hydrocarbon radical. Such hydroperoxides are unstable[40] and are not likely to be recovered in quantity from a mixture reacting at several hundred degrees centigrade. This also applies to the monooxyalkyl-peroxides that may be formed by condensation of aldehydes with alkyl hydroperoxides, although it should be noted that Mondain-Monval and Quanquin[17,26] report that they detected such unstable peroxides among the recovered peroxides. Aivazov and Neumann suggest that the peroxides isolated by them and by others[17,26] working with normal paraffins from pentane to octane are of the latter type. However, the experimental material appears to be insufficient at present to establish the origin of the peroxides recovered from reacting mixtures.

That alkyl hydroperoxides are very active in promoting reaction in the τ_1 regime has been shown by several investigators.[5,37]

With respect to lead tetraethyl as an additive, the outstanding fact is the observation reported by Rögener that the induction period τ_1 is unchanged, whereas the induction period τ_2 is lengthened considerably. Thus, addition of 2 per cent by volume of lead tetraethyl to liquid n-heptane left the equation for τ_1 in Table 2 unaffected but resulted in values of τ_2 expressed by the empirical equation,

$$\tau_2 = 2 \times 10^4 \times p^{-2.24} \times e^{-7,000/T} \tag{14}$$

In the temperature and pressure range of Rögener's experiments this exceeds the value of τ_2 obtained from the corresponding equation in Table 2 by a factor of the order of 10. The effect of lead tetraethyl on the pressure-temperature limits of two-stage ignition is shown for pentane-air mixtures in Figure 5.[52] This figure comprises the ignition limits as a function of temperature, pressure, mixture composition, and addition of $Pb(C_2H_5)_4$ in an amount of 0.05 per cent. Along the vertical dotted lines, no ignition is obtained. If the data for a mixture, for example 3.7 per cent pentane, are plotted in a temperature-pressure diagram, the curves shown in Figure 5 are obtained. It is seen that $Pb(C_2H_5)_4$ causes displacement to higher temperatures and pressures, which appears moderate in a diagram of this type but might, in certain regions of the diagram, lead to very large temperature increases if the pressure remains constant or very large pressure increases if the temperature remains constant. Similar curves have been obtained for butane, isobutane, and hexane with air.[50,51] For isobutane and hexane, the $Pb(C_2H_5)_4$ curves are so displaced toward higher temperatures, without changing the peninsula shape, that they cross the curves for the nonleaded mixtures in several places. In such places the ignition pressure at constant temperature is actually lowered by addition of $Pb(C_2H_5)_4$. There is also shown in Figure 5 a set of isoinduction period curves for $\tau_1 + \tau_2 = 4 \times 10^{-3}$ sec calculated for n-heptane from Rögener's data. The displacement of these curves by $Pb(C_2H_5)_4$ is of similar character. It might be expected that the cool-flame region similarly shifts with addition of $Pb(C_2H_5)_4$. In experiments of the type performed by Prettre, described and discussed earlier in this section, where the pressure of the mixture remained constant as the temperature was changed, addition of $Pb(C_2H_5)_4$ might therefore cause diminution of luminosity effects and even elimination of cool flames, depending on the amount of $Pb(C_2H_5)_4$ added. Such has been the experience of Prettre.

It should be mentioned that the length of the induction period in the τ_1 region depends somewhat on the nature of the vessel surface. All

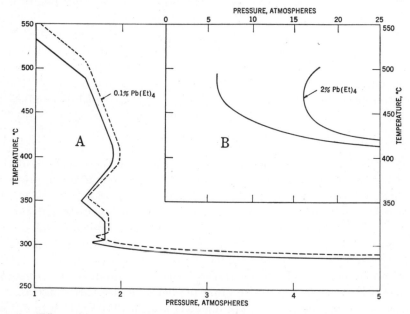

Fig. 5.   Effect of lead tetraethyl on ignition limits and induction periods. (A). Ignition limits of 3.7 per cent pentane-air mixture with and without lead tetraethyl (Townend and Mandlekar). (B). Curves of equal induction periods τ of stoichiometric n-heptane-air mixture with and without lead tetraethyl $\tau = 4 \times 10^{-3}$ sec.

experimenters report that to obtain reproducible values, treatment of the reaction vessel is necessary. This treatment usually consists of a number of blank runs preceding the measurement. This applies to the glass-vessel experiments at low pressures as well as to the high-pressure experiments of Rögener. Photographs by Taylor and co-workers[46] taken through a glass window in a rapid compression chamber, under experimental conditions similar to Rögener's, show that luminous spots appear preferentially at the chamber surface, and that ignition develops inward toward the center. Concerning the role played by surfaces, one is reminded of an observation of Beatty and Edgar,[4] who passed mixtures of n-heptane and air through a pyrex tube of 2.4 cm diameter at various temperatures. Although the initial diffuse luminosity at about 250°C seemed to occupy the whole column of the mixture, the cool flames that formed at about 270°C appeared in the shape of rings; that is, the luminosity was more intense near the wall than in the center.

Although the nature of the surface has a recognized influence on the length of τ_1 and probably also τ_2, it does not, according to Day and Pease,[9] greatly affect the pressure-temperature limits of cool flame and the second-stage ignition. These investigators, who studied the propane-oxygen system, observed approximately the same limits, including the closed regions of periodicity (see Figure 2) in pyrex vessels that were treated with nitric acid, etched with hydrofluoric acid, and coated with KCl. In the latter vessel the induction periods were lengthened considerably, particularly at lower temperatures. Analysis of the products in flow experiments, using similarly prepared tubes, revealed the presence of peroxides in all but the KCl-coated vessel.* Day and Pease, therefore, cast doubt on the role of peroxides in the cool-flame mechanism. Similarly, they question the role of acetaldehyde in the mechanism, as, according to a previous investigation of Pease,[34] a KCl coating causes the concentration of acetaldehyde to be substantially lower than in the two other vessels. It appears to us that as the reaction does not tend toward a steady state, surface chain-breaking may decrease the rate of acceleration of the reaction but cannot prevent the ultimate attainment of critical concentrations of aldehydes and peroxides that determine the burst of reaction that is the cool flame. The values of these critical concentrations depend primarily on pressure and temperature and are reached after some shorter or longer time, depending on surface conditions. The fact that in a flow system peroxides are not recovered from a KCl-coated tube is no proof against their transient existence; similarly, the heterogeneous catalysis of acetaldehyde oxidation on a KCl surface need not preclude attainment of a critical concentration during the course of the self-accelerating reaction.

The development of waves of cool flames is linked to the fact that the chemical reaction accelerates in some volume elements more rapidly than elsewhere in the volume of reacting mixture. In this way, centers of ignition are formed within which temperature and concentrations of active species are relatively high. From such centers, heat and chain carriers flow to an adjacent layer by the processes of heat transfer and diffusion. The layer then becomes activated to chemical reaction and serves as a source of ignition for the next layer, and so forth. Behind the cool-flame wave there exists an accumulation of peroxides and aldehydes, and a large part of the chemical enthalpy of the mixture is still unex-

* Similar observations were made by Newitt and Thornes.[30]

pended. In the wake of the cool flame, therefore, the reactions of the τ_2 regime take place, which accelerate to explosion. In the final stage of the latter process, discrete sources of ignition also probably appear. As the process is very fast, it is difficult to resolve the details of the final explosion. Neumann and Aivazov believe that in the experiment quoted in Table 1 a hot-flame wave developed that traveled with a velocity of 500 to 1,000 meters per second. Similar hot-flame waves have been observed by Miller[25] in high-speed schlieren photographs of knocking combustion in the internal-combustion engine.

When a cool flame propagates from a spontaneously formed ignition source, the mixture that is being overrun by the wave has itself progressed more or less along the same reaction path as the volume element that now constitutes the ignition source, and it may be surmised that the reaction, prior to the arrival of the cool-flame wave, assists in the propagation process. There is no reason to believe, however, that a preparatory reaction is essential for the propagation of the cool flame. That is, it is quite imaginable *a priori* that cool flames may be induced in a nonreacting cold mixture by means of a suitable ignition source. This is fully borne out by experiment. Such observations were made originally on diethyl-ether-air mixtures by White,[59] and extensive studies were carried out later by Townend and his co-workers[16,24,48,49] It is even possible to stabilize a cool-flame wave in a manner similar to the combustion wave of a Bunsen burner.[45]

We conclude this section with the observation that the CO formed in the slow reaction between hydrocarbons or related compounds with oxygen can, under suitable conditions, give rise to explosion and thus produce an apparent shift of the ignition region toward lower temperatures and pressures. This phenomenon was originally observed by Russian investigators[3,21,28,42] for methane and ethane with oxygen and has been investigated further for higher hydrocarbons by French workers.[10,13] If, for example, a 1 per cent mixture of hexane and air at a pressure of 100 mm of Hg is heated rapidly in a quartz vessel, the normal ignition limit is found at approximately 700°C with an induction period of about 1 second; if the same mixture is heated to about 600°C, ignition takes place after an induction period of the order of 1 hour. The region of ignition, with accompanying long induction periods, corresponds to the CO explosion peninsula. For details the reader is referred to the original papers.

Mechanism of n-Paraffin Oxidation

The problem of the mechanism of hydrocarbon oxidation has been re-examined in the last few years by Walsh.[56] From various chemical and kinetic evidence, this author proposes that in the τ_1 regime peroxide molecules are formed according to the chain reaction

$$R \xrightarrow{O_2} ROO \xrightarrow{RH} ROOH + R \tag{15}$$

and that these peroxides decompose into free radicals by fission at the O—O bond and other bonds, depending on the structure of the peroxides, thus giving rise to intense branching. In agreement with the suggestion made by the present authors,[22] Walsh visualizes the branching reaction to be catalyzed by aldehydes, which condense with peroxides and are regenerated according to:

$$RCH_2OOH + HCHO \rightarrow RCH_2OOCH_2OH \rightarrow RCH_2O + OH + HCHO \tag{16}$$

In the τ_2 regime, unbranched chains are operative that are analogous to the methane oxidation chains discussed earlier; that is, the peroxide radicals formed by association of a radical RCH_2 with O_2 decompose into OH and aldehyde:

$$RCH_2OO \rightarrow OH + RCHO \tag{17}$$

Decomposition of the peroxide radical destroys the chance that a peroxide molecule is formed, and in this way branching by O—O fission is prevented.

There can be little disagreement with the basic concept of branching in the τ_1 regime by O—O fission and the competing straight-chain reaction in the τ_2 regime. However, it appears to us that the exclusive operation of the peroxide chain (reaction 15) in the τ_1 regime, to be followed always by fission of the O O bond and therefore branching at every chain link, places an undue burden on the theory. Walsh himself has modified this position by admitting the possibility of competition of radical decomposition (reaction 17) with the peroxide-forming chain (reaction 15) in the τ_1 regime. However, he proposes that a major part of the molecular transformation occurs via the branching reaction. This is illustrated by his scheme of oxidation of long-chain n-paraffins such as n-octane:

$$RCH_2CH_2CH_3 \xrightarrow{OH} H_2O + RCH_2CHCH_3 \xrightarrow{O_2} RCH_2CH(OO)CH_3 \xrightarrow{RCH_2CH_3}$$
$$RCH_2CH(OOH)CH_3 + RCH_2CH_2$$
$$\downarrow$$
$$RCH_2 + CH_3CHO + OH \tag{18}$$
$$RCH_2 \xrightarrow{O_2} RCH_2OO \rightarrow OH + RCHO \rightarrow RH + CO \tag{19}$$

In this scheme, every attack on the original hydrocarbon molecule leads to chain branching. The self-accelerating character of the reaction is evidence in itself that chain-breaking processes are inadequate to keep the branching rate under control. Consequently, if one assumes that branching occurs every time the original hydrocarbon molecule is attacked, it is difficult to see how induction periods τ_1 of comparatively long duration (seconds and minutes) could be commonly observed. One would have to postulate very effective chain-breaking reactions, which, however, must not interfere with the self-accelerating character of the reaction. The kinetic problem posed by this concept appears to be extraordinarily complex even when approached on a purely speculative basis. We are inclined to the view that the branching reaction is comparatively rare, and that the bulk of the reaction products is formed in a straight-chain reaction throughout the τ_1 regime. In support of this, we may quote dissociation energies of O—O bonds compiled by Walsh[55] (Table 3).

TABLE 3. STRENGTHS OF O—O BONDS IN ORGANIC PEROXIDES

Peroxide	K cal/mole
C_2H_5OOH	51
C_3H_7OOH	54
$C_2H_5OOC_2H_5$	62

These values in Table 3 may be lowered somewhat by the condensation reaction between peroxides and aldehydes, but they would still be of an order of magnitude that makes it unlikely that chain branching could be anything but a rare event. We are inclined to accept the chain-branching reaction,[16] at least with respect to the principle of O—O fission, but consider the bulk of the reaction products to be formed by chains of the type exemplified by the propane-oxygen reaction:

$$CH_3CHCH_3 \xrightarrow{O_2} CH_3CH(OO)CH_3 \rightarrow CH_3CHO + CH_3O \xrightarrow{C_3H_8} CH_3OH + C_3H_7 \quad (20)$$

This scheme is consistent with the observation of Pope, Dykstra, and Edgar[36] that no oxide of carbon is formed in the initial attack of O_2 on a paraffin molecule; it explains the simultaneous appearance of methyl alcohol and aldehydes observed by Pease[35] and Harris and Egerton;[15] and it also explains the observation of Newitt and Thornes[30] that in the initial stages of the reaction no formaldehyde but only higher aldehydes are formed. The point of attack along the carbon chain is assumed to be at the secondary carbon atom; this is in agreement with evidence discussed by Walsh showing that secondary carbon atoms are more readily attacked than primary ones. If the scheme is applied to an n-paraffin of more than three C atoms, it would seem that initial attack is possible with equal facility on any of the CH_2 groups. We would therefore write, in general:

$$R'CHCH_2R'' \xrightarrow{O_2} R'CH(OO)CH_2R'' \rightarrow R'CHO + R''CH_2O \quad (21)$$

Unlike propane, where the methoxyl radical is stable and can react further to form methyl alcohol, the higher oxyalkyl radicals formed in this fashion are not stable but decompose according to reaction:

$$R''CH_2O \rightarrow R'' + HCHO \tag{22}$$

We thus have an explanation of the commonly observed fact that formaldehyde appears among the first products of the oxidation of higher hydrocarbons.[8] Cullis and Hinshelwood, who studied the oxidation of n-hexane at various mixture ratios, report that initially the ratio of total aldehydes to formaldehyde always tends to a value of about two, one molecule of formaldehyde being formed for every higher aldehyde formed. They, themselves, propose reaction (22) as the source of formaldehyde. The scheme (reactions 21 and 22) is evidently consistent with this observation.

We do not believe that available evidence warrants specific formulation of the mechanism by which the higher aldehydes are oxidized further. We are inclined to the view that the CHO group is the preferred position of attack by chain carriers, and that the resulting radical RCO decomposes into R and CO. The radicals that thus result are CH_3, CH_2CH_2, $CH_3CH_2CH_2$, etc. Such radicals are expected to add O_2 and decompose either into OH and aldehyde or into H_2O and radicals of the type $RCO(\rightarrow R + CO)$, viz.,

$$RCH_2 \xrightarrow{O_2} RCH_2OO \underset{\searrow H_2O + RCO \rightarrow R + CO}{\overset{\nearrow OH + RCHO}{}} \tag{23}$$

It is felt that the chain mechanism (21) to (23) is operative in both the τ_1 and τ_2 regimes and that the true difference between the two regimes lies in the suppression of O—O fission-chain branching in the τ_2 regime. This comes about because, with increasing temperature, the decomposition of the peroxidic radicals in the manner of reactions (21) and (23) becomes increasingly more probable than the formation of saturated peroxides capable of O—O fission-branching. It is understandable, therefore, that on increasing the temperature, all other conditions remaining constant, one passes through a temperature range of maximum branching rate, characterized under suitable conditions by vigorous cool-flame development, into a temperature range of weakly developed branching. Two aspects of the cool-flame phenomenon require discussion. The first concerns the fact that the reaction rate does not tend toward a steady state even though chains are broken at the surface. This indicates that the branching reaction is kinetically of a higher order than the chain-breaking reaction. The suggestion that branching occurs by condensation of aldehyde and peroxide is consistent with this, as the rate of production of chain carriers becomes proportional to the product of the concentrations of two intermediate reaction products, whereas the rate of chain breaking is proportional to the first power of the chain-carrier concentration. The second concerns the arrest of the cool-flame reaction short of complete release of chemical enthalpy. In line with the earlier discussion concerning the ineffectiveness of the formyl radical CHO as a chain carrier, and in harmony with the observation that formaldehyde inhibits the reaction in the τ_1 regime, we believe that cool flames are quenched by their own reaction product, formaldehyde. The latter reacts with active free radicals like OH or CH_3O to form the inactive formyl radical.

On the other hand, on analogy with the methane-oxygen system, we believe that formaldehyde initiates chains in the τ_2 regime where otherwise no effective source for chain carriers exists. The reaction rate in the τ_2 regime, viz., the length of the induction period τ_2, is therefore strongly dependent on the concentration of formaldehyde remaining at the end of the τ_1 regime. The end of the latter regime is brought about by the rise in temperature accompanying the reaction. The amount of formaldehyde remaining will be smaller the higher the initial temperature of the system, because the higher the temperature the less chain branching will have occurred over the duration of the τ_1 regime, and, correspondingly, the consumption of reactants and formation of formaldehyde will be less. The τ_2 regime thus starts with decreasing amounts of formaldehyde as the temperature is increased; for this reason, the induction period τ_2 increases. It is understood that during the τ_2 regime more formaldehyde is produced, and therefore the reaction rate is self-accelerating in the sense of "degenerate branching"; it may become so large that thermal explosion ensues. If the heat is dissipated to the surroundings at a sufficient rate, the system may lapse back into the τ_1 regime. We may see in this process a possible cause for the frequently observed periodicity of cool flames.

It is also imaginable that the periodicity of cool flames has its origin in the reaction mechanism and would occur under isothermal conditions. This suggestion has been made by Frank-Kamenetzki[12] and is discussed further by Walsh.[56] It appears to us that a reaction mechanism in which a concentration of intermediate products passes through periodic changes is an interesting possibility, but that an attempt to identify, if only approximately, the actual elementary reactions involved leads to serious difficulties and contradictions. This point is amplified in another place.[23]

Knock Limit in Otto Engines

The knock limit is determined by both fuel and engine factors. The following analysis, although approximate, illustrates the interplay of these two sets of factors. We shall first examine the process of normal engine combustion by determining the amount, the pressure, and the temperature of the unburned part of the charge at any instant during the time interval between spark ignition and completion of burning. Next we shall determine the induction period τ (preceding knock) that corresponds to the pressure and temperature of the unburned charge at

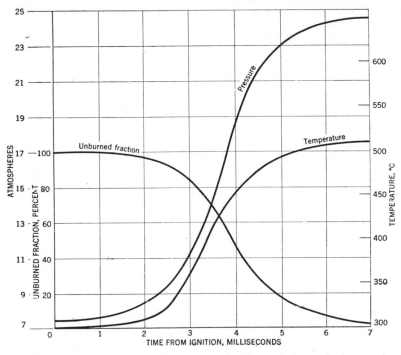

Fig. 6. Pressure, temperature and per cent of unburned charge during combustion in an Otto-cycle test engine. Engine data: $2\frac{7}{8}$ inch bore; compression ratio 4.8; 900 revolutions per minute; 12 degree spark advance; fuel, isooctane; air fuel ration 13.7; 1 by weight. Time counted from instant of spark ignition. Data on pressure and per cent of unburned charge from Withrow and Cornelius. Temperature calculated for isentropic compression with $\gamma = 1.35$.

any instant. As long as τ is large as compared to the time required for the remainder of the charge to burn, knock cannot occur. However, when τ approaches or becomes smaller than this time, knocking will follow, the severity of the knock depending on the amount of unburned charge left.

The example shown in Figure 6 is based on data of Withrow and Cornelius.[60] These investigators analyzed high-speed flame photographs taken through the transparent head of a test engine in conjunction with the pressure record by a method previously described by Rassweiler and

Withrow.[39] The investigators constructed mechanical models from the flame pictures to determine the flame volume. The test engine was operated at 900 rpm, and time was measured by degrees of crank-angle, 8 degrees corresponding to 1.48 milliseconds. In Figure 6, curves of

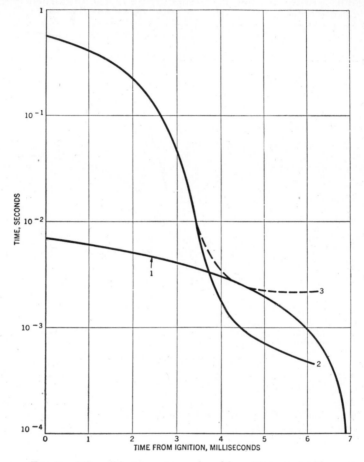

FIG. 7.   "Race" between normal and knocking combustion.
Curve 1. Time remaining for completion of normal combustion.
Curve 2. Ignition lag τ for n-heptane.
Curve 3. τ for n-heptane $+$ 2 per cent lead tetraethyl. The curves are calculated from data in the preceding figures using Rögener's equations for $\tau = \tau_1 + \tau_2$.

per cent mass burned and pressure are constructed from a typical experiment; these curves are subject to change of operating conditions, such as engine speed, throttle, and spark advance; they are also dependent on stoichiometry but are otherwise not greatly dependent on the nature of the fuel. The temperature curve is based on an initial temperature of 70°C and is calculated from the equation for isentropic compression, using $\gamma = 1.35$. The curves show the pressure and temperature of the unburned charge at any time, together with the percentage of charge remaining unburned. In Figure 7, curve 1 represents the time remaining for completion of combustion at any instant; curves 2 and 3 represent the induction period τ preceding knock at any instant of the cycle calculated for n-heptane and leaded n-heptane from the pressure and temperature data of Figure 6 and by means of equations listed in Table 2 and equation (14) for τ_2. The calculated τ's represent the sums of τ_1 and τ_2. The calculations are summarized in Table 4. As was discussed, τ_1 is unaffected by Pb(Et)$_4$, whereas τ_2 is increased strongly. It is seen from Table 4 that during the first half of the combustion period the induction

TABLE 4. INDUCTION PERIODS τ_1, τ_2 AND τ FOR n-HEPTANE AND n-HEPTANE PLUS 2 PER CENT Pb(Et)$_4$ CORRESPONDING TO AN EXPERIMENTAL ENGINE CYCLE

Time from ignition, millisec	0	2.40	3.35	3.82	4.40	5.80
Pressure, atm	7.3	9	13	17	21	24
Temperature, °K	576	607	668	717	748	782
Charge, unburned, %	100	95	74	55	30	8
n-Heptane τ_1, millisec	576	141	10	1.91	0.69	0.26
n-Heptane τ_2, millisec	1.13	0.86	0.55	0.39	0.29	0.25
n-Heptane τ, millisec	577	142	11	2.3	0.98	0.51
n-Heptane + 2% Pb(Et)$_4$ τ_1, millisec	576	141	10	1.91	0.69	0.26
n-Heptane + 2% Pb(Et)$_4$ τ_2, millisec	12	1.3	1.65	1.89	1.76	1.98
n-Heptane + 2% Pb(Et)$_4$ τ, millisec	588	142	12	3.80	2.45	2.24

period τ is essentially equal to τ_1, but that during the critical second half the contribution of τ_2 becomes decisive. The τ-curve for n-heptane intersects curve 1, and it is evident that a large part of the end charge must knock. As is well-known, n-heptane is referred to as the fuel of zero octane number. No experiments with this fuel are reported by Rassweiler and Withrow, but they observed[61] that knock occurred under these test conditions with a 48-octane fuel. The effect of Pb(Et)$_4$ is strikingly demonstrated, in that the τ-curve approaches curve 1 when 3 milliseconds are still left for completion of the burning and then draws away, so that under such conditions one should expect no or very mild knock. Unfortunately, no engine tests are available for the n-heptane leaded fuel.

Summary

For the slow oxidation of methane, the experimental evidence points to the attainment of a steady state in which chains are initiated at a rate proportional to the formaldehyde concentration, and the latter remains constant because formaldehyde is formed and destroyed by the chain reaction at the same rate. The experimentally observed dependence of the steady-state reaction on vessel diameter, pressure, and mixture composition corresponds in the first approximation to the skeletonized reaction mechanism:

$$HCHO + O_2 \rightarrow \text{free radicals} \tag{I}$$
$$OH + CH_4 = H_2O + CH_3 \tag{II}$$
$$CH_3 + O_2 = HCHO + OH \tag{III}$$
$$OH + HCHO = H_2O + HCO \tag{IV}$$
$$OH \xrightarrow{\text{wall}} \text{destruction} \tag{V}$$
$$CHO \rightarrow \text{destruction}$$

A more complete representation of the experimental observations is obtained when the surface-catalyzed oxidation of formaldehyde is added to the scheme and suitable assumptions are made concerning reactions of the radical CHO.

For higher hydrocarbons and related compounds, the steady-state concept is not applicable. There are two regimes of self-accelerating reaction characterized by induction periods τ_1 and τ_2. The former may lead to "cool" flames and the latter to "true" ignition. In a given fuel-oxygen mixture enclosed in a vessel at a suitable temperature and pressure, one observes that the reaction at first accelerates—this period comprises the τ_1 regime—then decelerates, and then accelerates again—this period comprises the τ_2 regime. Ignition thus occurs in two stages. Under suitable conditions, cool flames appear and disappear periodically. Depending on the range of kinetic factors such as pressure, temperature, and mixture composition, the bulk of the chemical change may occur either in the τ_1 regime or in the τ_2 regime. With increasing temperature, τ_1 decreases and τ_2 increases; with increasing pressure, both τ_1 and τ_2 decrease. The reaction in the τ_1 regime is inhibited by formaldehyde but promoted by acetaldehyde and notably alkyl hydroperoxides. Lead tetraethyl leaves the induction period τ_1 unchanged, whereas the induction period τ_2 is considerably lengthened. For a given mixture composition, it is possible to represent τ_1 and τ_2 by empirical equations as functions of temperature and pressure. The cool flames that appear at the end of τ_1 represent combustion waves that pass through the mixture but produce only a partial release of the chemical enthalpy. Aldehydes and peroxides are left in their wake. By suitable ignition sources it is possible to produce cool flames at temperatures and pressures below the range of spontaneous formation.

The evidence suggests that the reaction chains in the τ_1 regime are branched and those in the τ_2 regime are unbranched. Branching occurs via peroxide formation by fission of the peroxidic bond. Walsh proposes a mechanism according to which virtually every attack of an oxygen molecule on a hydrocarbon molecule leads to chain branching. To the present authors, it seems far more probable that branching is a comparatively rare molecular event. Transition from the τ_1 regime to the τ_2 regime occurs with rising temperature, because peroxides are destroyed with increasing probability by decomposition without chain branching.

From the empirical equations that represent τ_1 and τ_2 as functions of pressure and temperature, and from the pressure-temperature history of the fuel-air mixture in an Otto engine, it is possible to calculate the occurrence and estimate the severity of engine knock with fair approximation.

References

1. Aivazov, B., and Neumann, M. B., Z. physik. Chem., **B33,** 349 (1936).
2. Andreev, E. A., Acta Physicochim. (U.R.S.S.), **6,** 57 (1937).
3. Andreev, E. A., and Neumann, M. B., Physik. Z. (U.R.S.S.), **4,** 14 (1933).
4. Beatty, H. A., and Edgar, G., J. Am. Chem. Soc., **56,** 112 (1934).
5. Blat, E., Gerber, M., and Neumann, M., Acta Physicochim. (U.R.S.S.), **10,** 273 (1939).
6. Bone, W. A., and Gardner, J. B., Proc. Roy. Soc. (London), **A154,** 297 (1936).
7. Chamberlain, G. H. N., and Walsh, A. D., Rev. inst. franc. pétrole et ann. combustibles liquides, **IV,** No. 9, p. 29 (1949).
8. Cullis, C. F., and Hinshelwood, C. N., "The Labile Molecule," Discussion Faraday Soc., No. 2, p. 117 (1947).
9. Day, R. A., and Pease, R. N., J. Am. Chem. Soc., **62,** 2234 (1940).
10. Dugleux, P., and Freling, E., "Cinétique et Mécanisme des Réactions d'Inflammation et de Combustion en Phase Gazeuse," p. 179, Paris, 1948.
11. Eméléus, J. Chem. Soc., 2948 (1926); 1733 (1929).
12. Frank-Kamenetzki, A. A., J. Phys. Chem. (U.R.S.S.), **14,** 30 (1940).
13. Freling, E., "Cinétique et Mécanisme des Réactions d'Inflammation et de Combustion en Phase Gazeuse," p. 174, Paris, 1948.
14. Gaydon, A. G., "Spectroscopy and Combustion Theory," London, Chapman & Hall, Ltd., 1948.
15. Harris, E. G., and Egerton, A., Chem. Rev., **21,** 287 (1937).
16. Hsieh, M. S., and Townend, D. T. A., J. Chem. Soc., 332, 337, 341 (1939).
17. Ivanov, K. I., and Savinova, V. K., J. App. Chem. (U.R.S.S.), **8,** 64 (1935).
18. Jost, W., "Third Symposium on Combustion and Flame and Explosion Phenomena," p. 424, Baltimore, Williams and Wilkins Co., 1949.
19. Jost, W., and Teichmann, H., Naturwissenschaften, **27,** 318 (1939); Z. Elektrochem., **47,** 262, 297 (1941).
20. Kane, G. P., Proc. Roy. Soc. (London), **A167,** 62 (1938).
21. Kowalsky, A., Sadovnikov, P., and Chirkov, N., Physik. Z. (U.R.S.S.), **1,** 451 (1932).
22. Lewis, B., and von Elbe, G., J. Am. Chem. Soc., **59,** 976 (1937); see also, Lewis, B., and von Elbe, G., "Combustion, Flames and Explosions of Gases," p. 108 et seq., Cambridge University Press, 1938.
23. Lewis, B., and Von Elbe, G., "Combustion, Flames and Explosions of Gases," Academic Press Inc., New York.
24. Maccormac, M., and Townend, D. T. A., J. Chem. Soc., 143, 151 (1940).
25. Miller, C. D., Soc. Automotive Engrs. Quart. Trans., **1,** 98 (1947).

26. Mondain-Monval, P., and Quanquin, B., *Compt. rend.*, **191**, 299 (1930); *Ann. chim. phys.*, **15**, 309 (1931).
27. Neumann, M., and Aivazov, B., *Nature*, **135**, 655 (1935); *Acta Physicochim. (U.R.S.S.)*, **4**, 575 (1936); **6**, 279 (1937).
28. Neumann, M., and Serbinov, A., *Physik. Z. (U.R.S.S.)*, **1**, 536 (1932); **4**, 433 (1933).
29. Neumann, M., and Tutakin, P., *Compt. rend. acad. sci. (U.R.S.S.)*, **4**, 122 (1936).
30. Newitt, D. M., and Thornes, L. S., *J. Chem. Soc.*, 1656, 1669 (1937).
31. Norrish, R. G. W., *Proc. Roy. Soc. (London)*, **A157**, 503 (1936); see also Norrish, R. G. W., *Rev. inst. franc. pétrole et ann. combustibles liquides*, **IV**, No. 9, p. 16 (1949).
32. Norrish, R. G. W., and Foord, S. G., *Proc. Roy. Soc. (London)*, **A157**, 503 (1936).
33. Norrish, R. G. W., and Reagh, J. D., *ibid.*, **A176**, 479 (1940).
34. Pease, R. N., *J. Am. Chem. Soc.*, **55**, 2753 (1933).
35. Pease, R. N., *ibid.*, **57**, 2296 (1935).
36. Pope, J. C., Dykstra, F. J., and Edgar, G., *ibid.*, **51**, 1875, 2203, 2213 (1929).
37. Prettre, M., *Ann. combustibles liquides*, **11**, 669 (1936).
38. Prettre, M., "Third Symposium on Combustion and Flame and Explosion Phenomena," p. 397, Baltimore, Williams and Wilkins Co., 1949.
39. Rassweiler, G. M., and Withrow, L., *J. Soc. Automotive Engrs.*, **42**, 185 (1938).
40. Rieche, A., "Alkylperoxyde und Ozonide," Dresden, 1931.
41. Rögener, H., (in collaboration with W. Jost), U. S. Govt. Tech. Oil Mission microfilm reel 242; Photoduplication Service, Library of Congress (1945). *Z. Elektrochem.*, **53**, 389 (1949).
42. Sadovnikov, *Physik. Z. (U.R.S.S.)*, **4**, 735, 743 (1933).
43. Scheuermeyer, M., and Steigerwald, H., *Motortech. Z.*, Stuttgart, **8–9** (1943).
44. Schmidt, F. A. F., "Verbrennungsmotoren" (Springer, Berlin), 2d ed. with supplements; FIAT (U.S.) Rep. 709 (1946).
45. Spence, Kate, and Townend, D. T. A., *Nature*, **155**, 330 (1945); "Third Symposium on Combustion and Flame and Explosion Phenomena," p. 404, Baltimore, Williams and Wilkins Co., 1949.
46. Taylor, C. F., Taylor, E. S., Livengood, J. C., Russell, W. A., and Leary, W. A., *Soc. Automotive Engrs. Quart. Trans.*, **4**, 232 (1950).
47. Tizard, H. T., and Pye, D. R., *Phil. Mag.*, **44**, (VI), 79 (1922); *ibid.*, **1**, (VII), 1094 (1926).
48. Topps, J. E. C., and Townend, D. T. A., *Trans. Faraday Soc.*, **42**, 345 (1946).
49. Townend, D. T. A., and Chamberlain, E. A. C., *Proc. Roy. Soc. (London)*, **A158**, 415 (1937).
50. Townend, D. T. A., Cohen, L. L., and Mandlekar, M. R., *ibid.*, **A146**, 113 (1934).
51. Townend, D. T. A., and Mandlekar, M. R., *ibid.*, **A141**, 484 (1933).
52. Townend, D. T. A., and Mandlekar, M. R., *ibid.*, **A143**, 168 (1934).
53. Vanpee, M., *Ann. mines Belg.*, **47**, 1053 (1948).
54. von Elbe, G., and Lewis, B., *J. Chem. Phys.*, **10**, 366 (1942).
55. Walsh, A. D., *Trans. Faraday Soc.*, **42**, 264 (1946).
56. Walsh, A. D., *ibid.*, **42**, 197 (1946); **43**, 297, 305 (1947).
57. Walsh, A. D., *ibid.*, **43**, 297 (1947).
58. Walsh, A. D., *Rev. inst. franc. pétrole et ann. combustibles liquides*, **IV**, No. 9, p. 45 (1949).
59. White, A. G., *J. Chem. Soc.*, 498 (1927).
60. Withrow, L., and Cornelius, W., *J. Soc. Automotive Engrs.*, **47**, 529 (1940).
61. Withrow, L., and Rassweiler, G. M., *ibid.*, **39**, 297 (1936).

CHAPTER 33

LOW-TEMPERATURE OXIDATION OF PARAFFIN HYDROCARBONS; OXIDATION OF PARAFFIN WAX

William E. Vaughan,

AND

Frederick F. Rust

Shell Development Company, Emeryville Research Center, Emeryville, California

The oxidation of the paraffin hydrocarbons at low temperatures (about 100 to 150°C) is inextricably involved with the reaction of alkyl radicals and oxygen. Therefore, knowledge of this primary process and the fate of the successive intermediates is essential to an understanding of alkane oxidation processes in general.

Bates and Spence,[4] who carried out the photolysis of methyl iodide in the presence of oxygen, concluded the reaction of methyl and oxygen to be

$$\dot{C}H_3 + O_2 \rightarrow H_2CO + \dot{O}H \tag{1}$$

This idea is concurred in by Norrish[14] and Chamberlain and Walsh;[8] the latter two authors also postulate the existence of a transient, energy-rich CH_3OO. Raley, Porter, Rust and Vaughan[17] conclude that CH_3OO is the essential intermediate and that the subsequent reactions involve hydrogen abstraction or degradation:

$$CH_3O\dot{O} + RH \rightarrow CH_3OOH + \dot{R} \tag{2}$$

$$2CH_3O\dot{O} \rightarrow 2CH_3O + O_2 \tag{3}$$

This suggestion is substantiated by Gray,[9] who obtained high yields of CH_3OOH from the mercury-sensitized photooxidation of methane.

Studies of the organic peroxides and of the radicals derivable from them have also contributed considerable information about the intermediates which participate in low-temperature oxidation processes. It is generally appreciated that in most oxidations in this region the initial breach in the hydrocarbon structure is accomplished by the abstraction of a hydrogen atom by some radical.

$$\dot{X} + RH \rightarrow XH + \dot{R} \qquad (4)$$

There is also general concurrence that step (4) is followed by association with oxygen.

$$R + O_2 \rightarrow RO_2 \qquad (5)$$

However, the point of initial attack has been subject to considerable speculation.

The earlier ideas of Pope, Dykstra, and Edgar[16] that initial attack occurred on the methyl group at the end of the longest alkyl chain has given way before the general appreciation that in an absolute sense the hydrogen atoms in a hydrocarbon molecule are all vulnerable to free radical attack, and that the frequency of attack at any one position will be compounded of such factors as hydrogen atom reactivity, the numbers of available atoms at any position, and, in some cases, steric factors. In general, the order of increasing reactivity of hydrogen atoms will be primary, secondary, and then tertiary. In the normal paraffins, for example, initial attack will be directed predominantly toward, and more or less randomly among, the methylene groups. This has been admirably demonstrated by Benton and Wirth,[6] who in a study of the autoxidation of n-decane at 145°C, have shown that all of the four pairs of methylenic groups are, within their experimental accuracy, equally vulnerable to attack, while the two methyl groups are far less reactive. This lack of specificity of attack on the methylenic groups is not unexpected on the basis of previously investigated free-radical chlorination reactions, but the proof by Benton and Wirth is at variance with claims by others that the 2-position is favored.[11] Thus the initial association of the radical and oxygen will usually lead to a secondary alkyl peroxy radical:

$$\begin{array}{cc} R & R \\ \diagdown & \diagdown \\ CH + O_2 \rightarrow & CHOO \\ \diagup & \diagup \\ R' & R' \end{array} \qquad (6)$$

Hydrogen abstraction by peroxy radicals to give hydroperoxides is a well accepted process in oxidation systems:

$$ROO + RH \rightarrow ROOH + R \qquad (7)$$

However, except in the case of the tertiary hydrocarbons, aliphatic hydroperoxides are not usually found in appreciable amounts on oxidation, but their transitory existence may be deemed certain on the basis of the alcohols and ketones which are formed in high yields in the early stages.

Indeed, at quite low levels of conversion of n-paraffins, hydroperoxides can be detected.[6]

The role of hydroperoxides in the over-all process of paraffin oxidation is by no means concluded with their formation. The autocatalytic character of the oxidation of many paraffins is attributed to the formation of peroxides. Certainly they are excellent oxidation chain initiators which function through their ability to dissociate into free radicals:

$$ROOH \overset{\Delta}{\rightarrow} R\dot{O} + \dot{O}H \tag{8}$$

Although evidence for a thermal dissociation in accordance with the above equation has been obtained by adding the hydroxy radical to the double bond,[5] Bateman and Hughes[3] has shown that in liquid phase the disappearance of cyclohexene hydroperoxide follows second-order kinetics. This is interpreted to show that a transition state involving two hydroperoxide molecules precedes the decomposition step. Whichever kinetics is involved, alkyl hydroperoxide, upon decomposition, passes through the alkoxy radical.

The alkoxy radical stage need not necessarily be reached by way of the hydroperoxide because the hydrogen abstraction reaction, which possesses a sensible activation energy, competes with other reaction opportunities of the peroxy fragment. However, the alternative fates of the peroxy entity have been difficult to assess because this radical is usually formed in the presence of oxygen. As a consequence, it has been almost impossible to distinguish between end products arising from peroxy radical reactions and secondary oxidations.

The tert-butyl peroxy radical has been obtained by reacting tert-butyl hydroperoxide with both di-tert-butyl and di-tert-amyl peroxides.[21] These reactions can be summarized as follows:

$$R_3'COOCR_3' \rightarrow 2R_3'CO- \tag{9}$$

$$R_3COOH + R_3'CO \rightarrow R_3COO + R_3'COH \tag{10}$$

$$R_3'CO \rightarrow R_2'C{=}O + R' \tag{11}$$

$$R_3COO + R' \rightarrow R_3COOR' \tag{12}$$

If oxygen is present, $R' + O_2 \rightarrow RO_2$ will be so rapid that the association shown by Equation (12) will not take place. Instead the degradation of alkyl peroxy to alkoxy

$$2RO_2 \rightarrow 2RO + O_2 \tag{13}$$

will compete with hydrogen abstraction, as given by Equation (7).

Thus alkoxy radicals eventually appear as intermediates, regardless of whether or not the hydroperoxide was formed, and the properties of these intermediates are prime determinants of the end products.

There are four competitive reactions of alkoxy, as follows:

(1) Hydrogen atom capture which yields either primary, secondary or tertiary alcohols:

$$R_3'CO + RH \rightarrow R_3'COH + R \tag{14}$$

(2) Carbon-carbon bond scission:

$$R_3'CO \rightarrow R_2'C\!\!=\!\!O + R' \tag{15}$$

Scission will be β to the oxygen atom and, if there is a choice, will generally involve rupture of the weakest C—C bond in that position. For example, ethyl, propyl, and larger groups will be cleaved in preference to methyl. This is well shown in the decomposition of di-tert-amyl peroxide to give initially two tert-amyloxy radicals, $(C_2H_5)(CH_3)_2CO$, which in turn decompose to two molecules of acetone and two ethyl radicals; the latter dimerize to butane.[13,18] As a consequence of carbon-carbon bond scission, tertiary alkoxy leads to ketone and alkyl radical; secondary alkoxy to aldehyde and alkyl; and primary alkoxy to formaldehyde and alkyl.

(3) Disproportionation:

$$2R_2'CHO \rightarrow R_2'CHOH + R_2'C\!\!=\!\!O \tag{16}$$

(4) Ether formation:

$$R' + RO \rightarrow R'OR \tag{17}$$

The sequence of steps between initiation and the formation of the first stable molecular products is diagrammed in Figure 1; these steps are based on experimental evidence derived from studies of generations [summarized in Equation (5)] of specific free radicals and their subsequent reactions. This rather clean-cut delineation of the individual incidents has only been possible by the use of organic peroxides and hydroperoxides. It should be emphasized that this scheme carries only to the first stable molecular species, and other products, such as acids (whose synthesis is described in the latter part of this discussion), water and carbon oxides, generally arise from subsequent radical attack upon the primary products.

As has just been pointed out, in many oxidations where hydrogen donors are not readily available, chain propagation is possible by radical-radical reactions [for example, Equation (3)] and neither branching nor termination need be involved. In the course of such reactions the formation of relatively unstable fragments, such as alkoxy radicals, is usually followed by carbon skeleton breakdown. In most oxidations of the lower paraffin hydrocarbons, the difficulty of hydrogen capture by intermediate peroxy radicals is reflected in rather extensive carbon-carbon bond scission. However, if a good hydrogen donor is present, for example, hydrogen bromide, the oxidation chains are modified so that peroxy radicals, instead of degrading, are converted to hydroperoxides (Equation 2) and thence into stable end products without carbon chain rupture.

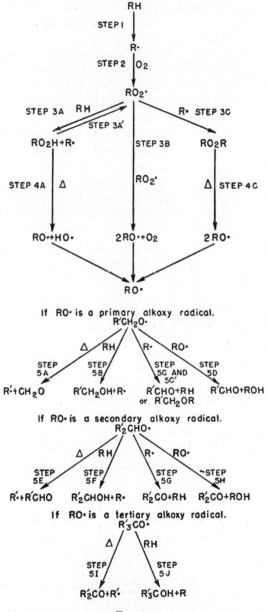

Fig. 1.

These oxidations utilizing hydrogen bromide[18] not only are characterized by discreteness of reaction, but also in some cases lead to products not previously derived in quantity from reactions with oxygen. High yields of relatively simple mixtures are obtained at temperatures far below those usually encountered in hydrocarbon oxidations.

Thus, the hydrogen bromide-catalyzed oxidation of paraffins containing tertiary carbon-hydrogen linkages appears to proceed by a relatively simple chain reaction, which is fundamental to the oxidations of the other types of compounds. In general, it can be said that branched-chain hydrocarbons are converted in high yield to stable organic hydroperoxides. For example, the oxidation of *isobutane*, in particular, the simplest member of the series, at temperatures as low as 160°C produces tert-butyl hydroperoxide in yields as high as 75 per cent based on the consumed oxygen from a 10-to-10-to-1 mixture of isobutane, oxygen, and hydrogen bromide under conditions where 87 per cent of the oxygen is reacted. tert-Butyl alcohol and di-tert-butyl peroxide are also formed. Breakdown of the carbon skeleton during the oxidation is minor. Further, the hydrogen bromide catalyst is regenerated semiquantitatively; losses are attributable to oxidation to bromine or to formation of organic bromides, the possibilities for the production of which will be apparent from a consideration of the following mechanism developed to explain the principal reaction:

$$HBr + O_2 \rightarrow Br + (HO_2\ldots\ldots?) \tag{18}$$

$$R-\overset{\displaystyle R}{\underset{\displaystyle R}{C}}-H + Br \rightleftarrows HBr + R-\overset{\displaystyle R}{\underset{\displaystyle R}{C}}- \tag{19}$$

$$R-\overset{\displaystyle R}{\underset{\displaystyle R}{C}}- + O_2 \rightarrow R-\overset{\displaystyle R}{\underset{\displaystyle R}{C}}-O_2- \tag{20}$$

$$R-\overset{\displaystyle R}{\underset{\displaystyle R}{C}}-O_2- + HBr \rightarrow R-\overset{\displaystyle R}{\underset{\displaystyle R}{C}}-O_2H + Br \tag{21}$$

It is seen that the over-all reaction is simply:

$$(R)_3CH + O_2 \xrightarrow{\text{HBr}} (R)_3COOH \tag{22}$$

Equation (18), a chain-initiating step which probably occurs largely at the wall, generates a bromine atom. The bromine atom, in reacting with a molecule of a tertiary hydrocarbon, attacks at relatively low temperatures virtually exclusively the tertiary hydrogen atom, forming hydrogen bromide and the tertiary-alkyl radical (19). The latter may, with due consideration for the probable reversibility of the previous reaction, undergo an association reaction with oxygen (20), and the peroxy radical thus produced is stabilized as the hydroperoxide molecule by an exchange reaction with hydrogen bromide (21), the equivalent of (2). By this process a bromine atom is regenerated and the sequence is repeated. It is reaction (21) which distinguishes these oxidations from others which are less clean-cut, for without such a hydrogen donor, the peroxy radical cannot become a stable molecule and instead breaks down with varying degrees of carbon-carbon bond scission. Further and important is the specificity of the attack of the bromine atom on the hydrocarbon.

If the compound undergoing oxidation contains only secondary and primary carbon-hydrogen linkages, the principal product is a ketone. *Propane,* for example, can be converted to acetone in a yield of 75 per cent, based on the consumed propane in a 2-to-2-to-1 mixture of propane, oxygen, and hydrogen bromide. Approximately 75 per cent of both of the first two components are converted, and 83 per cent of the catalyst is recovered. The operating temperature is somewhat higher than that required for *isobutane* (190° as compared to 160°C), and the catalyst requirements are somewhat greater. Propionic acid accounts for about 8 per cent of the consumed propane. The mechanism of ketone formation strictly parallels that previously given for the branched-chain compounds:

$$H-\overset{\overset{\textstyle R}{|}}{\underset{\underset{\textstyle R}{|}}{C}}-H + Br \rightleftarrows H-\overset{\overset{\textstyle R}{|}}{\underset{\underset{\textstyle R}{|}}{C}}- + HBr \qquad (23)$$

$$H-\overset{\overset{\textstyle R}{|}}{\underset{\underset{\textstyle R}{|}}{C}}- + O_2 \rightarrow H-\overset{\overset{\textstyle R}{|}}{\underset{\underset{\textstyle R}{|}}{C}}-O_2- \qquad (24)$$

$$H-\overset{\overset{\textstyle R}{|}}{\underset{\underset{\textstyle R}{|}}{C}}-O_2- + HBr \rightarrow \left[H-\overset{\overset{\textstyle R}{|}}{\underset{\underset{\textstyle R}{|}}{C}}-O_2H \right] + Br \qquad (25)$$

$$\left[H-\overset{\overset{\textstyle R}{|}}{\underset{\underset{\textstyle R}{|}}{C}}-O_2H \right] \rightarrow \overset{\overset{\textstyle R}{|}}{\underset{\underset{\textstyle R}{|}}{C}}=O + H_2O \qquad (26)$$

The bromine atom attacks principally the secondary carbon-hydrogen bonds [Equation (23)] and the isoalkyl radical thus formed associates with oxygen [Equation (24)]. In turn, the peroxy radical is stabilized by hydrogen bromide [Equation (25)], but in this instance the hydroperoxide molecule undergoes elimination of water, giving the major product [Equation (26)]. The chain steps may be summarized thus:

$$R_2CH_2 + O_2 \xrightarrow{\text{HBr}} R_2C{=}O + H_2O \tag{27}$$

The hydrogen bromide-catalyzed oxidative attack on primary carbon-hydrogen bonds leads to the formation of organic acids. Just as propane required somewhat higher temperatures than isobutane for comparable amounts of reaction (190°C instead of 160°C for the cited example), so the oxidation of *ethane* is a slower reaction and the temperatures of operation are somewhat greater than those for propane (220°C *vs* 190°C). Even this temperature is far below that usually required for ethane oxidation, and, whereas there were realized yields of acetic acid equivalent to 75 per cent of the consumed oxygen (which is 85 to 90 per cent of the input), the uncatalyzed reactions at 300°C and higher lead to complex mixtures.[12] Operation at elevated pressures resulted in an increased amount of product, retardation of side reactions, and a lowering in catalyst requirements. Surface plays an important role in these chain processes and its effects are lessened by an increase in the total pressure in the system.

The reactions have been interpreted by the following mechanism:

$$R{-}\overset{\displaystyle H}{\underset{\displaystyle H}{\overset{|}{\underset{|}{C}}}}{-}H + Br \rightleftarrows R{-}\overset{\displaystyle H}{\underset{\displaystyle H}{\overset{|}{\underset{|}{C}}}}{-} + HBr \tag{28}$$

$$R{-}\overset{\displaystyle H}{\underset{\displaystyle H}{\overset{|}{\underset{|}{C}}}}{-} + O_2 \rightarrow R{-}\overset{\displaystyle H}{\underset{\displaystyle H}{\overset{|}{\underset{|}{C}}}}{-}O_2{-} \tag{29}$$

$$R{-}\overset{\displaystyle H}{\underset{\displaystyle H}{\overset{|}{\underset{|}{C}}}}{-}O_2{-} + HBr \rightarrow \left[R{-}\overset{\displaystyle H}{\underset{\displaystyle H}{\overset{|}{\underset{|}{C}}}}{-}O_2H \right] + Br \tag{30}$$

$$\left[R{-}\overset{\displaystyle H}{\underset{\displaystyle H}{\overset{|}{\underset{|}{C}}}}{-}O_2H \right] \rightarrow R{-}\overset{\displaystyle H}{\overset{|}{C}}{=}O + H_2O \tag{31}$$

There is good evidence for the dehydration shown in Equation (31), as it is known that aldehydes are among the major products of decomposition of normal alkyl hydroperoxides.[10,19] However, the expected aldehyde is, for all practical purposes, only a transitory intermediate which is presumably converted to the end product, organic acid, thus:

$$R\overset{\overset{\displaystyle H}{|}}{C}{=}O + Br \rightarrow R\overset{|}{C}{=}O + HBr \tag{32}$$

$$R\overset{|}{C}{=}O + O_2 \rightarrow R\overset{\overset{\displaystyle O_2-}{|}}{C}{=}O \tag{33}$$

$$R\overset{\overset{\displaystyle O_2-}{|}}{C}{=}O + HBr \rightarrow \left[R\overset{\overset{\displaystyle O_2H}{|}}{C}{=}O \right] + Br \tag{34}$$

The peracid in the atmosphere of hydrogen bromide or in the collection vessels is reduced:

$$\left[R\overset{\overset{\displaystyle O_2H}{|}}{C}{=}O \right] + 2HBr \rightarrow R\overset{\overset{\displaystyle O}{\|}}{C}{-}OH + Br_2 + H_2O \tag{35}$$

Step (35) as written is an over-all reaction, not a step in a chain. Actually, free bromine in considerable quantity is found in the product, in contrast to the *propane* oxidation where the final product can be formed without reduction of the peroxy compound. However, the amount of free halogen is far less than that required by the stoichiometry of Equation (35), and the major portion of it apparently reacts to form alkyl bromide which, in turn, is also converted to acid. Thus:

$$R\overset{\overset{\displaystyle H}{|}}{\underset{\underset{\displaystyle H}{|}}{C}}{-} + Br_2 \rightarrow R\overset{\overset{\displaystyle H}{|}}{\underset{\underset{\displaystyle H}{|}}{C}}{-}Br + Br \tag{36}$$

$$R\overset{\overset{\displaystyle H}{|}}{\underset{\underset{\displaystyle H}{|}}{C}}{-}Br + Br \rightleftarrows R\overset{\overset{\displaystyle Br}{|}}{\underset{\underset{\displaystyle H}{|}}{C}}{-} + HBr \tag{37}$$

$$R\overset{\overset{\displaystyle Br}{|}}{\underset{\underset{\displaystyle H}{|}}{C}}{-} + O_2 \rightarrow R\overset{\overset{\displaystyle Br}{|}}{\underset{\underset{\displaystyle H}{|}}{C}}{-}O_2{-} \tag{38}$$

$$R\overset{\overset{\displaystyle Br}{|}}{\underset{\underset{\displaystyle H}{|}}{C}}{-}O_2{-} + HBr \rightarrow \left[R\overset{\overset{\displaystyle Br}{|}}{\underset{\underset{\displaystyle H}{|}}{C}}{-}O_2H \right] + Br \tag{39}$$

$$\left[R\overset{\overset{\displaystyle Br}{|}}{\underset{\underset{\displaystyle H}{|}}{C}}{-}O_2H \right] \rightarrow \left[R\overset{\overset{\displaystyle Br}{|}}{C}{=}O \right] + H_2O \tag{40}$$

$$\left[R\overset{\overset{\displaystyle Br}{|}}{C}{=}O \right] + H_2O \rightarrow R\overset{\overset{\displaystyle O}{\|}}{C}{-}OH + HBr \tag{41}$$

The equations dealing with the oxidation of primary carbon-hydrogen bonds may be summarized by the following equation:

$$2R{-}\overset{\displaystyle H}{\underset{\displaystyle H}{\vphantom{|}C}}{-}H + 3O_2 \xrightarrow{\text{HBr}} 2R{-}\overset{\displaystyle O}{C}{-}OH + 2H_2O \tag{42}$$

and it is seen that under ideal conditions there would be no loss of hydrogen bromide, which then would function strictly as a catalyst—a condition which has been closely approximated.

In oxidations of the paraffins, products more complex than simple acids, ketones, aldehydes, alcohols or hydroperoxides are always found in the final product. The appearance of more highly oxygenated products is not necessarily a consequence of re-attack upon already existing oxygenated products. Such complex products can appear at lowest levels of conversion; in fact, Pardun, and Kuchinka,[15] conclude that compounds such as lactones are produced *"in statu nascendi."* More recent work on the fundamentals of oxidation suggest that attacks beyond the point of initial oxidation may be consecutive reactions.

Wibaut and Strang[22] have shown the liquid phase oxidation of 2,5-dimethylhexane to be productive of a dihydroperoxide which certainly is formed by the following sequence:

$$(CH_3)_2CHCH_2CH_2CH(CH_3)_2 \xrightarrow{R} (CH_3)_2CCH_2CH_2CH(CH_3)_2 \xrightarrow{O_2} \tag{43}$$

$$(CH_3)_2\underset{\underset{O-}{O}}{C}CH_2CH_2CH(CH_3)_2 \rightarrow (CH_3)_2\underset{\underset{OH}{O}}{C}CH_2CH_2C(CH_3)_2 \xrightarrow{O_2} \tag{44}$$

$$(CH_3)_2\underset{\underset{OH}{O}}{C}CH_2CH_2\underset{\underset{O-}{O}}{C}(CH_3)_2 \xrightarrow{C_8H_{18}} (CH_3)_2\underset{\underset{OH}{O}}{C}CH_2CH_2\underset{\underset{OH}{O}}{C}(CH_3)_2 \tag{45}$$

A similar sequence of reactions has been proposed by Barusch, *et al.*[2] to explain 1,3-dicarbonyl formation in the gas phase oxidation of pentane and by Bailey and Norrish[1] for the formation of substituted furans during the vapor-phase oxidation of hexane; e.g.

$$CH_3CH_2CH_2CH_2CH_2CH_3 \xrightarrow{R} CH_3\overset{|}{C}HCH_2CH_2CH_2CH_3 \xrightarrow{O_2}$$

$$CH_3\underset{\underset{OO-}{}}{C}HCH_2CH_2CH_2CH_3 \rightarrow CH_3CHCH_2CH_2CHCH_3 + OH \tag{46}$$

Thus there is a previously unsuspected configurational property of the peroxy radical favorable to internal attack.

In passing to practical applications of the foregoing theoretical considerations on the low-temperature oxidations of paraffin hydrocarbons, it can be stated that there exists a wide gap between the use of C_3—C_4 paraffins and the waxes ($>C_{20}$).* Mention should be made of the extensive operations of both Celanese Corporation and Cities Service Company on propane and the butanes to produce aliphatic acids, ketones, and the like. However, these operations are presumably carried out at much higher temperatures ($>300°C$) than this account has concerned itself with and, further, since little information about them has appeared in the literature, it is probably advisable to conclude these remarks with a brief description of the oxidation of paraffin wax as was practiced in Germany.

This technique was utilized by several concerns and was directed principally to the manufacture of acids in the C_{10}-C_{20} range for soap. It was very extensively studied by various Allied Forces investigators after the Second World War and numerous reports[7] thereon have been issued. The reader is recommended to one other compilation in particular, the book by Wittka,[23] which is replete with data, even to the extent of listing several hundred pertinent patents from various countries. The article by Pardun and Kuchinka[15] is also an excellent one, as it gives quite comprehensive distributions of products derived from oxidations using many different heavy metal catalyst combinations.

Suffice it for the present to outline the operation as practiced by the I. G. Farbenindustrie A.G. at Oppau, since all the processes were basically the same, differing in details such as sensitizer, materials of construction, and work-up procedures. The Oppau operation is singled out as one of the authors (WEV), as a FIAT investigator, personally inspected that plant and discussed it at length with the engineer in charge.

In view of the fact that soap manufacture was the primary object of paraffin wax oxidation in Germany during World War II, it is obvious that straight-chain paraffinic stocks with little or no branching were the desired base. This qualification was well met by hydrogenating Saxony brown coal at high temperature to yield a hard, straight-chain paraffin (mp 48–52°C), which was comprised essentially of C_{18}-C_{35} hydrocarbons. Another synthetic wax (or "gatsch") was derived *via* the Fischer-Tropsch process; this material had a melting point of 35–45°C and, if made at sufficiently high pressures, was only about 5 per cent branched. Indigenous paraffins derived from petroleum, both from German and American

* The autoxidation of cumene exemplifies the industrially important application of Equation (2) as it yields the hydroperoxide, which upon acid treatment gives phenol and acetone.

sources, were also used. The latter, when properly selected, was considered a very satisfactory material. It was essential that the feedstock have low sulfur and phenol content. If this condition was not met, it would be purified by one of three processes: (1) aluminum chloride treatment; (2) hydrogenation; or (3) solvent extraction. The latter, however, was not commercially practiced, although it was considered to be eminently satisfactory on an experimental scale.

At Oppau the wax was run into high aluminum towers holding 30 metric tons of wax. To this, while molten at 140°C, was added potassium permanganate to give a final concentration of between 0.1 and 0.2 per cent on the salt. To waxes less amenable to oxidation there was also added potassium and/or sodium carbonates in concentrations of 0.1 to 0.2 per cent. In other operations different initiators of the reaction were used; for example, cobalt or manganese stearates at Witten in the Ruhr and, in at least one instance, a small amount of previously oxidized wax at Magdeburg (Russian zone). These sensitizers were added to reduce the induction period, which otherwise would be invariably found. However, even with them, induction periods of approximately one hour were experienced.

After thorough incorporation of the sensitizer and while the wax was still held at 140°C, air was introduced at the bottom of the tower through a perforated ceramic or aluminum cross at a rate between 40 to 60 cubic meters per hour per ton of wax. After the oxidation had been initiated, the temperature was lowered to 100 to 115°C by means of water cooling on the outside of the tower. Pure straight-chain waxes could be oxidized at 100° at a satisfactory rate, but one with much branching or impurities would require a temperature of 115°. The oxidation times varied from 20 to 30 hours, in which one-third of the wax was converted to acids. The rate of oxidation was followed by measurement of acid and saponification values, and the oxidation was considered to have proceeded to a sufficient extent with attainment of an acid number of 70 and a saponification number of 120 to 150. The gas stream emergent from the top of the tower passed through a cooler and was washed countercurrently with water, yielding a two-phase mixture; the oily layer was recycled and the aqueous condensate, comprising approximately 10 per cent formic acid, 10 per cent acetic acid, 10 per cent C_3–C_5 acids, 2 per cent lactones, and the remainder water, was sold as such.

To separate the fatty acids from the unreacted paraffin* 35 per cent aqueous sodium hydroxide was added to the reaction mixture, which was

---

* Efforts to remove the manganese had been attempted by various extraction methods; these not only failed in their original objective but also caused excessive loss of product.

then led into an autoclave operating at 120–150°C. wherein an aqueous lower layer separated from the unreacted paraffin which was returned to the oxidation unit. The aqueous phase was then fed by a high-pressure pump through a series of hairpin finned tubes, which were gas fired to temperatures of 270 to 320°C and pressures of 100 to 120 atmospheres for a residense time of 10 minutes. In this stabilization step hydroxy acids were dehydrated to unsaturated compounds of which there were approximately 10 per cent in the finished fractions. Following this treatment the soap solution passed through pressure releases and the temperature dropped to 150 to 160°C and the pressure to 5 atmospheres. In a second series of finned tubes the temperature was again raised, this time to 300 to 350°C and the water and unsaponifiable material vaporized in iron vessels attached to the end of this second series of tubes. At the top of this unit the vapors passed overhead and were condensed and returned to the oxidation units after removal of water. The molten soap at 300°C was fed from the vessel and mixed with 80°C water to give 30 to 40 per cent soap solution, which in turn passed to the hydrolyzer, a tank lined with acid-resistant tile, into which the stoichiometric amount of aqueous sulfuric acid was fed at a temperature of 70°C. The crude fatty acids were washed with water to remove the salt and a portion of the remaining manganese.

At this point the crude acid consisted of C_3–C_{25} materials, and these were fed through a preheater and then separated by distillation in four continuous columns. The fractions obtained were as follows:

> (1)   To 150°C, 4 mm, C_3–C_{10}
> (2)   150–250°C, 4 mm, C_{10}–C_{18}
> (3)   250–270°C, 4 mm, C_{17}–C_{20}
> (4)   270–300°C, 4 mm, C_{20}–C_{25}

In the distillation a small amount of water was added to break surface films and thus speed distillation. During this separation any acids in the off-gases from the columns were washed out countercurrently with water at 5°C.

Approximate yields were as follows:

Per 100 kg of paraffin oxidized:	Fischer "Gatsch"	ex brown coal
Aqueous condensate	25.0 kg	20.0
C_3–C_{10}	12.1	7.6
C_{10}–C_{20}	46.1	50.2
C_{20}–C_{25}	5.7	1.8
Residue	7.1	17.1
	96.0	96.7

Although, as stated previously, this operation was directed principally toward soap manufacture, there were a number of other uses. These were as follows:

(1) *Aqueous condensate*—used in the leather industry for dehairing.
(2) C_3–C_{10} fraction:
    (a) used during the war with poly alcohols for plasticizers
    (b) reduced to alcohols for plasticizers
    (c) in alkyd type resins
    (d) in foaming agents
    (e) reacted in liquid phase in the presence of iron to cause a coupling reaction, making ketones with evolution of water and carbon dioxide; these ketones were hydrogenated to alcohols for special uses
(3) C_{10}–C_{20} fraction:
    (a) in soap
    (b) a small amount to synthetic fat
    (c) sulfonates
    (d) a special fraction, C_{10}–C_{15}, was used exclusively for making soap for emulsion polymerization in making Buna rubber
(4) C_{20}–C_{25} fraction:
    (a) for greases
    (b) special lubricants for extrusion presses
(5) *Residue*
    (a) bonding agent in sand for castings
    (b) used in making a heat-resistant lacquer
    (c) Grease

The crude mixed fatty acids prior to distillation were used to some extent at textile mills for dispersing and hydrolyzing the fibers.

In conclusion, it is of interest to note that peroxidic materials were not produced in detectable amounts. It should be emphasized, also, that the products were not pure aliphatic acids but were mixtures containing unsaturated linkages, keto and hydroxy groups as well as a certain amount of lactones. While with extensive purifications it was possible to make a fairly white and attractive soap, the usual product was dark brown and highly odorous, requiring the use of masking agents, which gave a product which, to some noses, was more offensive than the original soap.

References

1. Bailey, H. C., and Norrish, R. G. W., *Proc. Roy. Soc.*, **212,** 311 (1952).
2. Barusch, M. R., Neu, J. T., Payne, J. Q., and Thomas, J. R., *Ind. Eng. Chem.*, **43,** 2766 (1951).
3. Bateman, L., and Hughes, H., *J. Chem. Soc.*, 4594 (1952).
4. Bates, J. R., and Spence, R., *J. Am. Chem. Soc.*, **53,** 1689 (1931).
5. Bell, E. R., Raley, J. H., Rust, F. F., Seubold, F. H., and Vaughan, W. E., Faraday Soc. Discussion No. 10, "Hydrocarbons," **1951,** 242.
6. Benton, J. L., and Wirth, M. M., *Nature*, **171,** 269 (1953).

7. See, for example, BIOS 274; 274 (addendum); 748; 805; CIOS XXVIII–35; XXXI–79; FIAT 213; 362.
8. Chamberlain, E. A. C., and Walsh, A. D., *Rev. Inst. franc. Pétrole Ann. Combust. Liq.*, **4**, 301 (1949).
9. Gray, J. A., *J. Chem. Soc.*, **1952**, 3150.
10. Harris, E. J., *Proc. Roy. Soc. (London)*, **173a**, 126 (1936).
11. Ivanov, K. I., Savinova, V. K., and Zhakhovskaya, V. P., *Doklady Akad. Nauk. U. S. S. R.*, **72**, 903 (1950).
12. Jost, W., "Explosions- und Verbrennungsvorgänge in Gasen," pp 416–21, Berlin, Julius Springer, 1939.
13. Milas, N. A., and Surgenor, D., *J. Am. Chem. Soc.*, **68**, 205, 643 (1946).
14. Norrish, R. G. W., *Rev. Inst. franc. Pétrole Ann. Combust. Liq.*, **4**, 288 (1949).
15. Pardun, H., and Kuchinka, R., *Erdöl u. Kohle*, **3**, 109 (1950).
16. Pope, J. C., Dykstra, F. J., and Edgar, G., *J. Am. Chem. Soc.*, **51**, 2203 (1929).
17. Raley, J. H., Porter, L. M., Rust, F. F., and Vaughan, W. E., *J. Am. Chem. Soc.*, **73**, 15 (1951).
18. Raley, J. H., Rust, F. F., and Vaughan, W. E., *J. Am. Chem. Soc.*, **70**, 88 (1948).
19. Rieche, A., "Alkylperoxyde und Ozonide," Leipzig, Steinkopf, 1931.
20. Rust, F. F., and Vaughan, W. E., *Ind. Eng. Chem.*, **41**, 2595 (1949).
21. Seubold, F. H., Rust, F. F., and Vaughan, W. E., *J. Am. Chem. Soc.*, **73**, 18 (1951)
22. Wibaut, J. P., and Strang, A., *Proc. Acad. Sci. Amsterdam*, Series B, **54**, 102 (1951).
23. Wittka, F., "Gewinnung der höheren Fettsäuren durch Oxydation der Kohlenwasserstoffe," Leipzig, J. A. Barth, 1940; also lithoprinted by Edwards Bros., Inc., Ann Arbor, Michigan, 1945.

CHAPTER 34

OLEFIN AUTOXIDATION

R. H. ROSENWALD

Universal Oil Products Co., Riverside, Ill.

Olefin Oxidation

Hydrocarbons are susceptible to attack by oxygen. The ease and extent of this attack are determined by a number of factors, among which are nature of the hydrocarbon, the presence of certain foreign materials, and the conditions (i.e., temperature, oxygen pressure, hydrocarbon concentration) under which oxygen is brought into contact with the hydrocarbon. In numerous cases oxidation is undesirable, leading to deterioration in the properties of the hydrocarbon-containing product.

The object of this chapter is to summarize the present-day concept of the chemistry involved in the oxidation process, particularly of olefins, including only oxidations in the liquid phase and at temperatures not above about 100°C. The discussion of oxidation within the above limits broadly considers some of the basic aspects of the process, but with emphasis on those points believed pertinent to the problem of gum formation in gasoline. Such oxidation is commonly referred to as autoxidation.

The union of oxygen and hydrocarbon is indeed a complex process, composed of a number of individual steps which lead to a variety of products. However, in spite of such apparent derangement of the overall process, there are several features common to all oxidation reactions to be considered here. First, oxygen is initially incorporated into the hydrocarbon molecule by formation of a peroxide of which there are two principal types, the hydroperoxide and the disubstituted peroxide. The formation of these two types of peroxides can be schematically pictured as follows:

$$C_xH_y + O_2 \rightarrow C_xH_{y-1}OOH$$
$$nC_xH_y + nO_2 \rightarrow (-C_xH_yOO-)_n$$

In the first reaction, oxygen can be considered as entering into a substitution reaction to form a hydroperoxide, whereas in the second reaction a type of addition leads to a disubstituted peroxide.

The second general feature of hydrocarbon oxidation is that a chain

TABLE 1

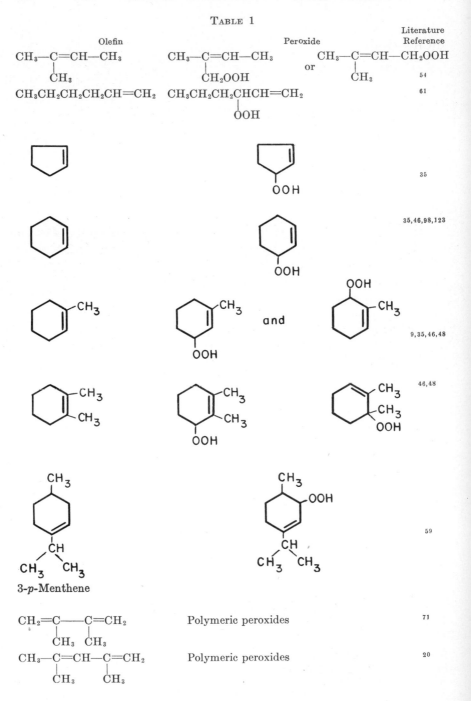

Olefin	Peroxide	Literature Reference

3-p-Menthene

Polymeric peroxides [71]

Polymeric peroxides [20]

TABLE 1 (*Continued*)

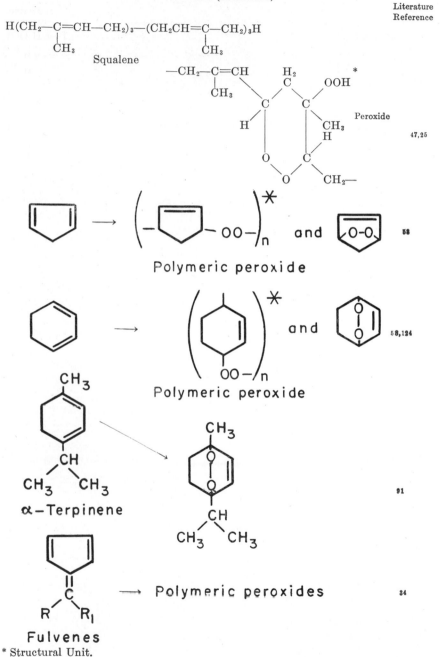

H(CH₂—C=CH—CH₂)₃—(CH₂CH=C—CH₂)₃H

Squalene

Peroxide

47,25

Polymeric peroxide

58

Polymeric peroxide

58,124

α−Terpinene

91

Fulvenes

Polymeric peroxides

34

* Structural Unit.

TABLE 1 (Continued)

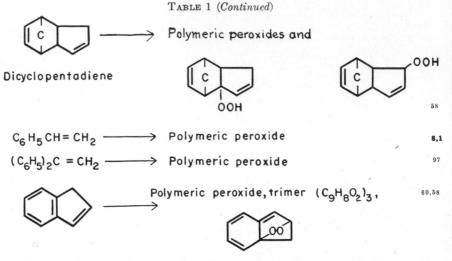

Dicyclopentadiene → Polymeric peroxides and

[58]

$C_6H_5CH=CH_2$ ⟶ Polymeric peroxide [8,1]

$(C_6H_5)_2C=CH_2$ ⟶ Polymeric peroxide [97]

⟶ Polymeric peroxide, trimer $(C_9H_8O_2)_3$, [60,58]

mechanism is operative. Explanation of the course of oxidation on the basis of a chain mechanism has been notably successful in conjunction with the concept of free radicals, a concept which defines the intermediate chain carriers. On these two general premises an attempt will be made to describe the over-all oxidation process.

Peroxides from Olefins. The presence of a double bond in a hydrocarbon molecule increases the susceptibility of attack by oxygen. The incorporation of oxygen into the molecule occurs via formation of a peroxide, a fact crudely comprehended by early investigators.[44] The isolation of peroxide materials as the initial oxidation product has been experimentally established in a number of specific examples. A listing of such examples is presented in Table 1.

The two main types of peroxides, namely, the hydroperoxides and the disubstituted peroxides, are recognized among the oxidation products of the olefins listed. In order to differentiate more clearly the types of peroxides, the following examples are briefly considered.

The most thoroughly studied example of hydroperoxide formation from an olefin is the autoxidation of cyclohexene to form 2-cyclohexenyl hydroperoxide.

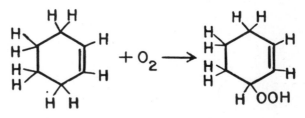

The unpromoted oxidation proceeds at a comparatively slow rate to form a well characterized, distillable hydroperoxide, the structure of which has been definitely established. Owing to the unstable nature of the hydroperoxide, oxidation products other than the hydroperoxide may result, particularly during advanced stages of oxidation. This instability is also evident in the distillation of the peroxide under high vacuum; a nonvolatile residue (a dimer) may remain from this thermal treatment.[46]

In the above example, the hydroperoxide results by substitution of an oxygen molecule on the activated carbon atom adjacent to the double bond. In the substitution process, the double bond may shift but is not destroyed. In the formation of disubstituted peroxides, the oxidation process involves a direct union of the oxygen with the double bond. Such is the case with styrene, which forms a polymer by a process similar to copolymerization. The polymeric peroxide is characterized as a non-volatile, resin-like polymer composed of the following structural unit.

$$nC_6H_5CH{=}CH_2 + nO_2 \rightarrow \left(-\overset{\displaystyle C_6H_5}{\underset{\displaystyle H}{\underset{|}{\overset{|}{C}}}}{-}CH_2{-}OO{-} \right)_n$$

As observed in Table 1, hydrocarbons possessing a double bond active for most addition reactions are prone to produce the polymeric peroxides. The formation of polymeric peroxides actually is a normal and common phenomenon, broadly described by a number of investigators but explicitly characterized by few.

Included in Table 1 are examples of 1–4 addition of oxygen to a conjugated system as in the case of 1,3-cyclohexadiene.

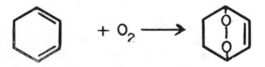

The extent of such reaction is small and represents only a minor and secondary portion of the reaction.

Each hydrocarbon need not oxidize in one definite manner. One observes that several types of peroxides can be isolated from a single olefin. Furthermore, a polyolefin can produce a single oxidation product containing both types of peroxide linkages in a single molecule; such an example is the diperoxide from squalene. Thus, oxidation products in general are often heterogeneous, not only due to the diverse peroxides formed, but also to decomposition products of these peroxides.

Kinetics. A study of the kinetics of oxidation concerns two principal factors: the over-all rate of the reaction, and the intermediates involved in converting hydrocarbons to the final oxidation products. This conversion is not a one-step reaction, dependent on a single rate-controlling reaction, but is a sequence of reactions subject to a number of rate-controlling factors. Since the oxidation reaction is composed of a series of individual steps, attention of investigators has centered on efforts to segregate each step and then to interpret the final results in terms of the information gained about each component reaction.

The sequence of the reactions to produce a hydroperoxide has been identified as follows:

(A) Initiation   (1) $RH \xrightarrow{k_1} R^\cdot$

(B) Propagation   (2) $R^\cdot + O_2 \xrightarrow{k_2} ROO^\cdot$

                    (3) $ROO^\cdot + RH \xrightarrow{k_3} ROOH + R^\cdot$

(C) Termination   (4) $R^\cdot + R^\cdot \xrightarrow{k_4} RR$

                    (5) $ROO^\cdot + R^\cdot \xrightarrow{k_5} ROOR$

                    (6) $ROO^\cdot + ROO^\cdot \xrightarrow{k_6} ?$

RH is the hydrocarbon oxidized and the dot signifies one electron deficiency of the fragment to form a free radical. One recognizes in this sequence the three major factors which compose a chain reaction, namely, initiation, propagation, and termination. The oxidation is initiated by some process, have vaguely pictured as abstraction of a hydrogen atom from the hydrocarbon molecule RH to produce $R^\cdot$. The free radical thus produced reacts with oxygen to form a peroxy free radical, $ROO^\cdot$, which in turn propagates the chain by abstracting a hydrogen atom from the hydrocarbon. The chains as started are subject to termination reactions by which products are formed that cannot propagate the chain. The products for two of the three possible termination reactions are hypothetical but possible compounds which can be formed.

The oxidation of an olefin to form a disubstituted peroxide is controlled by the same three factors. An example of such an oxidation is as follows:

(A) Initiation   (1) $C{=}C \xrightarrow{k_1} C{-}C^\cdot$

(B) Propagation   (2) $C{-}C^\cdot + O_2 \xrightarrow{k_2} CC{-}OO^\cdot$

                    (3) $CCOO^\cdot + C{=}C \xrightarrow{k_3} CC{-}OO{-}CC^\cdot$

(C) Termination   (4) $CC^\cdot + CC^\cdot \xrightarrow{k_4} CC{-}CC$

                    (5) $CCOO^\cdot + CC^\cdot \xrightarrow{k_5} CC{-}OO{-}CC$

                    (6) $CCOO^\cdot + CCOO^\cdot \xrightarrow{k_6} ?$

The oxidation in this case is comparable to a copolymerization reaction involving two monomers (olefin and oxygen) to produce a polymer. Again the sequence can be resolved into the three principal component reactions of initiation, propagation, and termination.

The essential role of the three basic reactions (initiation, propagation, and termination) as the rate-controlling factors is depicted by the following consideration. The function of the initiation step is to supply active centers, each of which instigates a recurring cycle of reaction. In general, the over-all oxidation rate is a function of the number of active centers formed per unit time (initiation rate $= r_i$) and the number of times each cycle is repeated. The last factor is the kinetic chain length (L). Thus, the product of the rate of polymerization and the chain length describes the over-all oxidation rate.

$$\text{Oxidation rate} = r_i \times L$$

However, the chain length L is equal to the rate of propagation (r_p) divided by the rate of termination (r_t), so the generalized equation becomes:

$$\text{oxidation rate} = \frac{r_i r_p}{r_t}$$

Equations which have been found to describe kinetically an oxidation reaction are fundamentally derivatives of this parent form.

Examination of the kinetic aspects of oxidation reactions has revealed pertinent information as to the basic nature of the entire process.[21] Kinetic analysis has identified the intermediates involved with a discernment impossible solely by inspection of the final oxidation products. The equations representing the chain cycle have been established as a result of kinetic analysis.

The rate of oxygen absorption at oxygen pressures of about 100 mm or higher follows the kinetic expression:

$$-\frac{d[O_2]}{dt} = k_3 k_6^{-\frac{1}{2}}[RH]r_i^{\frac{1}{2}}$$

for a number of hydrocarbons such as cyclohexene, methylcyclohexene, 1-octene, dihydromyrcene and decalin. The k factors represent specific velocity constants for the accompanying equations, $[RH]$ is the concentration of the hydrocarbon, and r_i is the rate of initiation.[12,13]

The oxidation rate shows a square-root dependency on the rate of initiation owing to the bimolecular nature of the termination reaction. The termination step is that of reaction (6), whereas reactions (4) and (5) are not of consequence. For the propagation step, reaction (2), $R^{\cdot} + O_2$, is not rate-controlling but rather reaction (3), $ROO^{\cdot} + RH$, determines the time needed for each cycle. Of the chain carriers, the $ROO^{\cdot}$ radical is present in comparatively high concentration (due to stability factors as indicated in Table 2), and consequently the rate equations for propagation and termination are functions of the concentration of this intermediate.

A decrease in oxygen pressure to a value of 1 mm or less of mercury changes the relationship to that of:

$$-\frac{d[O_2]}{dt} = k_2 k_4^{-\frac{1}{2}}[O_2]r_i^{\frac{1}{2}}$$

The same dependency is found for the initiating rate, but now the propagation step is controlled by reaction (2), $R^{\cdot} + O_2$, owing to the low concentration of oxygen. Likewise, the termination step is a function of the concentration of the $R^{\cdot}$ intermediate, although reaction (5), $ROO^{\cdot} + R^{\cdot}$, may be involved at pressures of 1 to 5 mm.[11]

TABLE 2

Temperature, °C	Cyclohexene 15	Tetralin 25
Rate of Oxidation, mole L^{-1} sec^{-1}	4.25×10^{-6}	4.03^{-6}
Chain length	9.5	86
Lifetime per chain cycle, sec	0.17	0.86
Lifetime of ROO°, sec	0.02	0.01
Lifetime of R°, sec	—	2.75×10^{-5}
k_2, gmole^{-1} L sec^{-1}	ca 10^6	6.76×10^7
k_3, gmole^{-1} L sec^{-1}	0.65	13.3
k_6, gmole^{-1} L sec^{-1}	0.95×10^6	0.215×10^6

The preceding kinetic formulas are derived using only two chain carriers, namely, the $R^{\cdot}$ and $ROO^{\cdot}$ fragments. Kinetically, no differentiation can be made between hydroperoxide formation or dialkyl peroxide formation; both types of peroxidation in case of squalene and 2,6-dimethyl-2,6-octadiene follow the same kinetic expression.[26]

The oxidation rate equations as presented express the dependency of the rate on certain variables. A more complete analysis of the over-all reaction includes not only the identification of the chain carriers and the end products, but also the lifetime and concentration of these intermediates. Since the concentration of these intermediate fragments in a liquid phase generally does not exceed 10^{-7} mole per liter, indirect calculations of concentration must be made.[77]

The lifetime of a kinetic chain (τ) is determined by the concentration of the chain carrier, $[ROO^{\cdot}]$ in case of oxidation at high oxygen pressure, and the rate of initiation (r_i),

$$\tau = \frac{[ROO^{\cdot}]}{r_i}$$

As the reaction reaches a steady state, the rates of radical formation and removal are equal. The termination rate (r_t) is a function of the square of the concentration of $ROO^{\cdot}$ and of k_6:

$$r_t = r_i = k_6[ROO^{\cdot}]^2$$

Substitution of values for $[ROO^{\cdot}]$ gives:

$$\tau = \frac{1}{\sqrt{k_6 r_i}}$$

The use of photochemical technique permits oxidations with known values of r_i; the use of either the rotating sector method[14] or photochemical pre- and after-effects[11,13] allows estimation of the values of τ.

By means similar to those briefly described, the oxidation process has been kinetically characterized with a select group of olefins. Table 2 presents data so obtained with cyclohexene, along with data for the oxidation of tetralin at 100 mm of oxygen pressure.[6]

The rate-controlling role of reaction corresponding to k_3 is evident by comparing the large value for k_2 (ca 10^{+6} for cyclohexene) with k_3 (value 0.65). These values substantiate the correctness of the kinetic interpretation of the oxidation process.

The rate of oxidation of an olefin or an olefin mixture is a function of the individual component parts, namely, initiation, propagation and termination. Those factors which regulate these three component parts are briefly considered.

Initiation. *Self-Initiation.* The oxidation of a highly purified sample of olefin requires formation of active centers or free radicals to start the initial chain. This ability, at present undefined, is an inherent property of each olefin. Certain active olefins, e.g., polyenes, are particularly capable of generating these initial centers and, hence, show a high degree of oxidizability. The initiation process probably involves a bimolecular process between the olefin and oxygen,[12] and hence oxygen concentration probably is a factor in this rate-controlling step, as experimentally established with aldehydes.[32]

Sensitized Oxidations. The over-all oxidation rate as observed is generally not governed by self-initiation, particularly at low temperatures with olefins not highly active. The over-all initiation rate is regulated by free-radical-forming components or conditions. The free radicals thus formed prompt a sensitized oxidation which dominates the slow self-induced reaction.

Sensitization is achieved by the addition of free-radical-forming materials. The initiation rate thus obtained can be estimated with some degree of accuracy, and this procedure has been consequently used in investigations of the kinetics of reaction. The additions of benzoyl peroxide,[22,23,26,27] azobis(isobutyronitrile),[15] and linoleate hydroperoxide,[23,27] have been kinetically studied as to initiation of oxidation. Benzoyl peroxide and azobis(isobutyronitrile) decompose essentially in a monomolecular fashion to liberate free radicals:

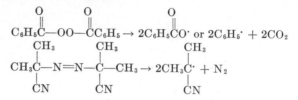

In view of the square-root dependency of the rate of oxidation on the initiation rate, the rate of a sensitized oxidation is accordingly dependent on the square root of the concentration of these initiators.

$$r_1 = k_1 \text{ [Initiator]}$$

$$-\frac{d[O_2]}{dt} = k_3 \frac{[RH]r_1^{1/2}}{k_6^{1/2}} = k_3 \frac{[RH](k_1 \text{ [Initiator]})^{1/2}}{k_6^{1/2}}$$

In case of an initiator, the decomposition of which is a bimolecular process, the rate of oxidation is linearly proportional to the initiation concentration.

The dependency of oxidation rate on initiator concentration is appraised by determining the slope of the line obtained by plotting log concentration *vs* log of rate of oxidation.

Autocatalysis has been a characteristic commonly associated with autoxidation. Autocatalysis occurs owing to the labile nature of the peroxide formed. The peroxide as generated in the oxidation process is subject to a decomposition depending on the properties of the peroxide and condition of oxidation.

A slow thermal decomposition occurs with both types of peroxides to form, from each molecule of peroxide, two free radicals,

$$ROOH \rightarrow RO\cdot + \cdot OH$$
$$ROOR \rightarrow 2RO\cdot$$

each of which is considered able to instigate new chains. Consequently, the oxidation rate accelerates with duration because of the sensitizing nature of the product.

In general, the dialkyl peroxides possess a relatively high stability and occasionally the rate of formation of new centers is usually small. Consequently, autocatalysis is inconspicuous or even lacking.

The oxidation of most olefins, e.g., cyclohexene, forms hydroperoxides, and autocatalysis is observed. The rate of such oxidation, accelerated because of the phenomenon of degenerative branching, is described by the equation

$$\text{rate} = Ae^{-\phi t}$$

where A and ϕ are constants and t is the time.[92]

Irradiation, particularly in the ultraviolet spectra, of an olefin mixture is an effective means to initiate oxidation. According to the laws of photochemistry, the absorption of one quantum of radiation activates one molecule, thereby starting a chain. In order for initiation to occur, absorption is a prerequisite. The conjugated polyenes and aromatic compounds absorb light in the ultraviolet range, but simple olefins are poor absorbers. Irradiation in the range of 2000 to 4000 Å is effective in accelerating oxidation, even with the simple olefins, owing to a photolysis of hydroperoxides, thereby liberating free radicals.[10] Such photolysis is a means to accentuate the autocatalytic nature of the oxidation reaction.

Ultraviolet absorption can be assured by the addition of certain dyes. This effect is due to the ability of the dye molecule to become activated by absorption of irradiation and thereby initiate chains.[6]

The rate of oxidation is proportional to the square root of light intensity. The plot of the log of intensity against log of oxidation rate gives a line with a slope of 0.5.

The presence of certain heavy metal compounds, such as copper and cobalt salts, exerts a strong accelerating effect on the rate of oxidation. This acceleration is due to an increase in rate of initiation as brought about by the decomposition of hydroperoxides. The liberation of free radicals from hydroperoxides is generally conceived as follows, where M^+ represents a metal in a lower state of oxidation.[65]

$$ROOH + M^+ \rightarrow RO^{\cdot} + M^{++} + OH^-$$

or,[86]

$$ROOH + M^+ \rightarrow RO^- + M^{++} + {\cdot}OH$$

Initiation is due to the fragment liberated, either $RO^{\cdot}$ or ${\cdot}OH$.

Initiation can be also brought about by the reducing properties of the hydroperoxide. t-Butyl hydroperoxide is decomposed by certain cobalt salts to yield a peroxy free radical that can undergo reactions typical of this species.[69] The alternating reduction

$$ROOH + Co^{+++} \rightarrow ROO^{\cdot} + Co^{++} + H^+$$

and oxidation of heavy metal cations by hydroperoxides is thus able to prompt an efficient initiation.

This explanation for heavy metal catalysis is applicable to the autoxidation of saturated hydrocarbons[119] and trimethylethylene in a solution of acetic acid.[17]

The extent of heavy-metal-accelerated oxidations depends on the metal employed, the concentration, the hydrocarbon oxidized, and the nature of the anion of the metal salt.[52]

An unusual metal-catalyzed oxidation without hydroperoxide decomposition is the oxidation of tetrahydrocarbazole in the presence of a platinum catalyst.[121]

In order for sensitization by metals to occur, the presence of hydroperoxides is believed essential; the oxidations of olefins that form exclusively disubstituted peroxides (e.g., styrene) is not subject to normal catalysis by copper salts.

A continued increase in the rate of initiation brings about a maximum rate of oxidation, beyond which further initiation is without effect in increasing the over-all oxidation rate. This maximum rate has been shown to be a function of temperature alone, and at sufficiently high temperatures is not dependent on irradiation or added activators which decompose hydroperoxides.[106]

The over-all energy of activation (E) for oxidations described by the kinetic equation:

$$-\frac{d[O_2]}{dt} = k_3 k_6^{-\frac{1}{2}}[RH]r_i^{\frac{1}{2}}$$

is equal to $E_3 + \frac{1}{2}E_1 - \frac{1}{2}E_6$, where E_3, E_1 and E_6 refer to activation energies for the propagation, initiation, and termination steps, respectively. The value of E_1 is subject to wide variations and is dependent on the particular initiating method employed. For olefin oxidations initiated by benzoyl peroxide, the over-all activation energy is in the range of 22 to 28 kcal/mole.[22] The activation energy for the decomposition of benzoyl peroxide is 31 kcal/mole, and the energy for the termination process ($ROO^{\cdot} + ROO^{\cdot}$) can be considered as zero. The value for E_3 is consequently in the range of about 6 to 12 Kcal/mole, depending on the structure of the olefin. With a photochemical initiation process, the value of E_1 is zero and the over-all activation energy drops to a value for the propagation step.

Propagation. According to the oxidation scheme, the propagation step in the presence of sufficient oxygen primarily concerns the more stable peroxy free radical. The selectivity of this radical in chain propagation is of prime importance in determining the nature of the oxidation product. Addition of this intermediate to the double bond leads to polymeric peroxides, whereas abstraction of hydrogen from an active methylene group leads to hydroperoxide formation. Thermochemical consideration reveals that these two reactions proceed with comparable facility energetically.[24] Those active olefins, such as conjugated dienes which are prone to enter into polymerization reactions, tend to give peroxides of the polymeric type. In some cases lack of the methylenic function or steric conditions may direct the propagation step, but no generalization has been offered to decide which type of reaction will predominate. The place of oxygen attack may be dependent on the temperature; higher temperatures (above 80°C) favor the direct attack of the double bond.[5]

The effect of structure variations in olefins of the type:

$$H—C—C=C$$
$$123$$

has been investigated as to the effect on the specific velocity constant k_3 for the propagation reaction.[22] The values obtained refer to the reaction in which the hydrogen atom on carbon 1 is abstracted by the peroxy free radical. It was found that:

(1) Replacing one or two hydrogen atoms at 1 or 3 by an alkyl group increases k_3 by 3.3^m, where m is the total number of alkyl groups introduced. Replacement of a hydrogen atom on 2 has no effect.

(2) Replacement of a hydrogen atom at 1 by a $C=C—$ group increases k_3 107-fold.

(3) The k_3 value of a methylene group contained in a cyclic structure is 1.7 times greater than that contained in the analogous, acyclic olefinic group.

The above findings are in agreement with the general rule that substitution occurs with least difficulty on a tertiary carbon atom and with greatest difficulty on a primary carbon atom.

Hydroperoxide formation is often accompanied by a double bond shift, as recorded in Table 1 in case of dimethylcyclohexene. This shift is explained as due to the rearrangement during the propagating step of the intermediate free radical in the mobile allyl system.

$$C=C—C\cdot \longleftrightarrow \cdot C—C=C$$
$$\downarrow \text{2 steps} \qquad \downarrow \text{2 steps}$$
$$\underset{\underset{OOH}{|}}{C=C—C} \qquad \underset{\underset{OOH}{|}}{C—C=C}$$

In case of a 1,4 diene, the intermediate stabilizes itself by formation of a conjugated system. Thus, the oxidation of a 1,4 diene (*cis, cis*) in

$$C=C—\underset{\cdot}{C}—C=C \rightarrow C=C—C=C—C\cdot \text{ or } \cdot C—C=C—C=C$$

case of a fatty acid ester gives under controlled conditions at least a 90 per cent yield of a conjugated (*cis, trans*) hydroperoxide.[82]

Termination. *Self-Termination.* Reactions expressed by Equation (4) and (6) are responsible for chain termination in the uninhibited process. In the presence of sufficient oxygen (pressures about 50 mm or higher), the interaction of two $ROO\cdot$ radicals leads to products incapable of continuing the chain. The product of this interaction has not been established, but may involve reaction as follows:[6]

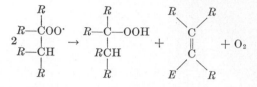

The value of k_6, the specific velocity constant, is rather insensitive to wide structural differences in the hydrocarbon.[13] In the oxidation of 1-octene, cyclohexene, 1-methylcyclohexene, dihydromyrcene, and digeranyl, the value of k_6 (10^{-6} mole^{-1} 1. sec^{-1}) was found to be of equal magnitude for all compounds.

The value of k_6 is also insensitive to temperature, for the interaction between the two radicals proceeds with little or no activation energy.

Termination by Antioxidants. The rate of oxidation can be markedly reduced by the addition of antioxidants. It is evident that reduction in rate can be accomplished by a proper adjustment in rates of the three component reactions involved. The addition of antioxidants primarily affects the termination rate and, consequently, chain length.

Of the two transient intermediates involved in the chain, the more stable peroxy free radical is the more vulnerable link in the cycle. Since compounds that serve as effective antioxidants generally, but not invariably, possess an extractable hydrogen, the following reaction appears as a reasonable chain-terminating step:

$$ROO \cdot + A H \rightarrow k_7 ROOH + A \cdot$$

The antioxidant AH forms a radical $A \cdot$ which is unable to continue the chain. Chain termination is achieved with simultaneous formation of a hydroperoxide, which is a potential initiator, but only after a fission process has occurred. By the addition of an effective antioxidant in suitable concentration, the self-termination reaction involving two radicals is replaced by a new reaction, as indicated above.

Observations have been made to substantiate the above terminating reaction. Reactions between phenolic compounds and the peroxy free radical have been proposed as appropriate by a number of investigators.[6,26,27,28,33,125]

According to the preceding scheme for inhibition, the ease of abstraction of the hydrogen atom is a critical factor in determining the efficacy of a compound as an antioxidant. Indeed, a relationship is found to indicate that the oxidation-reduction potential or the critical oxidation potential[49] is an index of antioxidant activity of compounds possessing either amino or hydroxyl functions.[35,38,41,42 a,75]

The preceding reaction is a direct and reasonable means to explain inhibition of oxidation. However, inhibition most likely is not achieved because of one specific reaction. Inhibition effected by aromatic amines probably involves other simultaneous side reactions.[9]

The rate of oxygen absorption in the presence of a phenolic type of antioxidant, AH, has been shown to follow an equation of the type:

$$ -\left(\frac{d[O_2]}{dt}\right)_{\text{Inhib.}} = \frac{k_3[RH]r_1}{[AH]k_7} $$

where k_7 is the reaction constant for the terminating reaction of the peroxy radical and the antioxidant.[6,26,27] According to this equation, the inhibition process does not alter the rate of initiation, but does reduce the chain length. Consequently, the effect of antioxidants is most evident in autoxidations involving a low rate of initiation and a long kinetic chain length.

Peroxide Decomposition. Compounds other than peroxides are often detected and isolated as end products from the autoxidation reaction. The literature records numerous instances of the formation of such products as mono- and polyhydric alcohols, aldehydes, ketones, olefin oxides, esters, and acids. General methods for analysis of these products have been suggested.[70]

These products are derived from the initially formed peroxide. The chemical properties of the peroxides are therefore factors of importance in any attempt to account for the nature of the final oxidation product. A number of articles have summarized present-day knowledge of peroxides, particularly alkyl hydroperoxides.[36,55,74,84,85,100]

The oxygenated products from autoxidation can be considered as arising from the following types of peroxide reactions, namely, thermal decomposition, catalytic decomposition, and olefin oxidation. As a rule a number of products are formed by autoxidation (via peroxidation), and no single reaction can be identified as responsible for the type of product. The following discussion indicates reactions which may be involved.

Thermal Decomposition. Peroxides are subject to a thermal decomposition which leads to diverse products. The weakest bond in the peroxide is the O—O linkage,[80] and consequently is the place of rupture in this decomposition. Fission produces two free radicals:

$$ ROOH \rightarrow RO\cdot + \cdot OH $$
$$ ROOR \rightarrow 2RO\cdot $$

The ultimate compounds isolated depend on the decomposition products of the resulting free radicals or reactions induced by these free radicals.

In general, the stability of both dialkyl peroxides and alkyl hydroperoxides is dependent on the size and configuration of the hydrocarbon group(s). Primary alkyl groups tend to give minimum stability, and tertiary alkyl groups favor a comparatively high stability.

The alkoxy free radical, liberated by the peroxide decomposition, can react in varied ways, as indicated by the following tabulation.

(1) The $RO^{\cdot}$ radical abstracts hydrogen from a hydrocarbon molecule (R_1H) to form an alcohol:[45,66,67]

$$RO^{\cdot} + R_1H \rightarrow ROH + R_1^{\cdot}$$

(2) The alkoxy radical can form a carbonyl compound with ejection of a smaller free radical, as in the decomposition of α-cumyl hydroperoxide.[65,66] The active methyl radical abstracts a hydrogen atom from the solvent RH:

$$
\begin{array}{c}
\quad\quad CH_3 \\
\quad\quad | \\
C_6H_5\overset{|}{\underset{|}{C}}O^{\cdot} \rightarrow C_6H_5\overset{|}{C}CH_3 + CH_3^{\cdot} \\
\quad\quad CH_3 \quad\quad\quad O
\end{array}
$$

$$CH_3^{\cdot} + RH \rightarrow CH_4 + R^{\cdot}$$

(3) The free radical adds to an olefin, followed by further reaction in case of butadiene.[63]

$$RO^{\cdot} + CH_2{=}CH{-}CH{=}CH_2 \rightarrow ROCH_2CH{=}CHCH_2^{\cdot} \rightarrow \text{dimer}$$

(4) An induced decomposition of hydroperoxides is effected, with the formation of carbonyl derivatives. Two such examples involving chain reactions are as follows:[65,67]

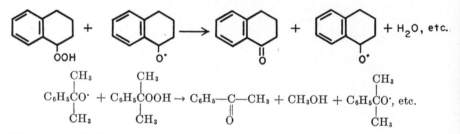

$$
C_6H_5\overset{CH_3}{\underset{CH_3}{C}}O^{\cdot} + C_6H_5\overset{CH_3}{\underset{CH_3}{C}}OOH \rightarrow C_6H_5{-}\overset{O}{\overset{\|}{C}}{-}CH_3 + CH_3OH + C_6H_5\overset{CH_3}{\underset{CH_3}{C}}O^{\cdot}, \text{ etc.}
$$

The thermal decomposition of peroxides in the presence of olefins is, to a large extent, a process involving induced fission.

A further oxidation of carbonyl derivatives leads to acids. Aldehydes, which are derived from primary hydroperoxides, are oxidized to acids by either oxygen or hydroperoxides.[56] Likewise ketones are oxidized by oxygen to acids, but with greater difficulty.[93,94]

The oxidative process is occasionally accompanied by cleavage of the olefin to products of lower molecular weight. The details of this chain scission have not been identified, but most likely involve a peroxide decomposition process.

The thermal decomposition of peroxides into two fragments is fundamentally a first-order reaction. However, the unimolecular scission is accompanied by side reactions induced by attack of radicals on the peroxide. Consequently the over-all process is complex and subject to influences of solvent,[96] additives, and concentration.

The decomposition of 2-cyclohexenyl hydroperoxide at a temperature of 60 to 80°C and a concentration of 0.02 M or greater is best described as a bimolecular reaction, conceived as:[16]

$$2ROOH \rightarrow RO\cdot + ROO\cdot + H_2O$$

In benzene the order of reaction is 1.95, whereas in cyclohexene the order drops to 1.77. With an olefin as solvent, the olefin (R_1H) is subject to attack by radicals, leading to an accelerated decomposition of the peroxide.

$$R_1H + RO\cdot \text{ or } ROO\cdot \rightarrow R_1\cdot + ROH \text{ or } ROOH$$
$$R_1\cdot + ROOH \rightarrow R_1OH + RO\cdot$$

The addition of stearic acid reduces the order to 1.0. Thus, the dependency of the rate of oxidation of an olefin on the concentration of 2-cyclohexenyl hydroperoxide depends on the absence or presence of the acid.

Catalytic Decomposition. The presence of bases leads to decomposition of hydroperoxides. In case of cyclohexenyl hydroperoxide, the products are 2-cyclohexenol and unidentified hydroxy and dibasic acids.[35,46] In case of α-tetralyl hydroperoxide, the decomposition in the presence of a base resembles that of dehydration to form the ketone.[101]

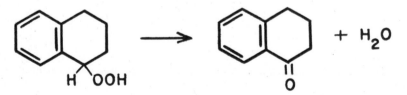

In the presence of alkali, tertiary hydroperoxides decompose at 90°C, with the liberation of oxygen along with formation of alcohols, ketone, and acids.[68]

Disubstituted peroxides with a hydrogen atom on the carbon adjacent to the peroxide linkage are subject to decomposition. The following decomposition has been observed:[73]

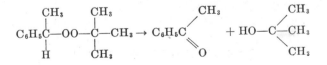

Hydroperoxides are subject to decomposition by acids. In an acetic acid solution with a trace of perchloric acid, 2-cyclohexenyl hydroperoxide decomposes with rearrangement.[64]

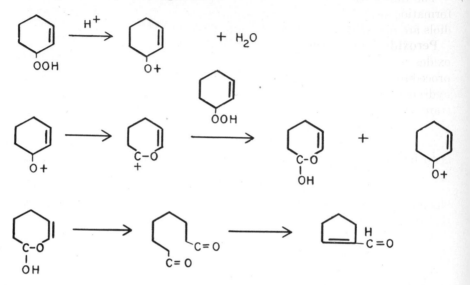

A great variation of stabilities of various hydroperoxides toward acids in acetic acid solution has been observed; the basicity of the hydroperoxide (ability to add a proton to form an oxonium complex) is a factor in determining stability.[68]

2-Cyclohexenyl hydroperoxide, in the presence of aqueous acid, is converted to cyclohexanetriols, most likely through the intermediate cyclohexene oxide.[35,46]

The catalytic decomposition of hydroperoxides has been previously considered in relation to heavy metal catalysis in autoxidation. The catalytic decomposition by metals leads to formation of free radicals, primarily alkoxy radicals, which, in turn, form alcohol and carbonyl derivatives. The catalytic effect of iron phthalocyanine on hydroperoxides leads to formation of ketones.[31]

The liberation of oxygen has been observed in the decomposition of certain hydroperoxides. In certain solvents *t*-butyl peroxide is decomposed by mercaptobenzimidazole with the liberation of oxygen.[62] In the presence of certain additives, such as succinonitrile or carbon disulfide, and alkali metals, hydroperoxides are decomposed with oxygen liberation.[68] The oxygen liberated is considered to involve the following reaction:

$$RO_2^- + ROOH \rightarrow RO^- + ROH + O_2$$

Oxygen liberation has also been observed in peroxide decompositions without catalysts (*t*-butyl hydroperoxide in chlorobenzene at 140°C).[18]

The direct oxidation of the double bond by hydroperoxides leads to formation of 1,2-diols, probably via the olefin oxide.[46] For this reason diols are occasionally encountered as oxidation products.

Peroxide Determination. The quantitative determination of peroxides is based on their oxidative properties. However, the analytical procedure is not without faults and limitations. In the reduction of a hydroperoxide by some reagent, here depicted as a metal M^+ in a reduced state, the first reaction involving one electron change

$$ROOH + M^+ \rightarrow RO^. + OH^- + M^{++}$$

is to be followed by a second reaction, also involving a single electron

$$RO^. + M^+ \rightarrow RO^- + M^{++}$$

change. However, the $RO^.$ fragment is subject to various other reactions and the stoichiometry is thereby destroyed.

The main methods of analyses include the use of ferrous, stannous, or arsenous salts and iodide.[7,72,105,112,113]

The inertness or sluggishness of the dialkyl peroxides prevents a convenient and adequate method of analysis. In order to reduce this peroxide by the usual reagents, more severe conditions must be employed.[8,37] The inertness of di-*t*-butyl peroxide prevents its detection using the polarograph.[120]

Oxidation of Petroleum Products

Gum Formation. Motor fuels produced by present-day refining techniques contain unsaturated hydrocarbons and, consequently, are susceptible to the attack of oxygen. The oxidation causes a deterioration made manifest by the formation of gums, development of color, and loss of octane value. Although the loss of octane value may be a factor of concern,[110] particularly in advanced stages, the formation of gums is perhaps the most serious effect of oxidative deterioration.

The spark ignition engine is constructed to use a fuel possessing certain volatility characteristics. Gasoline is drawn, by means of a vacuum created by the downward movement of the piston, through the carburetor, where vaporization of the fuel and mixing with air occurs. The vaporization process is dependent on (1) the addition of heat to evaporate the liquid, (2) the vacuum created to assist the vaporization process, and (3) the mechanical action of the jets in atomizing the liquid fuel into a fine spray. Droplets of liquid fuel are carried along by the gaseous air-fuel mixture and reach the combustion chamber in this state. However, the carburetor system is designed to operate on a fuel that can be aspirated and transported in a vapor phase. Fuel constituents of low volatility will tend to deposit in the carburetor, in the manifold system, on the inlet valves, and even in the combustion chambers. Those deposits of resinous or "gum-like" properties adhere to the engine parts and can accumulate to such an extent that mechanical difficulties and failures are encountered.

In order to avoid gum difficulties, certain specifications as to maximum amount of nonvolatiles have been accepted. The amount of these non-volatiles is measured by a comparatively simple test in which a sample of motor fuel is rapidly evaporated at a temperature of 155°C (311°F) under a jet of air, and the residue thus obtained is weighed.[3] The gum content is expressed as mg of gum per 100 ml of fuel.

A motor fuel containing less than 7 mg of gum is considered satisfactory as regards gum content; more than 7 mg is considered objectionable. This value has been found a suitable criterion in judging the acceptability of fuels.[2] However, the seriousness of gum deposition with a given fuel is dependent on engine operating conditions.[76]

The presence of oxidized hydrocarbons can be ascertained by determination of the peroxide concentration, using a standardized procedure with ferrous iron.[122] However, since gum comprises a variable fraction (less than 50 per cent) of total oxidation products,[111] the peroxide determination is not a true criterion for the estimation of nonvolatiles in a fuel.

At the time of preparation, a properly fractionated gasoline contains practically no gum. A poorly fractionated fuel will contain high-boiling constituents and will leave an oily residue upon evaporation in the gum test. The gasoline as it leaves the refinery must be so treated that the maximum tolerable gum content is not exceeded at the expected time of consumption. Generally, sufficient stability is required to prevent excessive (i.e., more than 7 mg) gum formation for a period up to about one year.

Gum formation is an oxidation process involving primarily the hydrocarbon unsaturates and atmospheric oxygen. Combined oxygen is a component of gum, as determined by elemental analysis.[19,51,79,90,95,99,115] A typical gum composition is as follows:[115]

	Weight %
C	75.2
H_2	7.6
O_2	15.5
S	1.5
N	0.15

Since oxygen is a prerequisite for gum formation, a restriction in the amount of air available will limit the maximum gum level attainable in a given fuel, and the gum content will remain constant after oxygen depletion.[115]

The essentiality of olefins for gum formation has been demonstrated by the preparation of olefin-containing blends and by determining the gum-forming properties of those blends.[30,34,50,78]

The following facts have been recognized as pertinent to the effects of certain hydrocarbons on gum formation.

(1) The saturated constituents of all types (paraffinic, naphthenic, or aromatic) are not responsible for gum formation.

(2) The presence of simple olefins in concentrations of about 20 per cent or less does not impart a serious instability.

(3) The presence of reactive olefins, particularly conjugated olefins, produces a blend readily oxidized, with formation of gum.

(4) Blends containing both conjugated diolefins in low concentrations (about 2 per cent) and simple olefins are particularly unstable.

A close examination of gum composition reveals that nitrogen and sulfur are incorporated in appreciable amounts (0.1 to 2.0 weight per cent). However, while nitrogen- and sulfur-containing constituents are involved in some unknown manner in the gum-forming process, the olefins are the prime offenders.

Gum formation is indeed a complicated process, involving certain olefins of a complex hydrocarbon mixture along with certain unspecified nitrogen- and sulfur-containing compounds. No comprehensive exposition has been formulated and established to elucidate the chemistry of gum formation. The best description of the chemistry of gum formation is to consider this process as fundamentally that of autoxidation.

In view of the oxidizability of olefins, the formation of gum is not an unexpected phenomenon. Furthermore, the nature of the oxidation product, as to both physical and chemical properties, is revealed by consideration of the oxidation products from pure olefins. The prime characteristics of gum are its low volatility and varnish-like nature. These properties are characteristic of the polymeric peroxides. The gum deposited in the engine is primarily the polymeric peroxides formed from the active olefins, e.g., conjugated diolefins. Simple olefins are potential gum formers, but their contribution to the process is secondary. The presence of hydroperoxides, the main oxidation product of simple olefins, is not as serious in respect to volatility as the presence of the polymeric peroxides. The simple olefins are capable of initiating chains (particularly autocatalysis due to hydroperoxides) and continuing chains, thereby accentuating the gum-forming abilities of the active olefins.

The methods of production and treating of a motor fuel determine the composition and consequently the degree of instability. Thermal cracking, particularly vapor-phase cracking, produces a fuel containing active olefins and hence is susceptible to form gums. By comparison, catalytic cracking produces a fuel possessing a greater stability because the concentration of olefins is decreased and the concentration of aromatics increased. The preparation of fuels by catalytic reforming processes carried out in the presence of hydrogen, such as UOP platforming, produces fuels of high stability. Any auxiliary process that reduces the concentration of highly active olefins will markedly decrease the gum-forming tendency.

Since gum formation is an autoxidation process, a certain control can be exercised by the proper addition of antioxidants. This control has been successfully practiced throughout the petroleum industry, and the addition of antioxidants to gasoline is a standard practice. Three antioxidants have been accepted as satisfactory for general use, the exact choice depending on the specific stabilization problem in question. These three materials, in order of their decreasing popularity, are:

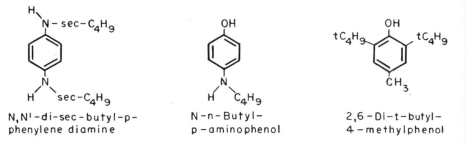

N,N'-di-sec-butyl-p-
phenylene diamine

N-n-Butyl-
p-aminophenol

2,6-Di-t-butyl-
4-methylphenol

By the addition of an antioxidant in concentration from 0.001 weight per cent to 0.010 weight per cent, a sufficient stabilization is effected for storage periods up to one year.

The commercial selection of these materials as suitable additives is based on their properties, such as potency as antioxidant, difficulty of extraction from gasoline by water solutions, solubility in gasoline, volatility, compatibility to other additives, and cost.

Antioxidant effectiveness is dependent to a large extent on structural factors of the compound in question. General structure requirements have been considered.[40,42,75] The configuration of the alkyl group in case of derivatives of p-phenylene diamine is of consequence.[81] In case of the alkyl phenols, the inhibitor effectiveness is a function of the number, size, position, and configuration of the alkyl substituents.[89]

A motor fuel may contain a soluble copper compound owing to the use of either copper alloys in refinery equipment or treating processes involving copper. Copper in excess of concentrations of about 0.01 part per million is detrimental to stability. Fortunately, certain compounds upon addition to a gasoline possess the ability to chelate the copper effectively and thereby nullify its effect.[39,118] In order to deactivate copper, an additive employed is disalicylal-1,2-diaminopropane in concentration of about 0.001 weight per cent.

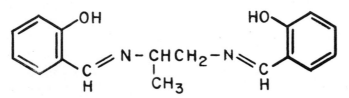

The stability of a gasoline is dependent upon a composite of factors such as composition, treatment, metal contaminants, and the presence of additives. In order to evaluate stability for future storage, at the time of refining an accelerated test is essential. A suitable test has developed, based on the accelerating effects of raising temperature to 100°C and oxygen pressure to 100 pounds per square inch.[4,108]

With the accelerated oxygen bomb test, an estimate of stability is obtained by observing one of two factors, namely, the rate of formation of gum or the length of the induction period. During the induction period, the added antioxidant protects the gasoline against rampant oxidation, but does not completely eliminate gum formation. The amount of gum formed in a given time during the induction period is indicative of stability.

Consumption of the antioxidant brings to an end the stabilization period, and rapid oxidation follows. The length of this induction period, generally recognized with facility, is likewise a measure of stability.

With increasing antioxidant concentrations, gasoline stability in terms of induction period continued to improve,[88] but in terms of gum formation, a rate is reached at a relatively low antioxidant concentration beyond which no improvement results by larger dosage.[115]

Gum formation during the induction period proceeds at an exponential rate, as shown in Fig. 1.[116] The time required to reach a certain gum time (gum value) can be determined from such a curve for each condition plotted.

The effects of temperature and oxygen pressure on the length of the induction period and the gum time are expressed by the equations:

$$\log \text{time} = A + \frac{B}{T}$$

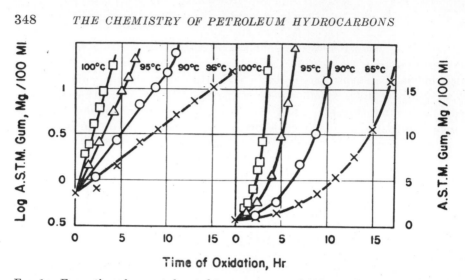

FIG. 1.   Formation of gum at elevated temperatures and 100 pounds oxygen pressure.

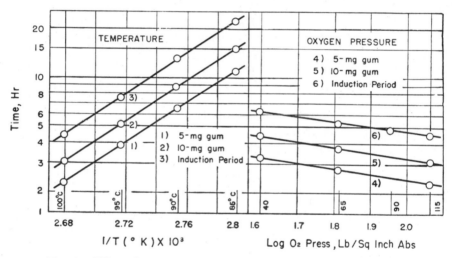

FIG. 2.   Effect of temperature and oxygen pressure on stability times.

where A and B are constants characteristic for each gasoline, and T is the absolute temperature, and

$$\log \text{time} = C + D \log P$$

where C and D are constants and P is the oxygen pressure.[116] These relationships are shown graphically in Figure 2.

By the use of these fundamental relationships, the stability of a gasoline under ambient storage conditions can be estimated from the accelerated test conditions.[117]

Copper Dish Gum Test. Evaporation of gasoline in a copper dish is another means of conducting an accelerated stability test.[107,109] The amount of nonvolatiles, as determined by this test, is considered a measure of the potential gum that may form in storage. This test is of value in conjunction with other stability data, but is not a suitable sole criterion for evaluating stability. In general, this test is able to distinguish those fuels of high stability from those of low stability, but does not effectively rate fuels of intermediate stability.

Tetraethyl Lead. Tetraethyl lead, a constituent of motor and aviation gasolines, is susceptible to attack by oxygen. The effect of tetraethyl lead

TABLE 3. STORAGE OF THERMALLY CRACKED GASOLINE

Antioxidant	Conc., wt %	Stor-age	Gasoline Properties	Duration of Storage, months						
				0	1	3	5	7	9	11
None	—	Dry	Peroxide No.	0.08	2.0	11.1	37.2	85.2	97.0	—
			ASTM Gum	1	5	43	480	549	823	750
			Cu Dish Gum	81	156	335	940	997	1274	1163
		Wet	Peroxide No.	0.08	1.49	1.67	3.85	3.41	6.80	6.30
			ASTM Gum	1	1	4	11	14	30	20
			Cu Dish Gum	81	118	150	124	—	182	222
N-*n*-Butyl-*p*-aminophenol	0.0025	Dry	Peroxide No.	0.08	0.45	1.27	0.47	0.99	2.08	1.23
			ASTM Gum	1	1	1	3	3	5	3
			Cu Dish Gum	4	3	9	12	47	—	51
		Wet	Peroxide No.	0.08	0.62	0.48	0.60	0.66	1.20	1.07
			ASTM Gum	1	4	2	3	3	6	3
			Cu Dish Gum	4	69	53	41	59	84	—
N,N'-Di-sec-butyl-*p*-phenylene diamine	0.0035	Dry	Peroxide No.	0.08	0.24	0.48	1.32	0.77	3.20	3.40
			ASTM Gum	1	4	4	2	1	8	1
			Cu Dish Gum	18	54	34	48	48	101	175
		Wet	Peroxide No.	0.08	0.41	0.48	0.60	—	1.57	2.07
			ASTM Gum	1	3	2	1	1	6	2
			Cu Dish Gum	18	48	44	30	—	56	105

on stability depends on the fuel. The problem of stabilizing a leaded motor fuel is primarily that of stabilizing the olefinic constituents of that fuel. In case of a leaded aviation gasoline which normally contains no olefinic components, the problem is primarily that of stabilizing the tetraethyl lead. The addition of antioxidants is effective in stabilizing leaded aviation fuels.[114]

The addition of a suitable antioxidant to an unstable fuel is an effective and practical means of increasing the time that a fuel can be safely stored. The data in Table 3 are typical of the stabilization that can be gained by the use of antioxidants. The fuel, a thermally cracked gasoline, was inhibited with two commercial antioxidants in concentrations as recorded, increasing the length of the accelerated oxygen bomb induction period from an original value of 60 minutes to 300 minutes. This fuel was stored, at room temperature, dry, and in the presence of 10 volume per cent of water, since water is often present in actual refinery storage. The gasoline properties recorded are peroxide number (equivalents/1000 liters), and ASTM and copper dish gum values (mg gum/100 ml). The gasoline in the absence of an antioxidant, particularly stored dry, developed gum rapidly. The presence of either of these two antioxidants in low concentration imparted a stability of about eleven months.

Inhibitor Sweetening. The use of N,N'-di-*sec*-butyl-*p*-phenylene diamine as an antioxidant in a motor fuel has brought about an interesting and profitable practice involving mercaptan conversion. Under proper conditions, the addition of this antioxidant to an olefinic fuel containing mercaptan will prompt a consumption of mercaptan along with oxygen absorption. The reactions involved in this oxidation have been found to occur in two steps:[87]

$$(1) \quad C{=}C + R\mathrm{SH} + O_2 \rightarrow \underset{\underset{R}{\overset{|}{S}}}{C}{-}C{-}OOH$$

$$(2) \quad \underset{\underset{R}{\overset{|}{S}}}{C}C{-}OOH + 2R\mathrm{SH} \rightarrow \underset{\underset{R}{\overset{|}{S}}}{C}C{-}OH + RSSR + \mathrm{H_2O}$$

The function of the antioxidant is to tie these two reactions together by taking part in an alternating oxidation-reduction system. This can be visualized in several ways, of which the following is one:

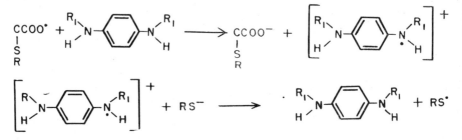

The peroxy free radical oxidizes the antioxidant to a stable ammonium free radical. This latter product, in turn, oxidizes the mercaptan anion to a free radical, followed by reaction with olefin and oxygen to complete a cycle. Thus, the antioxidant is able to induce a favorable oxidation.

Fuel and Diesel Oil Stability. The normal refinery must integrate into its operation the preparation and consumption of higher boiling distillates (over 200°C) such as kerosenes, fuel oils, and diesel oils. In general, acute stability problems of these materials have been minimized by the use of virgin (saturated) stocks.

However, with the advent of catalytic cracking and increased fuel oil demand, refineries have replaced the virgin distillates for domestic heating fuels and diesel fuels with catalytic cycle stocks. The cracked stocks, particularly blended with virgin distillates, are often unstable.[57]

Instability of domestic fuel oil manifests itself through formation of sediment and darkening of color. Sediment plugs filters and burner tips and is therefore not tolerable. Tests have been devised to estimate fuel oil deterioration, but none has gained wide acceptance.[83,104]

Although oxygen is believed essential to fuel oil deterioration, its role has not been established. Certain sulfur[104] and nitrogen compounds[103] are pertinent factors. The addition of common gasoline antioxidants is ineffective in preventing sediment formation.[102]

In refinery practice some alleviation of plugging difficulties is obtained by the addition of oil-soluble surface-active materials. The beneficial results, if obtained, are not due to the prevention of the formation of insolubles, but presumably due to the dispersion of the sediment by the additive.

Petroleum Lubricants. Petroleum lubricants are subject to oxidative deterioration and thereby become ill fitted for their intended purposes. In order to mitigate this deterioration the refiner carefully selects and refines stocks and incorporates additives. With lubricants, the oxidation process and its inhibition, competently reviewed by several authors,[29,126] are in many aspects unlike the previously considered oxidation process.

Lubricants, particularly those used for internal combustion engines, are subject to conditions characterized by high temperatures (up to 200°C) and presence of metallic salts. These severe conditions demand a greater resistance to oxidation, and consequently the more vulnerable hydrocarbons, such as olefins, are excluded as major components from lubricating oils. Under the more severe conditions (temperature 110 to 150°C) one observes a gradation in oxidizability of pure nonolefinic hydrocarbons, with certain alkyl aromatics the more susceptible to attack.[129]

The elevated temperature of engine operation effects a suitable rate of initiation to instigate peroxidation. The peroxides as formed are rapidly decomposed, either thermally or catalytically, to yield acids, water, and carbon dioxide, besides the usual carbonyls and some alcohol. This extended oxidation to acidic materials is a primary cause of lubricating oil deterioration in internal combustion engines.

Those materials effective as antioxidants at low temperatures generally are ineffective under engine conditions. For lubricating oils, additives have been developed[53] which resist direct oxidation by oxygen but which are able to intervene effectively in the oxidation process. The high concentration of additive employed (up to 10 per cent) is ample to allow for a reductive decomposition of the peroxide products and deactivation of metals, besides functioning in the chain terminating process.

References

1. Abere, J., Mark, H., and Hohenstein, W., *J. Appl. Chem.*, **1**, 363 (1951).
2. Alspaugh, M., *J. Soc. Automotive Engrs.*, **54**, 289 (1946).
3. Am. Soc. Testing Mat., Standards on Petroleum Products and Lubricants, Nov. 1952. A.S.T.M. Designation D381-50.
4. *Ibid.*, A.S.T.M. Designation D525-49; D873-49.
5. Atherton, D., and Hilditch, T., *J. Chem. Soc.*, **1944**, 105.
6. Bamford, C., and Dewar, M., *Proc. Roy. Soc. (London)*, **A-198**, 252 (1949).
7. Barnard, D., and Hargrave, K., *Anal. Chim. Acta*, **5**, 476 (1951).
8. Barnes, C., Elofson, R., and Jones, G., *J. Am. Chem. Soc.*, **72**, 210 (1950).
9. Bateman, L., *Trans. Inst. Rubber Ind.*, **26**, 246 (1950).
10. Bateman, L., *Discussions Faraday Soc.*, No. 10, 326 (1951).
11. Bateman, L., Bolland, J., and Gee, G., *Trans. Faraday Soc.*, **47**, 274 (1951).
12. Bateman, L., and Gee, G., *Proc. Roy. Soc.*, **195**, 376 (1949).
13. Bateman, L., and Gee, G., *Trans. Faraday Soc.*, **47**, 155 (1951).
14. Bateman, L., and Gee, G., *Proc. Roy. Soc. (London)*, **195**, 391 (1948).
15. Bateman, L., Gee, G., Morris, A., and Watson, *Discussions Faraday Soc.*, No. 10, 250 (1951).
16. Bateman, L., and Hughes, H., *J. Chem. Soc.*, **1952**, 4594.
17. Bawn, C., Pennington, A., and Tipper, C., *Discussions Faraday Soc.*, No. 10, 282 (1951).
18. Bell, E., Raley, J., Rust, F., Seubold, F., and Vaughan, W., *Discussions Faraday Soc.*, No. 10, 242 (1951).
19. Berger, B., and Bost, R., *Oil Gas J.*, **38**, No. 46, 81 (1940).
20. Bodendorf, K., *Arch. Pharm.*, **271**, 1 (1933).
21. Bolland, J., *Quart. Rev. (London)*, **3**, 1 (1949).
22. Bolland, J., *Trans. Faraday Soc.*, **46**, 358 (1950).
23. Bolland, J., and Gee, G., *Trans. Faraday Soc.*, **42**, 236 (1946).
24. Bolland, J., and Gee, G., *Ibid.*, **42**, 244 (1946).
25. Bolland, J., and Hughes, H., *J. Chem. Soc.*, **1949**, 492.
26. Bolland, J., and ten Have, P., *Trans. Faraday Soc.*, **45**, 93 (1949).
27. Bolland, J., and ten Have, P., *Proc. Faraday Soc.*, **43**, 252 (1947).
28. Bolland, J., and ten Have, P., *Trans. Faraday Soc.*, **43**, 201 (1947).
29. Bondi, A., "Physical Chemistry of Lubricating Oils," Chap. VII, New York, Reinhold Publishing Corp., 1951.
30. Brooks, B. T., *Ind. Eng. Chem.*, **17**, 1198 (1926).
31. Cook, A., *J. Chem. Soc.*, **1938**, 1774.
32. Cooper, H., and Melville, H., *J. Chem. Soc.*, **1951**, 1984.
33. Cooper, H., and Melville, H., *Ibid.*, **1951**, 1994.
34. Cassar, H., *Ind. Eng. Chem.*, **23**, 1132 (1931).

35. Criegee, R., Pilz, H., and Flygare, H., *Ber.*, **72**, 1799 (1939).
36. Criegee, R., *Fortschr. Chem. Forsch.*, **1**, 508 (1950).
37. Dickey, F., Raley, J., Rust, F., Treseder, R., and Vaughan, W., *Ind. Eng. Chem.*, **41**, 1673 (1949).
38. Doede, C., "Proceedings Rubber Technical Conference," p. 730, Cambridge, England, W. Heffer & Sons, 1938.
39. Downing, F., Clarkson, R., and Pedersen, C., *Oil Gas. J.*, **38**, No. 11, 97 (1939).
40. Dryer, C., Lowry, C., Jr., Egloff, G., and Morrell, J., *Ind. Eng. Chem.*, **27**, 315 (1935).
41. Dryer, C., Morrell, J., Egloff, G., and Lowry, C., *Ind. Eng. Chem.*, **27**, 15 (1935).
42. Egloff, G., Morrell, J., Lowry, C., and Dryer, C., *Ind. Eng. Chem.*, **24**, 1375 (1932).
42a. Elley, H., *Trans. Electrochem. Soc.*, **69**, 195 (1936).
43. Engler, C., and Frankenstein, W., *Ber.*, **34**, 1075 (1925).
44. Engler, C., and Weissberg, J., "Kritische Studien über die Vorgänge der Autoxydation," Braunschweig, 1904.
45. Farmer, E., and Moore, C., *J. Chem. Soc.*, **1951**, 131.
46. Farmer, E., and Sundralingam, A., *J. Chem. Soc.*, **1942**, 121.
47. Farmer, E., and Sutton, D., *J. Chem. Soc.*, **1942**, 139.
48. Farmer, E., and Sutton, D., *Ibid.*, **1946**, 10.
49. Fieser, L., *J. Am. Chem. Soc.*, **52**, 5204 (1940).
50. Flood, D., Hladky, J., and Edgar, G., *Ind. Eng. Chem.*, **25**, 1234 (1933).
51. Freund, M., *Proc. World Petroleum Congr. London*, 1933, Vol. 2, p. 108.
52. George, P., Rideal, E., and Robertson, A., *Nature*, **149**, 601 (1942).
53. Georgi, C., "Motor Oils and Engine Lubrication," Chap. VI, New York, Reinhold Publishing Corp., 1950.
54. Gray, U., and Steiner, H., British Patent 614,456; *Chem. Abs.*, **43**, 5032 (1949).
55. Hawkins, E., *Quart. Rev.*, (London), **4**, 251 (1950).
56. Hawkins, E., *J. Chem. Soc.*, **1950**, 2169.
57. Hill, J. B., "Progress in Petroleum Techn.," p. 246, Am. Chem. Soc., 1951.
58. Hock, H., and Depke, F., *Ber.*, **84**, 122, 349 (1951).
59. Hock, H., and Lang, S., *Ber.*, **75**, 300 (1942).
60. Hock, H., Lang, S., and Knauel, G., *Ber.* **83**, 227 (1950).
61. Hock, H., and Neuwirth, A., *Ber.*, **72**, 1562 (1939).
62. Kendall, C., *Ind. Eng. Chem.*, **43**, 452 (1951).
63. Kharasch, M., Arimoto, F., and Nudenberg, W., *J. Org. Chem.*, **16**, 1556 (1951).
64. Kharasch, M., and Burt, J., *J. Org. Chem.*, **16**, 150, (1951).
65. Kharasch, M., Fono, A., and Nudenberg, W., *J. Org. Chem.*, **15**, 763 (1950).
66. Kharasch, M., Fono, A., and Nudenberg, W., *Ibid.*, **16**, 105 (1951).
67. Kharasch, M., Fono, A., and Nudenberg, W., *Ibid.*, **16**, 113, (1951).
68. Kharasch, M., Fono, A., and Bischof, B., *J. Org. Chem.*, **17**, 207 (1952).
69. Kharasch, M., Pauson, P., and Nudenberg, W., *J. Org. Chem.*, **18**, 322 (1953).
70. Knight, H., and Swern, D., *Oil and Soap*, **26**, No. 7, 366 (1949).
71. Kogerman, P., *Chem. Abs.* **29**, 3297 (1935).
72. Kolthoff, I., and Medalia, A., *Anal. Chem.*, **23**, 595 (1951).
73. Kornblum, N., and De La Mare, H., *J. Am. Chem. Soc.*, **73**, 880 (1951).
74. Leffler, L., *Chem. Rev.*, **45**, 385 (1949).
75. Lowry, C., Egloff, G., Morrell, J., and Dryer, C., *Ind. Eng. Chem.*, **25**, 804 (1933).
76. Marley, S., and Gruse, W., *Ind. Eng. Chem.*, **24**, 1298 (1932).
77. Melville, H., *J. Chem. Soc.*, **1952**, 1547.

78. Morrell, J., Dryer, C., Lowry, C., and Egloff, G., *Ind. Eng. Chem.*, **26,** 655 (1934).
79. Morrell, J., Dryer, C., Lowry, C., and Egloff, G., *Ibid.*, **28,** 465 (1936).
80. Pauling, L., "Nature of the Chemical Bond," p. 53, Ithaca, N. Y., Cornell University Press, 1945.
81. Pedersen, C., *Ind. Eng. Chem.*, **41,** 924 (1949).
82. Privett, O., *et al.*, *J. Am. Oil Chemists Soc.*, **30,** 61 (1953).
83. Rescorla, A., Cromwell, J., and Milson, D., *Anal Chem.*, **24,** 1959 (1949).
84. Rieche, A., "Alkylperoxide und Ozonide," Stemkopff, 1931.
85. Rieche, A., "Die Bedeutung d. organischen Peroxyde fur die chem. Wissenschaft u. Technik," Samml. **34,** Enke, 1936.
86. Robertson, A., and Waters, W., *Trans. Faraday Soc.*, **42,** 197 (1946).
87. Rosenwald, R., *Petroleum Processing*, **6,** 969 (1951).
88. Rosenwald, R., and Hoatson, J., *Ind. Eng. Chem.*, **41,** 914 (1949).
89. Rosenwald, R., Hoatson, J., and Chenicek, J., *Ind. Eng. Chem.*, **42,** 162 (1950).
90. Schildwächter, H., *Brennstoff-Chem.*, **19,** 117 (1938).
91. Schlenck, G., and Ziegler, K., *Naturwissenschaften*, **32,** 157 (1944).
92. Semenoff, N., "Chemical Kinetics and Chain Reactions," p. 69, Oxford-Clarendon Press, 1935.
93. Sharp, D., Patton, L., and Whitcomb, S., *J. Am. Chem. Soc.*, **73,** 5600 (1952).
94. Sharp, D., Whitcomb, S., Patton, L., and Moorhead, A., *J. Am. Chem. Soc.*, **74,** 1802 (1952).
95. Smith, N., and Cook, M., *U. S. Bur. Mines, Report 2394*, Sept. 1922.
96. Stannett, V., and Mesrobian, R., *J. Am. Chem. Soc.*, **72,** 4125 (1950).
97. Staudinger, H., *Ber.*, **58,** 1075 (1925).
98. Stephens, H., *J. Am. Chem. Soc.*, **50,** 568 (1928).
99. Story, L., Provine, R., and Bennett, H., *Ind. Eng. Chem.*, **21,** 2079 (1929).
100. Swern, D., *Chem. Rev.*, **45,** 1 (1949).
101. Thompson, R., *Org. Synthesis*, **20,** 94 (1940).
102. Thompson, R., Fifth Annual Diesel Fuel Conference, Bartlesville, Okla., App. G., May 1951.
103. Thompson, R., Chenicek, J., Druge, L., and Symon, T., *Ind. Eng. Chem.*, **43,** 935 (1951).
104. Thompson, R., Druge, L., and Chenicek, J., *Ind. Eng. Chem.*, **41,** 2715 (1949).
105. Tanner, E., and Brown, T., *J. Inst. Petroleum*, **32,** 341 (1946).
106. Tobolsky, A., Metz, D., and Mesrobian, R., *J. Am. Chem. Soc.*, **72,** 1942 (1950).
107. United States Bur. Mines, R.I., 3152 Nov. 1931.
108. Universal Oil Prod. Co., Laboratory Test Methods for Petroleum and Its Products, Method H-6-40.
109. Universal Oil Prod. Co., Laboratory Test Methods for Petroleum and Its Products, Method H-11-43.
110. Veld, H., *Petroleum Refiner*, **25,** No. 6, 285 (1946).
111. Vellinger, E., and Radulesco, G., World Petr. Congr. (London), 1933, Vol. 2, p. 103.
112. Wagner, C., Smith, R., and Peters, E., *Anal. Chem.*, **19,** 976 (1947).
113. Walker, D., and Conway, H., *Anal. Chem.*, **25,** 923 (1953).
114. Walters, E., and Busso, C., *Ind. Eng. Chem.*, **41,** 907 (1949).
115. Walters, E., Minor, H., and Yarbroff, D., *Ind. Eng. Chem.*, **41,** 1723 (1949).
116. Walters, E., Yarbroff, D., and Minor, H., *Ind. Eng. Chem.*, **40,** 423 (1948).
117. Walters, E., Yarbroff, D., and Minor, H., and Sipple, H., *Anal. Chem.*, **19,** 987 (1947).

118. Watson, R., and Tom, T., *Ind. Eng. Chem.*, **41,** 918 (1949).
119. Wibaut, J., and Stang, A., *Proc. Kon. Nederland Akad. Wetenschap*, Series B. 55, No. 2, 102: No. 3, 229 (1951).
120. Willits, C., *et al.*, *Anal. Chem.*, **24,** 785 (1952).
121. Witkop, B., and Patrick, J., *J. Am. Chem. Soc.*, **73,** 2188 (1951).
122. Yule, J., and Wilson, C., *Ind. Eng. Chem.*, **23,** 1254 (1931).
123. Zelinski, N. D., and Borison, P., *Ber.*, **63,** 2362 (1930).
124. Zelinski, N. D., and Titova, A., *Ber.*, **64,** 1399 (1931).
125. Ziegler, K., *Ann.*, **551,** 206 (1942).
126. Zuidema, H., *Chem. Rev.*, **38,** 197 (1948).

CHAPTER 35

SYNTHESIS GAS FROM METHANE, OXYGEN, AND STEAM*

H. H. STORCH

Chief, Fuels-Technology Division, Bureau of Mines, Region VIII, Bruceton, Pa.

The oxidation of methane to produce carbon monoxide and hydrogen has been studied in both homogeneous and heterogeneous systems, in laboratory, pilot-plant, and industrial-scale equipment. Although this work has resulted in operable processes, comparatively little is known concerning the kinetics and mechanisms of the reactions of methane with oxygen, steam, and carbon dioxide. For both the homogeneous and heterogeneous reactions of equal volumes of methane and oxygen, at temperatures in the range 700° to 1300°C, it is probable the initial phenomenon is a flame,[22,19] in which a fraction of the methane and all of the oxygen react to produce carbon dioxide and steam. Subsequently the bulk of the methane is oxidized by the carbon dioxide and steam produced in the initial combustion. Discussions of the nature of this combustion are beyond the scope of this book.

The homogeneous oxidation of methane by steam or carbon dioxide is a highly endothermic and relatively slow reaction. Its rate is conveniently measurable above about 1000°C, where the thermal decomposition of methane also occurs at an appreciable rate. Indeed, one experimenter[6] makes the positive statement that at about 1000°C, steam and methane do not react, but that the more reactive carbonaceous products of the thermal decomposition of methane react to produce carbon monoxide and hydrogen. Outstanding among the readily isolable and identifiable products of the pyrolysis of methane are ethylene and acetylene.[25,26,27] These may react with steam to produce alcohols which then decompose, yielding carbon monoxide, methane, and hydrogen. This is purely speculative, for no significant data are available. The

* Contribution of Fuels-Technology Division, Bureau of Mines, Region VIII, Bruceton, Pa.

reaction of methane with carbon dioxide obviously is even more complex than that with steam.

In work on the heterogeneous catalysis of the methane-steam and methane-carbon dioxide reactions, only active nickel or cobalt catalysts have been used at temperatures in the range 700° to 1000°C. Refractory supports and promoters for these catalysts are of importance only at the lower temperatures (i.e., 700 to 800°C). At temperatures of about 1000°C, massive nickel has been shown to be an effective catalyst.[8,28] Dissociate adsorption of methane occurs on nickel catalysts even at very low (i.e., <300°C) temperatures.[18] It is probable that the carbonaceous fragments from such chemisorption (possibly carbon as metal carbide or a solid solution of carbon in the nickel) react at a suitable rate with steam or carbon dioxide to yield carbon monoxide.

The literature on the contact-catalytic reaction between methane and steam or carbon monoxide is very voluminous. Schmidt[23] and Stanley[24] list a large number of references to patents and technical papers. The most efficient catalysts are those containing about 20 per cent of nickel and 80 per cent of a refractory oxide such as thoria, magnesia, or silica. Most industrial catalysts for this reaction contain magnesia or alumina as the refractory support.[1,4,13] Experiments on the use of oxidation catalysts, such as vanadium oxides and promoted silver for the methane-oxygen reaction at moderate temperatures (i.e., 500 to 700°C), have not been reported. This may be due to the fact that for the production of synthesis gas (carbon monoxide plus hydrogen), temperatures not lower than about 850°C are thermodynamically necessary to avoid uneconomical concentrations of carbon dioxide in the product. For hydrogen production, however, such catalysts may be of interest. The use of metal oxides, such as cupric and ferric oxides, as reactants to oxidize methane to carbon monoxide and hydrogen has received some attention. Laboratory experiments with fixed beds of ferric oxide are described by Ogawa[20] and his co-workers, who concluded that this material was a suitable reactant for synthesis gas production from methane. Further work on a pilot-plant scale is needed. Lewis[14] and his co-workers found that cupric oxide was the most suitable of a number of oxides as a source of oxygen for synthesis gas production from methane. Their experiments were done with a fluidized bed of cupric oxide contained in a 1-inch (diameter) quartz tube, 48 inches in length, to which was supplied a continuous feed of methane and cupric oxide, and from which copper and product gas were continuously discharged. The most suitable solid reactant was 15 per cent of copper oxide deposited on silica gel. This was pulverized and screened, and a fraction which consisted of 50 per cent 100 to 200 mesh and 50 per cent below 200 mesh was used for the tests. At 1640°F, with flow rates of methane of 0.87 liter/minute and of copper oxide-silica gel of 22.1 grams/minute, a dry exit gas rate of 2.31 liters/minute was obtained. Volumes of gas are measured at 70°F and 1 atmosphere. The exit gas contained, in volume per cent: $63.5H_2$, $29.3CO$, $3.1CO_2$, $2.1CH_4$, $1.6N_2$. The inlet solid feed contained 13.9 and the exit solid feed 0.4 weight per cent of copper oxide. The calculated conversion of methane is 94 per cent, with a selectivity:

$$\frac{P_{CO} + P_{H_2}}{P_{CO} + P_{H_2} + P_{H_2O} + P_{CO_2}}$$

of 0.92. The authors[14] consider the reaction as probably proceeding in two steps: an initial rapid reaction of copper oxide with methane to produce chiefly carbon dioxide and water; and a subsequent slow, rate-determining step in which the residual methane reacts with carbon dioxide and water to produce carbon monoxide and hydrogen. The rate-determining step is probably a chemical process and not gaseous diffusion, in view of the high activation energy, which is 47,700 calories. The following rate equation correlates the data within the limits of experimental error:

$$- \frac{dw}{dn} = \frac{1.26 \times 10^{10} e^{-\frac{47,700}{RT}} \, p_{CH_4}(p_{CO_2} + p_{H_2O})}{[1 + 24(p_{CO_2} + p_{H_2O}) + 8p_{H_2}]^2}$$

In this equation n = liters of methane per minute measured at 70°F and 1 atmosphere, w = grams of fluidized catalyst per minute, p = partial pressure in atmospheres, R = gas constant, T = temperature in °K. The results of experiments in which mixtures of methane and carbon dioxide or water at 1500°F were passed through a fluidized bed of reduced copper oxide on silica gel also are accurately represented by this equation. The addition of about 1 per cent of nickel to the reduced copper-oxide-silica gel resulted in a slightly higher rate of reaction.

In all of the experiments by Lewis *et al.*[14] equilibrium in the water-gas reaction

$$CO + H_2O = H_2 + CO_2$$

was reached, whereas for the reactions

$$CH_4 + CO_2 = 2CO + 2H_2 \text{ and } CH_4 + H_2O = CO + 3H_2$$

equilibrium was not established. No carbon was found in the reaction products of any of the tests.

Herbst[9] studied the behavior of mixtures of iron oxide, manganese dioxide, and magnesium or chromium oxides as oxygen carriers in fluidized beds for conversion of methane to carbon monoxide and hydrogen. He found that higher reaction temperatures could be employed if the agglomerates in the solid feed were continuously removed by classification in a fluidized bed in a separate packed vessel. These agglomerates were then reground and mixed with the solid feed to the reactor. Symonds[29] suggests the use of three fluidized reactors for the conversion of methane to carbon monoxide and hydrogen via promoted (with manganese, vanadium, chromium, molybdenum, or nickel oxides) copper oxide as an oxygen carrier. In one reactor the copper is oxidized by air; in another the oxidized solid is fluidized in a stream of preheated methane so that the reaction temperature is in the range 1500 to 2000°F. A deficiency of methane is used in this second reactor so that the exit gas is chiefly carbon dioxide plus steam and a small proportion of oxygen from the thermal decomposition of the copper oxide. These hot exit gases are passed into the third reactor, where reaction between additional methane and the CO_2, H_2O, O_2 mixture yields chiefly carbon monoxide and hydrogen.

Processes employing metal oxides as carriers can use air as the source of oxygen. The lower cost of synthesis gas thus achieved, as compared with that from processes using pure oxygen, is partially offset by the following:

(1) The heat in the nitrogen in the exit gas from the oxidation step can be only partially recovered. The use of air and the recovery of heat from the nitrogen involve considerable expense because of the large volumes of air and nitrogen.

(2) For most synthetic fuel processes it is desirable to produce synthesis gas at about 30 atmospheres pressure. Although the oxidation of methane by fluidized metal oxides probably can be operated at 30 atmospheres, the handling of hot fluidized solids under pressure is a more difficult operation than the partial combustion at 30 atmospheres of methane with pure oxygen. It is known[21] also that elevated pressures reduce the rate of reaction of methane with steam or carbon dioxide.

Another process which uses air as the oxygen source employs a fluidized refractory such as alumina, magnesia, or silica. Atwell[3] heats the refractory to about 2000°F by air plus residual carbon (deposited on the refractory during the subsequent operation) and additional fuel gas. The hot solid is then passed into a fluidized bed of nickel catalyst along with preheated methane, steam, and carbon dioxide. The hot refractory provides the heat for the endothermic conversion of the methane to synthesis gas. Separation of the nickel catalyst from the refractory is based on proper sizing of these (smaller particle size of the refractory), so that the refractory will be "blown out" of the bed of coarser catalyst. Here again difficult engineering problems involved in transporting hot solids are encountered, and if operation at 30 atmospheres is desired the lower reaction rate[21] will necessitate higher temperatures for a given conversion.

The homogeneous partial oxidation of methane by oxygen has been of interest to industry as a means of (1) production of acetylene with synthesis gas as a co-product[5,10,7,12,2] and (2) production of synthesis gas at about 30 atmospheres pressure.[19,12,2] For the thermal process (no catalysts used) a temperature of 2350°F or higher is needed to obtain adequate conversion at a satisfactory rate.[19] The primary reaction is the highly exothermic, rapid conversion of part of the methane to carbon dioxide and steam.[22] This is followed by the endothermic and slow reaction of the residual methane with carbon dioxide and steam. To reduce

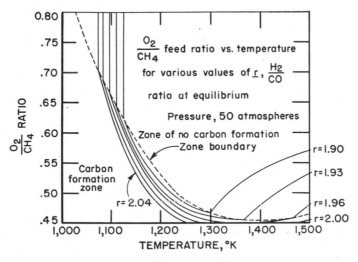

Fig. 1.   Oxygen-methane feed ratio vs temperature.

the consumption of oxygen per unit volume of synthesis gas, the German KW process[7] specified active nickel catalysts for the endothermic part of the reaction. In the United States the noncatalytic reaction at about 30 atmospheres has been selected as part of the Hydrocol process[19,2] for synthesis of liquid hydrocarbons from natural gas.

Thermodynamic studies[15,11,17,16] have shown the conditions (temperature, pressure, O_2/CH_4 ratio) for avoiding carbon deposition. Figures 1 and 2 show these conditions for 20 and 50 atmospheres pressure;[17] Figure 3 shows the effect of pressure on limits of carbon formation at constant O_2/CH_4 ratio. Figure 4 shows the composition of the product gas as a function of the O_2/CH_4 ratio at 20 atmospheres pressure.[16]

Mungen and Kratzer[19] operated a pilot plant for the partial oxidation of natural gas with oxygen to produce synthesis gas. The reactor was

10 inches in internal diameter and 6.5 feet long. Gas and oxygen entered the top of the reactor through a stainless-steel, water-cooled burner. The product gas was partially cooled in a water-cooled transfer line which conducted the gas to a packed tower for direct contact with cooling water. Although this plant was operated as a service-unit to supply gas for

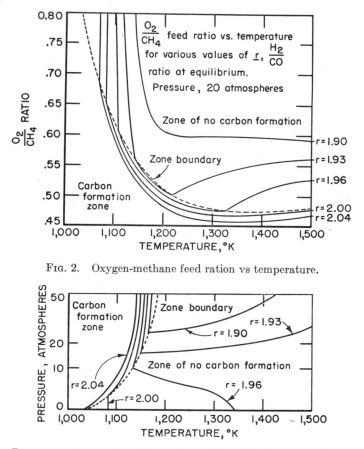

Fig. 2.   Oxygen-methane feed ration vs temperature.

Fig. 3.   Pressure vs temperature for various values of hydrogen- carbon monoxide ration at equilibrium. (Oxygen-methane feed ratio, 0.55.)

hydrocarbon synthesis, some data on the effect of the important process variables were obtained. Complete consumption of oxygen was always obtained in tests in which the O_2/C ratio varied from 0.52 to 0.67. The authors[19] suggested that the reaction proceeds in two steps, viz. complete conversion of the oxygen and part of the methane to carbon dioxide and water followed by a second, rate-controlling reaction of the residual methane with carbon dioxide and water to form hydrogen and carbon monoxide.

An appreciable amount of carbon was formed. Thus at $0.63O_2/C$ ratio about 0.02 per cent and at $0.53O_2/C$ ratio about 0.2 per cent of the carbon in the feed appeared as elemental carbon in the product gas. The operating pressure was 18 to 20 atmospheres and the exit gas temperatures (calculated) 2600°F and 2450°F for 0.63 and $0.53O_2/C$ ratios, respectively. Extrapolation of the curves of Figure 1 to these conditions indicates that at equilibrium no carbon should have been formed. The authors[19] suggest

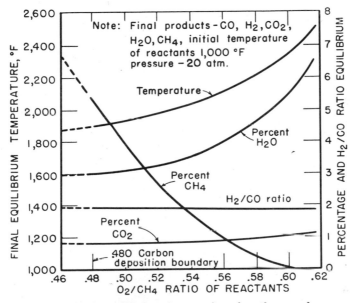

FIG. 4. Adiabatic equilibrium for reaction of methane and oxygen.

that the cooling of the exit gas was slow enough to permit some conversion of carbon monoxide to carbon and carbon dioxide.

The natural gas used in this pilot plant contained some (7 to 8 per cent) of C_2- to C_4-hydrocarbons and the feed gas included about 16 per cent of nitrogen. Although an exact calculation of equilibrium compositions and yields was not feasible, the approximations made by the authors[19] indicate that the conversions (95 per cent at $0.63O_2/C$ and 84 per cent at $0.53O_2/C$ ratio) were below the equilibrium values. The calculated exit gas temperatures were higher and the volumetric ratios of $H_2 + CO$ produced to hydrocarbon and oxygen in the feed were lower than those at equilibrium. The H_2/CO ratio in the product was between 1.75 and 1.90.

References

1. Arnold, M. R., Atwood, K.. Baugh, H. M., and Smyser, H. D., *Ind. Eng. Chem.*, **44,** 999 (1952).
2. Arnold, J. H., *Advances in Chem.*, Series **5,** 120 (1951).
3. Atwell, H. V., U. S. Patent 2,632,690 (1953).
4. Clark, E. L., Kallenberger, R. H., Browne, R. Y., and Phillips, J. R., *Chem. Eng. Progress*, **45,** 651 (1949).
5. Fisher, F., and Pichler, H., *Brennstoff-Chem.*, **11,** 501 (1930).
6. Gordon, A. S., *J. Am. Chem. Soc.*, **70,** 395 (1948); *Ind. Eng. Chem.*, **44,** 1587 (1952).
7. Gordon, K., *et al.*, Report on the Petroleum and Synthetic Oil Industry of Germany, B.I.O.S. Overall Report **1,** 28, (1947), P.B. 88,981.
8. Hawk, C. O., Golden, P. L., Storch, H. H., and Fieldner, A. C., *Ind. Eng. Chem.*, **24,** 23 (1932).
9. Herbst, W. A., U. S. Patent 2,631,933 (1953).
10. Holroyd, R., C.I.O.S. Rept. **30-103,** 6 (1945): P.B. 23,750: Bur. of Mines, Inf. Circular **7375,** 5 (1946).
11. Hradek, V., *Paliva*, **31,** 266 (1951); *British Abs.*, **1952,** I, 639.
12. I. G. Farbenindustrie A.-G., British Patent 300,328 (1927).
13. Ipatieff, V. N., Monroe, G. S., and Fischer, L. E., *Ind. Eng. Chem.*, **42,** 92 (1950).
14. Lewis, W. K., Gilliland, E. R., and Reed, W. A., *Ind. Eng. Chem.*, **41,** 1227 (1949).
15. Lotteri, A., *Rev. combust. liquids*, **1,** 19 (1947).
16. Mayland, B. J., and Hayes, G. E., *Chem. Eng., Progress*, **45,** 452 (1949).
17. Montgomery, C. W., Weinberger, E. B., and Hoffman, D. S., *Ind. Eng. Chem.*, **40,** 601 (1948).
18. Morikawa, M., Benedict, W. S., and Taylor, H. S., *J. Am. Chem. Soc.*, **58,** 1445 (1936).
19. Mungen, R., and Kratzer, M. B., *Ind. Eng. Chem.*, **43,** 2782 (1951).
20. Ogawa, T., Matui, A., and Senco, H., *Chem. Abs.*, **33,** 3327 (1939); **34,** 5627 (1940).
21. Pichler, H., *Brennstoff-Chem.*, **12,** 325 (1931).
22. Prettre, M., Eichner, C. H., and Perron, M., *Trans. Faraday Soc.*, **42,** 335 (1946).
23. Schmidt, J., "Das Kohlenoxyd," p. 47, Leipsig, Akademische Verlagsgesellschaft, 1950.
24. Stanley, H. M., *Science of Petroleum*, **3,** 2164 (1938).
25. Storch, H. H., *J. Am. Chem. Soc.*, **54,** 4188 (1932).
26. Storch, H. H., and Golden, P. L., *Ind. Eng. Chem.*, **25,** 768 (1933).
27. Storch, H. H., *Ind. Eng. Chem.*, **26,** 56 (1934).
28. Storch, H. H., Anderson, R. B., Hofer, L. J. E., Hawk, C. O., and Golumbic, N., *U. S. Bur. Mines*, Techn. Paper, 709, (1948).
29. Symonds, F. L., U. S. Patent 2,631,094 (1953).

CHAPTER 36

THE PARTIAL OXIDATION OF THE SIMPLE PARAFFINIC HYDROCARBONS

N. C. ROBERTSON

National Research Corporation, Cambridge, Mass.

The conversion of the lower aliphatic hydrocarbons by direct reaction with oxygen to products of a degree of oxidation intermediate between the hydrocarbon and the carbon oxides has been actively investigated for fifty years. As early as 1903 Bone and Wheeler[7] circulated a mixture of two parts methane and one part oxygen through a furnace maintained at 500°C for a period of several days and positively identified formaldehyde among the products collected in a cold trap at the furnace exit.

Academic research on partial oxidation has had the object of developing satisfactory mechanisms for the combustion of hydrocarbons. The vast amount of industrial research in this field, reported largely in patents, has been aimed at utilizing the cheap and available paraffinic hydrocarbons as sources of aldehydes, ketones, alcohols, and acids, which are the building blocks of the aliphatic chemical industry.

Despite the volume of published information our knowledge of the oxidation reactions of the simple hydrocarbons is still far from satisfactory. In fact, the oxidation of such relatively complex molecules as cumene or the higher olefins in the liquid phase is better understood than that of ethane or propane. The critical faculty of the interested investigator will seldom be so taxed as in reviewing the vast literature of hydrocarbon oxidation. The pronounced effect of surface conditions and of the presence or absence of small amounts of impurities on the reaction rates, and the fact that the nature of the products as well as the kinetics may often change completely with a change in temperature or in the proportion of the reactants used, account for many of the disagreements among research workers. All too frequently no satisfactory material balances have been obtained; for only recently have instrumental methods capable of analyzing the complex mixture of liquid and gaseous reaction products become available. Considerable confusion has been caused by reactions occurring between the condensed products of oxidation processes which have no bearing on the primary oxidation reaction itself.

For all the foregoing reasons, unequivocal statements about oxidation are dangerous in the extreme, but it is possible to list some characteristics of oxidation reactions which are observed with almost all the saturated aliphatic hydrocarbons in the vapor phase.

(1) An induction period whose duration may range from fractions of a second to hours is observed in either static or flow systems. During this time a slight rise in temperature is usually noticed and small amounts of reaction products may be measured, but no appreciable consumption of hydrocarbon or oxygen can be detected.

Mulcahy[38] has found that for constant surface conditions the induction period varies inversely with the product of the hydrocarbon and oxygen concentrations. This fact he relates to the build-up of a concentration of chain carriers by the initial step

$$RH + O_2 \rightarrow R + HO_2$$

until a concentration sufficient to cause rapid reaction is obtained.

The induction period is much more sensitive to temperature than the rapid reaction which follows it. It can often be reduced or completely eliminated by the addition of higher aldehydes, peroxides, alkyl nitrites, or ethers, which are sources of free radicals by thermal decomposition or oxidation.

(2) At the end of the induction period the rate of reaction increases rapidly to a maximum. In the case of propane and higher hydrocarbons, at temperatures below 400°C, the rate of the rapid reaction is strongly dependent on the hydrocarbon concentration, but almost independent of the oxygen concentration after this passes a certain minimum.[38]

(3) The structure of the hydrocarbon affects both the rate of oxidation and the nature of the products. The rate of oxidation is much more sensitive to hydrocarbon structure than is the rate of thermal cracking.[15,26] Mulcahy compared the maximum rates of oxidation of pairs of hydrocarbons at temperatures convenient for measuring the rate of pressure increase in a static system.[37] Results for the series ethane through pentane appear in Table 1.

TABLE 1. RELATIVE REACTION RATES OF SOME NORMAL PARAFFIN HYDROCARBONS[37]

Temperature, °C	Hydrocarbon	Ratio of Maximum Reaction Rates
263	n-Pentane:n-Butane	2:1
289	n-Butane:Propane	5:1
461	Propane:Ethane	90:1

Within a group of isomers, chain branching decreases the rate of oxidation. Cullis and Hinshelwood found n-hexane to oxidize about 1580 times as rapidly as 2,3-dimethyl butane.[15]

It is now generally agreed that the point at which a hydrocarbon molecule is initially attacked either by an oxygen molecule or by a free radical depends upon the molecular structure. A tertiary hydrogen is more readily abstracted than a secondary, and a secondary more readily abstracted than a primary. Walsh[66] has presented the evidence for this conclusion, and Boord[10] has correlated the order of ease of abstraction in oxidation reactions with that obtaining in similar free-radical reactions such as halogenation and nitration.

(4) The nature of the surface of the reaction vessel and the surface:volume ratio often affect the rate of oxidation and the partial oxidation products which can be isolated.

Packing the reaction vessel usually, but by no means always, decreases the duration of the induction period. This was observed by Steacie for the oxidation of ethane at 452°C.[59] The most plausible interpretation is that at least some of the chains are being initiated at the surface. The effect of packing on the rapid reaction following the induction period is almost always inhibitory. Furthermore, low-pressure oxidations of many hydrocarbons will not proceed in vessels whose diameter is below a certain critical value. This is the result of surface destruction of atoms and radicals produced by chains starting in the gas phase. The quantitative relation of the surface:volume ratio to rate of oxidation processes has been developed by Semenov.[56] With oxidation, as with other chain reactions, the effect of increased pressure or of the addition of an inert diluent is to decrease the influence of surface on reaction rate by impeding the diffusion of chain carriers to a surface before they can undergo reaction to generate new atoms or radicals.

Our understanding of the specific effects of various kinds of surface on oxidation processes is still very poor. In some instances they cause the destruction of certain partial oxidation products. Alkali halide surfaces, for example, destroy the hydrogen peroxide produced in the low-pressure oxidation of ethane and higher hydrocarbons; but the distribution of the other reaction products may or may not be affected, depending upon the precise experimental conditions.[25,51]

When a surface participates in vapor-phase partial oxidation of the paraffinic hydrocarbons, it usually does so by creating chain carriers or by causing the destruction of certain chain carriers. There is much evidence that many radical recombination reactions occur at surfaces. On the other hand, partial oxidation products almost never result from the chemisorption of paraffinic hydrocarbons and of oxygen on a catalytic surface followed by chemical transformation on the surface and desorption of the stable products into the gas phase. Reactions analogous to the conversion of ethylene to ethylene oxide on silver catalysts have not been found with the paraffinic hydrocarbons.* Instead, conventional oxidation catalysts, such as the oxides of metals of variable valence, usually cause complete combustion of the paraffins to carbon dioxide and water. For example, the supported metal oxides which catalyze the oxidation of propylene to acrolein and isobutylene to methacrolein catalyze the combustion of propane or isobutane under the same conditions.

Margolis and Todes[35] found that catalysts of the chromia spinel type supported on asbestos caused the oxidation of such hydrocarbons as pentane and heptane to proceed all the way to carbon dioxide and water. Their effect on the oxidation of methyl ethyl ketone and butyraldehyde, which are among the products of partial oxidation of such hydrocarbons in the vapor phase, was to convert them to organic acids. These partial oxidation products were therefore not formed as intermediates in the surface combustion reaction.

Oxidation of Individual Members of Paraffinic Series

Methane and its lower homologs must be discussed separately not only because there are pronounced differences in the oxidation behavior of each, but also because far more information has been accumulated about the oxidation of these simple hydrocarbons than about those with six or more carbon atoms. This discussion is not primarily concerned with reaction mechanisms (see Chapter 32), and mechanisms will be dealt with only insofar as they can be related to the formation and destruction of the major partial oxidation products.

Methane. Much of our knowledge of the low-pressure oxidation of methane we owe to Norrish.[48] Lewis and von Elbe[32] have recently reviewed the available information, and Hoare and Walsh[27] have discussed the effect of surfaces.

Thermal oxidation becomes detectable above about 400°C but is not rapid below 575°C. During the induction period the concentration of formaldehyde builds up exponentially to a steady state. During the fast reaction following the induction period carbon monoxide and water are the principal products. Addition of formaldehyde can shorten or eliminate the induction period; and, if still more formaldehyde is added, the rate of the fast reaction also increases and formaldehyde is destroyed until the normal steady-state concentration is again attained. The importance of the role of formaldehyde is also emphasized by the fact that, if a

---

* A possible exception may develop in the catalytic oxidation of normal butane to maleic anhydride over certain mixed oxide catalysts. M. J. P. Hartig (U.S. Patent 2,625,519 (Jan. 13, 1953)) has claimed yields of over 60% of maleic anhydride from normal butane in 1–5% concentration in air over promoted molybdenum oxide-cobalt oxide catalysts.

reacting mixture of methane and oxygen at 485°C is exposed to a strong beam of ultraviolet light of wavelength 2400 to 3800 Å, the rate is markedly accelerated; but it returns to normal when the light is cut off.[47] This wavelength is known to effect dissociation of formaldehyde into hydrogen atoms and carbon monoxide, and it should have no effect on the reactants or on any other intermediate which could reasonably be postulated.

According to current views on mechanism,[32] the reaction is "triggered" by some process the net effect of which is to convert methane to formaldehyde and which must be written simply as

(a) $$CH_4 + O_2 \rightarrow HCHO + H_2O$$

One or more reactions of formaldehyde with oxygen lead to chain branching and a rapid increase in the formaldehyde concentration.

(b) $$H_2CO + O_2 \rightarrow H_2CO_2 + O$$
(c) $$O + CH_4 \rightarrow OH + CH_3 \cdot \qquad \text{(Norrish)}$$

or

(d) $$H_2CO + O_2 \rightarrow HCO + HO_2 \qquad \text{(Walsh)}$$

Chain propagation involves the reactions,

(e) $$CH_4 + OH \rightarrow H_2O + CH_3 \cdot$$
(f) $$CH_3 \cdot + O_2 \rightarrow HCHO + OH$$

Formaldehyde is destroyed by reactions with radicals such as

(g) $$OH + HCHO \rightarrow H_2O + HCO \cdot$$
$$HCO \cdot \rightarrow H + CO$$
(h) $$H + O_2 + HCHO \rightarrow H_2O_2 + HCO$$

Reactions of chain termination include

(i) $$OH + Wall \rightarrow Destruction$$
(j) $$HO_2 + Wall \rightarrow Destruction$$
(k) $$HCHO + O_2 + Wall \rightarrow Destruction$$

Hoare and Walsh[27] observed that coating a clean or acid-washed silica vessel with lead oxide had little effect on the induction period, but greatly decreased the rate of pressure rise in the rapid reaction and considerably increased the activation energy of the rapid reaction. Since there is evidence that lead oxide destroys HO_2 radicals in other reactions, they interpreted their results on the basis of destruction of the chain-carrying HO_2 radical from reaction (d) above, so that this reaction no longer leads to branching and any branching must occur from a reaction of methane with oxygen such as

$$CH_4 + O_2 \rightarrow CH_3 \cdot + HO$$

It will be noted that none of these reactions leads to methanol, for no more than traces of methanol are found among the products of the unsensitized oxidation of methane at low pressures. Such small quantities as are found might be explained by surface reactions.

Neither can methyl hydroperoxide be detected among the oxidation products under these conditions. Gray[21] has prepared this hydroperoxide in good yield by the mercury-photosensitized oxidation of a 90 per cent methane-10 per cent oxygen mixture at 25°C. The reactions involved are:

(a) $Hg(^1S_0) + H_2 \rightarrow Hg(^3P_1)$
(b) $Hg(^3P_1) + CH_4 \rightarrow Hg(^1S_0) + CH_3 \cdot + H$
(c) $CH_3 \cdot + O_2 \rightarrow CH_3OO \cdot$
(d) $CH_3OO \cdot + CH_4 \rightarrow CH_3OOH + CH_3 \cdot$

Although Gray believes the hydroperoxide may be involved in low-pressure oxidation of methane at temperatures as high as 400°C, it seems doubtful that this peroxy radical is stable at high temperatures for long enough to abstract a hydrogen.

Because formaldehyde is so readily decomposed on attack by oxygen or free radicals in the temperature range of reasonably rapid oxidation of methane, its concentration in the reaction mixture is always low; and the thermal oxidation of methane is not well suited to the preparation of formaldehyde.

The effect of the variables of temperature, contact time, and methane: oxygen ratio on the yields of formaldehyde at atmospheric pressure have been rather thoroughly studied by Patry and Monceaux.[49,50] Working in a quartz-tube flow system with mixtures of methane and air and in the temperature range 500 to 900°C, they found that the maximum yields of formaldehyde based on methane fed are seldom greater than one per cent, and the highest concentration of formaldehyde in the exit gas was 0.2 per cent. As a function of contact time the conversions of methane to formaldehyde passed through maxima which occurred at lower contact times as the temperature was raised. Feed compositions with methane:air ratios less than one gave the highest yields, particularly above 700°C. It is noteworthy that packing the reactor with quartz chips drastically lowered the formaldehyde yields.

Patry and Monceaux also studied the thermal decomposition of formaldehyde in streams of nitrogen (0.1 to 0.2 per cent concentrations of formaldehyde) in this same temperature range. Figure 1 shows curves taken from their data for the yield of formaldehyde from a methane-air mixture and for the thermal decomposition of formaldehyde as a function of contact time at 700°C. Replacing nitrogen by air had little effect on the rate of formaldehyde decomposition.

Much effort has been expended in the search for gaseous catalysts capable of initiating methane oxidation at temperatures low enough for formaldehyde to be stable or of so altering the mechanism of the reaction that the formaldehyde produced can be preserved and recovered. Nitric acid and the oxides of nitrogen were tried by several investigators in the 1920's. Experiments on pure methane and oxygen with added nitrogen dioxide were made by Smith and Milner.[58] In a typical run at 700°C and

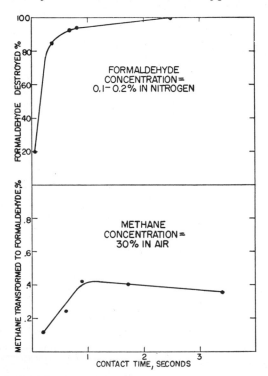

Fig. 1.   Comparison of conversion of methane to formaldehyde and thermal decomposition of formaldehyde at 700°C and atmospheric pressure.[50]

0.1 second contact time the effect of adding 7.5 per cent nitrogen dioxide to a mixture of 1.5 parts methane and 1.0 parts oxygen was to increase the methane reacted from virtually nil to 25 per cent and to increase the proportion of the methane fed going to formaldehyde from 0.2 to 3.4 per cent. Bibb[5] added small percentages of nitric acid to mixtures of one part natural gas (containing 16.6 per cent ethane) and 2.4 parts air, reacted the mixture at 735°C, and obtained yields of approximately six pounds of 40 per cent formalin per thousand cubic feet of gas fed in a single pass and 26 pounds per thousand cubic feet in a recycle system.

Yields of 40 per cent formalin based on nitrogen dioxide consumed ranged from six to eight pounds.

The fact that the sizable amounts of nitrogen dioxide added cannot be recovered shows that the effect cannot be a true catalysis and renders the results of doubtful practical value.

More recently claims have been made for processes which require only a few tenths of a per cent of added nitric oxide or nitrogen dioxide and which result in ultimate yields of 45 per cent or more of formaldehyde based on methane consumed.[40,41,59] Certain types of surfaces such as silica or nonreducible metal oxides are frequently specified in conjunction with the homogeneous catalyst.

Ozone has also been reported to accelerate the oxidation of methane and to improve the yields of formaldehyde.[18,36]

Fujimoto[19] obtained hydrogen peroxide in addition to formaldehyde and methanol by passing a mixture of two parts methane and one part oxygen through a brushy spark discharge. Substantial amounts of hydrogen were also produced so that it is not possible to say whether the peroxide was a primary product of methane oxidation or was formed by further oxidation of molecular hydrogen. The hydrogen peroxide was actually isolated in the form of its formaldehyde addition product, dioxydimethyl peroxide. Dioxydimethyl peroxide decomposes on heating into formic acid and hydrogen.

$$\underset{\underset{H}{|}}{\overset{\overset{OH}{|}}{H-C}}-O-O-\underset{\underset{H}{|}}{\overset{\overset{OH}{|}}{C}}-H \rightarrow 2HCOOH + H_2$$

In fact, it is now fairly clear that most of the acids which have been identified among the products of hydrocarbon oxidation have been produced by the action of hydrogen peroxide on aldehyde in the condensed products.

The oxidation of methane at superatmospheric pressures differs markedly from the low-pressure oxidation, in that methanol becomes the principal partial oxidation product recoverable. Newitt and his coworkers have investigated the oxidation of methane in both static and flow systems at pressures ranging from 10 to 150 atmospheres.

Table 2 shows the results obtained by Newitt and Haffner[43] for the effect of pressure on the yields of methanol and formaldehyde from a mixture of 8.1 parts methane and 1.0 parts oxygen in a static system consisting of a 500-ml steel cylinder. In these experiments the temperatures were adjusted to give roughly comparable reaction rates. It is apparent that both the methanol yield based on methane consumed and the methanol:formaldehyde ratio increase rapidly with increasing pressure.

The effect of replacing methane by nitrogen or carbon dioxide at a constant total pressure was to lower the yields of both methanol and formaldehyde.

TABLE 2. EFFECT OF INITIAL PRESSURE UPON THE SURVIVAL OF PRODUCTS OF OXIDA-
TION OF METHANE IN A STATIC SYSTEM AT VARIOUS TEMPERATURES[43]
Initial mixture $= 8.1CH_4 + 1.0O_2$

Initial Pressure, atm.	Initial Temp., °C	Rise of Temp., °C	Duration of Oxidation, min	Ratio CO/CO_2 in Gaseous Products	Survival as Per Cent on Methane Burnt		Ratio $CH_3OH/H.CHO$
					CH_3OH	H.CHO	
10	400	2	10	0.06	1.1	nil	—
25	385	4	7	0.15	4.8	0.66	7.3
40*	372	6	15	0.05	6.1	1.20	5.1
48	373	12	4	0.35	13.7	0.80	17.1
106.4	341	14	12	—	22.3	0.75	29.7
149*	341	17	16	0.08	19.0	0.60	31.6

* Not quite optimum temperature conditions.

At each pressure there appeared to be an optimum temperature for obtaining the best yields of partial oxidation products, this optimum being several degrees above the lowest temperature at which reaction could be effected. However, heterogeneous reactions may have been involved in the reaction at the lowest temperatures where induction periods of as long as 50 minutes were encountered.

The effect of duration of reaction on the concentrations of methanol and formaldehyde produced in a static system is shown in Table 3 from

TABLE 3. PRODUCTS AT VARIOUS STAGES OF THE OXIDATION OF METHANE IN A STATIC
SYSTEM AT HIGH PRESSURE[43]
Initial pressure $= 106.4$ atm
Temperature $= 341°C$

Duration of Experiment, min	Composition of Gaseous Medium, cc at N.T.P.						Ratios	
	O_2	CH_4	CO_2	CO	CH_3OH	H.CHO	CO/CO_2	$CH_3OH/H.CHO$
0	2332	18790	—	23	—	—	—	—
6.5	1905	18360	191	82	59	8	0.31	7.4
7.25	1390	18330	334	120	115	16	0.28	7.2
9.0	413	17570	564	460	192	17]	0.77	11.3
12.0	nil	17310	461	695	330	10	1.45	33.3
30.0	nil	17240	766	502	325	4	0.63	81.2
1000.0	nil	17480	1030	160	147	3	0.13	49.0

the work of Newitt and Haffner. Formaldehyde reaches a maximum concentration before methanol does and decomposes more rapidly than methanol in the period after all the oxygen is consumed.

Working in a flow system and at higher ratios of methane to oxygen,

Newitt and Szego[45] were able to obtain considerably better yields of methanol, as high as 50 per cent based on methane consumed (Table 4).

Boomer and Naldratt[8] and Boomer and Thomas[9] have also investigated the oxidation of methane at pressures up to 180 atmospheres, packing their reaction vessel with nickel, copper, zinc, or Monel in various shapes. Oxidizing three to five per cent of hydrocarbon per pass, they obtained methanol yields of up to 60 per cent on the hydrocarbon consumed; but it is doubtful that their results are superior to those of Newitt,

TABLE 4. THE OXIDATION OF METHANE IN A FLOW SYSTEM AT FIFTY ATMOSPHERES PRESSURE[45]

Initial Mixture		Initial Temp. of Reaction Tube, °C	Rise of Temp., °C	Duration of Heating, sec	Percentage of Methane Burnt Surviving as	
					CH_3OH	HCHO
(1) $CH_4 =$	90	430	5	5	51	4.1
$O_2 =$	3	430	5	7	49	3.2
$N_2 =$	7	410	15	10	43	3.2
	100	400	28	20	12	2.16
(2) $CH_4 =$	90	410	35	5	29.0	1.4
$O_2 =$	5	410	46	7	18.0	0.9
$N_2 =$	5	400	75	30	3.0	1.0
	100					

or that the added surface served any useful function except possibly to aid in dissipating heat and maintaining a more uniform temperature.

The available data permit little more than speculation about the mechanism of the high-pressure oxidation. At high hydrocarbon pressures, the methyl peroxy radical may abstract a hydrogen atom instead of decomposing unimolecularly, and this could result in the reaction sequence:

$$
\begin{array}{ll}
\text{(a)} & CH_3\cdot + O_2 \rightarrow CH_3OO\cdot \\
\text{(b)} & CH_3OO\cdot + CH_4 \rightarrow CH_3OOH + CH_3\cdot \\
\text{(c)} & CH_3OOH \rightarrow CH_3O\cdot + OH \\
\text{(d)} & CH_3O\cdot + CH_4 \rightarrow CH_3OH + CH_3\cdot
\end{array}
$$

Ethane. The oxidation of ethane at pressures in the neighborhood of an atmosphere is more complex than that of methane. The reaction does not proceed at reasonable rates (residence times of one to 20 seconds) until temperatures of higher than 400°C are attained, and under these conditions ethylene instead of oxygenated substances is the principal product.

Working at reaction times of the order of 30 minutes or more, Bone and Hill[6] were able to obtain reaction of ethane-oxygen mixtures in a static system at 316°C. Formaldehyde was the major partial oxidation product, and smaller amounts of acetaldehyde and formic acid were found. At this low temperature little ethylene was made. A long induction period was observed, which could be drastically reduced by addition of nitrogen dioxide or aldehydes. The induction period could also be shortened by increase in the total pressure or the temperature. Analyses made at various stages after the onset of rapid reaction showed that the aldehyde concentration passed through a maximum with time and that the partial oxidation products were being rapidly destroyed by the time most of the oxygen had been consumed.

It might be noted that at approximately the same temperature, 310°C, Nalbandyan[39] found that the mercury-photosensitized oxidation of ethane yielded formaldehyde and acetaldehyde in the ratio of five parts formaldehyde to one of acetaldehyde.

The oxidation of ethane to ethylene at much higher temperatures has been investigated by Steacie and Plewes,[59] and most recently by Gray.[22] Steacie and Plewes found ethylene to be the principal product of the oxidation at 452°C. In one experiment at this temperature, charging a 33 per cent ethane-67 per cent oxygen mixture, ethylene accounted for 63 per cent of the consumed ethane at the point where half the oxygen was consumed. Moreover, substituting ethylene for ethane did not alter the kinetics of the main reaction. They concluded that some sort of dehydrogenation process is the first step in the oxidation. Gray, working with ethane-rich mixtures in a flow system, also found ethylene to be the major product above 400°C.

The synthesis of ethylene by low-pressure oxidation of ethane with air or oxygen was operated on a substantial scale in Germany and has also been developed to the point of commercial feasibility in the United States.[17]

Some light is thrown upon the possible mechanism by which ethane is converted to ethylene by an important coproduct of the low-pressure oxidation in the temperature range in question, namely, hydrogen peroxide.

Kooijman has explored the synthesis of hydrogen peroxide by oxidation of a 90 per cent ethane- 10 per cent oxygen mixture.[30] Figure 2 shows his results for effect of temperature on oxygen consumption and yields of unsaturates and peroxides. The peroxide yields include the oxyalkyl peroxides formed by addition of hydrogen peroxide to aldehydes and were determined by a potassium iodide titration.

Gray[22] has discussed probable mechanisms for the oxidation. Reactions which seem plausible are:

(a)	$C_2H_6 + O_2 \rightarrow C_2H_5\cdot + HO_2$
(b)	$C_2H_5\cdot + O_2 \rightarrow C_2H_4 + HO_2$
(c)	$C_2H_6 + HO_2 \rightarrow H_2O_2 + C_2H_5\cdot$
(d)	$HO_2 + Wall \rightarrow Destruction$
(e)	$H_2O_2 + Wall \rightarrow H_2O + \frac{1}{2}O_2 \text{ or } H_2 + O_2$
(f)	$H_2O_2 \rightarrow 2OH$
(g)	$OH + C_2H_6 \rightarrow H_2O + C_2H_5\cdot$

From the foregoing discussion it is evident that any oxygenated hydrocarbons such as aldehydes, alcohols, etc., produced by the low-pressure

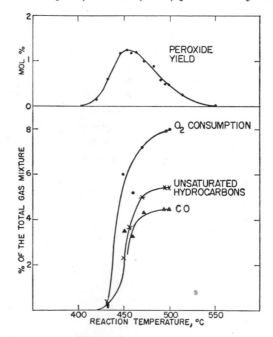

FIG. 2. Production of peroxides and unsaturates from oxidation of 90 per cent ethane–10 per cent oxygen mixture at a contact time of 8.0 seconds.[30] Peroxide yield is based on hydrocarbon fed and determined by K I oxidation.

oxidation of ethane in the temperature range where reaction is reasonably fast, are probably derived from the further oxidation of ethylene. Some years before the work cited above, Curme[16] oxidized ethane with air at 700 to 710°C in a recycle system, while adding fresh ethane continuously, allowing ethylene to accumulate in the recycle, and withdrawing purge gas to maintain constant pressure. From a hundred parts of ethane fed he obtained 33.4 parts of ethylene and 7.4 parts of aldehydes, with 46.3

parts of unreacted ethane. The ratio of formaldehyde to acetaldehyde was 6:1. The product distribution is similar to that obtained from ethylene in the same temperature range.

At pressures of several atmospheres, ethylene is not produced in appreciable quantities, but the proportion of ethane oxidizing to ethylene as a function of pressure has not been accurately established. Formaldehyde is the principal partial oxidation product at these moderate pressures, but unfortunately no quantitative data are available.[68]

Newitt has shown that, as was the case with methane, oxidation at high pressures yields alcohols instead of aldehydes. Table 5 shows the

TABLE 5. THE EFFECT OF INITIAL PRESSURE ON THE SURVIVAL OF INTERMEDIATE PRODUCTS FROM THE REACTION OF AN 88.4 C_2H_6/11.6 O_2 MEDIUM IN A STATIC SYSTEM[42]

Initial Pressure, atm	Initial Temp., °C	Duration of Reaction, min	Percentage of the Carbon of the Ethane Burnt Surviving as						Total in Condensable Products
			C_2H_5OH	CH_3OH	CH_3CHO	$H.CHO$	CH_3COOH	$HCOOH$	
15	315	3.0	16.0	19.4	1.9	4.5	Nil	Nil	41.8
50	294	3.25	17.2	14.1	5.2	1.9	Nil	0.7	39.1
75	279	2.5	18.0	16.6	6.8	0.4	3.6	0.6	46.0
100	270.5	4.5	34.6	14.0	9.7	0.1	12.5	0.5	50.4

results of Newitt and Bloch[42] for the effect of initial pressure on product distribution in a static system. Again, the temperature was adjusted to give comparable residence times for a given degree of reaction. The ratio of C_2 to C_1 products is seen to increase as the pressure is raised.

The precision of Newitt's data in static systems may be seriously questioned. The sizable effects of small changes in reaction temperature on the distribution of products, and especially on the $CO_2:CO$ ratio, is hard to explain unless surface effects are involved. The acetic acid found in the products must have been derived from acetaldehyde by oxidation at the vessel surface or in the condensed products. No data are given that permit the degree of oxygen consumption to be calculated.

In a flow system Newitt and Szego[45] were able to improve the yields of partial oxidation products still further, and Table 6 shows the results

TABLE 6. THE SLOW OXIDATION OF ETHANE IN A FLOW SYSTEM AT FIFTY ATMOSPHERES PRESSURE[45]

Reacting medium: $C_2H_6 = 90$, $O_2 = 3$, $N_2 = 7\%$

Initial Temp. of Reaction Tube, °C	Temp. Rise, °C	Duration of Heating, sec	Products as Percentages of Carbon of the Ethane Burnt							Total Carbon Accounted for, %
			C_2H_5OH	CH_3CHO	CH_3OH	CH_3COOH	CH_4	CO	CO_2	
360	11	4	62.6	4.8	Trace	1.1	9.3	9.2	4.7	91.7
360	22	7	47.4	6.2	2.5	2.9	10.1	11.5	15.8	96.4

of two runs at 50 atmospheres pressure with a mixture containing three per cent oxygen. Yield of two-carbon products was better than 50 per cent based on ethane consumed. The authors attribute most of the improvement over the results in the static system to the rapid cooling of partial oxidation products. In all probability the increased hydrocarbon:oxygen ratio in the flow experiments was the more important factor.

Again, the high partial pressures of the reactants favor bimolecular reactions of the ethoxy and ethyl peroxy radicals such as,

$$CH_3CH_2OO\cdot + C_2H_6 \rightarrow C_2H_5\cdot + CH_3CH_2OOH$$
$$\downarrow$$
$$CH_3CH_2O\cdot + OH$$
$$CH_3CH_2O\cdot + C_2H_6 \rightarrow CH_3CH_2OH + C_2H_5\cdot$$
$$CH_3CH_2O\cdot + O_2 \rightarrow CH_3CHO + HO_2$$

over unimolecular decompositions such as,

$$CH_3CH_2O_2 \rightarrow C_2H_4 + HO_2$$
$$CH_3CH_2O\cdot \rightarrow CH_3\cdot + HCHO$$

Propane. The oxidation of propane has probably been studied more than that of any other saturated hydrocarbon. This has not resulted in adequate explanations for all the observed phenomena and may mean only that our ignorance is more diffuse. Many characteristics of the oxidation of ethane are observed with propane; but cool flames, two-stage ignition, and a negative temperature coefficient are encountered for the first time in ascending the paraffinic series.*

The rate and products of the oxidation are much influenced by the reaction conditions. The important effects of temperature and pressure can be summarized:

(1) At pressures of about an atmosphere and temperatures below about 360°C and in clean vessels, the reaction yields mainly aldehydes and methanol plus some propylene. In this region the rate is highly dependent on propane concentration and almost independent of oxygen concentration.

(2) As the temperature is raised, a range is reached in which the rate of oxidation decreases with increasing temperature. This negative temperature coefficient was first noted by Pease[52] and has since been observed for almost all the paraffins higher than propane and for some of the olefins. The exact range of the negative temperature coefficient can vary with the partial pressures and ratios of the reactants and with the surface

---

* Gray[22] has recently reported some evidence for cool flames in ethane oxidation.

conditions. With further increase in temperature the rate passes through a minimum and then increases. The temperature at which the minimum rate is observed may vary from about 380° to 430°C.

In the range of negative temperature coefficient as the temperature is raised and the rate becomes lower, the proportion of oxygenated products becomes less, and that of olefins, especially propylene, becomes greater. The author has observed that for the case of high hydrocarbon to oxygen ratios, i.e., very limited conversions of hydrocarbon, the minimum rate corresponds to the point of maximum production of propylene based on hydrocarbon consumed. This is also true of n-butylene from n-butane and isobutylene from isobutane.

(3) As the reaction rate increases after passing through the minimum, the proportion of reacted hydrocarbon going to oxygenated products continues to decrease, and the proportion going to the olefins, to increase. Production of ethylene increases very rapidly, and above about 500°C the reaction becomes essentially an oxygen-sensitized cracking of propane. Schultz[55] has found that the ratio of propylene to ethylene in this range agrees with the prediction of the Rice-Kossiakoff theory for hydrocarbon cracking.

In this region the rate becomes much more dependent on oxygen concentration. Several moles of propane can react per mole of oxygen consumed, and the ratio becomes greater as the oxygen concentration is reduced.[55]

(4) The formation of hydrogen peroxide in the low-pressure oxidation was observed by Pease, and the peroxide and its aldehyde adducts are important products in the range 300 to 500°C. Figure 3 shows the results of Kooijman[30] for oxygen consumption and yields of peroxide, carbon monoxide, and unsaturates from a 90 per cent propane-10 per cent oxygen mixture in a flow system. Unfortunately, no breakdown of the unsaturates is given.

(5) Packing the reactor inhibits the low-temperature oxidation. Coating the reactor surface with substances such as alkali chlorides destroys hydrogen peroxide and slows down the reaction.[51,52]

(6) At moderate superatmospheric pressures of the order of four atmospheres and higher, the production of olefins is drastically reduced and the negative temperature coefficient is no longer observed. At pressures just high enough to suppress olefin formation, the nature and distribution of the products at temperatures up to about 400°C resemble those found in atmospheric pressure oxidation below the range of negative temperature coefficient.

(7) At high pressures, of the order of 20 atmospheres or more, the three-carbon compounds, isopropyl alcohol and acetone, become impor-

tant oxidation products, and the production of olefins becomes entirely negligible.[44]

Some information about the oxidation products in the lowest temperature range in which low-pressure oxidation can be carried out, 300 to 330°C, was obtained by Pease[53] and by Harris and Egerton[25] for 1:1 mixtures of propane and oxygen. The data of Pease, working in a flow system, showed the methanol yield to approach correspondence to the propane consumed at low conversions. Analyses at various stages of reaction were obtained by Egerton and Harris for a static system in this

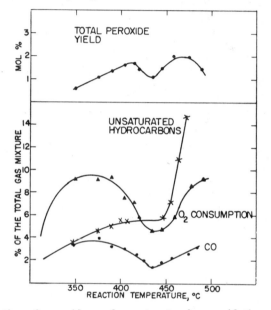

Fig. 3. Production of peroxides and unsaturates from oxidation of a 90 per cent propane–10 per cent oxygen mixture at a contact time of 4.0 seconds.[30] Peroxide yield is based on hydrocarbon fed and determined by K I oxidation.

temperature range. These showed: (a) the concentrations of carbon oxides and methanol calculated as moles per mole propane consumed increase throughout the reaction whereas concentrations of water and aldehydes are about constant; (b) when propylene was added to the charge, its concentration in the products was unaltered, an indication that any propylene produced may be further oxidized under these conditions, so that part of the oxygenated products may be derived from propylene.

All these data are open to question, and the degrees of conversion are usually so high as to make it doubtful that many of the substances determined were primary products.

Recent data obtained by Satterfield and Wilson[54] for the products of oxidation of a 5.6:1 propane-oxygen mixture at various stages of reaction and at temperatures of 375°C and 475°C appear in Figures 4(A) and 4(B). Under their conditions in a flow system, 375°C was just below the region of negative temperature coefficient and 475°C was above the minimum rate which was observed at 425°C. The decrease in the proportion of

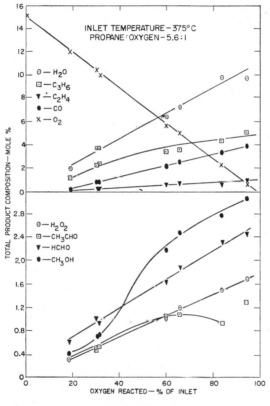

FIG. 4(A).

oxygenated products and increase in olefin production at the higher temperature are quite apparent.

The composition of the reaction products from a mixture with an initial composition of 1:1 propane-oxygen and an initial pressure of 282 mm has been reported by Chernyak and Shtern[13] for a temperature of 350°C. In the early stages the product ratios are roughly the same as those of Satterfield and Wilson. Deanesly and Watkins[17] have reported the yields of propylene and ethylene obtainable by the oxidative cracking of propane in the high temperature region.

At this point a very brief consideration of the mechanisms which have been proposed to account for the kinetics and products of propane oxidation may be worthwhile, since many features of propane oxidation are

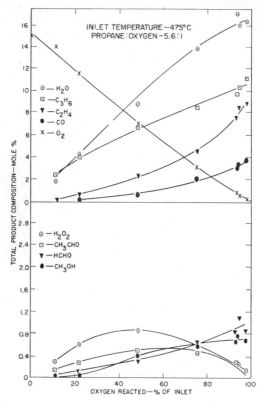

FIG. 4(B).   Products of propane oxidation at one atmosphere pressure as function of oxygen consumed.[54]

observed with higher hydrocarbons. Attack on the hydrocarbon molecule by a free radical or an oxygen molecule yields a propyl radical:

(a) $C_3H_8 + R(\text{or } O_2) \rightarrow C_3H_7\cdot + RH (\text{or } HO_2)$

At low temperatures, abstraction of a secondary hydrogen undoubtedly occurs most easily. The propyl radical, like other alkyl radicals, reacts readily with oxygen; and in the low-temperature range most of the radicals will undergo the reaction,

(b) $C_3H_7\cdot + O_2 \rightarrow C_3H_7OO\cdot$

The subsequent reactions of this radical are still in doubt. Confining attention for the moment to the radicals produced as the result of secondary attack, the hydroperoxide mechanism proposed by Ubbelohde and extended by Walsh[66] has the peroxy radical abstracting hydrogen to yield a hydroperoxide molecule which can then decompose.

(c) $\qquad i\text{-}C_3H_7OO\cdot + RH \rightarrow i\text{-}C_3H_7OOH + R$

(d) $\qquad i\text{-}C_3H_7OOH \rightarrow i\text{-}C_3H_7O\cdot + OH$

(e) $\qquad i\text{-}C_3H_7O\cdot \rightarrow CH_3CHO + CH_3\cdot$

To overcome the objection that the reaction sequence leads to chain branching for each hydroperoxide molecule formed, which is not in accord with the kinetics, Walsh and Malherbe[33] have modified the mechanism to allow for branching by some reaction of hydroperoxide with oxygen, such as:

$$
\text{(f)} \qquad i\text{-}C_3H_7OOH + O_2 \rightarrow HO_2 + \cdot\underset{\underset{\displaystyle CH_3}{|}}{\overset{\overset{\displaystyle CH_3}{|}}{C}}\!\!-\!OOH \rightarrow \text{Free Radicals}
$$
$$
(CH_3, OH, \text{etc.})
$$

The major portion of the hydroperoxide would decompose by a non-branching route, which is not specified. Objection to a mechanism that requires formation of a hydroperoxide molecule can still be made on the grounds that only a negligibly small amount of acetone, the product of dehydration of isopropyl hydroperoxide, is formed in the noncatalytic oxidation of propane at moderate pressures, whereas acetone is an important product under conditions where hydroperoxides are known to be intermediates.

Lewis and von Elbe[32] have suggested that the peroxy radical decomposes unimolecularly,

(g) $\qquad i\text{-}C_3H_7OO\cdot \rightarrow CH_3CHO + CH_3O\cdot$

and that the methoxy radical then abstracts a hydrogen atom:

(h) $\qquad CH_3O\cdot + RH \rightarrow CH_3OH + R$

This mechanism affords a satisfying explanation of the fact that at low temperatures, at low or moderate pressures, and at limited conversions of hydrocarbon the mole ratio of acetaldehyde to methanol is unity. On the other hand, the decomposition as written requires an alignment of atoms which would seem somewhat unlikely.

Vaughan and his co-workers[4] would have the peroxy radical react with an alkyl radical or with another peroxy radical:

(i) $\qquad i\text{-}C_3H_7OO\cdot + R \rightarrow i\text{-}C_3H_7OOR \rightarrow i\text{-}C_3H_7O\cdot + RO\cdot$

(j) $\qquad i\text{-}C_3H_7OO\cdot + ROO\cdot \rightarrow i\text{-}C_3H_7O\cdot + RO\cdot + O_2$

The alkoxy radical would then undergo decomposition as in the hydroperoxide case,

(k) $i\text{-}C_3H_7O\cdot \rightarrow CH_3CHO + CH_3\cdot$

The methyl radical could either abstract hydrogen to form methane, react with oxygen to yield formaldehyde, or react to produce methanol via the dialkyl peroxide route,

(l) $CH_3\cdot + O_2 \rightarrow CH_3OO\cdot$
.(m) $CH_3OO\cdot + R \rightarrow CH_3OOR \rightarrow CH_3O\cdot + \cdot OR$
(n) $CH_3O\cdot + RH \rightarrow CH_3OH + R$

The dialkyl peroxide mechanism requires reaction of one radical with another for each mole of oxygen consumed and would appear to require a higher concentration of radicals than seems likely to exist in many reacting mixtures. If radical-radical reactions were frequent, certain stable products of radical combination such as ethane or dimethyl ether might be expected as major products of the over-all reaction, and these are almost completely absent from propane oxidation products in the temperature range in question. On the other hand, if, as seems very likely, the reaction of alkyl with oxygen is fast and that of the resulting alkyl peroxy radical with hydrocarbon is slow by virtue of a very sizable activation energy, the concentration of $RO_2\cdot$ radicals attained would be large and reactions with other radicals could become important.

In the opinion of the author, it is doubtful that any one of the mechanisms advanced can account for all the known facts about propane oxidation over the entire range of temperatures, pressures, and hydrocarbon: oxygen ratios. The hydroperoxide mechanism, for example, suffers from certain deficiencies as regards low-pressure oxidation, but explains many of the known facts about high-pressure oxidation satisfactorily.

According to the mechanisms discussed, attack at a primary hydrogen in the propane molecule can result in formation of the radicals,

$CH_3CH_2O\cdot$ and $CH_3CH_2CH_2O\cdot$

and these decompose to give formaldehyde and an alkyl radical. It is likely that much of the formaldehyde produced in propane oxidation results from decomposition of these alkoxy radicals. Methyl radicals can, of course, react with oxygen to give formaldehyde, but Chernyak and Shtern observed that the addition of acetaldehyde, which is surely a source of methyl radicals, to a propane-oxygen reaction mixture resulted in no measurable increase in the formaldehyde produced. Also the results of Marcotte and Noyes[34] on the rate of reaction of methyl with oxygen indicate that the competing reaction of hydrogen abstraction should become important in hydrocarbon-rich mixtures at temperatures of 350°C and higher.

It should be noted that formaldehyde can also be produced by further oxidation of the olefins ethylene and propylene if the conditions are such that they build up to high concentrations. Thomas has disclosed the low-pressure oxidation of propane to formaldehyde in a recycle system in which ethylene and propylene were the major hydrocarbons present in the reactor feed.[60]

Cook has disclosed the production of propylene oxide by the oxidation of propane at moderate pressures in vessels packed with inert surfaces.[14] In the absence of further information, it seems likely that propylene was an intermediate in the process.

Some propionaldehyde is undoubtedly formed from the n-propyl peroxy radical,

$$CH_3CH_2CH_2OO\cdot \rightarrow CH_3CH_2CHO + OH$$

but propionaldehyde is such an unimportant product that the extent of this reaction cannot be great.

To explain the negative temperature coefficient, Pease postulated an intermediate in the oxidation which in the low-temperature region reacts to give a branched reaction chain and at higher temperatures reacts by way of an unbranched chain. The change in product distribution in the range of the negative temperature coefficient has suggested to several authors that the intermediate is the isopropyl or isopropyl peroxy radical which can react:

$$i\text{-}C_3H_7\cdot + O_2 \rightarrow i\text{-}C_3H_7OO\cdot \longrightarrow \text{oxygenated products}$$
$$\text{capable of}$$
$$\searrow \text{branching reactions}$$

$$C_3H_6 + HO_2$$

In the second reaction the peroxy radical may not be formed as a discrete intermediate. The second reaction would be favored as the temperature is increased. The HO_2 radical can undergo the reactions discussed under ethane oxidation, namely, hydrogen abstraction from a molecule or radical to yield hydrogen peroxide or reaction at a surface to form stable products.

The chain-branching agent among the oxygenated products is not definitely established. Lewis and von Elbe have pointed out that only a moderate amount of branching is required to explain the kinetic data in the low-temperature region. Malherbe and Walsh proposed oxidation of the hydroperoxide as the branching reaction. Chernyak and Shtern[13] have recently argued for acetaldehyde as the branching agent in the low-temperature range via the reaction:

$$CH_3CHO + O_2 \rightarrow HO_2 + \cdot CH_2CHO$$

In support of this proposal Antonovskii and Shtern[1] found that addition of acetaldehyde results in a considerable increase in the maximum reaction rate in the low-temperature range, but no increase above the range of the negative temperature coefficient.

As the temperature is increased, the increased proportion of attack on primary hydrogens results in formation of more n-propyl radicals which decompose largely into methyl plus ethylene, and it is this reaction which becomes dominant in the high-temperature range. Thus, all the phenomena of low-pressure oxidation of propane can now be explained in a very crude and tentative fashion.

The oxidation of propane at pressures of more than ten atmospheres results in increased yields of alcohols with respect to aldehydes and increased yields of two- and three-carbon compounds with respect to one-carbon products. Table 7 shows the data of Newitt for the effect

TABLE 7. PRODUCTS FROM THE REACTION OF A 1:3.6 PROPANE-AIR MEDIUM AT 1, 20, 60, AND 100 ATMOSPHERES[44]

Pressure, atm	1	20	60	100
Reaction temp., °C	373	281	252	250
Products	Percentages of the Carbon of the Propane Burnt			
Total aldehydes	20.5	21.8	13.5	13.7
Normal alcohols	19.7	21.0	17.5	15.2
Isopropyl alcohol	1.3	2.8	6.2	16.0
Acetone	0.5	4.3	12.5	7.9
Acids	4.3	17.0	19.0	18.9
Carbon dioxide	7.3	17.1	21.4	20.6
Carbon monoxide	21.3	16.0	9.9	7.7
Propylene	25.1	Nil	Nil	Nil

of pressure on the products of oxidation of a 1.0 part propane—3.6 parts air mixture at increasing pressure, temperature being adjusted to give comparable rates of reaction.[44] It will be noted that as the pressure is increased, the temperature required for reaction at a convenient rate is decreased, so that the effects of pressure and temperature are interrelated.

Table 8 shows the increase in the proportion of normal and isopropyl alcohols as the pressure is increased.

Wiezevich and Frolich[69] reacted a 92 per cent propane-8 per cent oxygen mixture at 170 atmospheres and 350°C and at a contact time of less than 10 seconds to obtain a product mixture in which the mole ratio of the compounds present was approximately 1.0 formaldehyde : 14 acet-aldehyde : 5 acetone : 39 methanol : 15 ethanol : 7 propanol : 3 acetic acid. Again the very high proportion of alcohols stands out, although the yields of individual products are of questionable accuracy.

TABLE 8. RELATIVE QUANTITIES OF ALCOHOLS SURVIVING FROM THE SLOW REACTION OF A 1:3.6 PROPANE-AIR MEDIUM[44]

Pressure, atm	5	30		65
Products		Mole Per Cent of Total Alcohols		
Methyl alcohol	76.3	58.0	55.3	50.1
Ethyl alcohol	19.1	17.6	13.2	9.8
Propyl alcohol	4.6	4.3	7.3	12.2
Isopropyl alcohol		20.0	24.2	27.9

As was postulated for the lower hydrocarbons, the most important effect of carrying out reaction at high pressure upon the product distribution is to increase the proportion of products which may be considered to derive from the abstraction of hydrogen by methoxy, ethoxy, and propoxy radicals. On the one hand, the elevated pressures cause the reaction to proceed at temperatures at which these radicals are more stable toward unimolecular decomposition. On the other, the increased concentration of hydrocarbon favors the bimolecular hydrogen abstraction reaction.

The increased yield of acetone may also be related to the isopropoxy radicals' being sufficiently stable to react:

$$
\begin{array}{cc}
CH_3 & CH_3 \\
| & | \\
HC{-}O\cdot + R \rightarrow & C{=}O + RH \\
| & | \\
CH_3 & CH_3
\end{array}
$$

Alternately, there may be a sufficient quantity of hydroperoxide formed at high pressures to yield appreciable amounts of acetone by dehydration at a surface.

Butane. The kinetic behavior of the low-pressure oxidation of *n*-butane or isobutane resembles that of propane so closely that detailed discussion is not required. The temperature range of low-temperature oxidation, i.e., below the range of the negative temperature coefficient, is longer than with propane, since the oxidation of *n*-butane proceeds at an easily measurable rate as low as 260°C and that of isobutane at 300°C. Again, the product yields at low temperatures and long contact times are about the same as those obtained at moderate pressures at temperatures ranging from 250 to 400°C, if the reaction times are adjusted to give comparable conversions.

With n-butane the product distribution indicates the predominant reaction to be (according to the Lewis and von Elbe theory):

(a)
$$n\text{-}C_4H_{10} + R \rightarrow \overset{\displaystyle CH_3}{\underset{\displaystyle C_2H_5}{CH\cdot}} + RH$$

(b)
$$\overset{\displaystyle CH_3}{\underset{\displaystyle C_2H_5}{CH\cdot}} + O_2 \rightarrow \overset{\displaystyle CH_3}{\underset{\displaystyle C_2H_5}{CHOO\cdot}}$$

(c)
$$\overset{\displaystyle CH_3}{\underset{\displaystyle C_2H_5}{CHOO\cdot}} \rightarrow CH_3CHO + C_2H_5O\cdot$$

(d)
$$C_2H_5O\cdot \rightarrow HCHO + CH_3\cdot$$

(e)
$$CH_3\cdot + O_2 \rightarrow \text{Methanol, Formaldehyde, or Carbon Oxides}$$

(f)
$$CH_3\cdot + RH \rightarrow CH_4 + R$$

Since the ratio of primary to secondary hydrogens is only half that of propane, fewer products result from primary attack.

Isobutane has one tertiary and nine primary hydrogens, and attack on the tertiary hydrogen leads mostly to acetone by the splitting off of methoxy radical from the tertiary butyl peroxy radical or of methyl from the tertiary butoxy radical.[66] Abstraction of a primary hydrogen, which of course becomes more frequent as the temperature is raised, results mainly in acetaldehyde, formaldehyde, and a methyl radical via:

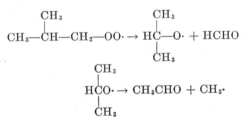

In all these oxidations lesser amounts of higher alcohols and aldehydes are produced by competing reactions.

Wiezevich and Frolich[67] found alcohols to be the major products from the oxidation of n-butane at very high pressures. The alcohol distribution obtained under conditions of 160 atmospheres total pressure, 410°C reaction temperature, less than 10 seconds contact time, and 6.2 per cent oxygen in the feed gas was one part methanol:2 parts ethanol:3 parts propanol:0.4 part butanol. The effect of increasing the pressure over the range 33 to 133 atmospheres was to increase the yields of higher alcohols and lower the yields of methanol.

Bretton, Wan, and Dodge[11] obtained small amounts of maleic acid and formaldehyde and a trace of glyoxal from the oxidation of *n*-butane over a supported vanadium pentoxide catalyst at high ratios of air to hydrocarbon. Eighty per cent of the reacted hydrocarbon went to carbon oxides.

Grosse and Snyder[23] were able to conduct a high-pressure, vapor-phase oxidation of butane at very low temperatures by initiating the reaction with a surface film of cobalt acetate in acetic acid. Two- and four-carbon compounds were the principal products.

Harris[24] has disclosed the synthesis of hydrogen peroxide by the oxidation of normal butane or isobutane at low pressures and high ratios of hydrocarbon to oxygen. The maximum yields per pass of hydrogen peroxide were obtained at temperatures just above the minimum rate following the range of the negative temperature coefficient.

Pentane and Hexane. The straight-chain hydrocarbons higher than *n*-butane produce some new types of products on oxidation.

Ubbelohde obtained sizable amounts of products boiling above the C_1 to C_4 carbonyl compounds from the oxidation of *n*-pentane at atmospheric pressure. He carried out the oxidation in a circulating system at 320 to 350°C, stripping off *n*-pentane and low-boiling products from the condensate, and returning them to the reaction.[63] From the 65 to 95°C fraction of the condensate he isolated 2-methyl tetrahydrofuran and found some unsaturated substances believed to be dihydropyrans. Ubbelohde's suggestion that the cyclic oxide is formed by internal dehydration of a hydroperoxide is probably as good an explanation as can be advanced

$$CH_3-CH_2-CH_2-CH_2-CH_2OOH \rightarrow \underset{\underset{O}{\diagdown\diagup}}{\overset{CH_2-CH_2}{\underset{CH_2\quad CH-CH_3}{|\qquad|}}} + H_2O$$

The initial formation of the secondary rather than the primary hydroperoxide is more likely.

In studying the preflame spectra of C_4 and higher hydrocarbons, Ubbelohde also observed an absorption band at 2600 Å which could not be attributed to any commonly known partial oxidation product. Recently Barusch and co-workers have identified the substances responsible as β-dicarbonyl compounds.[2] They isolated 2,4-pentanedione from the products of oxidation of 150 mm pentane and 610 mm air at 304°C. Butanal-3-one was identified in the absorption spectrum of *n*-butane during oxidation but was too reactive to be isolated. From studies of the intensity of absorption and of the rate of decomposition of 2,4-pentanedione added to cool flames, the authors conclude that under their conditions a considerable amount of hydrocarbon oxidizes by way of such intermediates. An intramolecular abstraction of hydrogen by a peroxy radical, followed by reaction of the resulting hydroperoxide radical with oxygen, has been proposed very tentatively as a route by which the β-dicarbonyl structure can be approached.[3]

The major products from the oxidation of n-pentane at moderate pressures are acetaldehyde, propionaldehyde, formaldehyde, methanol, ethanol, and n-propyl alcohol. Such products would, of course, be predicted from the oxidation of this hydrocarbon by the mechanisms developed for propane and butane. Isopentane yields acetone, methyl ethyl ketone, acetaldehyde, formaldehyde and the lower alcohols. The ratio of acetone to methyl ethyl ketone should be 1:2 if each carbon-carbon bond in the 2-methyl 2-butoxy or 2-methyl 2-peroxy butul radical, which result from tertiary attack, had the same ease of rupture. The fact that it is considerably higher reflects both the greater tendency of the larger alkyl group to split off[20] and the greater stability of acetone toward decomposition or oxidation.

Wiezevich and Frolich[67] oxidized a mixture of 60 per cent n-pentane and 40 per cent isopentane at 240°C and 200 atmospheres. A large amount of acetaldehyde was produced even at these pressures, although alcohols predominated. About a quarter of the alcohols were amyl alcohols.

The products of oxidation of n-hexane in two temperature ranges, 275 to 280°C and 300 to 400°C, were investigated by Kahler, Bearse, and Stoner.[28] The ratios of hydrocarbon to oxygen used approximated 1:2. Most striking was the formation of stable organic peroxy compounds at the lower temperature. These were not positively identified, but hydrogenation of the condensate gave very appreciable yields of dihydroxy compounds in the four- and six-carbon range, suggesting that cyclic peroxides may have been produced.

Oxidation in the higher temperature range gave much more carbonyl compounds and olefins and much hydrogen peroxide, but little or no organic peroxides.

It is apparent that our knowledge of the processes involved in oxidation of these higher saturated hydrocarbons is very sketchy indeed and that reactions and products not encountered with the lower members of the series must be dealt with. Although the separation and analysis of the products is a forbidding problem, it is one which must be solved before much further progress can be made.

Synthesis of Oxygenated Chemicals by Partial Oxidation

The incentive to develop commercial processes for oxidizing the simple paraffins to aliphatic chemicals is found in the relatively low price at which they have always been available in large refineries and near natural gas fields. The hydrocarbons propane through pentane can be obtained in high purity by fractionation of the natural gasoline and liquefied petroleum gas recovered at natural gasoline and cycling plants. Concentrated streams of ethane are also produced at these plants, and larger amounts can be recovered if desired by low-temperature absorption or condensation operations carried out on the dry gas. Methane and ethane can be transported by pipeline and the liquefiable hydrocarbons by pipeline, tank car, or ocean-going tanker.

Acetylene and the lower olefins are, in general, the competitive raw materials for the manufacture of oxygenated compounds, and in recent years acetylene has been more expensive than the saturates by a factor of five to ten and the olefins have been more expensive by a factor of two to five. Moreover, some of the routes based upon olefins require two steps to arrive at compounds which are produced by oxidation in one step.

In spite of this superficially favorable economic relationship, the development of direct oxidation processes has not been rapid. This has been caused by poor understanding of the chemical processes involved, difficulties in controlling the fast and highly exothermic reactions, and difficulties in recovering and separating the components of the complex mixtures which are often produced. Much has already been done to solve these problems, and further advances can be expected to come swiftly.

The important classes of compounds which might be produced by partial oxidation of the saturated hydrocarbons are:

(1) *Aldehydes.* The lower aldehydes can be made by oxidation at low or moderate pressures. As has been shown, they usually result from reactions in which carbon-carbon bonds are broken, so that aldehydes with fewer carbon atoms than the hydrocarbon oxidized almost always predominate.

(2) *Ketones.* Although high-pressure oxidation of normal hydrocarbons will produce small amounts of ketones of the same carbon number, ketones are best synthesized from branched-chain hydrocarbons. As has been noted with isopentane, the larger alkyl group can be expected to split off most readily from tertiary radicals to yield the lower of the possible ketones.

(3) *Alcohols.* Methanol is made in large amounts by the low- and moderate-pressure oxidation of the hydrocarbons with three or more

carbon atoms and by the high-pressure oxidation of methane and ethane. High-pressure oxidation can produce alcohols of the same carbon numbers in good yields. These will be predominantly secondary and tertiary alcohols if secondary or tertiary hydrogens are present.

(4) *Acids*. Acids higher than formic acid do not appear to be made in appreciable amounts by vapor-phase oxidation of the C_1- to C_5-hydrocarbons. They may be found among the products if there is an opportunity for any hydrogen peroxide made to react with an aldehyde or for a liquid-phase reaction or possibly a surface reaction to take place.

(5) *Peroxides*. Hydrogen peroxide can be an important product of the oxidation of the C_2 and higher hydrocarbons in the low-pressure range. There is no good evidence that any appreciable quantity of alkyl hydroperoxides or dialkyl peroxides is produced by oxidation of the C_1- to C_4-hydrocarbons without the use of special gaseous catalysts. Some evidence that they are products of the noncatalytic oxidation of higher saturated hydrocarbons when oxidation can be effected below 300°C has been cited.[28]

The basic problem in obtaining good yields of many valuable partial oxidation products is that their rate of destruction by decomposition or oxidation is comparable to the rate of oxidation of the hydrocarbon from which they are derived. It is possible to make a crude comparison of stability if it is considered that the initial step in the decomposition or

TABLE 9. ACTIVATION ENERGIES AND RELATIVE RATES OF ABSTRACTION OF HYDROGEN BY METHYL RADICALS FROM SOME HYDROCARBONS AND OXYGENATED SUBSTANCES

Compound	$E_1 - \frac{1}{2}E_2$, kcal/mole	$k_1/k_2^{1/2} \times 10^{13}$ at 182°C
Ethane	10.4	3.8
2,2-Dimethyl propane	10.0	6.3
n-Butane	8.3	21
n-Pentane	8.1	27
Isobutane	7.6	42
Methanol	8.2	11
Ethanol	8.7	38
Isopropanol	7.3	60
Methyl ether	9.5	17
Isopropyl ether	7.3	72
Acetone	9.7	19
Acetaldehyde	7.6	430

Rate constants are in molecules, cubic centimeters, and seconds.
Subscript (1) refers to hydrogen abstraction reaction.
Subscript (2) refers to recombination of methyl radicals:

$$CH_3 + CH_3 \rightarrow C_2H_6, \quad E_2 \simeq 0.$$

Acetaldehyde values from Volman and Brinton.[64] Other values from Trotman-Dickenson and Steacie.[62]

oxidation of the oxygenated molecule as well as of the hydrocarbon molecule is the abstraction of a hydrogen atom by a free radical or an oxygen molecule. The rates of hydrogen abstraction by methyl radicals have been intensively studied by Steacie and his school, and Table 9 shows the activation energies for hydrogen abstraction from some common hydrocarbons and oxygenated molecules and the ratios of the rate constant for hydrogen abstraction to the square root of the rate constant for methyl radical recombination at 182°C. All the values were obtained by Trotman-Dickenson and Steacie,[62] except that for acetaldehyde, which is taken from the recent work of Volman and Brinton.[64]

In spite of the fact that the temperatures at which many of the measurements were made is lower than the range of rapid oxidation of hydrocarbons and that many radicals besides methyl are capable of abstracting hydrogen, the data are in accord with some well-known facts about partial oxidation, such as the relative stability of methanol and acetone compared to acetaldehyde.

It should be emphasized that the behavior of a pure compound with regard to thermal decomposition is no criterion for its behavior in a reacting system of hydrocarbon and oxygen. Niclause and Letort have shown that the presence of 0.04 per cent of oxygen causes decomposition of acetaldehyde to proceed at measurable rates at temperatures as low as 200°C, where the thermal decomposition in the absence of oxygen is too slow to measure.[46] One oxygen molecule can induce the decomposition of 100 to 300 aldehyde molecules. Furthermore, the oxidation of one substance can induce oxidation or decomposition of a second substance under conditions at which mixtures of the second substance and oxygen will not react. This is frequently observed with both hydrocarbons and oxygenated compounds.

With these facts in mind, the variables which can be controlled to give the highest yields of the desired products from a partial oxidation process can be considered.

(1) The feed stock should obviously be selected to give good yields of the desired products, but the value of any by-products and the cost of their recovery must be carefully appraised and may determine the choice between competitive feeds. If unreacted hydrocarbon is to be recovered from the purge gas stream, the cost of recovery will also affect the choice, since the higher hydrocarbons are more easily removed by condensation or absorption than the lower ones.

(2) The pressure at which the reaction is carried out affects the nature of the reaction products, as discussion of the individual hydrocarbons has shown. The fundamental variables are the partial pressures of hydrocarbon and oxygen; and, if air is used instead of oxygen, the nitrogen

simply serves as a diluent. High pressures favor alcohols over carbonyl compounds and also favor preservation of the carbon structure of the hydrocarbon.

The optimum pressure at which to operate the process will be determined by the degree to which the operating pressure affects not only the reaction but also equipment cost, ease of recovering oxygenated products from the reactor exit gas, and ease of recovering unreacted hydrocarbon from the purge gas.

(3) The reaction temperature, contact time, and degree of conversion of hydrocarbon are all interrelated. In superatmospheric pressure operation where production of olefins is suppressed, temperature can be allowed to vary over a wide range, provided reaction is stopped after the desired degree of conversion is attained. Heat of reaction may be removed by heat exchange. If the reaction is carried out adiabatically, diluents may be added to control the reaction temperature. Steam, in particular, has been patented.[12] An excess of hydrocarbon may also serve as a diluent.

The relationship between the rate of oxidation of the hydrocarbon and the rate of oxidation or decomposition of the products makes it plain that only a limited proportion of the hydrocarbon should be converted in a single pass if the yields of products based on raw material consumed are to be high. The ratio of unreacted hydrocarbon to partial oxidation products should be high at all times. Various practical methods for achieving this condition have been disclosed.[61,65] The conversions per pass must, of course, be appreciable if the equipment is to be of reasonable size, so here again an economic balance must be achieved.

The data of Newitt in Table 3 show that the reaction mixture should be cooled no later than the point at which virtually all the oxygen has disappeared, in order to prevent thermal decomposition of the products.

The fact that reacting hydrocarbon can sensitize the decomposition of oxygenated products shows that any back-mixing of products into the zone of rapid reaction should be avoided.

(4) Inert surfaces are often specified. Several patents have stressed the avoidance of metal oxide surfaces.[40,60] The desirability of preserving or destroying any hydrogen peroxide formed in low-pressure oxidations may influence the choice of reactor surface. Acid surfaces tend to preserve peroxide.

(5) Homogeneous catalysts such as nitrogen oxides or ozone may have beneficial effects, but no reliable data are available to assess them. The hydrogen halide catalysis of oxidations in the very low-temperature range is discussed elsewhere (see Chapter 33).

Figure 5 shows a schematic diagram, synthesized from a number of patents, of the process flows for a typical hydrocarbon oxidation in which only part of the hydrocarbon is converted on each pass through the reactor.

Several partial oxidation processes based on the lower saturated hydrocarbons have reached commercial operation. Some of these deserve particular mention.

The low-pressure oxidation of methane to formaldehyde, using traces of nitrogen oxides as catalyst, has been developed in Germany by the Gutehoffnungshütte. In 1940, a plant was erected in Rumania for which a detailed description is available.[18] The process was operated at very

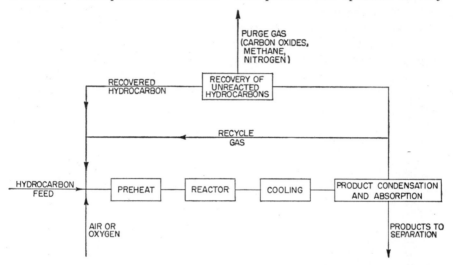

Fig. 5.   Flow plan for partial oxidation of C_2 and higher hydrocarbons.

low conversion per pass with the reaction carried out at 400 to 600°C in short tubes lined with ceramic material. The fresh feed consisted of 1.0 part methane and 3.7 parts air to which was added 0.08 per cent nitric oxide as catalyst. The ratio of methane-air feed to recycle was 1:9. The formaldehyde was scrubbed out of the reactor exit gas to give an aqueous solution of about five per cent concentration. The yield based on methane consumed was 35 per cent.

Further work since World War II has resulted in process improvements. It is claimed that the use of alkali silicates and borates as catalysts and better design of reactors have made possible yields which are not far from quantitative.[40] This process is reported to be under development in this country.

The direct oxidation of methane at high pressures to produce methanol selectively has not been exploited successfully, and this route probably cannot compete with the very efficient and well-developed process of hydrogenation of carbon monoxide.

The Cities Service Oil Company has been engaged in oxidation operations since the 1920's. Their patents and published information disclose oxidation of mixtures of methane and some higher hydrocarbons at moderately high pressures (preferably 250 psig or more), temperatures of 300 to 500°C, and high ratios of hydrocarbon to oxygen. Formaldehyde, methanol, and acetaldehyde are the principal products.[65,68]

Celanese Corporation of American built a plant for the oxidation of propane and higher hydrocarbons near the end of World War II and has since constructed several such units in the United States and Canada.[29] The primary purpose of the operation is to produce acetaldehyde and acetone for the company's cellulose acetate facilities, but by-products such as formaldehyde, methanol, and n-propanol are also sold.

References

1. Antonovskii, V. L., and Shtern, V. Ya., *Doklady Akad. Nauk S.S.S.R.*, **78**, 303 (1951).
2. Barusch, M. R., Crandall, H. W., Payne, J. A., and Thomas, J. R., *Ind. Eng. Chem.*, **43**, 2764 (1951).
3. Barusch, M. R., Neu, J. T., Payne, J. Q., and Thomas, J. R., *Ind. Eng. Chem.*, **43**, 2766 (1951).
4. Bell, E. R., Raley, J. H., Rust, F. F., Seubold, F. H., and Vaughan, W. E., *Discussions Faraday Soc.*, **1951**, No. 10, 242.
5. Bibb, C. F., *Ind. Eng. Chem.*, **24**, 10 (1932).
6. Bone, W. A., and Hill, S. G., *Proc. Roy. Soc. (London)*, **A129**, 434 (1930).
7. Bone, W. A., and Wheeler, R. V., *Trans. Chem. Soc.*, **83**, 1074 (1903).
8. Boomer, E. H., and Naldratt, S. N., *Can. J. Research*, **25B**, 494 (1947).
9. Boomer, E. H., and Thomas, V., *Can. J. Research*, **15B**, 401, 414 (1937).
10. Boord, C. E., "Third Symposium on Combustion and Flame and Explosion Phenomena," p. 416, Baltimore, Williams and Wilkins Co., 1949.
11. Bretton, R. H., Wan, S., and Dodge, B. F., *Ind. Eng. Chem.*, **44**, 594 (1952).
12. British Celanese Limited, British Patent 463,389 (Mar. 30, 1937).
13. Chernyak, N. Ya., and Shtern, V. Ya., *Doklady Akad. Nauk S.S.S.R.*, **78**, 91 (1951).
14. Cook, G. A., U. S. Patent 2,530,509 (Nov. 21, 1950).
15. Cullis, C. F., and Hinshelwood, C. N., *Discussions Faraday Soc.*, **1947**, No. 2, 117.
16. Curme, H. R., U. S. Patent 1,729,711 (Oct. 1, 1929).
17. Deanesley, R. M., and Watkins, C. H., *Chem. Eng. Progress*, **47**, 134 (1951).
18. Field Information Agency, Technical, Final Report No. 1085, "The Oxidation of Methane" by M. M. Holm and E. H. Reichl (1947).
19. Fujimoto, H., *Bull. Chem. Soc. Japan*, **13**, 281 (1938).
20. George, P., and Walsh, A. D., *Trans. Faraday Soc.*, **42**, 94 (1946).
21. Gray, J. A., *J. Chem. Soc.*, **1952**, 3150.
22. Gray, J. A., *Chem. Soc.*, **1953**, 741.
23. Grosse, A. V., and Snyder, J. C., U. S. Patent 2,492,985 (Jan. 3, 1950).
24. Harris, C. R., U. S. Patent 2,533,581 (Dec. 12, 1950).

25. Harris, E. J., and Egerton, A., *Chem. Rev.*, **21**, 287 (1937).
26. Hinshelwood, C. N., *J. Chem. Soc.*, **1948**, 531.
27. Hoare, D. E., and Walsh, A. D., *Proc. Roy. Soc. (London)*, **A215**, 454 (1952).
28. Kahler, E. J., Bearse, A. E., and Stoner, G. G., *Ind. Eng. Chem.*, **43**, 2777 (1951).
29. Keck, D. R., *Oil Gas J.*, **51**, No. 1, 159 (1952).
30. Kooijman, P. L., *Rec. trav. chim.*, **66**, 5 (1947).
31. Kooijman, P. L., *Rec. trav. chim.*, **66**, 491 (1947).
32. Lewis, B., and von Elbe, G., "Combustion, Flames and Explosions of Gases," New York, Academic Press, Inc., 1951.
33. Malherbe, F. E., and Walsh, A. D., *Trans. Faraday Soc.*, **46**, 824, 835 (1950).
34. Marcotte, F. B., and Noyes, W. A., Jr., *Discussions Faraday Soc.*, **1951**, No. 10, 236.
35. Margolis, L. Ya., and Todes, O. M., *Zhur. Obshchey Khim.*, **18**, 1043 (1948).
36. Monceaux, P., *Mem. services chim. etat (Paris)*, **33**, 423 (1947).
37. Mulcahy, M. F. R., *Discussions Faraday Soc.*, **1947**, No. 2, 128.
38. Mulcahy, M. F. R., *Trans. Faraday Soc.*, **45**, 575 (1949).
39. Nalbandyan, A. B., *Doklady Akad. Nauk S.S.S.R.*, **66**, 413 (1949).
40. Nashan, P., *Erdoel und Kohle*, **5**, No. 7, 423 (1952).
41. Nashan, P., U. S. Patent 2,244,210 (June 3, 1941).
42. Newitt, D. M., and Bloch, A. M., *Proc. Roy. Soc. (London)*, **A140**, 426 (1933).
43. Newitt, D. M., and Haffner, A. E., *Proc. Roy. Soc. (London)*, **A134**, 591 (1932).
44. Newitt, D. M., and Schmidt, W. G., *J. Chem. Soc.*, **1937**, 1665.
45. Newitt, D. M., and Szego, P., *Proc. Roy. Soc. (London)*, **A147**, 555 (1934).
46. Niclause, M., and Letort, M., *Compt. rend.*, **226**, 77 (1948).
47. Norrish, R. G. W., *Discussions Faraday Soc.*, **1951**, No. 10, 269.
48. Norrish, R. G. W., *Rev. inst. franc. pétrole*, **4**, 288 (1949).
49. Patry, M., and Monceaux, P., *Compt. rend.*, **221**, 259, 300 (1945).
50. Patry, M., and Monceaux, P., *Trans. Faraday Soc.*, **42**, 341 (1946).
51. Pease, R. N., *Chem. Rev.*, **21**, 279 (1937).
52. Pease, R. N., *J. Am. Chem. Soc.*, **51**, 1839 (1929).
53. Pease, R. N., *J. Am. Chem. Soc.*, **57**, 2296 (1935).
54. Satterfield, C. N., and Wilson, R. E., *Ind. Eng. Chem.*, In publication (1953).
55. Schultz, R. D., (Aerojet Engineering Corp.), Private communication.
56. Semenov, N., "Chemical Kinetics and Chain Reactions," Oxford, 1935.
57. Sherwood, T. K., U. S. Patent 2,412,014 (Dec. 3, 1946).
58. Smith, D. F., and Milner, R. T., *Ind. Eng. Chem.*, **23**, 357 (1931).
59. Steacie, E. W. R., and Plewes, A. C., *Proc. Roy. Soc.* (London), **A146**, 583 (1934).
60. Thomas, C. A., U. S. Patent 2,365,851 (Dec. 26, 1944).
61. Thompson, C. L., Bacon, T. S., and Bludworth, J. E., U. S. Patent 2,004,714 (June 11, 1935).
62. Trotman-Dickenson, A. F., and Steacie, E. W. R., *J. Chem. Phys.*, **19**, 329 (1951).
63. Ubbelohde, A. R., *Proc. Roy. Soc. (London)*, **A152**, 378 (1935).
64. Volman, D. H., and Brinton, R. K., *J. Chem. Phys.*, **20**, 1764 (1952).
65. Walker, J. C., U. S. Patent 2,042,134 (May 26, 1936).
66. Walsh, A. D., *Trans. Faraday Soc.*, **42**, 269 (1946).
67. Wiezevich, P. J., and Frolich, P. K., *Ind. Eng. Chem.*, **26**, 267 (1934).
68. Wirges, M. F., and Palm, J. W., *Oil Gas J.*, **48**, No. 1, 90 (1949).

CHAPTER 37

SPECIAL OXIDATION REACTIONS OF UNSATURATED HYDROCARBONS

Nicholas A. Milas

Department of Chemistry, Massachusetts Institute of Technology

There are two types of oxidation reactions with unsaturated hydro-carbons: (1) the direct attack of double or triple bonds by electrophilic reagents such as ozone, photosensitized molecular oxygen, organic per-acids, free hydroxyl radicals, hydrogen peroxide catalyzed by light or various inorganic oxides capable of forming inorganic peracids, perman-ganates, inorganic oxides including osmium tetroxide, vanadium pentox-ide, chromic oxide, manganese dioxide, mercuric salts, silver iodobenzoate, diazoacetic ester and the like; (2) indirect attack of the methylene groups adjacent to double and triple bonds and to aromatic nuclei by reagents such as molecular oxygen, organic peroxides, selenium dioxide, lead tetra-acetate, chromyl chloride, t-butyl chromate, N-bromosuccinimide, etc. The first type seems to proceed via an ionic mechanism while the second type probably proceeds through a free radical mechanism. Some of these reactions will be discussed in greater detail in the following sections.

Section One

OZONIZATION OF UNSATURATED HYDROCARBONS

The direct attack of double and triple bonds by ozone has been known for a long time and has been utilized by organic chemists to determine the structure of organic compounds. In spite of the immense knowledge in this field only recently has the mechanism of ozonization been eluci-dated. It is now known with certainty that ozone cleaves double bonds and through the researches of Rieche *et al*[17] the structure of ozonides has been clarified. The simplest explanation of the ozonization of a double bond is illustrated by equation (1). In reality ozonides can be classed as

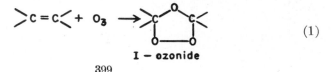

$$\text{>C=C<} + O_3 \longrightarrow \text{>C}\underset{O-O}{\overset{O}{\diagup\diagdown}}\text{C<} \tag{1}$$

I — ozonide

oxydialkyl peroxides.[15] However, it is very difficult to visualize under the extremely mild conditions of ozonization, how the double bond is completely cleaved and the above ozonide formed in one step. Staudinger[19] was the first to suggest that an unstable "molozonide" (II) is initially formed which rearranges to the more stable ozonide (I). To explain this

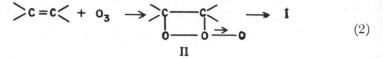

$$(2)$$

rearrangement Criegee[3,11] proposed that the molozonide undergoes an intramolecular change with the momentary formation of a positively polarized oxygen atom which abstracts the remaining two electrons from the carbon-carbon bond and rearranges into the neutral ozonide. The whole process of ozonization therefore may be viewed as an ionic reaction in which the ozone acts as an electrophilic reagent.

The polar nature of ozone has been established by Lewis and Smyth[8,12] who proposed that the middle oxygen atom is positively polarized, thus the structure most generally accepted for ozone is the obtuse-angled structure with the oxygen at the apex being positive. Under the influence of the polar ozone molecule a double bond is also polarized in such a manner that the π-electrons attach themselves to the positive oxygen atom of the ozone molecule. The mechanism of such a reaction may be illustrated as follows:

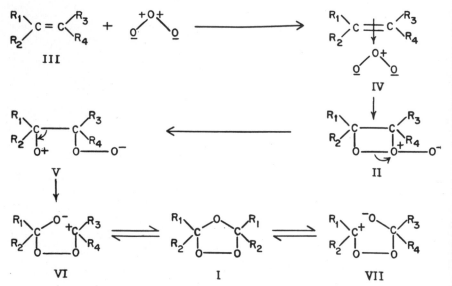

All ionic intermediates are probably formed instantaneously with the zwitter ions (VI) and (VII) existing in equilibrium with the neutral ozonite (I). If there are no other ionic species present to combine with the zwitter ions (VI or VII) either the *neutral* ozonide is formed or these ions decompose spontaneously into ketones or aldehydes and the zwitter ions (VIII) and (IX) which dimerize to form the highly explosive alkylidene peroxides (X) and (XI). As a rule these peroxides are not the main prod-

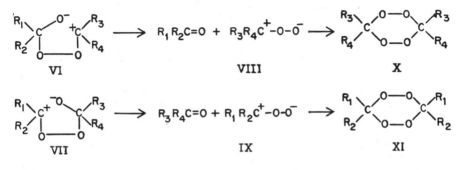

ucts of ozonization and the amounts formed depend upon the solvent, the temperature of ozonization and the groups attached to the double bond.[7,14,16] Owing to their stability and relative insolubility in various organic solvents these peroxides can be isolated easily from ozonization reactions. Table I shows some of the yields of these peroxides under various solvent and temperature conditions.

TABLE I. ALKYLIDENE PEROXIDES FROM THE OZONIZATION OF OLEFINS

Olefin	Solvent	Temp. of Ozonization (°C)	Peroxide	M.P.	Yield (%)
Tetramethylethylene[16]	n-Pentane	−20°	Diacetone	132–133°	15.2
iso-Butylene[16]	n-Pentane	−50°	"	131–132°	20.0
Styrene[14]	CCl₄	Room	Dibenzaldehyde	200°(d.)	1.7
Stilbene[14]	C₆H₆	"	"	"	9.6
α-Methylstyrene[16]	n-Pentane	−20°	Diacetophenone	182–183°	13.0
2-Phenyl, 3-methyl butene-2[16]	n-Pentane	−50°	Diacetone	132–133°	10.7
1,1-Diphenylethylene[14]	n-Hexane	Ice-salt	Dibenzophenone	206–208°	5.8
1,1-Diphenylethylene[16]	n-Pentane	−20°	"	"	15.1
1,1-Diphenylbutene-1[14]	CCl₄	Room	"	"	12.0
1,1-Diphenyl-2-acetoxy-ethene[16]	n-Pentane	−20°	"	"	13.0
Triphenylethylene[14]	CCl₄	Ice-salt	Mixture	184°(d.)	—
Tetraphenylethylene[14]	CCl₄	0°	Dibenzophenone	206–208°	53–57
Tetraphenylethylene[16]	CCl₄	0°	"	"	56
Tetraphenylethylene[16]	Ethylacetate	20°	"	200–205°	20

With the possible exception of 1,2-dimethylcyclopentene ozonide (XII)[6] very few ozonides have been isolated in the monomeric form from the ozonization of compounds containing tertiary-tertiary double bonds.[7] Other ozonides isolated in the pure state include those from cyclopentene (XIII) and cyclohexene (XIV) and their monomethyl derivatives.[4]

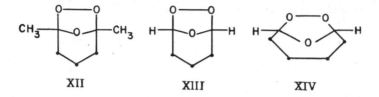

When ozonizations are carried out in the presence of carbonium ions neither the ozonides nor the alkylidene peroxides (X, XI) are formed but instead peroxides of the type (XV) and (XVI) have been isolated in good yields as the primary products.[16] The formation of these peroxides can be accounted for by the assumption that carbonium ions react with the intermediate zwitter ions (VI and VII). Using *t*-butyl carbonium ions this can be illustrated as follows:

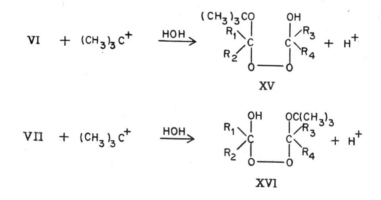

The method most suitable for these ozonizations, and one which is practical and easily adapted to large scale operations is the countercurrent circulatory method.[16] Fig. 1 shows the apparatus employed and consists of two independent circulatory systems. One consists of a circulating pump A and a copper coil B which is immersed in a bath which is usually kept at 0° but may be anywhere between room temperature and −70°C, depending upon the temperature desired for the ozonization. The liquid (ethylene glycol, or any other suitable liquid) circulates around the reaction chamber C, then through a column D filled with glass beads to increase the surface, then back to the pump A. This gives a very efficient cooling system. The other circulating system is composed of a solid glass piston E machined to fit into a block of Teflon F which is not attacked by ozone. The piston E is attached to an eccentric G which is operated by a motor of variable speed. On the other side of the Teflon block is a ground glass joint which is sealed as shown to two ground glass valves H and H'. The product to be ozonized is dissolved in *tert*-butyl alcohol containing enough sulfuric acid to produce one mole of

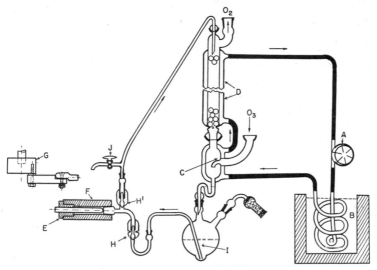

Fɪɢ. 1.   Countercurrent ozonization apparatus.

tert-butyl carbonium ions per double bond present in the compound to be ozonized. The mixture is placed in the flask I which can be refrigerated if necessary and from which it is pumped and circulated through the column and the reaction chamber. The stopcock J serves as a convenient outlet for withdrawing samples for the study of the course of ozonization.

To study the efficiency with which ozone is converted into stable organic peroxides, the latter were estimated quantitatively by the iodometric method and the values compared with the amount of ozone used. The peroxides formed were isolated and analyzed and the values obtained compared with those calculated on the basis that one mole of ozone was converted to one mole of peroxide of the type shown by (XV or XVI). These values are shown in Table II.

TABLE II. OZONIZATION OF CERTAIN OLEFINS IN THE PRESENCE OF *tert*-BUTYL CARBONIUM IONS

Olefin	Yield of Peroxide per Mole of O_3 Used (in %)	Peroxide Isolated	Active Oxygen (O) (in %)	
			Calcd.	Found
2-Methylbutene-2	45.0	$C_9H_{20}O_4$	8.33	7.20
Tetramethylethylene	57.0	$C_{10}H_{22}O_4$	7.76	8.0
Styrene	92.0	$C_{12}H_{18}O_4$	7.08	7.11
α-Methylstyrene	86.0	$C_{13}H_{20}O_4$	6.67	6.60
1,1-Diphenylethylene	100.0	$C_{18}H_{22}O_4$	5.33	5.19
D-Limonene (one —C=C—)	85.7	$C_{14}H_{26}O_4$	6.20	5.50
p-Menthene-8	68.0	$C_{14}H_{28}O_4$	6.16	6.0

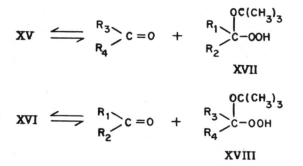

Peroxides of the type (XV) and (XVI) may be considered as either hemiperketals or hemiperacetals depending on the nature of the groups originally attached to the double bond, and therefore are expected to lose easily aldehydes or ketones and go over to more stable peroxides of the type (XVII or XVIII). This is especially true if such peroxides are subjected to a high vacuum. Thus, the peroxides obtained from tetramethylethylene, α-methylstyrene, p-menthene-8 and 1,1-diphenylethylene were converted to the peroxides (XIX), (XX), (XXI) and (XXII) respectively.

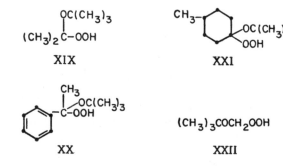

The corresponding methyl derivatives of peroxides of this type (**XXIII**, **XXIV** and **XXV**) have also been isolated by Criegee and Lohaus[7] from the ozonization in methanolic solutions of tetramethylethylene, bicyclohexylidene and $\Delta^{9,10}$-decalin respectively.

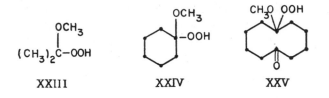

XXIII	**XXIV**	**XXV**

The ozonization of acetylenes follows somewhat along the same lines as that of the olefins. Acetylene ozonides are not known but the course of the ozonization has been clarified recently by Criegee and Lederer[5] who succeeded in isolating the peroxide (**XXX** or **XXXI**) from the ozonization of the dibenzoate of 1,4-butynediol in a mixture of acetic acid and carbon tetrachloride. In the mechanism ($R = C_6H_5COOCH_2$—) outlined below peroxides of the type shown (**XXX**) are known to decompose into dicarboxylic acids or their derivatives. In most of the ozonizations of acetylenes prior to the work of Criegee and Lederer the main products isolated were dicarboxylic acids (see L. Long[13]).

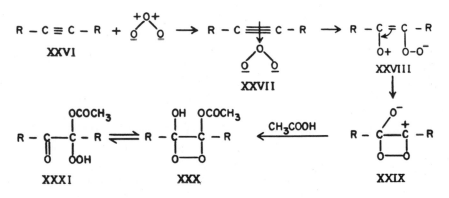

No account on ozonization reactions would be complete without a discussion of the extensive kinetic studies of Wibaut and his school on the ozonization of aromatic hydrocarbons.[20,21] The ozonization of aromatic hydrocarbons must proceed in a similar manner as that of an aliphatic double bond. Since there are no double bonds present in an aromatic ring system, it has been assumed by the Dutch workers[9,10] that under the influence of the polar ozone molecule the distribution of π-electrons is so modified that one pair is localized in one of the carbon atoms which is attacked by the ozone molecule while the other π-electrons are distributed over the remaining five carbon atoms to form a state of lowest energy. On the basis of kinetic measurements Wibaut et al[1,18,23] reported that the formation of benzene triozonide takes place by three bimolecular reactions, the first being much slower than the subsequent two reactions so that the total velocity of the reaction is determined by the speed of the first reaction. The velocity constant for benzene at $-30°$ has been found to be 5×10^{-5} (millimole^{-1}/min^{-1}). The mechanism of the reaction has been given as follows:

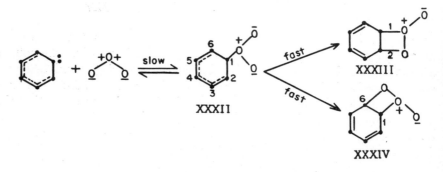

In the case of benzene (XXXIII) and (XXXIV) are identical but differ in alkylated benzenes. The complete cleavage of the 1,2 or 1,6 carbon-carbon bonds and the formation of the ozonides take place as has already been explained in connection with the cleavage of the aliphatic double bond. The remaining two double bonds have now assumed aliphatic properties and the subsequent two ozonization reactions are immeasurably fast.

Ordinarily the rate of ozone addition to most aromatic hydrocarbons is somewhat slow, but it can be catalyzed by "Lewis acids" such as aluminum chloride, ferric chloride and boron trifluoride.[2,25] This constitutes a strong evidence that the ozone attack of aromatic compounds is of an electrophilic nature. Apparently the catalyst forms a complex with ozone which enhances its electrophilic character by stabilizing one of its resonance structures. It also influences the polarizability of the aromatic nucleus.

$$F_3B + O \overset{+O+}{\diagdown} O \rightleftharpoons F_3\bar{B} \leftarrow O \overset{+}{-} O \overset{+}{-} O^-$$
$$XXXV$$

Kinetic measurements of ozonization reactions of aromatic compounds have yielded some very interesting results with regard to the effect of various substituents on the velocity of these reactions. A summary is given in Table III of the various series studied.

TABLE III. THE EFFECT OF SUBSTITUENTS ON THE VELOCITY OF OZONIZATION REACTIONS[22,23]

1. $C_6H_6 > C_6H_5F > C_6H_5Cl \simeq C_6H_5Br$
2. $C_6H_5CH_3 > C_6H_5CH_2Cl > C_6H_5CHCl_2 > C_6H_5CCl_3$
3. $C_6H_5CH_2COOC_2H_5 > C_6H_5COOC_2H_5$
4. $p\text{-}C_6H_4(CH_3)_2 > m\text{-}C_6H_4(CH_3)_2 \simeq o\text{-}C_6H_4(CH_3)_2 > C_6H_5CH_3 > C_6H_6$
5. $C_6H_6 < C_6H_5CH_3 < C_6H_5C_2H_5, C_6H_5C_3H_7, C_6H_5C_4H_9$
6. $C_6H_6 < C_6H_5CH_3 < C_6H_4(CH_3)_2 < C_6H_3(CH_3)_3 < C_6(CH_3)_6$
7. $C_6H_6 > C_5H_5N < \alpha\text{-}CH_3\text{-}C_5H_4N$
8. Naphthalene > quinoline, isoquinoline $\gg$ benzene

From these results it may be seen that alkyl substituents have a definite accelerating effect while halogens have a retarding effect on the velocity of ozonization. This is also true with pyridine and α-methyl pyridine. Then again, the position of the alkyl groups in the benzene ring influences the velocity of ozonization. Naphthalene, as one may expect, ozonizes more rapidly than quinoline or benzene. The velocity of these ozonizations seems to parallel the velocity with which the same compounds are brominated, chlorinated or nitrated.

References to Section One

1. Badger, G. M., *Rec. trav. chim.*, **71**, 468 (1952).
2. Boer, H., Sixma, F. L. j., and Wibaut, J. P., *ibid.*, **70**, 509, 1005 (1951).
3. Criegee, R., *Ann.*, **560**, 127 (1948).
4. Criegee, R., Blust, G., and Lohaus, G., *ibid.*, **583**, 2 (1953).
5. Criegee, R., and Lederer, M., *ibid.*, **583**, 29 (1953).
6. Criegee, R., and Lohaus, G., *Ber.*, **86**, 1 (1953).
7. Criegee, R., and Lohaus, G., *Ann.*, **583**, 6 (1953).
8. Dewar, M. J. S., *J. Chem. Soc.*, **1948**, 1299.
9. Ketelaar, J. A. A., and Van Dranen, J., *Rec. trav. chim.*, **69**, 477 (1950).
10. Kooyman, E. C., and Ketelaar, J. A. A., *ibid.*, **65**, 859 (1946).
11. Lefler, J. E., *Chem. Rev.*, **45**, 385 (1949).
12. Lewis, G. L., and Smyth, C. P., *J. Am. Chem. Soc.*, **61**, 3063 (1929).
13. Long, L., Jr., *Chem. Rev.*, **27**, 437 (1940).
14. Marvel, C. S., and Nichols, V., *J. Am. Chem. Soc.*, **60**, 1455 (1938).
15. Milas, N. A., *Encyclopedia of Chem. Technol.*, **10**, 71 (1953).
16. Milas, N. A., Davis, P., and Nolan, J. T., *J. Am. Chem. Soc.*, **76**, April (1955).
17. Rieche, A., Meister, R., and Sauthoff, H., *Ann.*, **553**, 187 (1942).
18. Sixma, F. L. J., and Wibaut, J. P., *Rec. trav. chim.*, **71**, 473 (1952).
19. Staudinger, H., *Ber.*, **58**, 1088 (1925).
20. Waters, W. A., *Ann. Reports*, **49**, 110 (1952).
21. Wibaut, J. P., *Bull. soc. chim.*, **1950**, M996.
22. Wibaut, J. P., and Sixma, F. L. J., *Rec. trav. chim.*, **71**, 761 (1952).
23. Wibaut, J. P., Sixma, F. L. J., Kampschmidt, L. W. F., and Boer, H., *ibid.*, **69**, 1355 (1950).

Section Two

PHOTOSENSITIZED OXIDATION OF UNSATURATED HYDROCARBONS

In 1926 Moureu, Dufraisse and Dean[5] made the significant observation that under the influence of light certain hydrocarbons of the acene family absorb molecular oxygen to form labile peroxides which upon heating in the dark revert to their original components. For example, under these conditions, 9,10-diphenyl anthracene (I) forms the transannular or endoperoxide (II) which loses oxygen on heating and reverts to the original hydrocarbon.[1,2,3] Somewhat later Windaus and Brunken[14] found that

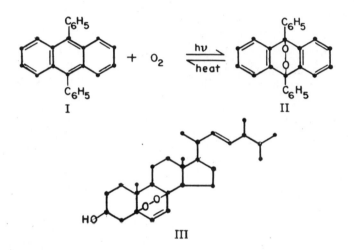

the photooxidation of ergosterol, to produce a similar type but more stable peroxide (III), was greatly accelerated by the presence of fluorescent dyes, such as eosin and erythrosin.

Ergosterol peroxide was found to be of the same type as ascaridole (V), a naturally occurring peroxide, which was synthesized by the photooxidation of a dilute alcoholic solution of α-terpinene (IV) in the presence of natural photosensitizers found in spinach or stinging nettle leaves.[12] More recently Schenck[9] reported that a number of photosensitizers such as eosin, methylene blue, methyl violet, fluorescein, protoporphyrin, chlorophyll, rubrene, anthracene, tetracene, acridine, etc. are capable of accelerating the autooxidation of α-terpinene to ascaridole. Of these, eosin and methylene blue are the ones most frequently employed as photosensitizers in these reactions. Unlike the labile peroxides of the acene family, ascaridole does not revert to its original components when heated, but isomerizes into the more stable 1-methyl-4-isopropyl-1,4-oxido-2-epoxy cyclohexane (VI).

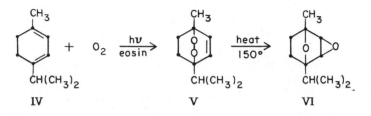

IV   V   VI

Photosensitized auto-oxidation reactions have now been extended to include numerous unsaturated hydrocarbons, both cyclic and open chain, with conjugated as well as isolated double bonds. As a rule the yields obtained in these reactions are good and owing to their high degree of selectivity and predictability they have been recommended for preparative purposes.

The photosensitized oxidation of cyclodienes leads to the formation of endocycloperoxenes while that of the open-chain dienes leads to the formation of the exocycloperoxenes (VII).[4] This reaction is analogous to the Deals-Alder reaction of dienophiles with conjugated systems.

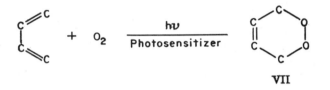

VII

As in the case of conjugated dienes, the photosensitized autoxidation of monoolefins leads to the direct addition of molecular oxygen to the double bond with a subsequent shift of a proton from the allylic carbon atom to form olefinic hydroperoxides in good yields.[6] This reaction, as it

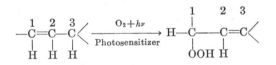

will be shown later, is an ionic reaction and differs from the unsensitized autoxidation of olefins which proceeds by a free radical mechanism. However, in certain unsubstituted cyclic olefins like cyclopentene and cyclohexene the products produced by either the photosensitized or unphotosensitized autoxidations are essentially the same. Table I gives a list of some of the unsaturated hydrocarbons oxidized by the photosensitized method and the type of peroxides obtained.

In order to clarify Table I, a few representative examples may now be considered in more detail. Among the cyclodienes the photosensitized oxidation of α-terpinene has already been discussed. The photosensitized oxidation of cyclopentadiene is of interest since it yields an endocyclo-peroxide (VIII) which decomposes at room temperature to give a mixture of the two unsaturated keto-alcohols (IX) and (X), both of which yield the same hydrogenation product (XI).

TABLE I. PHOTOSENSITIZED AUTOXIDATION OF UNSATURATED HYDROCARBONS

Cyclic Dienes	Type of Peroxide		Reference
Cyclopentadiene	Endocyclic Peroxide		6
1,3-Cyclohexadiene	"	"	7
2-Methyl-1,3-cyclohexadiene	"	"	6
α-Terpinene	"	"	7,11
α-Phellandrene	"	"	11
α-Pyronene	"	"	6
β-Pyronene	"	"	6
Open Chain Dienes			
1,3-Hexadiene	Exocyclic Peroxide		6
1,3-Dimethylbutadiene	"	"	6
2,3-Dimethylbutadiene	"	"	6
Alloöcimene	"	"	6
Fulvenes			
Dimethylfulvene	"	"	6
Methylethylfulvene	"	"	6
Pentamethylfulvene	"	"	6
Phenylfulvene	"	"	6
Diphenylfulvene	"	"	6
Cyclic Monoolefins			
Cyclopentene	Hydroperoxide		6
1-Methyl-1-cyclopentene	"		6
Cyclohexene	"		6
1-Methylcyclohexene	"		6
1,2-Dimethylcyclohexene	"		6
Cyclooctene	"		6
α-Pinene	"		10
β-Pinene	"		10
Dipentene	"		6
Limonene	"		6
Carvomenthene	"		6
Terpinolene	"		6
Open Chain Monoolefins			
1-Heptene	"		6
1-Octene	"		6
1-Dodecene	"		6
1-Hexadecene	"		6
Diisobutylene	"		6

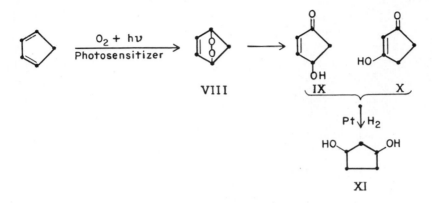

The photosensitized oxidation of 1,3-hexadiene yields the exocyclic peroxide (XII).

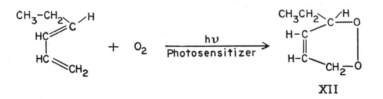

The photosensitized oxidation of 1,2-dimethylcyclohexene[6] leads exclusively to hydroperoxides (XIV) and (XV) which are produced by the shift of a proton either from one of the methyl groups or from the cyclohexane ring to the negatively polarized oxygen atom of the peroxy group.

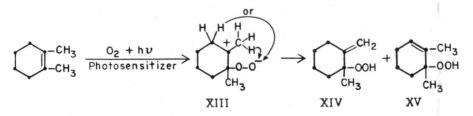

Of particular interest is the photosensitized oxidation of α- and β-pinenes. α-Pinene (XVI) gives in 80 per cent yield *trans*-pinocarveyl hydroperoxide (XVII)[10] which goes over on reduction with sodium sulfite to *trans*-pinocarveol (XVIII) and on spontaneous decomposition to pinocarveone (XIX). The autoxidation of α-pinene in the absence of photosensitizers yields only the verbenyl hydroperoxide (XX).[13]

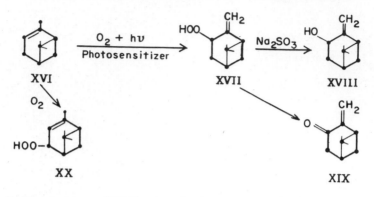

Similarly, β-pinene (XXI) gives in 80 per cent yield myrtenyl hydroperoxide (XXII)[10] which goes over on reduction with sodium sulfite to myrtenol (XXIII).

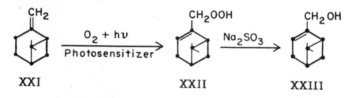

Schenck[6] also found that photosensitized oxidation of terminal double bonds proceeds more slowly than with other double bonds. For example, the ring double bond in dipentene can be preferentially oxidized into a hydroperoxide without affecting the terminal double bond.

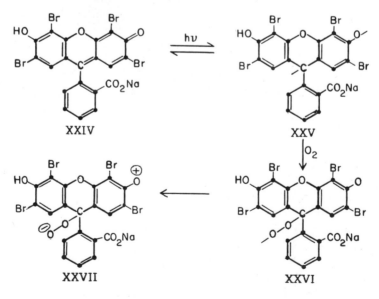

That photosensitized autoxidations are ionic in character was shown by Schenck.[9] He argued that in absorbing light a dye like eosin (XXIV) becomes activated and changes into a diradical (XXV). In the absence of any reactive species this diradical reverts to the normal eosin molecule with the evolution of energy (fluorescence). However, the presence of molecular oxygen, which also behaves as a diradical, converts the eosin diradical into a complex diradical (XXVI) which changes spontaneously into a zwitter ion (XXVII).

In the presence of light and zwitter ions the double bonds of an acceptor molecule become polarized so that the π-electrons become more easily available. The complex zwitter ion (XXVII) releases the oxygen molecule as another zwitter ion and goes back to the normal eosin (XXIV). To explain the final products of photosensitized autoxidations the oxygen molecule must be transferred as a zwitter ion with the positive end attached to the π-electrons of the double bond to form a new zwitter ion (XXVIII) which rearranges into a stable hydroperoxide. Using α-pinene as the acceptor these steps may be illustrated as follows:

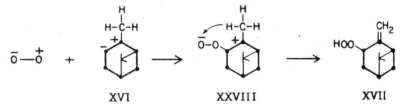

XVI   XXVIII   XVII

References to Section Two

1. Bergmann, W., and MacLean, M. J., *Chem. Rev.* **28**, 397 (1941).
2. Dufraisse, C., *Bull. soc. chim.*, **53**, 823 (1933); **6**, 422 (1939).
3. Etienne, A., *"Traite Chimie Organique"* **17**, 1299 (1949).
4. Milas, N. A., *Encyclopedia of Chem. Techn.*, **10**, 67 (1953).
5. Moureau, C., Dufraisse, C., and Dean, P. M., *C. rend.*, **182**, 1440, 1584 (1926).
6. Schenck, G. O., *Angew. Chem.*, **64**, 12 (1952).
7. *Ibid.*, **56**, 101 (1944).
8. *Idem., Naturwiss.*, **40**, 229 (1953).
9. *Ibid.*, **40**, 205 (1953).
10. Schenck, G. P., Eggert, H., and Denk, W., *Ann.*, **584**, 177 (1953).
11. Schenck, G. P., Kinkel, K. G., and Mertens, H., *ibid.*, **584**, 125 (1953).
12. Schenck, G. O., and Ziegler, K., *Naturwiss.*, **32**, 157 (1944).
13. Suzuki, K., *Bull. Inst. Phys. Chem. Res.* (Tokyo), **14**, 14 (1935).
14. Windaus, A., and Brunken, H., *Ann.* **460**, 225 (1928).

Section Three

OXIDATION OF UNSATURATED HYDROCARBONS BY PEROXYACIDS OR ORGANIC PERACIDS

The oxidation of unsaturated hydrocarbons by organic peracids was first accomplished by Prileschajew[31] who used perbenzoic acid to convert a number of olefinic substances into their α-epoxy derivatives or oxiranes. This reaction is quite general and is usually carried out under mild conditions in solvents such as chloroform, ether, acetone or dioxane. Other peracids which have since been introduced include, peracetic,[6] permonocamphoric,[24] perfuroic,[25] permonophthalic,[7,9] performic,[4,43] and peroxytrifluoroacetic[12] acid. Peracetic acid is available commercially in 40 per cent solution in acetic acid stabilized with α,α'-dipicolinic acid.[8] With performic, peracetic and trifluoroperacetic acids, the epoxy derivatives formed as intermediates react with the excess acids present and lead to the formation of α-glycol derivatives.

Most of the low molecular weight peracids have been prepared by the direct reaction of the acid with strong solutions of hydrogen peroxide, while higher peracids have been prepared by the action of alkali alkoxides with the corresponding diacyl peroxides and subsequent acidification.[40,41] Since benzaldehyde yields, on auto-oxidation, perbenzoic acid, induced epoxidations have been carried out by the direct oxidation with oxygen of mixtures of benzaldehyde and olefinic substances.[19,44] Representative examples of epoxidations and/or hydroxylations with various organic peracids are listed in Table I.

TABLE I. OXIDATION OF HYDROCARBONS BY ORGANIC PERACIDS

Hydrocarbon	Formula	Peracid	Yield (in Per Cent)		Reference
			Epoxide	Glycol	
Straight Chain Hydrocarbons					
Ethylene	$C_2{}^{14}H_4$	PB	30–53		45
1,3-Butadiene	C_4H_6	PB	42 (mono)		33
"		PF		73	18
2-Butene	C_4H_8	PA		85	18
"		PF		54	4
Isoprene	C_5H_8	PB	30–60 (mono)		33, 34
1-Pentene	C_5H_8	PTFA		71(1:2)	12, 13
2-Pentene	C_5H_8	PTFA		74(2:3)	12, 13
3-Methyl-1,2-butadiene	C_5H_8	PB	—		15
1,4-Pentadiene	C_5H_{10}	PA	—		16
Amylenes	C_5H_{10}	PA	—		26
Diallyl	C_6H_{10}	PA	60–70	63–100	2, 3, 40, 41
"		PF		65–75	1, 18, 14
1,5-Hexadiene	C_6H_{10}	PB	66	—	15, 48
2,4-Hexadiene	C_6H_{10}	PC	mono		24
"		PF		58	1, 23
1-Hexene	C_6H_{12}	PTFA		80	12, 13
Tetramethylethylene	C_6H_{12}	PFU	—		23
1,6-Heptadiene	C_7H_{12}	PB	—		15
2,4-Dimethylpentene-2	C_7H_{14}	PC	—		24
1-Heptene	C_7H_{14}	PB	—		22
2,3-Dimethyl-2-butene	C_8H_{12}	PB	—		32

TABLE I. OXIDATION OF HYDROCARBONS BY ORGANIC PERACIDS. (*Continued*)

Yield (in Per Cent)

Hydrocarbon	Formula	Peracid	Epoxide	Glycol	Reference
1,7-Octadiene	C_8H_{14}	PB	—	58–70	42
1-Octene	C_8H_{16}	PF	—		15
"		PTFA		80	12, 13
1,8-Nonadiene	C_9H_{16}	PB	mono		15
"		PB	100		37
1-Dodecene	$C_{12}H_{24}$	PTFA		95	12, 13
1-Tetradecene	$C_{14}H_{28}$	PTFA		92	12, 13
Cyclic Hydrocarbons					
Cyclopentene	C_5H_8	PB	80–90		3, 47
"		PF		60 *trans*	28
"		PA		17 *trans*	28
Cyclopentadiene	C_5H_8	PA	46 (*trans*-cyclopentene-1,2-diol)		29
Cyclohexene	C_6H_{10}	PB	100		3, 21
"		PA		63–100 *trans*	3
"		PF		65–75 *trans*	3
"		PTFA		82 *trans*	12, 13
Cycloheptene	C_7H_{12}	PB	100		5
"		PF		53 *trans*	27
Cycloöctatetraene	C_8H_8	PB	40–60		17, 35
"		PA	55		11
Cycloöctene	C_8H_{14}	PB	65		35
"		PF		71 $\begin{cases} 1:2 \ trans \\ 1:4 \ (?) \end{cases}$	10
"		PA	86		10
cis-Cyclodecene	$C_{10}H_{18}$	PF		cyclodecene-1-ol-3 cyclodecandiol-1,6	30
trans-Cyclodecene	$C_{10}H_{18}$	PF		cyclodecanone cyclodecandiol-1,6	30

PB = Perbenzoic acid. PF = Performic acid. PA = Peracetic acid. PC = Percamphoric acid. PFU = Perfuroic acid. PTFA = Pertrifluoroacetic acid.

Like ozone organic peracids are electrophilic reagents and reactions with olefins containing π-electrons may be considered ionic and the reaction rate normally increases as the availability of these electrons increases. For example, as the hydrogen atoms of an olefin are successively replaced by electron-releasing groups the rate of reaction with an organic peracid increases.[39] If the rate of reaction of ethylene with an organic peracid is taken as unity, propylene will react twenty-two times faster, 2-methyl-1-propene 484, 2-butene 490, 2-methyl-2-butene 6526, cyclobutene 107, cyclopentene 1026, 1-methyl-cyclopentene 11,684 and tetramethyl-ethylene is too fast to be measured. On the basis of these results one can predict that a compound containing multiple double bonds like α- or β-carotenes would tend to form an epoxide preferentially on a tertiary-tertiary double bond, namely on the double bond of the β-ionone ring. This has actually been found to be the case.[20]

Since peracids are electrophilic reagents they tend to provide electro-positively polarized hydroxyl groups[36] which lose protons readily, as soon as they attach themselves to the π-electrons of the double bond; the epoxide and the acid corresponding to the peracid used are the final products of the reaction.

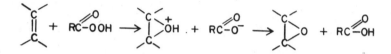

In epoxidations the oxygen addition to the double bond is usually considered to be a *cis*-addition,[49] but when the epoxide is hydrolized or allowed to react with an organic acid an inversion occurs with the formation of the *trans* glycol or its hemiacylated derivative. With performic, peracetic and pertrifluoroacetic acids the principal products are the *trans* hemiacylated glycols.

Acetylenes are also known to react with organic peracids but in most cases the triple bond is completely cleaved.[38]

References to Section Three

1. Adkins, H., and Roebuck, A. K., *J. Am. Chem. Soc.*, **70**, 4041 (1948).
2. Arbusow, B. A., and Michailow, B. M., *J. Prakt. Chem.*, **127**, 92 (1930).
3. Böeseken, J., *Rec. trav. chim.*, **47**, 683 (1928).
4. Böeseken, J., and Cohen, R., *ibid.*, **47**, 839 (1928).
5. Böeseken, J., and Derx, H. G., *ibid.*, **40**, 529 (1921).
6. Böeseken, J., Smit, W. C., and Gaster, A., *Proc. Acad. Sci.*, Amsterdam, **32**, 377 (1929).
7. Böhme, H., *Ber.*, **70**, 379 (1937).
8. Buffalo Electrochemical Co.
9. Chakravorty, P. N., and Levin R. H., *J. Am. Chem. Soc.*, **64**, 2317 (1942).
10. Cope, A. C., Fenton, S. W., and Spencer, C. F., *ibid.*, **74**, 5884 (1952).
11. Cope, A. C., and Tiffany, B. D., *ibid.*, **73**, 4158 (1951).
12. Emmons, W. D., and Ferris, A. F., *ibid.*, **75**, 4623 (1953).
13. Emmons, W. D., Pagano, A. S., and Freeman, J. P., *ibid.*, **76**, 3472 (1954).
14. English, J., and Gregory, J. D., *ibid.*, **69**, 2120 (1947).
15. Everett, J. L., and Kon, G. A. R., *J. Chem. Soc.*, **1950**, 3131.
16. Findley, T. W., and Swern, D., U. S. Pat. 2,567,930; *Chem. Abs.*, **46**, 3560 (1952).
17. Friess, S. L., and Boekelheide, V., *J. Am. Chem. Soc.*, **71**, 4145 (1949).
18. Himel, C. M., and Edmonds, L. O., U. S. Pat. 2,555,927; *Chem. Abs.* **46**, 524 (1952).
19. Jorissen, W. P., and van der Beck, P. A. A., *Rec. trav. chim.*, 45, 245 (1926).
20. Karrer, P., and Jucker, E., *Helv. chim. Acta*, **28**, 427, 471 (1945).
21. Kötz, A., and Hoffman, W., *J. prakt. chem.*, 110, 101 (1925).
22. Levy, J., and Pernot, R., *Bull. soc. chim.*, **49**, 1838 (1931).

23. Lutz, G. A., Bearse, A. E., Leonard, J. E., and Croxton, F. C., *J. Am. Chem. Soc.,* **70,** 4139 (1948).
24. Milas, N. A., and Cliff, I. S., *ibid.,* **55,** 352 (1933).
25. Milas, N. A., and McAlevy, A., *ibid.,* **56,** 1219 (1934).
26. Mousseron, M., and Winternitz, F., *Bull. soc. chim.,* **1948,** 79.
27. Owen, L. N., and Saharia, G. S., *J. Chem. Soc.,* **1953,** 2582.
28. Owen, L. N., and Smith, P. N., *ibid.,* **1952,** 4026.
29. *Ibid.,* **1952,** 4035.
30. Prelog, V., and Schenker, K., *Helv. chim. Acta* **35,** 2044 (1952).
31. Prileschajew, N., *Ber.,* **42,** 4811 (1909).
32. *Idem., J. Russ, Phys-Chem. Soc.,* **42,** 1387 (1910).
33. Pummerer, R., and Reindel, W., *Ber.,* **66,** 335 (1933).
34. Reindel, G. W., Thesis, Erlangen 1931; *Chem. Abs.,* **27,** 1637 (1933).
35. Reppe, W., Schlichting, O., Klager, K., and Toepel, T., *Ann.,* **560,** 1 (1948).
36. Roitt, I. M., and Waters, W. A., *J. Chem. Soc.,* **1949,** 3060.
37. Rothstein, B., *Bull. soc. chim.,* **2,** 1936 (1935).
38. Schlubach, H. H., and Franzen, V., *Ann.,* **577,** 60 (1952).
39. Swern, D., *J. Am. Chem. Soc.,* **69,** 1692 (1947).
40. *Idem., Chem. Rev.,* **45,** 1 (1949).
41. *Idem.,* in Organic Reactions, ed. by R. Adams, **7,** 378, J. Wiley and Sons, New York (1953).
42. Swern, D., Billen, G. N., and Scanlan, J. T., *J. Am. Chem. Soc.* **68,** 1504 (1946).
43. Swern, D., Billen, G. N. Findley, T. W., and Scanlan, J. T. *ibid.,* **67,** 1786 (1945).
44. Swern, D., Findley, T. W., and Scanlan, J. T. *ibid.,* **66,** 1925 (1944).
45. Tomisek, A. J., and Mahler, H. R., *ibid.,* **73,** 4685 (1951).
46. Weisenborn, F. L., and Taub, D., *ibid.,* **74,** 1329 (1952).
47. Wieland, H., Bergel, F., Schwartz, K., Schepp, R., and Fukelman, L., *Ann.,* **446,** 13 (1926).
48. Wiggins, L. F., and Wood, D. J. C., *J. Chem. Soc.,* **1950,** 1566.
49. Wittnauer, L. P., and Swern, D. L., *J. Am. Chem. Soc.,* **72,** 3364 (1950).

Section Four

DIRECT HYDROXYLATION OF UNSATURATED HYDROCARBONS

The direct hydroxylation of unsaturated hydrocarbons may be accomplished either by the direct attack of certain oxidizing reagents alone or in the presence of catalysts or by the addition of active hydroxyl groups to double bonds. In discussing these oxidations one must bear in mind that not all proceed by the same mechanism; some are stereospecific and lead exclusively to the production of *cis*-glycols while others lead to the production of *trans*-glycols. To the former belong oxidations by feebly alkaline or neutral potassium permanganate, osmium tetroxide, chlorates and hydrogen peroxide catalyzed by traces of osmium tetroxide and by active free hydroxyl groups. To the latter belong oxidations by hydrogen peroxide catalyzed by traces of oxides of metals belonging to the IV, V and VI sub-groups of the Periodic System and which are known to form with hydrogen peroxide unstable peracids rather than peroxides,[57] by

Caro's acid, mercuric salts, silver iodobenzoate, chromyl chloride, chromic acid, and di *tert*-butyl chromate.

a. *Permanganate Oxidations.* In spite of the immense amount of work that has been done in the field of hydroxylations of olefins with permanganate ions, the mechanism of the reaction still remains imperfectly understood. Reactions are usually carried out at low temperatures in dilute solutions in water, acetone or dry pyridine. Through the extensive researches of Wagner[73] and later those of Böeseken[9] it has been established beyond doubt that at low temperatures dilute feebly alkaline or neutral solutions of potassium permanganate attack olefins to yield mainly *cis*-α-glycols. To explain this fact both Wagner[74] and Böeseken[10] postulated the formation of the hypothetical cyclic intermediate (I) which hydrolyzes by a frontal attack to yield *cis*-glycols.

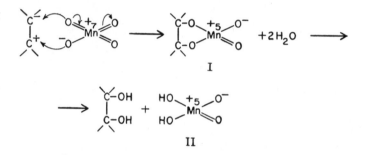

However, there is no experimental evidence at present in support of the existence of the cyclic intermediate (I). The reaction is so fast that attempts to detect such an intermediate met with failure. Oxidations with potassium permanganate, according to Drummond and Waters,[26] are multi-stage processes and while the olefin loses two electrons the manganese undergoes a 3-electron transition in neutral or alkaline medium.

The $\overline{MnO}_4$ ion attacks organic compounds by abstracting one electron from any substrate capable of electron release, and under these conditions no organic compound reduces the $\overline{MnO}_4$ ion beyond the $\overline{MnO}_4^{-2}$ ion which is known to disproportionate readily into the $\overline{MnO}_4$ ion and MnO_2.

Drummond and Waters argue further that if the Wagner-Böeseken cyclic scheme were valid one must assume (1) that an immediate reaction $\overline{MnO}_4^{-3} + \overline{MnO}_4^{-2} \rightarrow 2\overline{MnO}_4$ should follow the hydrolysis of the cyclic complex before the Mn^{+5} is further degraded to Mn^{+4}, and (2) that the formation of the complex should be very much slower than its hydrolysis and that enough $\overline{MnO}_4$ is available to insure the complete oxidation of

$\overset{-3}{\text{MnO}_4}$. These conditions appear to the authors to be too stringent and they feel that it is more probable that an olefin is attacked by two molecules of potassium permanganate and thus is oxidized in two consecutive one-electron stages by the transient radical-ion. An alternate hypothesis would be to retain the cyclic complex which so elegantly accounts for the production of *cis*-glycols by having a second permanganate ion attack the complex before hydrolysis to form a second complex (III)

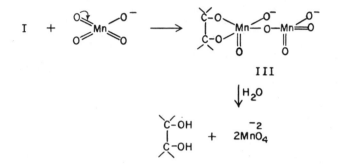

which hydrolyzes into the *cis*-glycol and two manganate ions. This would avoid the formation of the wholly improbable $\overset{-3}{\text{MnO}_4}$ ion and still fulfill the conditions imposed by Drummond and Waters.

b. *The Use of Osmium Tetroxide Alone or as a Catalyst in the Hydroxylation of Unsaturated Hydrocarbons.* About sixty years ago Phillips[54] found that osmium tetroxide was rapidly reduced by ethylene, propylene, isobutylene, acetylene, allylene and carbon monoxide. A little later Makowka[40] reported that acetylene reduces osmium tetroxide to a black lower oxide rather than to osmium metal. Moreover, this reduction was found to be general with all unsaturated substances and was adopted as a characteristic test for unsaturated fats in animal tissues.[29] Soon after these developments K. A. Hofmann[34] discovered that aqueous solutions of neutral chlorates which are poor oxidizing agents could be made to hydroxylate unsaturated substances in the presence of traces of osmium tetroxide. Subsequently this reaction has been modified and improved by several investigators[8] who definitely established that, like potassium permanganate, this reaction was stereospecific and led exclusively to the production of *cis*-α-glycols in good yields.

The use of the chlorate method, however, is limited to aqueous solutions and most of the olefinic hydrocarbons are insoluble in these solutions. A more general method was sought by Milas and his students[46] who discovered that although hydrogen peroxide in *t*-butyl alcohol failed to oxidize unsaturated hydrocarbons it effected their hydroxylation smoothly in the presence of traces of osmium tetroxide. This reaction is of general applicability and is stereo-specific always resulting in the formation of *cis*-glycols. Other solvents such as ether[20], aqueous methanol[16] and acetone[17] and *t*-butyl hydroperoxide[13,31] instead of hydrogen peroxide have been employed, but best results are obtained with the original reagent.

It was also discovered that with polyolefins hydroxylation may be controlled so that one double bond may be hydroxylated exclusively without affecting the others. For example, Maloney[41] found that with natural linoleic acid one of the double bonds was exclusively hydroxylated first before the other was attacked. Cyclopentadiene could also be selectively hydroxylated to give a mixture of 1,2 and 1,4-cyclopentene-diols.[46d,53] This method has been applied recently for the selective oxidation of β-carotene to vitamin A aldehyde.[30,76] In the course of this work it was found that this reagent attacks more readily double bonds which are least substituted and sterically most accessible. Table I records some of the unsaturated hydrocarbons hydroxylated by this method and the main products obtained.

TABLE I. CATALYTIC *cis*-HYDROXYLATION OF UNSATURATED HYDROCARBONS

Olefin	Main Product	Yield (%)
Ethylene[46b]	Ethylene glycol	92
Propylene[46b]	Propylene glycol	68
Isobutylene[46b]	Isobutylene glycol	37.6
Trimethylethylene[46b]	Trimethylethylene glycol	37.8
2-Methylbutene-1[46b]	2-Methylbutanediol-1,2	51
Pentene-2[46b]	Pentanediol-2,3	30
Hexene-3[46b]	Hexanediol-3,4	36
Diallyl[46b]	Hexanetetrol-1,2,5,6	45
Cetene[46b]	Cetene glycol	82
Styrene[46b]	Phenyl ethylene glycol	50
Cyclopentadiene[46d,53]	Cyclopentene-2-*cis*-diol-1,4 + 1,2	30.6
Cyclopentadiene[46d]	Cyclopentanetetrol-1,2,3,4	60.9
Cyclohexene[46b]	*cis*-Cyclohexanediol-1,2	58
Cycloöctene[18]	*cis*-1,2-Cycloöctanediol	11.4
D-Limonene[46b]	p-Menthanetetrol-1,2,8,9	35
Benzene[46b,17]	Phenol	23

Mention has already been made that osmium tetroxide attacks unsaturated groups and in the case of simple olefins it causes cleavage of the double bonds. Criegee,[21] however, discovered that with certain olefins like acenaphthylene, indene, Δ[2,3]-dihydronaphthalene and Δ[9,10]-octalin solid colored addition complexes could be isolated which contain one mole of osmium tetroxide per mole of the olefin. In accordance with a suggestion made by Böeseken[10] that osmium tetroxide adds on to a double bond in the same manner as permanganate ion, Criegee formulated the formation of these complexes or osmic acid esters as follows:

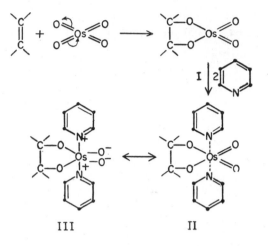

III   II

The osmic acid esters thus obtained are completely insoluble in all common solvents except tertiary bases, especially pyridine from which they were obtained as light colored crystalline products with two molecules of pyridine of crystallization. These are considered as co-ördination complexes having the possible structures II or III. The original osmic acid esters are not easily hydrolyzed even when refluxed with water for long periods of time. However, small quantities of *cis*-glycols can be obtained when the hydrolysis is accomplished in boiling alcoholic hydrochloric acid solutions. The glycols can also be obtained by oxidative hydrolysis with chlorates or hydrogen peroxide, or by reductive hydrolysis with aqueous-alcoholic sodium sulfite solutions, or in non-aqueous solutions with lithium aluminum hydride.

Somewhat later Criegee and his co-workers[21] found that the pyridine complexes can be formed directly and rapidly when the olefins together with osmium tetroxide and pyridine are allowed to react in chloroform solutions, although ethyl acetate, benzene and carbon tetrachloride have also been used as solvents. A large number of olefins have been studied by this method. Moreover, the *cis*-glycols can be regenerated in good yields from the pyridine complexes by mild reductive hydrolysis using formaldehyde and dilute alkali, or by ester interchange using dilute alkali in the presence of mannitol. Table II gives a summary of some of the glycols obtained by this method. It may be seen that with conjugated dienes osmium tetroxide adds always 1,2 rather than 1,4, as in the case of the osmium tetroxide-chlorate method,[8e,16] or the osmium tetroxide-hydrogen peroxide method,[46d] and the glycol obtained by the hydrolysis of the adduct has always the *cis*-1,2 configuration.

This method has been widely used for structural determinations, but the high cost of osmium tetroxide makes it prohibitive for preparative purposes. This method has also been applied to polynuclear and carcino-

TABLE II.[20,5] *cis*-GLYCOLS VIA THE HYDROLYSIS OF OSMIC ACID ESTERS OR OF THEIR PYRIDINE ADDUCTS

Olefin	Yield of osmic acid ester (in per cent)	Yield of ester pyridine adduct (in per cent)	Main hydrolysis product	Yield of glycol (in per cent)
Ethylene	—	100	—	—
Tetramethylethylene	89	69	—	—
Acetylene	—	82 (diester)	—	—
Diphenyl acetylene	—	100 (diester)	—	—
Cyclopentene	97	—	—	—
Cyclohexene	—	44	—	—
Cycloheptene	—	98	*cis*-Cycloheptane-1,2-diol	85
Cyclopentadiene	99 (mono)	98 (mono)	*cis*-Cyclopentane-1,2-diol	86*
α-Pinene	86	35	—	—
Acenaphthylene	98	—	*cis*-Acenaphthene-1,2-diol	84
Indene	99	—	*cis*-Hyndrindene-2,3-diol	66
1,4-Dihydronaphthalene	92	97, 81	*cis*-Tetralin-2,3-diol	78
Δ⁹,¹⁰-Octalin	99	—	*cis*-Decalin-9,10-diol	81
Phenanthrene	—	95	*cis*-9,10-Dihydrophenanthrene-9,10-diol	95

* Monoester first reduced with $H_2 + PtO_2$.

genic hydrocarbons.[17] Badger[5,6] has studied the kinetics of this reaction with several polynuclear hydrocarbons and found it to be of the second order. He further found that in polynuclear aromatic hydrocarbons osmium tetroxide attacks the double bonds which have a greater "double bond character," or greater concentration of π-electrons. It is therefore possible that, as in the case of ozone, osmium tetroxide influences the distribution of π-electrons in such a manner that one pair is localized in one of the carbon atoms which is attacked. For example, with pyrene (IV) and 1,2-benzanthracene (V) osmium tetroxide attacks first the same double bonds as ozone, namely 1,2 and 3,4 respectively while most

IV

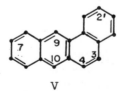

V

reagents substitute at positions 3,5,8 and 10 to give 3,8 and 10 disubstitution products or 3,5,8 and 10 tetrasubstitution products. In general it has been found that when electron-releasing groups were attached to, or were in close proximity to a double bond, the reaction rate with osmium tetroxide was increased, and when electron-attracting groups were present the reaction was retarded.

Mechanism of the Reaction

The fact that *cis*-glycols can be obtained either by the oxidative or reductive hydrolysis of the osmic acid esters led Criegee[20] to support the original hypothesis of Böeseken[10] for all hydroxylation reactions in which osmium tetroxide is used either as a hydroxylating agent or as a catalyst. There is some evidence, however, that seems to be against this view. Hofmann[34b] originally found that the solubility of potassium chlorate in water was increased in the presence of osmium tetroxide and the oxidation potential of the solution was greater than that of each of the components alone. This seems to indicate that a complex is formed between osmium tetroxide and the chlorate. Zelikoff and Taylor[80] have recently studied the kinetics of osmium tetroxide catalyzed oxidation of fumaric and maleic acids by chlorates and came to the conclusion that the rate controlling step was the formation of a complex between osmium tetroxide and the double bonded compounds, the subsequent production of the glycols being very rapid. However, they felt that the complex originally suggested by Böeseken was unlikely in view of the specificity of osmium tetroxide over other oxides. They suggested the possibility of carbon-osmium bonds, a suggestion which in our opinion is unlikely since such a complex should not yield glycols on hydrolysis.

In osmium tetroxide catalyzed hydroxylation of olefins by hydrogen peroxide Milas and co-workers[46] made the suggestion that the reactive species might be perosmic acid which breaks down to yield hydroxyl groups which, in turn, add on to double bonds to form glycols. This suggestion was supported by the fact that hydroxyl groups formed by the photochemical decomposition of hydrogen peroxide added to double bonds to form the same stereoisomeric glycols as those formed by the osmium tetroxide catalyzed hydroxylations.[47] This view, however, is not entirely consistent with our most recent experiments.[49] Osmium tetroxide is well known to form a very weak acid, H_2OsO_5, in water[63,79] It is therefore conceivable that osmium tetroxide would also form a peracid, H_2OsO_6, with hydrogen peroxide, but in water this peracid is so unstable that it decomposes spontaneously into molecular oxygen and osmic acid, H_2OsO_5. In fact, osmium tetroxide is one of the most efficient catalysts for the decomposition of hydrogen peroxide.[71] However, per-

oxyosmic acid, if formed, is perfectly stable for long periods of time, in
t-butyl alcohol. The peroxyosmic acid addition to olefins has been studied
spectroscopically.[49] It has been found that when equimolecular proportions of olefins, such as trimethylethylene and cyclohexene and hydrogen
peroxide in t-butyl alcohol were allowed to react in the presence of osmium tetroxide the maximum at 248 mμ, probably due to peroxyosmic
acid, slowly vanished and a new maximum appeared at 286 mμ. The new
maximum was attributed to the complex (VIII) and was found to be
identical with that observed when equimolecular proportions of osmium
tetroxide and various 1,2-glycols were allowed to react in the absence of
hydrogen peroxide. These results have been interpreted as follows:

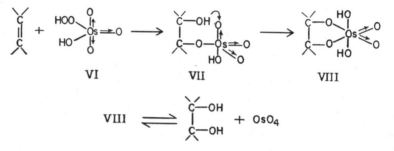

The reaction between osmium tetroxide and 1,2-glycols is an equilibrium reaction and the presence of water shifts the equilibrium to the
right and favors the formation of glycols while its absence causes a cleavage of the glycols with the formation of aldehydes and ketones.[67] Moreover, it is now clear that the intermediate (I) proposed by Böeseken and
supported by Criegee can be oxidized either by chlorates or by hydrogen
peroxide to give (VIII) which breaks down spontaneously into glycols
and osmium tetroxide. Such an interpretation avoids the unlikely hydrolysis step of the osmic acid ester (I) and brings this important reaction in line with the permanganate oxidation of olefins.

    c. Oxidations with Free Hydroxyl Radicals. It has already been men-
tioned that free hydroxyl radicals produced by the photodissociation of
hydrogen peroxide in solution oxidize olefins to 1,2-glycols.[47] For example, allyl alcohol yielded glycerol, crotonic acid dihydroxybutyric
acid, and maleic acid and diethyl maleate mesotartaric acid and diethyl
mesotartrate respectively. Somewhat later Dainton[23] showed that these
radicals can initiate the polymerization of vinyl compounds, while
Baxendale[7] found that they cause the oxidation of benzene to phenol
and diphenyl. Boyland and Sims[11] also reported that naphthalene, under
similar conditions, gives α- and β-naphthols in the ratio of 3.8 to 1. The
free hydroxyl radicals have a very high electron-affinity (~136 kcal)[72]

and are therefore powerful oxidizing agents. All of these reactions can be explained by the assumption that photochemically produced free radicals add on to carbon-carbon double bonds either singly or in pairs. It is not entirely clear at present how such additions lead to the formation of *cis*-glycols, but it is quite possible that hydroxylations of this type are stereospecific. The production of 1,2-glycols may be illustrated as follows:

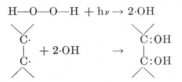

The initiation of the chain polymerization of vinyl compounds may be interpreted as being due to the initial addition of a hydroxyl radical to a double bond.

$$\cdot \overset{|}{C}\!-\!\overset{|}{C}\cdot + \cdot OH \rightarrow HO\!-\!\overset{|}{C}\!-\!\overset{|}{C}\cdot + \cdot \overset{|}{C}\!-\!\overset{|}{C}\cdot \rightarrow HO\!-\!\overset{|}{C}\!-\!\overset{|}{C}\!-\!\overset{|}{C}\!-\!\overset{|}{C}\cdot$$

Reactions of hydroxyl radicals produced by the action of ferrous salts on hydrogen peroxide in acid solution (Fenton's reaction[28]) are too numerous to discuss here.[44,75] However, it should be made clear that these hydroxyl radicals have essentially all the properties of the photochemically produced hydroxyl radicals except that they fail to yield 1,2-glycols with olefins.

In the gaseous state hydroxyl radicals produced by the dissociation of water in an electrodeless discharge seem to be much more powerful oxidizing agents than those formed in solution.[50] They cause the cleavage of olefins to aldehydes and even effect the oxidation of methane largely to carbon dioxide and water.

d. *Catalyzed Hydroxylations of Olefins by Metal Oxides Known to Form Peroxyacids with Hydrogen Peroxide.* 1,2-Glycols are also formed when olefins are allowed to react with hydrogen peroxide in the presence of catalytic amounts of oxides of metals belonging to the IV, V and VI sub-groups of the Periodic System.[45] These metals include Ti, Zr, Th, V, Nb, Ta, Cr, Mo, W and U. Of these only V_2O_5, CrO_3, Ta_2O_5, WO_3 and MoO_3 were investigated. At first the mechanism of hydroxylation in the presence of these oxides as catalysts was thought to be the same as the osmium tetroxide catalyzed hydroxylations. However, on careful examination of the glycol obtained from the hydroxylation of cyclohexene using vanadium pentoxide as catalyst Trepagnier[67] found that the glycol was *trans*-cyclohexanediol-1,2, m.p. 104°, and when a mixed m.p. was taken with the *cis*-cyclohexanediol-1,2 (m.p. 98°) obtained by the osmium tetroxide hydroxylation method a depression of about 40° was noted. Ten years later Mugdan and Young[51] confirmed Trepagnier's observation and made an extensive study of the efficiency of various oxides as catalysts in the hydroxylation of olefins. Although osmium tetroxide was found to be superior to all other catalysts and is in a class by itself, of all the other oxides tungstic oxide, especially when used in aqueous solution and at elevated temperatures, was favored by Mugdan and Young as the best catalyst. This catalyst has also been recommended by Church and Blumberg[15] for the commercial production of tartaric acid from maleic acid using hydrogen peroxide as the oxidizing agent.

In view of the fact that the oxides discussed under this section are known to form peroxyacids with hydrogen peroxide, it is conceivable that the mechanism of the reaction may follow the same course as that postulated for the epoxydation of olefins with organic peroxyacids. In no case, however, has an epoxide been isolated in any of these reactions. We therefore feel that the reaction proceeds through an oxonium intermediate (IX) which is attacked on the back side by the metallic oxide anion to form the intermediate (X) which is easily hydrolyzed to yield the *trans*-glycol. Using peroxyvanadic acid, the mechanism can be illustrated as follows:

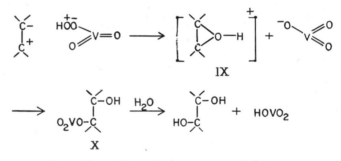

The metavanadic acid could easily be reconverted to peroxyvanadic acid with hydrogen peroxide.

Treibs and co-workers[68,70] studied the oxidation of cyclöolefins and hydroaromatic hydrocarbons with hydrogen peroxide in acetone solutions using peroxychromic, peroxymolybdic, peroxytungstic and peroxyvanadic acids as catalysts. Peroxyvanadic acid was especially suitable for the type of oxidations they observed. From cyclohexene they obtained, in addition to the expected *trans*-cyclohexanediol-1,2, 30–40 per cent cyclohexenone; from 1-methyl-cyclohexen-1 35 per cent of 1-methyl-cyclohexen-1-one-6 and 40 per cent of *trans*-1-methylcyclohexanediol-1,2; from 1-methylcyclopentene-1 25 per cent of 1-methyl-cyclopenten-1-one-5 and 30 per cent of *trans*-1-methylcyclopentanediol-1,2. Under the same conditions tetralin is oxidized to α-tetralone and hydrindene to α-hydrindone, while indene yielded only *trans*-hydrindenediol-1,2.

These results seem to indicate that peroxyvanadic acid attacks not only the double bonds but also the allylic hydrogen atoms. The latter reaction is analogous to the oxidation of allylic hydrogen atoms a reaction which, as a rule, proceeds via a free radical mechanism. With cyclohexene and peroxyvanadic acid this reaction may be illustrated as follows:

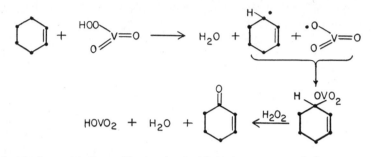

e. *Oxidation with Persulfuric Acid.* Albitzky[2] reported the preparation of dihydroxy acids from oleic, elaidic, brassidic and erucic acids by the use of a solution of sulfuric acid and ammonium persulfate. In later publications[3] he offered a mechanism of this reaction which is no longer feasible. Athanas'evskii[4] used Caro's acid for the hydroxylation of petroselic acid (6-octadecenoic acid) and its *trans*-isomer. In a search for a general method of hydroxylation Swann[65] used more dilute solutions of persulfuric acid than previous workers for the hydroxylation of olefins. Although the yields of the glycols were low, he was able to obtain glycerol from allyl alcohol and *trans*-cyclohexanediol-1,2 from cyclohexene.

Since Caro's acid leads to the formation of *trans*-glycols the mechanism of hydroxylation must be of the same type as that given under peroxyvanadic acid.

f. *Reaction of Mercuric Salts with Unsaturated Hydrocarbons.* Olefins are attacked by mercuric salts, especially by mercuric acetate and basic mercuric nitrate in either alcoholic (methanol) or aqueous solutions to produce addition products of varied stability. In many cases the olefin can be regenerated quantitatively from the adduct by allowing it to react with halogen acids[1] or compounds such as cyanides and thiocyanates which have a greater affinity for mercury than olefins.[35] Mercuric salts also add to aromatic hydrocarbons. For example, benzene yields phenyl mercuric acetate when heated with mercuric acetate under pressure.[25] Mercurations of olefins are accelerated by organic peroxides and boron trifluoride and inhibited by electron donors such as amines, nitriles and carbonyl compounds except acid chlorides which acylate the final products.[14] Oxidizing agents such as iodine remove mercury from the adducts as mercuric iodide and yield iodohydrins almost quantitatively.[60]

With gaseous olefins this reaction has been known for a long time.[24,35,37,61] *cis*-Olefins react much more rapidly than *trans*-olefins and each gives a characteristic diastereomer uncontaminated with the other.[32,62,78] With cycloölefins mercuric salts react to give only one diastereomer oxymercurial. For example, when cyclohexene is allowed to react with mercuric acetate in methanol only one *trans*-isomer is formed.[59]

The ease with which olefins are regenerated from these adducts by the addition of hydrochloric acid led the early investigators[42,43] to consider these adducts merely as coördination complexes similar to those of Werner complexes. However, the work of Adams *et al*[1] and that of Marvel and co-workers[32,62] showed quite definitely that mercuric salts add to double bonds to form saturated products.

Kinetic studies have been carried out by several investigators to elucidate the mechanism of this reaction. Of all the mechanisms proposed[12,35,38,61,78] only two need be considered here. In view of the fact that the mercuration of olefins is catalyzed by "Lewis acids" such as boron trifluoride it must be an electrophilic reaction. In fact Lucas, Hepner and Winstein[38] proposed that this reaction is ionic and proceeds *via* an "alkenemercurinium ion" (XIII).

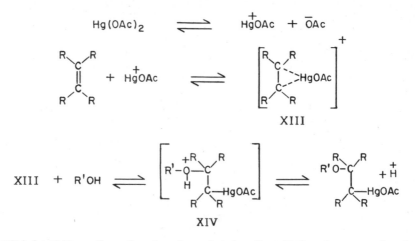

Wright,[12,78] on the other hand, maintains that if the above mechanism were correct the reaction should be a pseudo-unimolecular one but it is actually bimolecular. He argues that in the case of cyclohexene the addition of mercuric acetate in the absence of methanol is very slow and once the adduct is formed it is very slowly solvolyzed with methanol. This argues against the possibility of (XIII) and (XIV) as being the true intermediates because in the presence of methanol the reaction is very rapid with the methoxyl-mercurial forming exclusively. In a more recent publication Rodgman and Wright[58] have shown that prior to addition mercuric acetate reacts with methanol to form methoxylmercuric acetate which is the actual species that adds to the double bond in an non-ionic mechanism. According to this mechanism the attack of the

$$Hg(OAc)_2 + R'OH \rightleftharpoons R'OHgOAc + AcOH$$

double bond is frontal with the alkoxyl oxygen adding first presumably to a carbon of the double bond with a sextet, the other carbon becomes a carbanion which, having undergone an inversion, will accept the mercuric acetate group to yield the *trans*-alkoxymercurial.

However, since a free radical or a carbonium ion mechanism is excluded on the grounds that isomeric olefins retain their configuration, it is difficult to see how this mechanism will lead to the formation of *trans*-alkoxylmercurials. Furthermore, it is quite improbable that a double bond with π-electrons would coördinate with the oxygen of an alkoxyl group rather than with the mercury atom. Therefore, in spite of certain disadvantages of the ionic mechanism of mercuration of the double bond, the advantages far outweigh the disadvantages at present and it is the preferred mechanism.

Even in the case of high molecular weight olefins and cyclopolyolefins in which mercuration usually results in the complete reduction of mercuric salts to metallic mercury and the oxidation of the olefins, the ionic mechanism seems to be favored in the interpretation of the results. A good example of this type of reaction is the mercuration of cycloöctatetraene.[19,56] This also illustrates the effect which different hydroxylic solvents have on the course of the reaction. Reppe and co-workers[56] obtained from the mercuration of cycloöctatetraene: with mercuric sulfate in water, 70 per cent phenylacetaldehyde; with mercuric acetate in acetic acid, 96 per cent phenylethylidene diacetate; with mercuric acetate in methanol, 78 per cent phenylacetaldehyde dimethyl acetal. A more careful examination of these reactions by Cope and co-workers[19] led to the isolation of the products outlined below:

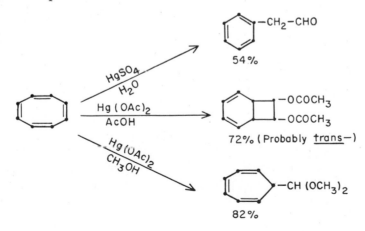

At elevated temperatures (130–150°) and in the absence of hydroxylic solvents mercuric acetate fails to attack the double bonds of cycloölefins, but it does attack the hydrogen atoms adjacent to them and yields the corresponding acetoxy derivatives of these olefins. For example, Treibs and Bast[69] obtained: from cyclohexene, 3-acetoxycyclohexene-1; from menthene-1, 6-acetoxymenthene-1; from menthene-3, 5-acetoxymenthene-3; and from D-limonene, besides p-cymene and dipentene, 6-acetoxy-D-limonene. These reactions are analogous to reactions of cyclic ketones, under similar conditions, with mercuric acetate. Unlike mercuration of olefins at ordinary temperatures, mercuration at elevated temperatures seems to proceed *via* a free-radical mechanism. Using cyclohexene and cyclohexanone this mechanism may be illustrated as follows:

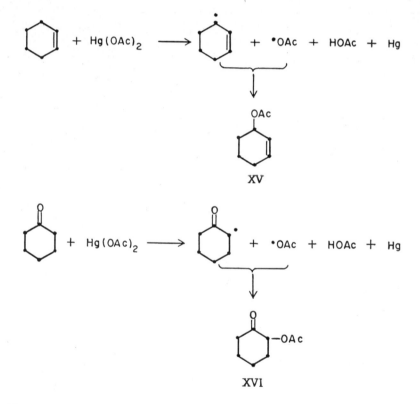

This type of oxidation is sometimes referred to as acetylative oxidation. That this type of reaction is a free-radical reaction was shown recently by Milas and Peters[48] who obtained among other products dicumene by allowing cumene to react with anhydrous mercuric acetate at the boiling point of cumene.

g. *Oxidation of Unsaturated Hydrocarbons by Iodosilverbenzoate*. When silver benzoate in benzene solution is allowed to react with iodine, a complex, iodosilverbenzoate, is formed in solution and silver iodide separates out as a solid. This reagent, sometimes referred to as the Prévost reagent, is a powerful oxidizing agent which has been extensively studied by Prévost and his co-workers.[55] With unsaturated hydrocarbons this reagent reacts to form *trans*-1,2-dibenzoates which are easily hydrolyzed to give in good yields the corresponding *trans*-1,2-glycols. With conjugated dienes the addition is always 1,2 rather than 1,4 as in the case of the addition of halogens to similar dienes. Although the iodosilverbenzoate gives the best results, iodosilveracetate and iodosilver complexes of other carboxylic acids have been tried with much inferior results. Likewise, chloro- and bromosilverbenzoates have also been tried in carbon tetrachloride solutions since they attack benzene, but the results obtained were not as satisfactory as those obtained with iodosilverbenzoate. Table III lists some of the olefins investigated by this method.

TABLE III. PRODUCTS FROM THE BENZOXYLATION OF CERTAIN OLEFINS WITH IODOSILVERBENZOATE

Olefin	Product	Yield (in per cent)	Ref.
$RCH=CH_2$	$RCH(C_6H_5CO_2)C(C_6H_5CO_2)H_2$	>90	55(a)
Diallyl	Diallyl tetrabenzoate	60	55(a)
1-Phenyl-1,3-butadiene	1,2-Dibenzoxy-butene-3	>80	55(e)
Anthracene	9,10-Dihydroanthracene-9,10-diol	50	55(d)
Hexadecene-1	1,2-Hexadecanediol	33	52
Octadecene-1	1,2-Octadecanediol	73	52
Eicosene-1	1,2-Eicosanediol	70	52
Methyl oleate	9,10-Dihydroxystearic acid (low melting)	93	77
Methyl elaidate	9,10-Dihydroxystearic acid (high melting)	76	77

The mechanism of this reaction consists of two parts: the formation of the complex and its reaction with the double bond. The complex, according to Prévost,[55(f)] is formed by the reaction of two moles of silver benzoate with one mole of iodine. Silver benzoate in solution probably exists as a complex salt in which one of the silver atoms assumes a coördination number of two. The existence of the complex anion in which the silver has this coördination number has been established by MacDougall and Allen.[09] Furthermore, Prévost[55(f)] established the positive nature of iodine in the complex by allowing it to react with phenyl acetylene. These reactions are illustrated by the following equations:

$$2C_6H_5COOAg \rightleftharpoons [(C_6H_5COO)_2Ag]\overset{-}{A}\overset{+}{g}$$
XVII

$$[(C_6H_5COO)_2Ag]\overset{-}{A}\overset{+}{g} + I_2 \rightarrow [(C_6H_5COO)_2Ag]\overset{-+}{I} + AgI$$
XVIII

$$[(C_6H_5COO)_2Ag]\overset{-+}{I} + C_6H_5C \equiv CH \xrightarrow{\text{fast}} C_6H_5C \equiv CI + [(C_6H_5COO)Ag]\overset{-+}{H}$$

$$C_6H_5COOH + C_6H_5COOAg \xleftarrow{\quad} \overset{\big|\text{slow}}{}$$

Since the glycols produced by this method are *trans*-1,2-glycols, the reaction of iodosilvenbenzoate (XVIII) with olefins may proceed *via* an iodonium ion intermediate (XIX) which adds a benzoate ion by a back

side attack to form the *trans*-iodobenzoate (XX). Such an intermediate has actually been isolated in several cases by Prévost who found that it reacts further with silver benzoate to give the dibenzoate (XXI). This reaction, too, seems to fall in line with other electrophilic reactions which are stereospecific in leading to the formation of *trans*-1,2-glycols.[64]

h. Reactions of Chromyl Chloride with Unsaturated Hydrocarbons. Chromyl chloride is a powerful electrophilic reagent and Etard[27] discovered long ago that it reacts with various hydrocarbons to give mixtures of aldehydes and ketones. From pentane and hexane he obtained mixtures of chlorinated ketones. From toluene he obtained a brown solid which gave benzaldehyde on hydrolysis. Recently Tillotson and Houston[66] applied this reaction to methylcyclohexane and found that the reaction proceeds only when 1 per cent of an olefin is added. A solid complex, $C_6H_{11}CH_3(CrO_2Cl)_2$ was isolated in 85 per yield and gave hexahydrobenzaldehyde on hydrolysis. Henderson and co-workers[33] applied this reaction to terpenes and always obtained brown solids which, when hydrolyzed, gave mixtures of aldehydes and ketones. It seems therefore that the reaction of chromyl chloride with olefins has always led to the cleavage of the double bond.

Recently, however, Cristol and Eilar[22] found that when cyclohexene was treated with chromyl chloride in carbon tetrachloride, a brown solid, similar to that obtained by previous investigators, was produced, and when carefully hydrolyzed it gave mainly *trans*-2-chloro-cyclohexanol and no aldehyde. Similarly, when propylene, butene-1, pentene-1 and hexene-1 were treated with chromyl chloride, the corresponding chlorohydrins were obtained in 35–50 per cent yields with the hydroxyl group occupying the primary position. Polychlorinated olefins failed to react with chromyl chloride a fact which is consistent with the electrophilic nature of the reaction.[36]

To account for the products of this reaction with olefins Cristol and Eilar assumed that the mechanism of the reaction must be similar to other reactions which lead to the formation of *trans*-glycols or *trans*-chlorohydrins. However, the formation of primary alcohols is consistent with the assumption that chromyl chloride donates a positive $\overset{+}{CrO_2Cl}$ to the olefin which hydrolyzes later to give the primary alcohol.

$$RCH{=}CH_2 + CrO_2Cl_2 \rightarrow [RCH{-}CH_2OCrOCl]\overset{+-}{Cl}$$
$$XXII \;\downarrow$$
$$\underset{Cl}{RCH{-}CH_2OH} \xleftarrow{H_2O} \underset{Cl}{RCH{-}\overset{}{C}H_2OCrOCl}$$

In order to make this mechanism consistent with the mechanisms of analogous reactions, the authors proposed a positive oxonium intermediate (XXIII) for the structure of the positive ion (XXII).

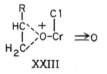

XXIII

Such an intermediate, in the case of cyclohexene, would add a chloride ion by a back side attack to give after hydrolysis the observed *trans*-chlorohydrin.

References to Section Four

1. Adams, R., Roman, F. L., and Sperry, W. N., *J. Am. Chem. Soc.* **44**, 1781 (1922).
2. Albitzsky, A., *Ber.*, **33**, 2909 (1900); *J. Prakt. Chem.*, (2) **61**, 65 (1900).
3. *Idem.*, *J. Russ Phys.-Chem. Soc.*, **34**, 810 (1902); *J. Prakt. Chem.*, (2) **67**, 357 (1903).
4. Athanas 'evskii, I., *J. Russ. Phys.-Chem. Soc.*, **47**, 2133 (1915).
5. Badger, G. M., *J. Chem. Soc.*, **1949**, 456; **1950**, 1809.
6. Badger, G. M., and Lynn, K. R., *ibid.*, **1950**, 1726.
7. Baxendale, J. H., *Faraday Soc. Discussions*, **14**, 249 (1953).

8. (a) R. Behrend and G. Heyer, *Ann.*, **418**, 294 (1919).
   (b) J. Böeseken and J. van Giffen, *Rec. trav. chim.*, **39**, 183 (1920).
   (c) N. A. Milas and E. M. Terry, *J. Am. Chem. Soc.*, **47**, 1412 (1925).
   (d) E. M. Terry and N. A. Milas, *ibid.*, **48**, 2647 (1926).
   (e) N. A. Milas, *ibid.*, **49**, 2005 (1927).
   (f) S. S. Medvedev and E. N. Alekseeva, *Papers Karpov. Chem. Inst. Bach. Mem. Vol.*, **1927**, 128.
   (g) J. W. E. Glattfeld and S. Woodruff, *J. Am. Chem. Soc.*, **49**, 2309 (1927).
   (h) Geza Braun, *ibid.*, **51**, 228 (1929).
   (i) I. S. Neuberg, *Biochem. Z.*, **221**, 492 (1930).
   (j) R. Lespieau and J. Wiemann, *Compt. rend.*, **194**, 1946 (1932); *Bull. soc. chim.*, **53**, 1107 (1933).
   (k) J. W. E. Glattfeld and J. W. Chittum, *J. Am. Chem. Soc.*, **55**, 3663 (1933).
   (l) J. W. E. Glattfeld and L. R. Forbrich, *ibid.*, **56**, 1209 (1934).
   (m) J. W. E. Glattfeld and R. E. Hoen, *ibid.*, **57**, 1405 (1935).
   (n) J. Wiemann, *Compt. rend.*, **200**, 840, 2021 (1935).
9. Böeseken, I., *Rec. trav. chim.*, **47**, 683 (1928).
10. *Ibid.*, **41**, 199 (1922).
11. Boyland, E., and Sims, P., *J. Chem. Soc.*, **1953**, 2966.
12. Brook, A. G., and Wright, G. F., *Can. J. Chem.*, **29**, 308 (1951).
13. Byers, A., and Hickinbottom, W. J., *J. Chem. Soc.*, **1950**, 47.
14. Chatt, J., *Chem. Rev.*, **48**, 7 (1951).
15. Church, J. M., and Blumberg, R., *Ind. Eng. Chem.*, **43**, 1780 (1951).
16. Clauson-Kaas, N., and Fakstrop, J., *Acta Chim. Scand.*, **1**, 216 (1947).
17. Cook, J. W., and Schoental, R., *J. Chem. Soc.*, **1950**, 47.
18. Cope, A. C., Fenton, S. W., and Spencer, C. F., *J. Am. Chem. Soc.*, **74**, 5884 (1952).
19. Cope, A., Nelson, N. A., and Smith, D. S., *ibid.*, **76**, 1100 (1954).
20. Criegee, R., *Ann.*, **522**, 75 (1936).
21. Cricgee, R., Marchand, B., and Wannowins, H., *ibid.*, **550**, 99 (1942).
22. Cristol, S. J., and Eilar, K. R., *J. Am. Chem. Soc.*, **72**, 4353 (1950).
23. Dainton, F. S., *J. Phys. and Coll. Chem.*, **52**, 490 (1948).
24. Deniges, G., *C. rend.*, **126**, 1043, 1145, 1868 (1898).
25. Dimroth, O., *Ber.*, **31**, 2154 (1898).
26. Drummond, A. Y., and Waters, W. A., *J. Chem. Soc.*, **1953**, 435.
27. Étard, M., *Ann. chim. phys.*, **22**, 218 (1881).
28. Fenton, H. J. N., *J. Chem. Soc.*, **65**, 899 (1894); **67**, 48, 775 (1895); **69**, 546 (1896).
29. Golodetz, L., *Rev. Fett-Harz Ind.*, **17**, 72 (1910).
30. Goss, G. C. L., and McFarlane, W. D., *Science*, **106**, 375 (1947).
31. Gresham, T. L., and Steadman, T. R., *J. Am. Chem. Soc.*, **71**, 737 (1949).
32. Griffith, E., and Marvel, C. S., *ibid.*, **53**, 789 (1931).
33. (a) Henderson, G. G., and Smith, R. W., *J. Chem. Soc.*, **55**, 49 (1889).
    (b) *Idem.*, and Gray, T., *ibid.*, **85**, 1041 (1904).
    (c) *Idem.*, and Heilbron, I., *ibid.*, 93, 288 (1908); **99**, 1887 (1911)
    (d) *Idem.*, and Chisholm, D., *ibid.*, **125**, 107 (1924).
34. (a) Hofmann, K. A., *Ber.*, **45**, 3329 (1912).
    (b) *Idem.*, Ehrhart, O., and Schneider, O., *Ber.*, **46**, 1657 (1913).
35. *Idem.*, and Sand, J., *ibid.*, **33**, 1340, 1353, 2692 (1900).
36. Ingold, C. K., *Chem. Rev.*, **15**, 225 (1934).
37. Keller, R. N., *ibid.*, **28**, 229 (1941).

38. Lucas, H. J., Hepner, F. R., and Winstein, S., *J. Am. Chem. Soc.*, **61**, 3102 (1939).
39. MacDougall, T. H., and Allen, M., *J. Phys. Chem.*, **46**, 730 738 (1942).
40. Makowka, O., *Ber.*, **41**, 943 (1908).
41. Maloney, L. S., Ph.D. Thesis, Part I, *Mass. Inst. Techn.*, (1939).
42. Manchot, W., *Ber.*, **53B**, 984 (1920).
43. *Idem.*, and Klüg, A., *Ann.*, **420**, 170 (1920).
44. Merz, J. H., and Waters, W. A., *J. Chem. Soc.*, **1949**, 2427, (Supplemental), 515.
45. Milas, N. A., *J. Am. Chem. Soc.*, **59**, 2382 (1937); U. S. Patents, 2,402,566 (1946); 2,414,383 (1947); 2,437,648 (1948).
46. (a) N. A. Milas and S. Sussman, *J. Am. Chem. Soc.*, **58**, 1302 (1936).
    (b) N. A. Milas and S. Sussman, *ibid.*, **59**, 2345 (1937).
    (c) N. A. Milas, S. Sussman and H. S. Mason, *ibid.*, **61**, 1844 (1939).
    (d) N. A. Milas and L. S. Maloney, *ibid.*, **62**, 1841 (1940).
    (e) R. C. Hockett, A. C. Sapp, and S. R. Millman, *ibid.*, **63**, 2051 (1941).
    (f) C. D. Hurd and C. D. Kelso, *ibid.*, **70**, 1484 (1948).
47. Milas, N. A., Kurz, P. F., and Anslow, W. P., *J. Am. Chem. Soc.*, **59**, 543 (1937).
48. *Idem.*, and Peters, J., Unpublished results.
49. *Idem.*, Trepagnier, J. H., and Nolan, J. T., Jr. Unpublished results.
50. *Idem.*, Stahl, L. E., and Dayton, B. B., *J. Am. Chem. Soc.*, **71**, 1448 (1949).
51. Mugdan, M., and Young, D. P., *J. Chem. Soc.*, **1949**, 2988.
52. Niemann, C., and Wagner, C. D., *J. Org. Chem.*, **7**, 227 (1942).
53. Owen, L. N., and Smith, P. N., *J. Chem. Soc.*, **1952**, 4035.
54. Phillips, F. C., *Z. anorg. chem.*, **6**, 299 (1894).
55. (a) C. Prévost, *Compt. rend.*, **196**, 1129 (1933); **197**, 166 (1933).
    (b) C. Prévost, and Losson, *ibid.*, **198**, 659 (1934).
    (c) C. Prévost, and R. Lutz, *ibid.*, **198**, 2264 (1934).
    (d) C. Prévost, *ibid.*, **200**, 408, 942 (1935).
    (e) C. Prévost, and J. Wiemann, *ibid.*, **204**, 700 (1937).
    (f) C. Prévost, *ibid.*, **204**, 989 (1937).
56. Reppe, W., Schlichting, O., Klager, K., and Toepel, T., *Ann.*, **560**, 1 (1948).
57. Riesenfeld, E. H., *Ber.*, **41**, 3536 (1908).
58. Rodgman, A., and Wright, G. F., *J. Org. Chem.*, **18**, 1617 (1953).
59. Romeyn, J., and Wright, G. F., *J. Am. Chem. Soc.*, **69**, 297 (1947).
60. Sand, J., *Ber.*, **34**, 2906 (1901).
61. *Ibid.*, **34**, 1385 (1901); *Ann.*, **329**, 135 (1903).
62. Sanborn, L. T., and Marvel, C. S., *J. Am. Chem. Soc.*, **48**, 1409 (1926).
63. Sauerbrunn, R. D., and Saundell, E. B., *ibid.*, **75**, 4170 (1953).
64. Sletzinger, M., and Dawson, C. R., *J. Org. Chem.*, **14**, 849 (1949).
65. Swann, S., Jr., *Univ. Ill. Eng. Exp. Sta. Bull.*, **204**, 14 (1930).
66. Tillotson, A., and Houston, B., *J. Am. Chem. Soc.*, **73**, 221 (1951).
67. Trepagnier, J. H., Ph.D. Thesis, *Mass. Inst. Techn.*, (1939).
68. Treibs, W., *Ber.*, **72**, 1194 (1939).
69. *Idem.*, and Bast, H., *Ann.*, **561**, 165 (1949).
70. *Idem.*, Franke, G., Leichsewring, G., and Röder, H., *Ber.*, **86**, 616 (1953).
71. Tschugajeff, L., and Bikerman, J., *Z. anorg. allgem. Chem.*, **172**, 230 (1928).
72. Uri, N., *Chem. Rov.*, **50**, 375 (1952).
73. Wagner, G., *Ber.*, **21**, 1230, 3343, 3347, (1888). **23**, 2307 (1890); **27**, 1636 (1894).
74. *Idem.*, *J. Russ. Phys-Chem. Soc.*, **27**, 219 (1895).
75. Waters, W. A., "Le Mécanisme de L'Oxydation" p. 81, Condenberg, Brussels (1950).

76. Wendler, N. L., Rosenblum, C., and Tishler, M., *J. Am. Chem. Soc.*, **72,** 234 (1950).
77. Wittcoff, H., and Miller, S. E., *ibid.*, **69,** 3138 (1947).
78. Wright, G. F., *ibid.*, **57,** 1993 (1935).
79. Yost, D. M., and White, R. J., *ibid.*, **50,** 81 (1928); Anderson, L. H., and Yost, D. M., *ibid.*, **60,** 1822 (1932).
80. Zelikoff, M., and Taylor, H. A., *ibid.*, **72,** 5039 (1950).

NOTE: Due to circumstances beyond the author's control the section covering oxidations by chromic acid di-*t*-butyl chromate, lead tetraacetate and selenium dioxide were received too late for publication.—The Editors.

SUBJECT INDEX